human anatomy and physiology

HOLT, RINEHART AND WINSTON, INC.
New York / Chicago / San Francisco / Atlanta / Dallas
Montreal / Toronto / London / Sydney

human anatomy and physiology

A CELLULAR APPROACH

David Shepro / Frank Belamarich / Charles Levy

Boston University

This book was set in Primer by Ruttle, Shaw & Wetherill, Inc.
The editor was Dorothy Crane;
the designer was Scott Chelius;
and the production supervisor was Robert Ballinger.
The drawings were done by Gail Cooper, M.D. Harvard Medical School.
The printer and binder was Kingsport Press.

Library of Congress Cataloging in Publication Data
Shepro, David.
Human anatomy and physiology.
1. Human physiology.   2. Anatomy, Human.
I. Belamarich, Frank, joint author.   II. Levy, Charles K., 1924-   joint author.   III. Title.
[DNLM: 1. Anatomy.   2. Physiology.   QT 104 S549h   1974]
QP34.5.S47   612   73-16092
ISBN 0-03-082840-6

Printed in the United States of America
4 5 6 7 8 9   071   9 8 7 6 5 4 3 2

To Lisa and Doug
Peter, Mark, Mathew, and Thomas
Brett, Adam, and Alison

preface

A book on human structure and function is written almost exclusively for students who are embarking on a career in some way connected to delivering health care; such a book is part of the professional curriculum of physicians, psychologists, nurses, physiotherapists, orthopticians, physical education instructors, and personnel in paramedical disciplines. The greatest proportion of the training in these fields is oriented toward preventing or solving a health problem, which implies a goal of 100 percent knowledge. Practically this endpoint can only be approximated because the amount of information available on the biology of a human far exceeds the limits imposed upon the student by a single formal introductory course. One goal of this book is therefore to convey sufficient information so that the reader has an understanding of how the body maintains its dynamic balance called life.

Books, classrooms, and teachers are merely prosthetic devices for learning. Study is purely a self-experience, and when students are ready to enhance their self-knowledge, they will learn and will grow in self-appreciation. However, prosthetic devices, even books, can make the process of awareness much easier. A new textbook obviously will provide the reader with up-to-date material, but the rationale of this book goes beyond this purpose. We have made several departures from the classical anatomy and physiology textbook. In each systems chapter, a section is devoted to cell microanatomy and physiology. The reason for this focus on the cell is that our knowledge about body function, therapy, and cure is directly related to our knowledge of subcellular structures and functions; this orientation means that educated individuals have to understand and utilize the language of the cell. Chapters on "Cellular Aspects of Disease and Defense" and on "Aging and Death" are included because we are convinced that questions related to who receives transplants, aging as a process, the validity of zero population growth, and even the value of death are all parts of a web that forms the body and its experiential world.

Another significant difference for an introductory text is the emphasis that has been placed on *integrative mechanisms* — notably the chapters on the nervous system and on the blood-cardiovascular system. The fairly extensive coverage on the nervous system is also prompted by the awareness that the knowledge of behavior will increase dramatically in the next decade, and basic information about constituents of the nervous system will be valuable to the clinically oriented.

The basic format of this book is as follows. In each chapter an abbreviated description of the *gross anatomy* of the system is initially provided. The next section deals with the microanatomy and cellular structure of the specialized cells; in certain instances, some detail on *ultrastructure* is provided (magnification that requires an electron microscope to enlarge the cellular components thousands of times). With a strong foundation of anatomy the reader is prepared to tackle the following section on *physiology* (function). The next section is on *control* (regulation), and here we deal primarily with the nerves and the hormones that have a direct effect on the organs. The section on *factors influencing function* is focused on conditions that indirectly affect the activity of the system. The final section, *clinical considerations*, describes some disease states. We hasten to add that the final section is merely a slightly more dramatic way of reinforcing knowledge of normal function, and that it was not our intention to make the reader knowledgeable about a specific disease. Finally, each chapter has at least one *module*, a diagrammatic-descriptive presentation that contains either the essence of the chapter or some aspect of the system under discussion that is deemed worthy of special consideration. Collectively knowledge of all the modules will give each reader a firm background upon which to build his present and future knowledge of life processes.

In addition, we hope that this text will give the reader some insight about the nature of a man that will be useful in dealing with a universal problem of undefined dimensions. H.G. Wells commented that mankind is in a "race between education and catastrophe," and his statement is more prophetic today than when it was made over a quarter of a century ago. It is our belief that the future of the human species is directly dependent upon knowledge of self, and certainly one of the first steps in this direction, regardless of career orientation, is to know raw materials of life and how they operate. Violence is the number one disease of our country and probably of the world. Every year hundreds of thousands of individuals are killed by trauma and millions are hopelessly maimed. Able men argue that the degree of violence is an indicator of man's inability to bridge his self with the environment and man is facing genocide. They argue that the focal point of man's existing behavior reflects a brain so overloaded with stimuli that he cannot focus on himself sufficiently to exercise restraint, and unfortunately there are no experts on behavior to whom he can turn for "the facts."

It is truly unimportant whether man is instinctively aggressive or whether environmental conditions produce this behavior. All factors are related, all constituents are connected: a vibration in one segment of one's system will manifest itself, within a short span of time, in some other area of the body. And a disturbance in one human being will eventually disturb another human being. Everything is part of a continuum. Cells, oxygen utilization, heart, bone, and muscle are inseparable from bigotry, joy, hate, love, nobility, fun, and dignity.

Because an understanding of one consciousness is a lifetime experience, a book can only deal with a small segment, and this book must be even more restricted. However, the intersection of any two pieces of knowledge does not create a dilemma but a new level of clarification of life. Hopefully, the knowledge derived from this book will increase your understanding of "why we are alive" and "why our life is worth living."

We wish to thank Gail Cooper, M.D., Harvard Medical School, who prepared most of the art for this textbook and Ms. Laurel Kologe for her valuable assistance in producing the manuscript. Our special thanks to Dorothy Carbose Crane and to Lyn Peters for their extraordinary editorial assistance.

November 1973   D.S.
                                                                                         F.A.B.
                                                                                         C.K.L.

contents

Preface vii

1 cell structure 1

2 cell functions 28

3 tissue, organ, system, and body organization 64

4 skeletal system 89

5 nerve cells 127

6 muscular system 153

7 central nervous system 183

8 peripheral nervous system and reflex activity 220

9 special sensory organs 241

10 blood 268

11 heart 290

12 blood vessels, lymphatics, and circulation 312

13 digestive system and nutrition 343

14 metabolism and energy exchange 384

15 respiratory system 411

16 urinary system 436

17   integumentary system and thermal regulation   455

18   endocrine system   468

19   male reproductive system   490

20   female reproductive system   504

21   prenatal development and birth   523

22   cellular aspects of disease and defense   547

23   aging and death   569

     glossary   581

     index   605

human anatomy and physiology

cell
structure

1

historical approach to cytology

cytological procedures
microscopy
cell and subcellular separation

structural components and their function

cytoplasm
membranes
organelles
inclusions
nucleus

cytology and disease
biopsy
chromosome analysis

It takes approximately 280 days for a new infant to develop from fertilization to birth, and in that span of time the single fertilized cell forms over 2 trillion cells; by adulthood this population of cells is increased 50 times. What is remarkable is that the machinery of these trillions of cells is quite similar. One could speculate that if the techniques were available, practically all of a cell's component parts could be readily exchanged with those of another cell, even with those of a different type and they would still work.

The science of the cell is *cytology,* and this discipline is concerned with the structure and the function of the cell's parts as well as with the cell itself. In recent years a new dimension in anatomy has been added, namely, *ultrastructure.* With instruments such as the electron microscope, cellular components that were not resolved by the light microscope are now visible and are labeled *subcellular components.* From electron microscopic and biochemical studies we have learned that individual cells are little worlds of their own and in essence are microcosms of the total organism they form. The combination of information revealed by the microscope and detailed studies of function provides greater insight into the workings of many tissues than could be gained from studying the gross anatomy of that tissue alone.

historical approach to cytology

If an individual were faced with the theoretical exercise of selecting the three events that have made the greatest impact on cytology (excluding Darwinism, the cornerstone of all biology), good arguments could be presented for the following: *the cell theory* of Schleiden and Schwann (1838–1939), *the cell lineage theory* of Virchow (1858), and *"the central dogma,"* which was the discovery of the structure and function of the deoxyribonucleic acid (DNA) molecule by Watson, Crick, and Wilkins (1953). These scientists are singled out because, in addition to adding to the general knowledge of the cell by their discoveries of some new structure or function, they also provided a generalization, the impact of which to the understanding of life itself overshadowed the specific discovery.

Contemporary and even earlier scientists than Schleiden and Schwann recognized the cell, the components of the cell, and even the importance of the cell. Robert Hooke in 1665 was the first to observe cells, but Schleiden and Schwann are deserving of the title "Fathers of Cytology" because they were the first to provide an all-embracing theory that *the cell is the functional and structural unit of life.* Their cell theory is as valid today as it was in 1838, and many scientists believe that this theory is the single most important contribution in the history of the anatomical sciences. To appreciate the impact of their theory, one must be reminded that it was less than a century ago that scientists were still asking the soul-searching question, "Does God wish man to peer into the bowels of a cell, and thus into the secrets of life itself?"

The realization that cells do not arise *de novo* (anew) was known in the middle of the nineteenth century, but Virchow by formulating a simple phrase "all cells from cells" (*omnis cellula a cellula*) focused attention on the fact that life was a continuum between one generation and the next and that the similarities as well as the differences exhibited by any cell were inherited from the parent cells.

The "central dogma" detailing how *DNA*, the hereditary material within the chromosomes, *duplicates* and *programs the cell to perform its many functions*, almost overnight brought the mass of cell data that had accumulated over the years into clear focus. It is somewhat paradoxical that a cell must be taken apart if it is to be understood; the Watson-Crick model of DNA provides the mold for bringing the parts together again. In many respects the advent of this model closed the old era of cytology, an era of great productivity but limited understanding, and opened the modern era.

Since the turn of the century there have been more than 40 Nobel laureates in physiology, but excluding Watson, Crick, and Wilkins, their names do not appear in this historical introduction. For the sake of argument let us assume that each year there were at least 10 scientists whose contributions to our knowledge of the cell were worthy of this distinguished award. This means that since 1900 over 700 major contributions have been of historical significance. It is obvious that the purpose of this introductory discussion was not to provide even an abbreviated history of cytology but to make the reader aware of the subject.

cytological procedures

microscopy

The growth of cytology paralleled the development and the improvement of the microscope, for until recently cytology was almost exclusively an anatomical discipline. The microscope provides an essential means of quantitating, since modern science has shown that *measurement, theory*, and *practice* are inseparable. If we can measure "something," we automatically know "something" about it. With the light microscope, structures as small as 0.2 μ (1 micron or 1 μ = 1/1000 mm, or approximately 1/25,000 inch) can be observed by using a total magnification of 2000X. In practice magnifications of specimens rarely reach the limits of resolution. However, many cell parts are of smaller dimensions than 0.2 μ and cannot be seen with this type of microscope. This limitation has restricted cellular research. The electron microscope (Figure 1-1), which uses a beam of electrons as its source of illumination, can resolve images of structures within a cell down to a level of 5 to 10 angstroms (1 angstrom or 1 Å = 1/10,000 of 1 μ). This instrument has truly opened up new vistas within the cells. For the first time we can see that a cell has an outside membrane with layers; that the "clear" cytoplasm is filled with channels containing all sorts of "floating structures." For the first time molecular units can be seen (Module 1).

The cellular anatomy discussed in the succeeding chapters is derived from both types of microscopic studies, and more frequently than not, studies were made on cells that were killed before viewing. Superficially, we might expect that killing a cell before microscopic viewing would provide very limited information, but surprisingly the more precise physiological and biochemical procedures have documented the value of studying *fixed* cells and tissues. The reasons for fixing a cell rather than viewing the cell in a live state will be better understood after reading further.

Figure 1-2 is a photomicrograph of a living blood cell as viewed by a special type of interference light microscope. This microscope takes advantage of the fact that even colorless objects have different densities

figure 1-1

ELECTRON AND
LIGHT
MICROSCOPES

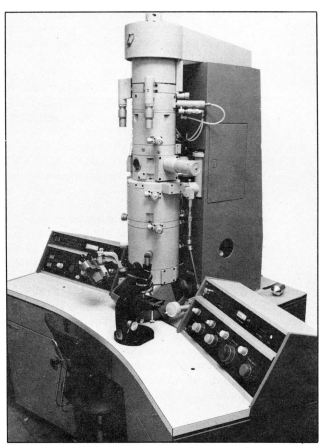

The large, cone-shaped instrument is an electron microscope (E.M.) that is capable of magnifying cells and other structures 500,000X. The E.M. uses an electron beam and not light as the source of illumination. Sitting on the working shelf of the electron microscope is another type of research instrument, a binocular light microscope, with a maximum meaningful magnification power of 2000X.

and that these differences can be enhanced by manipulating the light so that the colorless cell units appear as distinct entities. Certain cellular components are readily distinguished, as the labels indicate. However, this technique is limited, and more often than not, cell characterization requires *fixation* and *staining*.

The process of preserving cells in their "natural" form is called *fixing* and may be accomplished by several procedures. Placing a cell in a material known as a *fixative* serves to kill the cell rapidly and to preserve in death as many as possible of the structures that exist in life. The fixing substance should also prevent subsequent changes from occurring and not create structures that never existed (*artifacts*). Obviously, no one type of fixing fluid will meet all these requirements. Aqueous solutions (made with water) are frequently not acceptable because water will

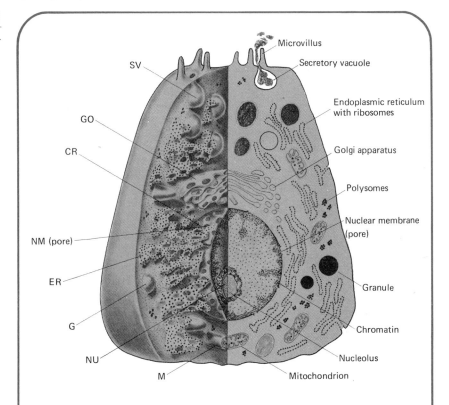

The three-dimensional cutaway is a schematic presentation of a typical animal cell. Although individual cells, even within the same organ, may differ enormously from one another, the basic structure of all cells is remarkably constant.

The cell is the structural and functional unit of the body, and the simplicity of the outside surface belies the extraordinary complex funtional organization within. The cell is a sack of rich broth (salts, minerals, and organic compounds) called the cytoplasm; (similar substance but contained within the nucleus is called the nucleoplasm), and within the cytoplasm are many types of substructures. Although the cytoplasmic organelles appear random and separate they are strategically located and functionally interconnected. In fact there is a nonlinear relationship between the constituents of a cell in that their total performance exceeds the sum of the activities of any of the parts. What cannot be appreciated in a drawing or even a photograph, regardless of the accuracy, is the activity and vitality of a cell. Labels cannot denote motion, the endless movement of raw materials or waste to and from the external membrane, or the programming and assembling of housekeeping products as well as secretions to be used by other cells, or that unique phenomenon of life, replication, the ability to make more of itself from non-living material. These activities seen within a cell are the fundamentals of life.

Legend: SV, secretory vacuole; GO, Golgi apparatus; CR, chromatin; NM, nuclear membrane; ER, endoplasmic reticulum; G, granule; NU, nucleolus; M, mitochondrion.

figure 1-2

LIVING CELLS
SEEN BY PHASE
MICROSCOPY

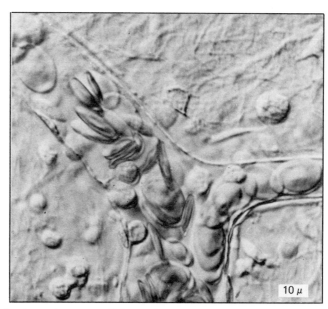

10 μ

The cells shown here were living and unstained when photographed with a light microscope that contains a series of lenses which interferes with the beam of light so that part of the light is different from the rest. Because of this light variation, parts of cells can be seen because of their different densities. Nonphase microscopy illumination would be too intense to show these minor differences in cell densities and the entire cell would appear transparent. An amphibian blood vessel was selected because the circulating blood cells are exceptionally large (much larger than human cells). The largest cells are erythrocytes, the smaller cells are leucocytes (defense mechanisms) and thrombocytes (blood clotting). If you look carefully, even the nuclei of the cells making up these small blood vessels are visible.

dissolve certain cellular materials. If the fixing medium contains alcohol, all alcohol-soluble components of the cell will disappear. Some fixatives are of little value because they do not penetrate rapidly, and thus parts of the cell are destroyed after death.

Once the cells are fixed they are embedded in a suitable medium so that they can be cut on an instrument called the *microtome*. For light microscopy most sections are cut between 2 to 10 μ; the electron microscope requires much thinner preparations, and sections are frequently cut below 900 Å. Translated into everyday terms, this difference means that a slice of a cell suitable for the light microscope ($\frac{1}{5000}$ inch) could be further cut into 200 thinner sections for the electron microscope.

The many procedures necessary to prepare cells or tissues for viewing generally make the cells transparent, and this necessitates the use of special stains to make the various parts visible. Staining for electron microscopy is still extremely limited, but staining for light microscopy is a relatively old technique and has given rise to a subdiscipline, *cytochemistry*, which is a combination of microscopy and biochemistry. Cells specially stained with both methyl green and pyronine have a bluish-green tinge in the central area. Methyl green is known to bind specifically to a nuclear component and pyronine has an equal specificity for a cytoplasmic component. This demonstrates the value of chemistry to microscopy. By this procedure of staining cells details of structure are available as well as information on the chemical composition.

From the standpoint of diagnosis, the microscope and cytochemistry are invaluable tools. For example, changes in cellular enzyme production associated with certain tumor cells can frequently be revealed by staining for the specific chemical. Procedures are being developed to identify alterations in the substructure and chemistry of aging cells.

cell and subcellular separation
In addition to microscopy the recent technological advances for separating cells and for fractionating the cells' components have provided valuable information in biology and medicine, and an impetus for new research. One example is the separation of blood platelets from whole blood and the utilization of the separated platelets in a study of their role in blood clotting.

Centrifugation
A centrifuge is an instrument for spinning a liquid suspension at speeds that can give the effect of thousands of times gravity. If blood (a suspension of red and white cells in plasma) is centrifuged at 5000 times gravity for a period of time, all of the cells will be packed into the bottom of the tube. After decanting the fluid, both a cell-free plasma and a pellet of blood cells would remain (Figure 1-3). Both fractions, the fluid portion and the packed cells, are of value in certain research and clinical situations. The system, of course, need not be limited to blood cells; any cells in a suitable liquid medium can be separated in this fashion.

We can modify this basic model of separation to a more narrowly defined system. Let us suppose a cell suspension contained three types of the cells A, B, and C, and one cell type was larger and more dense than the next. If a less than maximum gravitational force was exerted by the centrifuge, we could expect that the larger, more dense cells A would be the first to reach the bottom, that the B cells would be in the middle, and that the top layer would contain the smallest and least dense cells C. The separation of the cells is dependent upon their size and density and their ability to resist the gravitational force induced by the centrifuge; instead of varying the force, we can also increase the speed and shorten the time to achieve separation. In this case even though the centrifugal pull would be sufficient to pull down all the cells, because of the abbreviated period of time, the largest cells would be sedimented first followed by the next smallest, and so forth.

The ultracentrifuge can spin with as much as 400,000 times the force of gravity. This much gravitational energy can separate not only cells but even parts of cells. For example, if a group of cells in a fluid with a known density is broken, all particles will be randomly distributed. By manipulating time or speed of the centrifuge, we can achieve separation of the cellular subunits in a manner described above, and the isolated constituent particles can then be identified. A modification of this system is to put the mixture of cell parts into a tube that contains fluids of varying densities layered one on top of another. In this system, the cell parts will end up in different bands, according to the density of the cell part (Figure 1-4).

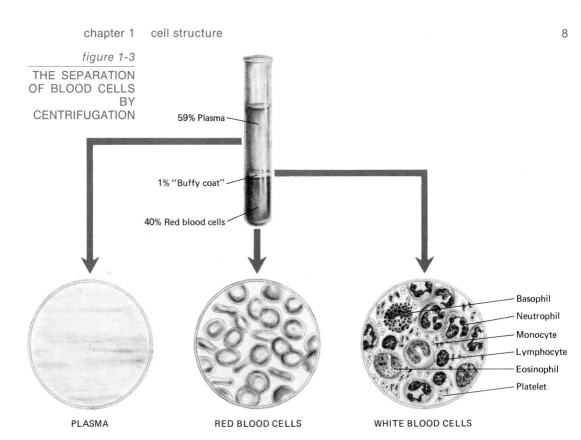

figure 1-3

THE SEPARATION
OF BLOOD CELLS
BY
CENTRIFUGATION

59% Plasma

1% "Buffy coat"

40% Red blood cells

Basophil
Neutrophil
Monocyte
Lymphocyte
Eosinophil
Platelet

PLASMA   RED BLOOD CELLS   WHITE BLOOD CELLS

Whole blood subjected to a force of about 2000X g by centrifugation separates into three major layers: the erythrocytes or red blood cells form a compact layer at the bottom; the adjacent thin white layer, also called the "buffy coat," is composed primarily of leucocytes (white blood cells) and platelets; the largest component, the plasma, is free of cells. The volumes, expressed in percentages, are averages and only indicate the normal values.

Chromatography

Another example of an analytical method for isolation and identification of materials is *chromatography* (Figure 1-5). The technique is used to separate different kinds of molecules, and the process is based upon the solubility of molecules for different kinds of liquids. Chromatographic separation is accomplished by many methods, but the most common types use paper or columns of material such as cellulose for the supporting medium. In paper chromatography, the molecules that are to be separated from one another are placed at a small spot at one end of the paper, and a mixture of liquids (*solvents*) is allowed to move along the paper by capillary action. The molecules, because of their different solubilities for the solvent mixture, will move varying distances along the paper. The components can be identified by staining or by other labeling techniques (radioisotopes).

Radioactive
Isotopes Tracers

Any element may exist in two forms that are chemically identical but physically different. One of the elements is said to be an *isotope* or a *nuclide* of the other. The isotopic form of the element undergoes a spon-

figure 1-4

SEPARATION OF
CELL COMPO-
NENTS BY ULTRA-
CENTRIFUGATION

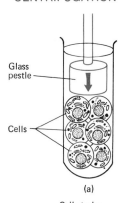

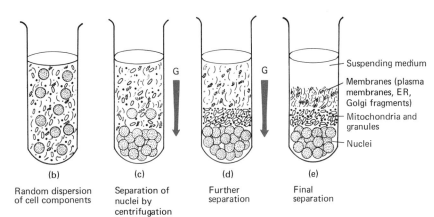

Glass pestle

Cells

Suspending medium

Membranes (plasma membranes, ER, Golgi fragments)

Mitochondria and granules

Nuclei

(a) Cells to be broken by plunging action of pestle

(b) Random dispersion of cell components

(c) Separation of nuclei by centrifugation

(d) Further separation

(e) Final separation

A force of 400,000X g (ultracentrifugation) will separate the subcellular components into several distinct bands. (a) The cells in a suspension medium are broken
by the plunging or spinning action of the glass rod. (b) The constituents freed from
the broken cells are randomly dispersed. (c) Suspension subjected to g force (↓)
begins to separate with the large nuclei first moving to the bottom of the tube.
(d) With time, the nucleus layer becomes more compact and a layer of mitochondria
and granules separate from the medium. (e) The least dense material, membranes,
form the third layer, and the uppermost layer, suspension medium is now free from
all cell fragments.

figure 1-5

CHROMATOG-
RAPHY

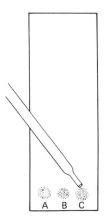

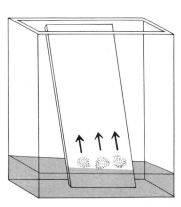

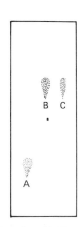

A B C

B C

A

Assume that A and B are known components and that C is either A or B. The
identity of C can be determined by placing all three materials on chromatography
paper or a chromatographic plate and placing the end of the chromatographic unit
in a solvent. The compounds will move with the solvent according to their solubility
in that particular solvent. After a period of time the chromatogram is taken out, dried,
and if necessary reacted in some way with chemicals to make the compounds more
visible. As seen in the last drawing compound C would be identified as being similar
to B because the extent of the solvent movement is the same for both compounds.

taneous decay process during which time it emits energy in the forms of rays or particles. These minute energetic emissions are detectable by a variety of means, for example, radiation detectors and photographic emulsion (Figure 1-6). Each isotope has well-defined physical properties such as a *half-life* (the time for one-half of the radioactive substance to disintegrate).

Since isotopic tracers are neither foreign nor chemically different from elements that compose biologically active molecules, the isotopes may be substituted and incorporated into specific cells. Once the isotopic label is incorporated into the cell, it can be used by the investigator to follow a process or to identify the location of a given substance, hence the name *tracer*.

figure 1-6

ISOTOPES IN
DIAGNOSIS AND
RESEARCH

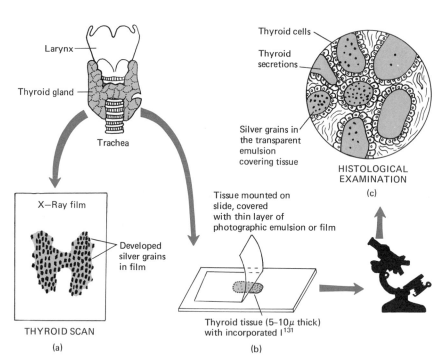

The patient receives an injection of radioactive iodine (I^{131}) into the bloodstream. The bulk of the injected iodine is selectively concentrated in the thyroid gland where it is incorporated into the hormone. Therefore the extent of thyroid activity (hormone synthesis) is reflected in the quantity of I^{131} utilized. This radioactivity can be indirectly measured by (a) scanning the patient's thyroid with a radiation detector which will indicate the quantity and distribution of the radioactive tracer. (b) Another procedure is to remove a small segment of the tissue and treat it for viewing with a microscope (see section on Microscopy). The tissue affixed to the slide is dipped in a photographic emulsion and the I^{131} within the tissue will eventually expose the overlaying photographic film. After the slide with the emulsion is developed, the exposure sites will appear as grains in the film directly over the site of incorporation. This technique is called radioautography.

For example, it is possible to label DNA molecules by using a radioactive *precursor* (one of the building constituents) for the DNA. As the cell makes the DNA, it picks up the labeled precursor material. By using the techniques described previously, one can demonstrate the rate of DNA synthesis as in repair. The procedure is called *radioautography.* Another example involves iodine, which is the major component of a hormone of the thyroid gland. Practically all ingested iodine is concentrated by this gland; therefore by using radioactive iodine (I^{131}) and *histology* (the study of tissues), a fair picture of the metabolic activities of the thyroid as it relates to making the specific hormone can be obtained (Figure 1-6).

structural components and their function

If it is necessary to study the cell in order to understand the physiology of an organ, then the same logic can be applied to cytology—namely, to understand the cell we have to study its parts. As stated previously, the electron microscope and equipment that permits cell fractionation provide a fairly detailed picture of a cell's functional components.

The objective of this section is to describe the life substance, *cytoplasm,* and then to work from the outside of the cell toward its center. As a matter of convenience the components of a cell can be divided into *membranes,* which include the outer limiting membrane and the internal cell membranes; *organelles,* which refer to structures that are generally nontransitory in nature and provide some vital function; *inclusions,* referring to structures usually more transitory which for the most part play a less important role; the *nucleus,* generally an oval or round body separated from the rest of the cell by a membrane and responsible for directing activities of the cell (Module 1).

cytoplasm

The term *cytoplasm* usually refers to the material external to the nucleus. The cytoplasm of the nucleus is termed *nucleoplasm,* to distinguish it spatially from the material external to the nucleus (Table 1-1).

table 1-1
CELLULAR
COMPONENTS

COMPONENTS	PERCENTAGES[a]	LOCATION
Water	80	Free or bound
Proteins	15	Membranes, granules, enzymes, dissolved membranes, inclusions
Lipids	2	Membranes, inclusions, droplets
Carbohydrates	1	Inclusions
Inorganic materials	1	Free or bound

[a] Percentages of water proteins and lipids vary; for example, water content ranges between 65 to 90 percent, and in brain tissue the lipid content would increase to 15 percent.

As we can see, cytoplasm is principally a "water-protein" complex, and in spite of its high water content, cytoplasm exists in a fairly solid state. The complexing of proteins and water into a *gel* and the properties of this type of organization are in themselves so important in understanding life that they are treated separately in greater detail in Chapter 2. For the present, several statements on the nature of cytoplasm are in order.

1. Although the percentages of the constituents remain relatively fixed, at no two moments are the subunits of the constituents of cytoplasm the same. This dynamic process is like a whirlpool in that it looks the same at any given moment of time, yet its water content is continuously changing.

2. Water, the most abundant constituent of cytoplasm, is a universal solvent. Lipids may also act as solvents.

3. The principal nonaqueous material is protein. Proteins either stimulate the metabolic rates of cell functions or are organized to provide structure to a cell.

4. Lipids are components of membranes, and a few types are involved in metabolism. Lipids can be stored as potential sources of energy.

5. Carbohydrates are the principal source of energy for cell activity.

6. The inorganic materials, for example, salts, although representing less than 1 percent of the solid material in protoplasm, are in most instances vital.

membranes

Cell Membrane

Maintaining the composition of cytoplasm in a fairly steady state requires a continual exchange in materials between the cell and its environment. Nutrients must be brought in and waste material must be excreted. Until the advance of the electron microscope, the presence of an outer membrane was theoretical, since the resolution of the light microscope did not permit the cell membrane to be observed. Previously only indirect evidence existed that made the theory plausible; for example, gentle pressure against a cell with a microprobe caused a crinkling of the outer edge. As this could not result from changes in surface tension alone, it was assumed that a membrane was present. Also, if a cell was damaged, the cytoplasm was observed to ooze out and then stop. This observation gave support to the speculation that the cell membrane was capable of repair if the damage was not too severe. The electron microscope provided the means for demonstrating that a cell membrane (plasma membrane or *plasmalemma*) does exist and that it has specific anatomical and chemical characteristics that help to explain the specific permeability and activity of cells.

The basic components of the membrane are lipids and proteins. They combine as a lipoprotein complex and appear as a three-layered (*trilaminar*) structure with proteins on the outside sandwiching the lipid material within (Figure 1-7). Collectively, the trilaminar membrane measures approximately 100 Å, although it varies slightly. As seen in the theoretical presentation in Figure 1-7, the protein-lipid orientation is uniform, but the molecules may exist in a nonuniform orientation, a *mosaic.* We can theorize that if there is a complete absence of the proteins and lipids, a "general pore" results. If only protein is missing or rearranged, a "lipid pore" might be formed and certain fatty substances would pass through the membrane. Conversely, if the lipid is missing, a "protein pore" exists that permits only the passage of certain proteins. The explanation of

figure 1-7

PLASMA
MEMBRANE—
TRILAMINAR
STRUCTURE

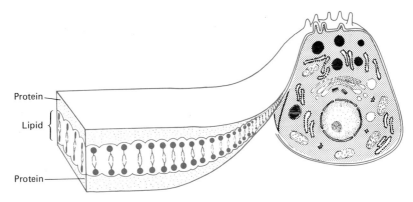

Protein

Lipid

Protein

An exploded diagrammatic view of the cell membrane showing the three-layered (trilaminar) arrangement. Not shown in this drawing is the fact that the outer protein layer has significant surface characteristics which are important in cell to cell interactions and immune responses.

pores is theoretical, but the possibility does exist, and the model illustrates that the membrane subunits need not be locked into a fixed position.

Surface
Specialization

In addition to interruptions in a membrane, modifications of the plasma membrane may exist. On the free surface of the cell small fingerline processes called *microvilli* may emerge. Cells with microvilli are found in the reproductive, urinary, and digestive systems. Generally speaking, microvilli appear on cells that specialize in absorption and provide an increase in surface area of the cell (Figure 1-8).

figure 1-8

MICROVILLI AND
CILIA

Microvilli

Cilia

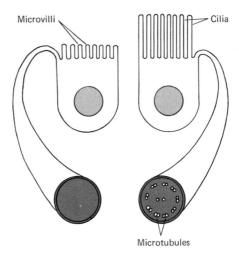

Microtubules

Two types of free surfaces are illustrated. The microvilli on the left are very small extensions of the plasma membrane and have no specialized substructure for support. The cilia shown on the right have an internal skeleton of microtubules. The microtubules are arranged in a very characteristic fashion with nine on the outside and two on the inside; each microtubule has a diameter of approximately 250 Å 40 millionths of an inch).

Larger extensions from the plasma membrane, called *cilia* (Figures 1-8), are found in tissues lining the respiratory and parts of the reproductive tract. Compared with microvilli, cilia are larger, structurally different, and they are motile. Cilia act in a coordinate manner to move substances along the surface of the cell. A lining of ciliated cells, as found in the respiratory system, serves to remove foreign material.

A coating of varying widths may appear on the surfaces of cells. Many theoretical functions have been assigned to this type of accessory coating such as protection, selective permeability, and adhesiveness. The coating is believed to be a complex of a carbohydrate and protein secreted by the cell.

Surfaces of cells are also modified for attachment. Several arrangements are seen in Figures 1-9 and 1-10. Cell membranes apparently fuse (Figure 1-9), a condition called the *tight junction*; in all probability, tight junctions have an adhesive secretion that facilitates the connection. A highly specialized structure, the *desmosome* (Figure 1-9), also affects a connection between cells by introducing an intercellular bridge. Anatomically, a desmosome connection consists of extraordinarily fine filaments that run from adjacent desmosomes and embed into the opposite cell cytoplasm. A very simple arrangement, in which one part of a cell extends over an adjacent cell, is called an *overlapping junction* (Figures 1-9 and 1-10). The result of these modifications is the maintaining of cell connections to provide for an intact lining or covering.

Plasma Membrane: A Penetrable Barrier

From the description of cell surface attachments, it is quite clear that a layer of cells presents a formidable barrier to the passage of materials.

This characteristic is as it should be, since it is important that the materials be contained within their respective systems and not leak throughout the body. However, there is also a continuing need for mate-

figure 1-9

CELL
CONNECTIONS

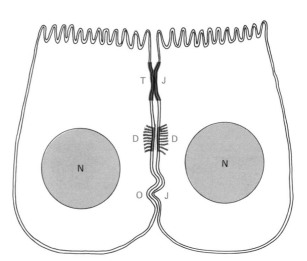

Three types of cell surface modifications for "connecting" cells are shown. The upper model demonstrates a tight junction (TJ); the middle figure is a desmosome (D); the bottom unit is an overlapping junction (OJ); nucleus (N).

figure 1-10

OVERLAPPING
CELL JUNCTIONS

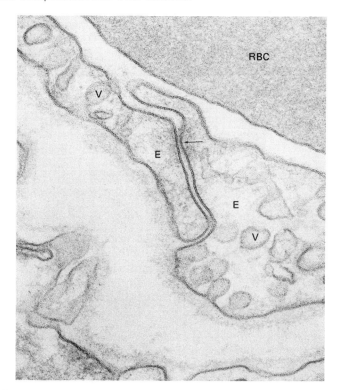

This tissue was taken from a heart blood vessel and magnified 200,000X; two endothelial cells (E) from a capillary and part of a red blood cell (RBC) cells are shown. The cell membrane (arrow) of the adjacent endothelial cells are in close approximation but not fused. A gap of about 40 Å exists. Note the flaplike projection of the right endothelial cell overlying the junction area. Note also the trilaminar membrane of the endothelial cells and of the RBC. The circles labeled with a V are vesicles, units for transport of materials across a cell; some are seen budding off the cell surface and others are seen lying free in the cytoplasm. (Micrograph courtesy of Dr. Morris Karnovsky, Harvard Medical School.)

rials to pass across a lining or covering. Providing nutrients to the tissues, absorption of nutrients from the digestive tract, the elimination of waste from the blood by the kidney, and the formation of hormones and enzymes in one part of the body to be used in another part of the body are examples of this need. The junctions between cells are so well constructed that most materials pass through the cells and not between them. One major exception is seen in the smallest blood vessels where rapid exchange is required, and special adaptations exist to permit materials to pass between cells as well as through the cells (Chapter 12).

The transport of materials across membranes and cytoplasm is quite complex, and it is obvious that certain materials pass through with ease, whereas other comparable materials are withheld. This is what is meant when a membrane is called a *semipermeable barrier* or by the term *selective permeability*. There are membranes that allow molecules to pass only in one direction, or allow one type of large molecule to pass through while restraining smaller molecules. This selective passage of molecules necessitates a controlled system and a great deal of energy to transport the molecules across a cell. The mechanism of permeability and membrane transit is discussed in detail in Chapter 2.

Intracellular Membranes

The membrane is not limited to the boundaries of the cell. Although the cytoplasm appears to be a homogeneous material, it is composed of a complex network of membranes that crisscross the cytoplasm. It is obvious that if a cell is capable of producing literally hundreds of different types of molecules, which in turn reflect a multiplicity of activity, a means for compartmentalizing the material must exist. Some cytologists are of the opinion that all of the intracellular membranes are modifications or extensions of the plasma membrane (Module 1).

organelles

The point was made earlier in this chapter that individual cells (like independent, one-cell organisms) perform all of the vital functions associated with body activity and that digestion, elimination, respiration, and transport are accomplished by the organelles. Many cells, however, are seen without one or more of these subcellular entities. This condition reflects the development of cells that adapt to specific roles in a multicellular organism.

Endoplasmic Reticulum

Some of the earliest electron micrographs show a complex network of membranes and channels. Because these membranes were first located deep within the cytoplasm, they were called the *endoplasmic reticulum.* Some endoplasmic reticulum (ER) has a rough appearance (Module 1) due to the presence of attached granules; thus we speak of *smooth* and *rough* ER, dependent on whether granules are present or not. The granular bodies are called *ribosomes;* they are 100 Å in diameter, and they can be found as free structures in the cytoplasm as well as attached to membranes. Ribosomes are composed of RNA, proteins, and some lipids. The ribosomes can also exist free of the membranes in clusters, called polysomes (Figure 1-11).

Many functions are assigned to the ER: (a) The membranes form a tubular intracellular *circulatory system* linking the plasma membrane with the nuclear membrane and also communicating with other parts of the cell. (b) The ribosomes attached to the ER make proteins. (c) The membranes also possibly transport the newly synthesized proteins. (d) In muscle cells the excitation impulses are conducted along the internal membranes. (e) Parts of the membrane separate into saclike structures, *cisternae* or *vesicles,* which package secretory products and wall them off from other parts of the cells. Some of these functions are still theoretical, although each has some experimental evidence to support it.

Mitochondria

The cell employs several means of producing and storing energy. The principal output occurs in another membranous structure, the *mitochondrion* (Figure 1-12). The number of mitochondria varies from as few as 50 in relatively inactive cells to thousands contained within an active secretory cell.

The average minimum dimensions of the mitochondria are 0.5 to 1.5 μ. As seen in the cutaway drawing in Figure 1-12, the organelle appears as

figure 1-11
INTERNAL
MEMBRANE:
ENDOPLASMIC
RETICULUM

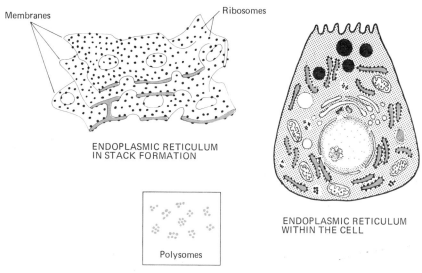

ENDOPLASMIC RETICULUM
IN STACK FORMATION

Polysomes

ENDOPLASMIC RETICULUM
WITHIN THE CELL

The endoplasmic reticulum (ER) is shown scattered throughout the cell and also magnified. Although the ER is shown with ribosomes (called rough ER), it may also be found devoid of ribosomes (smooth ER). Free ribosomes in the cytoplasm may also exist apart from the membrane, and occasionally they form clumps called polysomes.

a double-membrane structure. The mitochondrial membranes resemble the structure and composition of the plasma membrane, although one variation of the inner membrane is that it occurs in folds called *cristae*. The dual purpose of the cristae is to increase the surface area and provide sites for the assembly of important materials.

figure 1-12

MITOCHONDRION

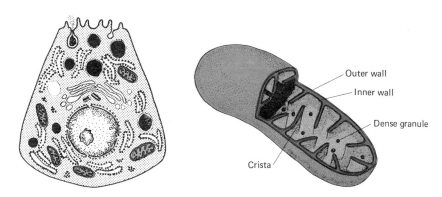

MITOCHONDRIA IN THE CELL

CUTAWAY OF A MITOCHONDRION

Mitochondria are scattered throughout the cytoplasm of the cell. The cutaway shows the internal structure of a mitochondrion, particularly the cristae, which provide more internal surface area. (Along the inner surfaces many chemical reactions occur.) The dense granules in the matrix are believed to be deposits of calcium phosphate.

The inner membrane is believed to be a site of cellular respiration, where raw materials (electrons) needed for the final production of the molecule *adenosine triphosphate* (ATP), a source of energy, are processed. The outer membrane also synthesizes the enzymes needed to move units of energy from the outside to the ATP assembly sites on the inner membranes (cristae).

Speculation is that mitochondria can produce themselves from pre-existing mitochondria, much as a cell reproduces. Both DNA and RNA are found in mitochondria, and evidently these nucleic acids provide for the production of a number of proteins needed by the mitochondrion to maintain itself and perhaps to reproduce.

In summary, mitochondria are large cellular organelles structurally organized as a membranous sac within a sac. Because of the compartmentalization, they are capable of several dynamic functions such as respiration synthesis, and release of a high energy compound. Mitochondria are frequently strategically located near sites of great intracellular activity, for example, where motility or secretion is observed.

Mitochondria may serve as a diagnostic parameter, because they frequently reflect certain disease states. Because the permeability of mitochondrial membrane is quite high, physiological as well as pathological conditions that affect cells in general will have a profound effect on mitochondria, such as in activation of respiratory enzymes. Many tumor cells have an increase of mitochondria that parallel the high metabolic activity of the cancer cells.

Golgi Complex   The *Golgi* unit or complex can be seen by both light and electron microscope, and it is generally located near the nucleus. The electron microscope reveals that the Golgi complex consists of parallel stacks of flat sacs or vesicles; interspersed between or adjacent to the stacks are vacuoles derived from the vesicles with smooth membranes (Module 1).

Because the Golgi apparatus in secretory cells is well formed and quite large, at one time it was believed to be actively involved in secretion. However, the absence of Golgi membrane enzymes and ribosomes leads us to assume that little synthesis occurs and that the Golgi unit functions as an adjunct system to the secretion parts of the cell. The precise activity is not clear-cut, but the Golgi complex acts principally to collect and concentrate secretions formed elsewhere in the cell, package the secretion into storage granules (0.1 to 0.3 μ), and bring about the release of the packaged material to the cell's exterior. The proximity of the Golgi unit to the ER of an actively secreting cell supports this concept. The notion that the Golgi unit is a specialized fragment of the ER has also been postulated.

The secretory material is believed to be transported from the rough endoplasmic reticulum to the Golgi apparatus. Within the vesicles the secretory products are concentrated and complexed and put into their final form (for example, joining a lipid to a protein to form a lipoprotein). Parts of the vesicles "pinch off" to form granules that may fuse with the cell membrane to bring about a release of granular material, or they may be forced out of the cell in the manner of a contractile vacuole (Figure 1-13). The release mechanism for the Golgi unit still is not very well understood.

figure 1-13
GOLGI FUNCTION

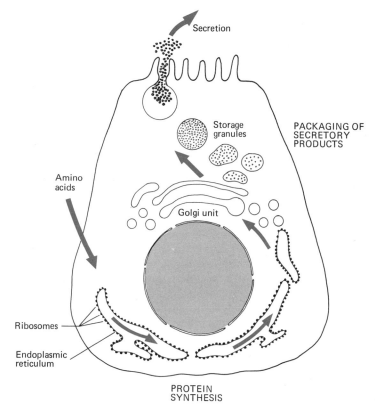

Amino acids are incorporated into the cell and are assembled into proteins by the ribosomes of the endoplasmic reticulum (ER). The newly synthesized proteins travel through the ER channels until they reach the Golgi unit. Here they are packaged into smaller granules for storage or for release. At the Golgi apparatus complexes of proteins with sugars or lipids may occur.

Centriole   A pair of structures lying close to the nuclear membrane are usually seen with the light microscope. These are the *centrioles* (Module 1), and show up under the electron microscope as twin cylinders composed of nine subunits. The centrioles have long been known to be associated with cell division, and they are frequently cited as the organizing center of the dividing cell. Details of centriolar activity in mitosis are discussed elsewhere.

The centriole is not restricted to dividing cells, for a centriole-type structure (*kinetosome*) appears in nondividing cells, always in relationship to motile units, for example, cilia. It is evident that the centriole has functions related to certain types of motility. The composition of the centriole is also poorly understood. Even the significance of the interesting feature that centrioles lie at right angles to one another is not known.

Another interesting observation is that the centriole, like the mitochondrion, is a replicating unit; that is, it is capable of making more of itself. This phenomenon is another illustration of a cell as a composite of semi-independent subunits.

Lysosomes   The word *lysosome* was coined to describe a dense particle found in most
cells that contains powerful chemicals (enzymes) that break down specific cellular material. These particles are the "digestive system" of a
cell.

Lysosomes are quite large, ranging in size from 0.25 to 0.50 μ. The example of lysosomal activity illustrated in Figure 1-14 provides a working
model. Certain cells, for example, white blood cells, are capable of *phagocytosis* (engulfing large particles of material); extracellular material is
engulfed by the plasma membrane and brought into the cytoplasm in a
vacuole. In an unexplained manner the phagocytic vacuole and lysosome
come to lie in close proximity, and when their membranes fuse or even
contact, the lysosomal membrane disrupts, spilling out the digestive enzymes. The contents of the two substructures intermingle, and the final
result is that the stored material is digested.

Lysosomal activity is not restricted to scavenging. There is evidence
that lysosomes work with the Golgi apparatus in expelling secretory material by digesting the plasma membrane to provide an exit for the Golgi
material. The lysosomal enzymes that are released from the cell may
erode the adjacent areas surrounding the cells and in this fashion provide "new room." In the development of an organism or any of its parts,
certain cells must die. Cells also age and wear out. The major purpose of
phagocytic cells is to engulf material until the phagocyte utilizes all of
its energy and space; then they, too, die. It is obvious that a mechanism
had to evolve to provide for the removal of the phagocytic cells. Normally,
phagocytes contain a great deal of lysosomal enzymes, which are released into the cytoplasm of the dying phagocyte, thus bringing about the
self-destruction of the cells.

figure 1-14

LYSOSOMAL
ACTIVITY

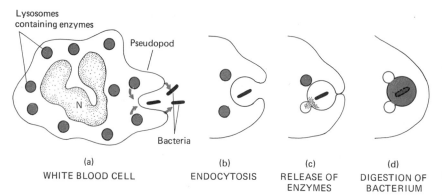

(a and b) The plasma membrane forms pseudopods that create a pocket which
surrounds a bacterium. Eventually the bacterium will be engulfed into the cell
cytoplasm by the projecting margins of the pseudopods, in a manner similar to
pinocytosis. Pinocytosis and phagocytosis are similar phenomenon for incorporat-
ing materials in bulk into the cytoplasm, and are sometimes referred to as endocytosis. (c) The bacterium is ingested and intact lysosome granules containing a
variety of enzymes move toward the vacuole containing the bacterium. (d) When the
lysosome comes in contact with the vacuole, their respective membranes fuse,
break down, and release the lysosomal digestive enzymes.

Vacuoles | Proteins have an affinity for water; that is, proteins readily form a bond with water molecules. If part of the membrane pinches off and encloses the protein bound with water, a *vacuole* is formed. Vacuoles vary in size from minute structures difficult to observe even with a microscope to vacuoles that fill almost the entire cell. After materials are discharged from the vacuole, the remaining empty unit is termed a *vesicle*. Vesicles may remain as containers to be refilled or they may rejoin the internal or plasma membranes. Vacuoles and vesicles are important internal features of the cell, because they can segregate chemically active substances from the rest of the cytoplasm (Module 1).

inclusions | Many of the components of cytoplasm are dissolved in the water component, but an equally large number remain suspended. It is the suspension of particles in water that makes cytoplasm a gel (Chapter 2). The suspended particles form the category of *inclusions*, and examples would be pigments, fat droplets, and large food molecules (Module 1-1). Some inclusions are highly transitory and may appear or disappear at any moment during a cell's lifetime.

Lipids, Glycogen, and Pigments | All cells contain significant amounts of lipids located within the membranes or finely dispersed through the cytoplasm. In special instances, such as in storage fat cells or in aging or dying cells, one type of lipid called *fat* will accumulate into sizable droplets (Figure 1-15).

Carbohydrates are stored intracellularly as glycogen particles (Module 1). A metabolically active cell will show little glycogen storage, since it is utilizing the energy supply for metabolism; conversely, a similar cell in a resting period will be characterized by large numbers of glycogen particles.

Examples of pigment inclusions would be the melanin granules synthesized by the cells of the skin. Melanin plus hemoglobin contribute most of the color observed in living tissue. Quite frequently melanin granules become more prevalent when cells age or become injured. The relationship of this increased pigmentation with aging is not yet clearly understood.

figure 1-15

FAT INCLUSIONS
AND FAT CELL

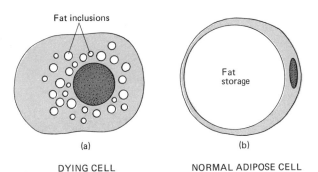

(a) DYING CELL

(b) NORMAL ADIPOSE CELL

(a) Fat droplets and inclusions are scattered throughout the cytoplasm. (b) The fat accumulation forms one large vacuole which occupies the greatest volume of the cell and pushes the cytoplasm and nucleus to the outer rim. Sometimes the cell is called a signet ring cell because of the narrow band of cytoplasm and nucleus restricted to the outside.

nucleus   The nucleus is the specialized functional center of the cell, and in the nondividing fixed cell, it usually appears as an oval body sharply defined from the surrounding, clearer cytoplasm (Module 1). Usually a cell has a single nucleus, except in striated muscle in which multinucleation is the rule not the exception. Whereas the cytoplasm contains the storage and production centers synthesizing the materials that drive the cells' machinery and that are also needed for the total functioning body, the nucleus is the operational center as well as the focal point for reproduction. Although some cells or parts of a cell can function without a nucleus (red blood cell), their life span is quite restricted, and the range of activity is not generally as great as is seen in the complete cell.

Separating the nucleus from the cytoplasm is the nuclear membrane, a double layer with micropores measuring up to 1000 Å (Figure 1-16). Within the nucleus the most important constituents are the nucleic acids DNA and RNA. Scattered throughout the nucleus are irregular clumps of material called *chromatin.* In the non-dividing cell, the DNA and the structural proteins are dispersed within the chromatin aggregates. When the cell divides, chromatin becomes threadlike and more compact, giving rise to the dense bodies called *chromosomes.* The chromosomes contain thousands of subunits, the genes, which hold the code that controls the functions of a cell.

A prominent body, the *nucleolus,* is found within the nucleus (Module 1). This intranuclear structure is rich in RNA and probably functions in transferring genetic messages from the nucleus to the cytoplasm. The remainder of the nucleus is composed of the clear *nucleoplasm,* the cytoplasm of the nucleus.

cytology and   In the diseased state the cell is the *unit* of pathology. Diagnosis can be
disease   made on the basis of changes in cell number or type, changes in cell structure or function, and the appearance of cell parts in the circulating fluids. Unique responses to drugs and physical agents are also utilized as criteria in cytological diagnosis; for example, tumor cells may be more susceptible than normal cells to antibiotics that inhibit synthesis.

figure 1-16

NUCLEAR
MEMBRANE

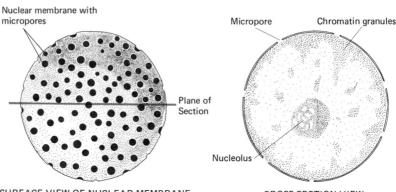

Nuclear membrane with
micropores

Micropore   Chromatin granules

Plane of
Section

Nucleolus

SURFACE VIEW OF NUCLEAR MEMBRANE   CROSS SECTION VIEW
OF NUCLEAR MEMBRANE

A diagrammatic reconstruction of the nuclear membrane as seen in cross section and surface view.

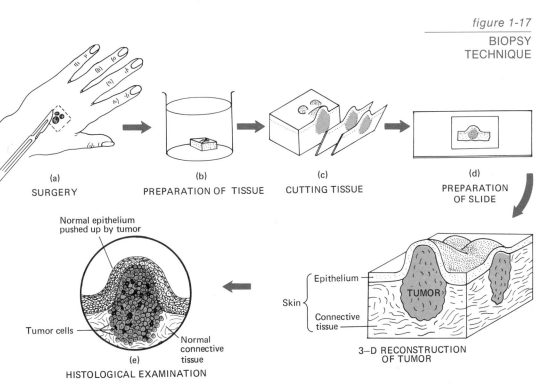

figure 1-17

BIOPSY
TECHNIQUE

(a)
SURGERY

(b)
PREPARATION OF TISSUE

(c)
CUTTING TISSUE

(d)
PREPARATION
OF SLIDE

Normal epithelium
pushed up by tumor

Tumor cells

Normal
connective
tissue

(e)
HISTOLOGICAL EXAMINATION

Skin { Epithelium

TUMOR

Connective
tissue

3–D RECONSTRUCTION
OF TUMOR

A technique that removes a small segment of living tissue for examination (diagnosis) is called a biopsy. For example, an area suspected of containing a tumor is sampled so that the pathologist can determine the characteristics of the growth. (a) A small segment of the diseased area is removed. (b) The tissue is treated to preserve as many of the living cytological characteristics as possible. (c and d) The excised tissue is cut for microscopic examination. (e) The tissue, as observed under the microscope, shows a tumor with malignant cells in the connective tissue layer of the skin. Two types of malignant cells are present, with and without the pigment melanin.

biopsy   Cells for cytological diagnoses may be obtained by *biopsy* (the removal and examination of cells and tissues). Areas that are open to the exterior (mouth, nose, ear, cervix, rectum) may be scraped or massaged to force some cells to the exterior. Cells are also obtained from the sputum, urine, and feces. When the region to be examined cytologically is not readily accessible, different instrumentations may be used as illustrated in Figure 1-17. Small pieces of tissue are removed in a biopsy using a plungerlike-needle device. The collected cells are then smeared onto a slide and stained for microscopic observation, or if the biopsy is a small piece of tissue, it is prepared for study by the procedure described at the beginning of the chapter.

    Examples of how cells obtained by biopsy afford the clinician a clue concerning the individual's health can be seen by studying the circulating blood cells. In certain types of anemia, the anemic state can be determined by merely counting the number of red blood cells. In certain diseases, for example, allergies or parasitic infestation, the frequency of one type of white blood cell (eosinophil) increases dramatically, and this measurement becomes a criterion for diagnosing the disease. The decision to operate when the signs signal appendicitis is made more incisive if the blood count shows an extraordinary high percentage of another type of white blood cell, the *neutrophil.*

Cancer of the cervix (the lower portion of the uterus that extends into the vagina) is readily detectable by swabbing the vaginal canal and cervical area with a cotton applicator and making a microscopic smear. If a cancer is present, alterations in some of the sloughed-off (shed, cast-off) cells may be recognized for cancer diagnosis. It would be diffi-

figure 1-18

PAPANICOLOAU
SMEAR

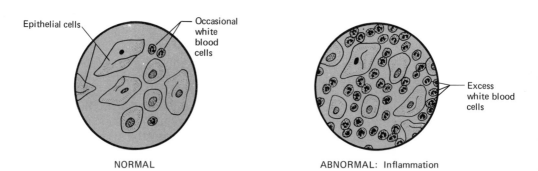

ENLARGEMENT OF CERVIX

PREPARATION OF SLIDE FOR
PAP SMEAR

MAKING THE PAP SMEAR

NORMAL

ABNORMAL: Inflammation

HISTOLOGICAL EXAMINATION

This technique is sometimes referred to as the "Pap" smear. A cotton swab is inserted into the vaginal canal until it touches the cervix, and by rotating the swab, a number of cells will be removed. The swab is then wiped on a slide and some cells remain on the slide. The slide is stained and placed under a microscope. At the left, a smear shows a number of epithelial cells, which form part of the outer mucosa, and a few white blood cells. At the right, the excessive number of white blood cells is an indication of an infection. If a tumor was present in the cervix, the smear would show a large number of tumor cells.

cult to devise a more simple technique for the detection and diagnosis of such a dread disease. The procedure was devised by Papanicolaou (1943) and bears his name, Papanicolaou or "Pap" smear (Figure 1-18). The importance of the Papanicolaou technique goes beyond detecting cancer of the cervix, because this method catalyzed the field of diagnostic cytology. A similar technique is also used as a means to obtain information about the secretion of specific female hormones. Vaginal smears will provide lining cells that differ in the sexually immature female when compared with cells obtained from a sexually mature female. Similar differences will also be observed at different stages of the menstrual cycle. Both situations reflect hormone levels. Thus, if a woman is experiencing a menstrual cycle abnormality, some insight into the causes of this disease is obtained by making a vaginal smear and looking for quantities of the large, flattened, lining cells that normally are present if a sufficient amount of female hormone (estrogen) is present. A paucity of these large lining cells indicates that insufficient female hormone is secreted.

chromosome analysis

The normal chromosome complement in humans is 46, composed of 22 pairs of *autosomal* (nonsex chromosomes) and 2 *sex chromosomes* (Figure 1-19). The chromosomes are recognized by their morphological characteristics, and the complete set is called the *karyotype*. Karyotypes of human chromosomes can be used as diagnostic tools, for some abnormalities in the karyotype correlate with certain medically recognizable disorders. The best known of these is *Down's syndrome* (previously and erroneously referred to as mongolism), which appears when there is an extra chromosome in the number 21 group (Figure 1-19). The presence of the additional chromosome produces severe mental retardation, a situation found in 1 out of every 650 live-born children. Other diseases

figure 1-19
KARYOTYPING OR
CHROMOSOME
ANALYSIS

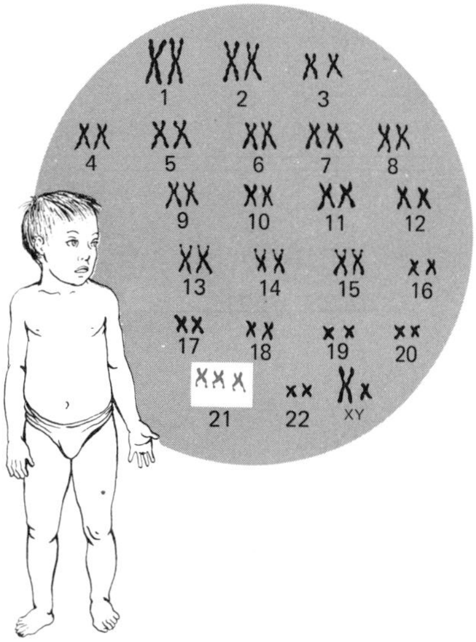

Within the past two decades visualization and classification of human chromosomes have been of diagnostic value in the identification of a number of diseases. The best known of such chromosomal defects is Down's syndrome in which an extra chromosome is found in the 21st pair.

may be also associated with chromosomal defects. Chromosome study in relation to disease is only some two decades old, and it seems reasonable to believe that only the surface has been scratched.

Many *intracellular* changes occur in disease tissue. Cells that are from a highly inflamed area frequently have a pale nucleus, slightly enlarged nucleoli, and a slight increase in the size of the nucleus itself. Cells removed from an area that is growing at an abnormal rate *(hyperplasia)* frequently have areas near the nucleus that do not stain. These alterations are small clues of dysfunction, but rarely is any one morphological change accepted as proof of the disease. However, if the cellular changes are correlated with the other manifestations exhibited by the patient, the clinician can make a diagnostic interpretation that contains fewer doubts than if he relied on just gross observations.

summary

historical

Examples of scientific discoveries that contributed to the development of the cell as the unit of life and to the field of cytology (study of the cell) are:

1. Cell theory by Schleiden and Schwann
2. Cell lineage theory by Virchow
3. Central dogma theory by Watson, Crick, and Wilkins

cytological procedures

1. Microscopy
   (a) light microscope provides magnification up to 2000×
   (b) electron microscopy provides magnification up to 1,000,000×
2. Cell and subcellular separation
   (a) centrifugation: uses gravitational forces to separate cells or their constituents; the separation is dependent upon cell or particle size and density, and resistance to gravity
   (b) chromotography: separation of molecules based upon their solubility in different kinds of solutions
   (c) radioactive isotopes: radioactive atoms that can be included in biologically active molecules incorporated into a cell as markers or tracers; since radioactivity can be measured, this tagging allows the investigator to follow a process or locate a special subcellular component

structural components

1. Cytoplasm: principally a water-protein complex; also contains lipids, carbohydrates, and inorganic materials
2. Membrane
   (a) structure composed of lipids and proteins that is organized into three layers; protein layers are on the outside
   (b) membranes surround the cell (plasma membrane) and the nucleus (nuclear membrane); membranes of organelles such as mitochondria, granules, endoplasmic reticulum have a similar basic structure and function as the plasma and nuclear membranes
   (c) membranes may contain pores, surface specialization (cilia and villi), and modifications for attachment and cell communication (tight junction, desmosome)

3. Organelles
   (a) endoplasmic reticulum: internal membranes that may contain ribosomes (seat of protein synthesis) and functions as an intracellular conducting system, packaging and storage of secretory materials
   (b) mitochondria: membranous sacs that are active in respiration, synthesis, and release of high-energy compounds.
   (c) Golgi complex: stack of flat membranous sacs believed to collect, concentrate, and package secretions made elsewhere in the cell
   (d) centriole: pair of structures near the nucleus that are known to be associated with cell division
   (e) lysosome: large granules containing digestive enzymes that are utilized in phagocytosis and secretion
   (f) vacuoles: pinched-off membranes that enclose proteins bound with water; after emptying their contents, the unit is called a vesicle; vacuoles are important because they segregate chemically active substances, such as enzymes, from the remainder of the cell
   (g) inclusions: a variety of suspended substances such as pigments, fat droplets, and glycogen
4. Nucleus: the functional center of the cell; the nucleoplasm or nuclear cytoplasm contains DNA dispersed within chromatin; chromatin is organized into chromosomes when the cell undergoes division

cytology and disease

1. The cell is also the unit of pathology in that diagnosis can be made on the basis of changes within a cell or in numbers and types of cells
2. Biopsy: the removal and examination of cells and tissue
3. Chromosome analysis: a diagnostic procedure; the presence of an additional chromosome is an excellent indication that the individual will have some type of mental disturbance.

2

cell functions

chemicals of life

molecules and compounds

biological compounds
water
elements in biological
  systems
organic compounds

energy conversion
energy flow
energy storage—ATP
metabolism

**movement of materials
through the cell membrane**
diffusion
active transport
pinocytosis

cell division
mitosis

motility
ameboid movement
cilia
muscle
common factors in motility

chemicals
of life

For centuries knowledge about human body function increased at a very slow rate because the unaided eye was the principal instrument for investigation. The examples of the technology described in the previous chapter provided new means for studying an organism, and as a result we now know so much more about the body at the level of chemical organization. The purpose of this chapter is to discuss the chemical and physical foundation of cellular activity and those cellular functions that are common to most cells: the utilization of energy, movement of materials across the cell membrane, cellular division, and cell motility. By having this basic knowledge, we can better understand the underlying causes for pathological conditions, as well as why certain treatments are used to bring the cells back to normal function.

molecules and
compounds

Atoms combine chemically to form *compounds,* the smallest unit of which is a *molecule.* Water is a compound consisting of two atoms of hydrogen and one atom of oxygen, H_2O. Common table salt is a compound consisting of one atom of the metallic element sodium and one atom of the poisonous gas chlorine, $NaCl$. The properties of the compound can be exceedingly different from the properties of the component atoms, as we see in sodium chloride. It is also possible to have molecules composed of like atoms as in the case of oxygen, which has two atoms chemically combined and is written as O_2. A similar picture is seen with hydrogen (H_2) and nitrogen (N_2). Two is not a required number, as the element sulfur is often found as a molecule of eight atoms (S_8).

Molecular weights can be calculated from *atomic weights** simply by adding the atomic weights in any given compound. For example, the molecular weight of water is

$$
\begin{array}{ll}
\text{atomic weight of hydrogen} = & 1 \times 2 = 2 \\
\underline{\text{atomic weight of oxygen}} = & \underline{16 \times 1 = 16} \\
\text{molecular weight of water} & = 18
\end{array}
$$

and for sodium chloride ($NaCl$),

$$
\begin{array}{ll}
\text{atomic weight of sodium} = 23 \times 1 & = 23 \\
\underline{\text{atomic weight of chlorine} = 35.5 \times 1} & \underline{= 35.5} \\
\text{molecular weight of sodium chloride} & = 58.5
\end{array}
$$

Gram molecular weight (or *mole*) is the molecular weight in *grams.* A gram molecular weight of any substance has the *same* number of molecules as a gram molecular weight of *any* other substance. This information is useful for preparations of solutions of salts, nutrients, and drugs, for the properties of a solution depend primarily on the number of molecules in a given volume rather than the weight of the molecule. Elsewhere in the chapter, the effect of concentration of solutions on cells is discussed.

* The atomic weight of each element is given in a periodic table found in practically every chemistry textbook and handbook.

biological
compounds

water

Properties

Life is dependent on the unique properties of water, a compound that constitutes about 70 percent of the bulk of the body. The ease with which a large number of compounds dissolve in water makes it the best-known solvent. Many molecules separate in water into particles that have a negative or positive charge (NaCl $\longrightarrow$ Na$^+$Cl$^-$); this process is called *ionization*, an essential prerequisite for many chemical reactions. Water has a high *specific heat* – that is, it takes a relatively large amount of heat to change the temperature of water 1°C – and a large amount of heat is given off when the temperature of water is lowered 1°C. Such a property is important in helping to maintain a constant body temperature, for the amount of heat given off during sweating is large, as is the loss of heat of a feverish patient during sponging. Water also acts as a lubricating medium and is the major component of the lubricants found in joints and organs. Water also serves as a mechanism of transport, carrying not only dissolved gases but also dissolved nutrients and wastes.

Solutions

Atoms and molecules exist in various sizes. Molecules can also form aggregates to produce particles of relatively large sizes. The size of atoms and molecules and their state in an aqueous solution determines the properties of the solutions.

TRUE SOLUTIONS *True solutions* are mixtures of two or more substances that produce a single-phase system. The system consists of the *solute*, which is evenly dispersed as ions or molecules throughout the *solvent*. An example is salt or glucose in water. Substances that form true solutions are also called *crystalloids* because they are capable of being crystallized.

COLLOIDAL SOLUTIONS In general, *colloidal systems* or solutions have larger particles (1 to 100 mμ) than true solutions. In a solution with two particles of equal size, however, one may form a true solution or a colloidal solution. Indeed, colloids may consist of unimolecular particles or aggregates.

We may distinguish colloids from crystalloids by the following:

1. Colloidal particles are not ordinarily capable of passing through a biological (natural) membrane, while crystalloids are.
2. Colloids scatter light.
3. Interfaces exist between the colloidal particle and the dispersing medium.
4. Colloid particles diffuse slowly.

Colloidal particles are kept in suspension by *Brownian motion,* the random movement of small solvent molecules that bounce into the larger colloidal particles and keep them from sedimenting under the force of gravity. Colloidal particles tend to be charged, either because they possess or because they attract charges (ions). Since they have *like* charges, they repel each other and are further aided in remaining in suspension.

Because colloidal particles do not usually pass through a natural membrane, small molecules present in colloidal solutions (for example, salts) can be removed by placing the colloid and salt solution in a membranous sac and immersing the whole in a large volume of distilled water. Initially, the concentration of the salts is zero on the outside, and the salts will diffuse from the interior of the sac to the outside. If several changes of the outside medium are made, the salt concentration can be reduced to near zero. The process is called *dialysis*, and it is an extremely important activity of certain organs such as the kidney.

Colloids also have the property of converting from a *sol* (a solution) to a *gel* (a solid) phase. The capacity to gel apparently resides in the presence and number of cross-links or bonds between long molecules. The heating of some gels will cause breaking of the cross-links, and the gel will convert to a sol. Certain gels are known to act in an opposite manner. In the cell, these phase changes can appear in localized regions; for example, during cell division the central area of the cell is in a gel state, whereas the peripheral areas are in a sol state. Gels are affected by changes in temperature, pressure, and acidity as well as by the concentration of the colloid.

IONIZATION When certain compounds are put into solution, the forces holding them together are weakened, and they come apart as electrically charged particles termed *ions*. The process of dissociation of the compound into ions is called *ionization*. The fact that the particles are charged is due to loss of electrons by one particle, leaving it positively charged, and the gain of electrons by the other particle, making it negatively charged. An example of ionization is as follows:

$$NaCl \rightleftharpoons Na^+ + Cl^-$$

The salt, sodium chloride, is ionized into the positive sodium ion and the negative chloride ion.

SOLUTION CONCENTRATIONS Solutions are prepared in various ways; some of the more common methods are listed below.

Weight per volume. This is a solution that contains a particular weight of solute in a given volume of solution. A 1 percent solution of glucose contains 1 g of glucose in 100 ml of solution.

Molarity. A molar *(M)* solution contains 1 g molecular weight (mole) of solute in 1 liter of solution. A 1 *M* solution of sodium chloride (NaCl) contains 58.5 g (1 mole) of NaCl in 1 liter of solution.

Osmolarity. Some of the properties of solution — for example, freezing temperature, boiling temperature, and osmotic pressure — depend on the *number* of particles rather than the concentration. The osmolar concentration of a solution is the concentration of solute given as the number of particles present in the solution. A 0.1 *M* solution of glucose would have half the number of particles as a 0.1 *M* solution of sodium chloride, since sodium chloride ionizes into Na$^+$ and Cl$^-$, whereas glucose molecules remain intact since they do not ionize.

Acids and Bases   The terms *acid* and *base* describe a particular quality of solutions. Vinegar and lemon juice have a sour taste and are acid, whereas the base ammonia has a bitter taste. The term acid is more precisely defined by the statement that acids are compounds that donate protons. Since hydrogen has an atomic structure consisting of a proton, a positively charged particle, and an electron, a negatively charged particle, when ionization of a hydrogen from a compound takes place, a proton is liberated. This proton is often termed a *hydrogen ion* (H⁺). Hydrochloric acid ionizes to produce hydrogen ions (protons) and chloride ions and is therefore an acid.

$$HCl \longrightarrow H^+ + Cl^-$$

Whether a solution is acid or basic *(alkaline)* has important implications for biological systems. Water, which is only slightly ionized, has a concentration of hydrogen ion of 0.0000001 *M* and is termed *neutral*.

$$HOH \longrightarrow H^+ + OH^-$$

Solutions that have higher concentrations of H⁺ than water are termed *acid*, and those with a lower concentration are termed *basic* or *alkaline* (Figure 2-1). However, to write the concentration in this way is awkward, and a system using exponentials (10^x is an exponent) has been devised. Thus the hydrogen ion concentration of water is 10^{-7} *M*, the exponent of which is −7. This revision is taken a step further by using the *negative* exponential of the concentration, a figure which is then called the *pH*.

$$0.0000001 \ M = 10^{-7} \ M$$
$$\text{negative exponent of } 10^{-7} = 7$$

An examination of Figure 2-1 indicates that the pH scale runs between 0 and 14, with the higher pH indicating a lower concentration of hydrogen ion and a lower pH indicating a higher concentration of hydrogen ion. The exponential nature of the scale means that there are *10 times* as many hydrogen ions at pH 1 as there are at pH 2. In biological systems many pH values fall between pH 6 and 8. However, the gastric juice has a pH value between 1 and 2 and is, thus, a very strong acid. The pH of the blood is about 7.4, and any marked deviation from this value results in severe physiological problems.

The pH of many fluids is maintained by *buffer systems* that are capable of combining with excess hydrogen ions. A buffer is a substance capable of neutralizing acids and bases and thereby maintaining the

figure 2-1

THE pH SCALE

Low pH values have a high concentration of hydrogen ions, while high pH values have a low concentration of hydrogen ions. The values for the hydroxyl ion (OH⁻) are the reverse of the hydrogen ion concentration.

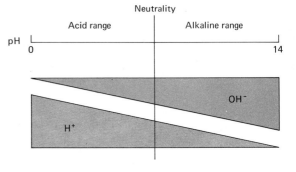

original hydrogen ion concentration of the solution. One of the main buffering systems of the body involves the bicarbonate ion, HCO^{3-}. When hydrogen protons are released by metabolic reactions, the excess H^+ combines with the HCO_3^- to form H_2CO_3, carbonic acid, thereby buffering against any major change in pH. Obviously, the capacity to buffer depends on the amount of buffering material available. Regulation of pH will be covered in detail in later chapters.

elements in
biological
systems

Of the 105 elements only a limited number constitute the molecules present in the human body. The more important of these are listed in Table 2-1. It is readily seen that carbon, hydrogen, oxygen, and nitrogen make up the bulk of the body. The relatively high concentration of calcium and phosphorus is easily accounted for by the deposition of these elements into the skeletal system.

All the other mineral elements found in the body are found as free ions or combined with organic compounds. Sulfur, for example, is found in many kinds of proteins as well as in the sulfate ion, SO_4^{2-}. Some of the other common ions found in the body are the sodium ion Na^+, chloride ion Cl^-, potassium ion K^+, hydrogen ion H^+, hydroxyl ion OH^-, magnesium ion Mg^{2+}, carbonate ion CO_3^{2-}, bicarbonate ion HCO_3^-, calcium ion Ca^{2+}, and the phosphate ion PO_4^{3-}.

Although iron constitutes about 0.01 percent of the composition of the body, its importance cannot be underestimated. It is an integral part of the hemoglobin molecule as well as other important molecules that deal with metabolism. Iodine, even less significant in percentage of composition (about 0.00003 percent), is classed as a *trace element;* yet it is necessary for normal activity of the body.

organic
compounds

Organic compounds were originally defined as those compounds that were synthesized by living organisms and that generally contained carbon. However, since so many compounds can be synthesized in the laboratory, the definition centers around the inclusion of carbon in the compounds. The cellular organic compounds are composed of carbon,

table 2-1
ELEMENTS
FOUND IN
HUMAN BODY

ELEMENT	PERCENT
Hydrogen	60.3
Carbon	10.5
Nitrogen	2.42
Oxygen	25.5
Sodium	0.73
Magnesium	0.01
Phosphorus	0.134
Sulfur	0.132
Chlorine	0.032
Potassium	0.036
Calcium	0.226
Iron	0.00059

Data given as percent of total atoms present.
From A. Loewy and P. Siekevitz, *Cell Structure and Function*, 2nd ed. New York: Holt, Rinehart and Winston, 1969.

hydrogen, oxygen, nitrogen, sulfur, and phosphorus, and these elements together constitute 98 percent of the composition of the body.

Carbohydrates

As the name implies, carbohydrate molecules are hydrates of carbon; that is, the ratio of hydrogen and oxygen to carbon atoms is almost always that of one water to one carbon ($1H_2O:1C$). The generalized formula $(CH_2O)_n$ is often used to designate carbohydrates. There are a large number of carbohydrates that are important in biological systems.

GLUCOSE The carbohydrate *glucose* is the most common energy-supplying molecule in the body. Its importance can be gauged by the efforts that go into keeping the level of glucose at 65 to 100 mg percent in the blood (*milligrams percent* is the number of milligrams of a substance in 100 ml of blood). Any sustained significant deviation from this value can cause illness and even death.

Glucose is a 6-carbon *monosaccharide* (single sugar) that is depicted in a linear fashion in Figure 2-2. These atoms can be arranged in several ways, and this figure demonstrates the arrangement of the same number of carbon, hydrogen, and oxygen atoms into the linear structure of *fructose*, another monosaccharide. When in solution, most glucose is in a ring form, and only a small part remains in the straight-chained form.

The adaptive value for storing glucose in some form is obvious. When amounts exceeding normal values prevail, glucose is stored as *glycogen* for future needs when there is a depletion of blood sugar. Glycogen is a *polysaccharide* made up of the many glucose units. Sometimes only two glucose units combine to form a *disaccharide (maltose)* by the dehydration reaction (Figure 2-3). Since other OH groups are available on a glucose molecule, long chains and branched chains can also be made. The fact that glycogen is a large molecule means that it is unlikely to move across a cell membrane, and it has to be broken down to glucose units before it can get out of the cell and into circulation.

The disaccharide maltose is only one of the many combinations that can be formed from the combination of two monosaccharides. The common table sugar is the disaccharide *sucrose*, a combination of glucose with fructose. Another one is the combination of glucose and *galactose* to form *lactose*, the common milk sugar.

figure 2-2

LINEAR STRUCTURE OF GLUCOSE AND FRUCTOSE

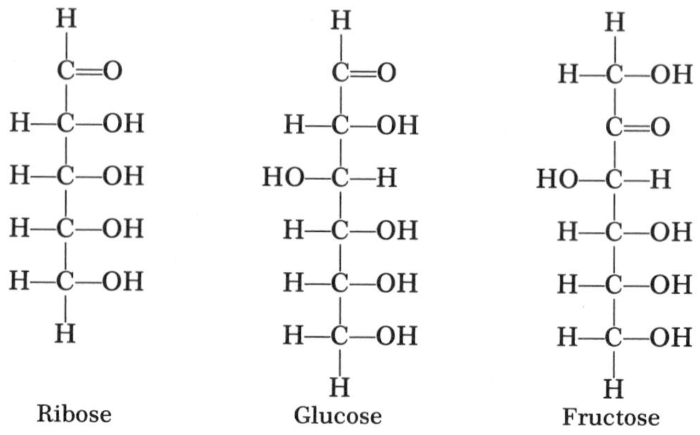

Ribose   Glucose   Fructose

figure 2-3

GLUCOSE,
MALTOSE, AND
POLYMER

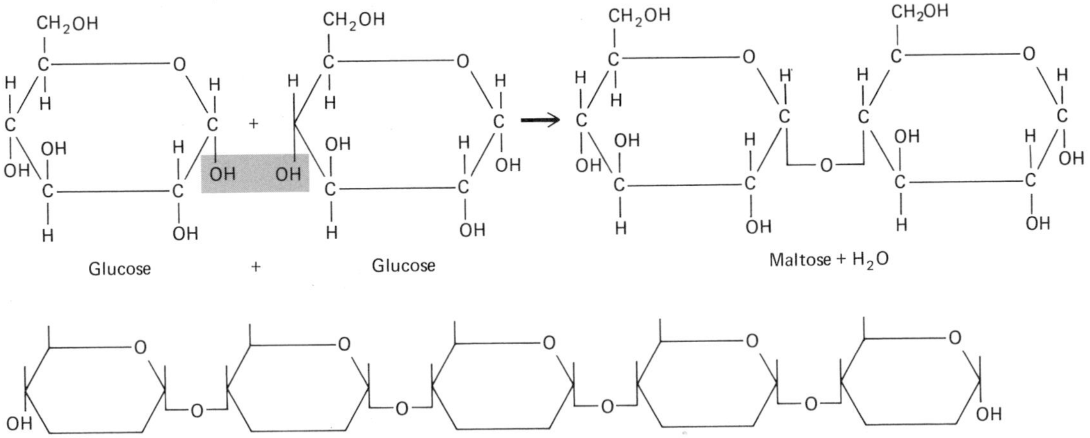

Glucose   +   Glucose   Maltose + H₂O

Long chain of glucose units

Maltose is formed by the removal of water from two glucose units. Similar reactions lead to formation of long chains of glucose units, as in glycogen.

Lipids   *Lipids* are somewhat harder to define because they constitute a diverse group of compounds. In general, they contain less oxygen than carbohydrates. The major share of the lipids are the fats, which are composed of glycerol and fatty acids (Figure 2-4). The fatty acids are straight-chained compounds with an acid group at one end. Palmitic acid with 16 carbons is the most frequently found type in the human body.

The acid groups of three fatty acids can combine with the three alcohol groups of glycerol to form a triglyceride (Figure 2-4). The properties of the fat or *triglyceride* are then determined by the type of fatty acids attached to the glycerol molecule.

Fatty acids can be saturated – that is, have hydrogen on all the available bonds; or they can be unsaturated – that is, have double bonds between carbons (Figure 2-5). As a general rule, animal fats tend to be more saturated, and plant fats tend to be more unsaturated. Most fats having a high degree of unsaturation are liquid, and those that are highly saturated tend to be solids, for example, corn oil versus lard.

The energy available from 1 g of fat is about twice that of an equiva-

figure 2-4

FORMATION OF
FATTY ACIDS

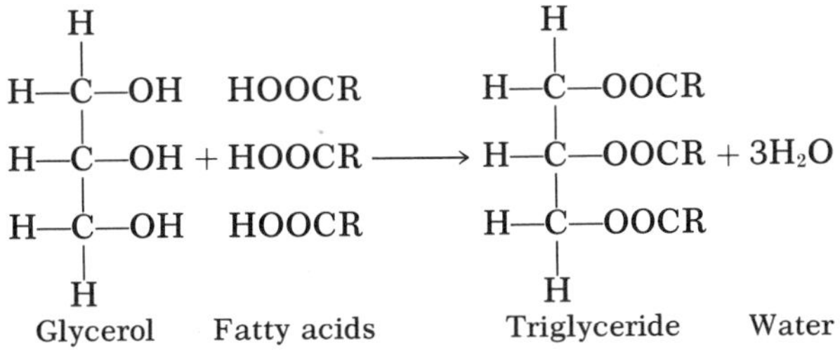

Glycerol   Fatty acids   Triglyceride   Water

Formation of a fat (triglyceride)

figure 2-5

SATURATED AND
UNSATURATED
FATTY ACIDS

$$H-\overset{\overset{\displaystyle H}{|}}{\underset{\underset{\displaystyle H}{|}}{C}}-\overset{\overset{\displaystyle H}{|}}{\underset{\underset{\displaystyle H}{|}}{C}}-\overset{\overset{\displaystyle H}{|}}{\underset{\underset{\displaystyle H}{|}}{C}}-\overset{\overset{\displaystyle H}{|}}{\underset{\underset{\displaystyle H}{|}}{C}}-\overset{\overset{\displaystyle H}{|}}{\underset{\underset{\displaystyle H}{|}}{C}}-\overset{\overset{\displaystyle H}{|}}{\underset{\underset{\displaystyle H}{|}}{C}}-\overset{\overset{\displaystyle H}{|}}{\underset{\underset{\displaystyle H}{|}}{C}}-\overset{\overset{\displaystyle H}{|}}{\underset{\underset{\displaystyle H}{|}}{C}}-\overset{\overset{\displaystyle H}{|}}{\underset{\underset{\displaystyle H}{|}}{C}}-\overset{\overset{\displaystyle H}{|}}{\underset{\underset{\displaystyle H}{|}}{C}}-\overset{\overset{\displaystyle H}{|}}{\underset{\underset{\displaystyle H}{|}}{C}}-\overset{\overset{\displaystyle H}{|}}{\underset{\underset{\displaystyle H}{|}}{C}}-\overset{\overset{\displaystyle H}{|}}{\underset{\underset{\displaystyle H}{|}}{C}}-\overset{\overset{\displaystyle H}{|}}{\underset{\underset{\displaystyle H}{|}}{C}}-\overset{\overset{\displaystyle H}{|}}{\underset{\underset{\displaystyle H}{|}}{C}}-COOH$$

Palmitic acid, a saturated fatty acid

Oleic acid, an unsaturated fatty acid

lent weight of carbohydrate. The reason for this difference is the relatively low number of oxygen atoms in fats, and more "oxidation" of fats is possible than of carbohydrates. Fats are not soluble in water and are therefore called *hydrophobic* (water hating) compounds.

Phospholipids are a class of lipids in which phosphoric acid is a component part (Figure 2-6). These molecules differ from fats in that they are *hydrophilic* (water loving) at one end, but with a large hydrophobic region making up most of the molecule. Any theoretical structure of the plasma membrane has to take into account the structural features of the phospholipids and how they might fit with the other molecules in the membrane, since up to 40 percent of the membrane is composed of phospholipids. Other lipid compounds, such as cholesterol, will be discussed in other sections of the book.

figure 2-6

PHOSPHOLIPIDS

$$CH_2OOCR_1$$
$$|$$
$$CHOOCR_2$$
$$| \qquad O$$
$$\qquad \parallel$$
$$CH_2-O-P-OCH_2CH_2N^+(CH_3)_3$$
$$|$$
$$OH$$

R_1, R_2 = Fatty acid chains

Phosphatidyl choline

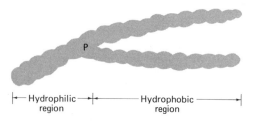

|← Hydrophilic →|← Hydrophobic →|
region　　　　　region

Proteins　　*Protein* compounds not only contain carbon, hydrogen, and oxygen but also nitrogen, and often sulfur. They are generally large molecules composed of long chains of *amino acids* and have a specific shape or configuration for each type of protein. The amino acid is the basic unit of the protein molecule and contains an amino group and an acid group attached to a central carbon. The acid group of one amino acid can react

figure 2-7

FORMATION OF A
DIPEPTIDE

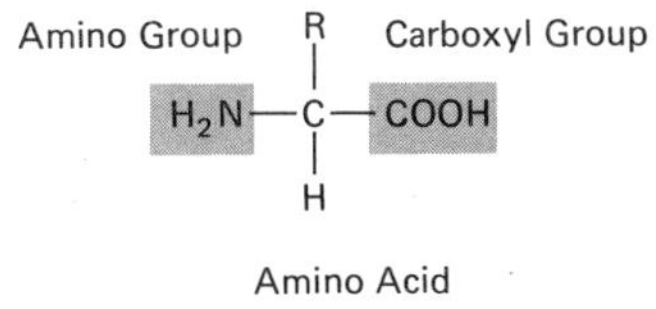

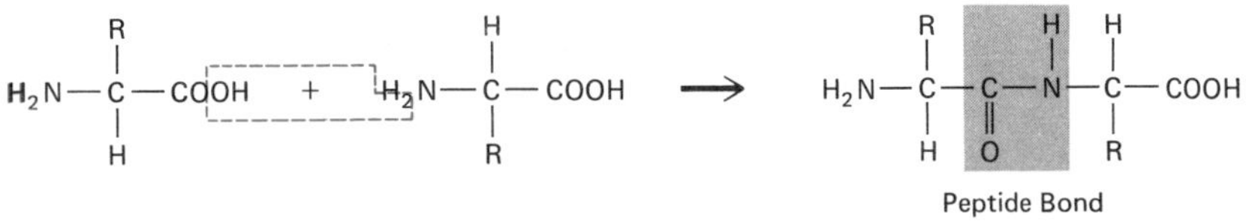

Amino Group   R   Carboxyl Group

$$H_2N-C-COOH$$

Amino Acid

$$H_2N-C-COOH \quad + \quad H_2N-C-COOH \quad \longrightarrow \quad H_2N-C-C-N-C-COOH$$

Peptide Bond

with the amino group of another by a dehydration reaction to form a dipeptide (Figure 2-7). Such a reaction does not preclude further reactions, since the amino group and the carboxyl group of the dipeptides are still available for combining with other amino acids. In this way, long chains can be built. There are 20 different amino acids commonly found in proteins, and, if we think of them as 20 different "letters," it is obvious that innumerable "words" (proteins) can be formed by combining them.

The reason for the large variation in properties of proteins is the varying properties of the different amino acids. Some have negatively or positively charged groups, and others have hydrophobic or hydrophilic groups. The reactions between these groups cause the folding of the protein chain into a particular configuration. Figure 2-8 shows the structure of two kinds of proteins.

ENZYMES The rates of chemical reactions depend on the amount of reactants and the temperature at which they react. In any living organism, *catalysts* are present that accelerate the rate of a reaction without being changed themselves. Catalysts in living systems are always proteins and are called *enzymes*. Without enzymes there would not be life as we know it, because the rates of uncatalyzed reactions are too slow to support life.

Enzymes function by lowering the energy needed for molecules to react (the *activation energy*). How this is accomplished is not entirely known, but the enzyme and the molecule that it works on (the *substrate*) must combine in order for the enzyme to work. This binding of the enzyme to the substrate requires a specific fit between the two and, in fact, is responsible for the specificity of enzyme action. A good analogy is that of the lock and key (Figure 2-9). The fit between the lock and key must be good if the lock is to open, and there must be a similar fit between the protein enzyme and the molecule (*substrate*) before the enzyme can function. Recent evidence indicates that enzymes can change their shape slightly to fit the substrate.

Nucleic Acids   The fact that the activity of the cell is controlled by the nucleus has been known for a long time. The degree of control is demonstrated by the experiments of Gurdon, who removed the nucleus from an intestinal cell of a tadpole, inserted it into a frog egg whose own nucleus had been destroyed, and after a period of development produced a perfectly normal

figure 2-8

STRUCTURE OF
PROTEINS

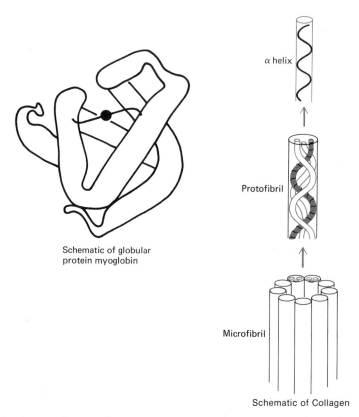

α helix

Protofibril

Schematic of globular
protein myoglobin

Microfibril

Schematic of Collagen

Proteins have various configurations. Two major types are shown above: fibrous, characterized by the structure of collagen, and globular, characterized by the structure of myoglobin.

frog. This experiment tells us not only that control comes from the nucleus, but that each nucleus has all the information for directing the development of the whole organism.

The information stored in the nucleus has been shown to be inherent in the molecules of *nucleic acid.* The nucleic acids are composed of chains of *nucleotides,* the latter being compounds containing one of five *nitrogenous bases,* a *5-carbon sugar,* and *phosphoric acid.* The components are shown in Figure 2-10. Four of these bases (*adenine, thymine, guanine,* and *cytosine*) are combined with the monosaccharide *deoxyribose* and phosphoric acid to form the nucleotides found in *deoxyribonucleic acid (DNA).* The bases are joined into long chains held together by a sugar-phosphorus backbone (Figure 2-11). Chains are also made with adenine, uracil (instead of thymine) guanine, and cytosine and ribose; this structure is called *ribonucleic acid (RNA).*

DNA There were several clues that DNA might be involved with information transfer in cells and control of cellular activity. First, DNA was found only in the nucleus (later, minute amounts of DNA were found to be present in mitochondria). Second, unlike many chemicals

figure 2-9

MECHANISM OF ENZYME ACTION

Enzyme recycles
Intact enzyme freed
Enzyme
Active site
Transient enzyme—substrate complex
Products of reaction
Substrate pool

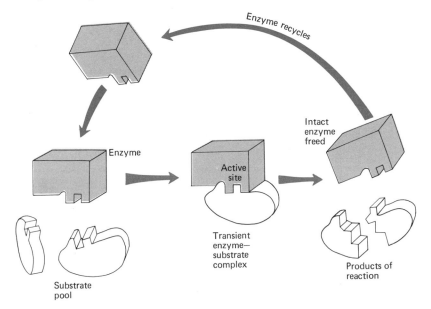

The enzyme is usually capable of converting thousands of molecules of substrate per minute to product.

figure 2-10

COMPONENT PARTS OF DNA AND RNA

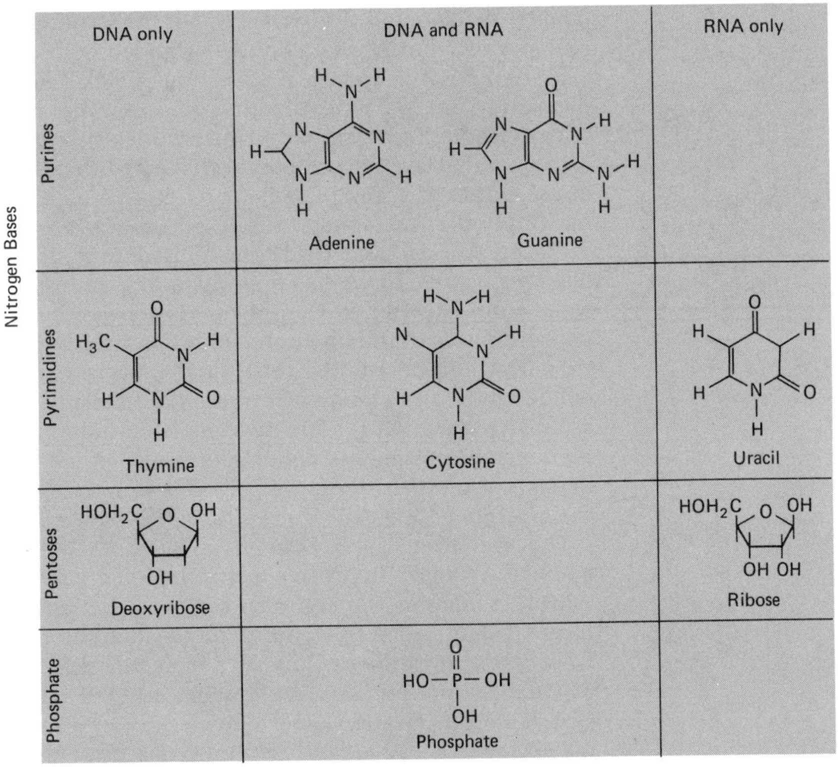

DNA only
DNA and RNA
RNA only
Nitrogen Bases
Purines
Adenine
Guanine
Pyrimidines
Thymine
Cytosine
Uracil
Pentoses
Deoxyribose
Ribose
Phosphate
Phosphate

figure 2-11

THE FORMATION
OF THE
NUCLEOTIDE
CHAIN IN DNA

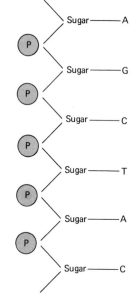

**DNA's components are joined together to form a
nucleotide chain in which alternating sugar (deoxyribose)
and phosphoric acid (P) units connect to side chains of
nitrogenous bases. (A for adenine, G for guanine, T for
thymine, and C for cytosine.)**

which vary in concentration in the cell, the concentration of DNA per
cell was constant, except in cells preparing to divide, where it was
double. Watson and Crick worked out the structure of DNA (Figure 2-12)
and showed that it was a double-stranded helix joined by the bases.

In making the model Watson and Crick found that adenine could
physically fit only with thymine, and guanine could physically fit only
with cytosine. This type of pairing is called *complementary* and is shown
as A-T and G-C. Chemical studies showed that the percentage of A was
equal to that of T and that the percentage of G was equal to C. (This does
not imply that the concentration of A-T was *equal* to the concentration
of G-C.) Watson and Crick postulated that prior to cell division, the
double-stranded DNA became unwound, and the strands became separated from each other. Complementary bases could now be added to the
exposed bases in the unwound and separated strands. If A were exposed,
then T would be bonded to it; or if C were exposed, then G would be
bonded to it, and along with ribose and phosphate, complete the second
strand (Figure 2-13). The two copies would then be exact copies or
replicas of the original. On cellular division, one of the copies would go
to each of the new daughter cells. Whatever information was present in
the original cell was now present in the new cells.

The fact that a cell exists is evidence of a carefully controlled sequence of events that are constantly being kept "in tune." The production of a copy of the cell also requires that the information be transferred intact from the parent to the daughter cell. The nucleic acid
DNA, present in the nucleus, is a molecule that meets the requirements
of stability and replicability that are needed for constancy of information. This information must be extended from the nucleus to the cytoplasm, where the actual synthesis of proteins is taking place. This

figure 2-12

THE WATSON-
CRICK MODEL OF
DNA

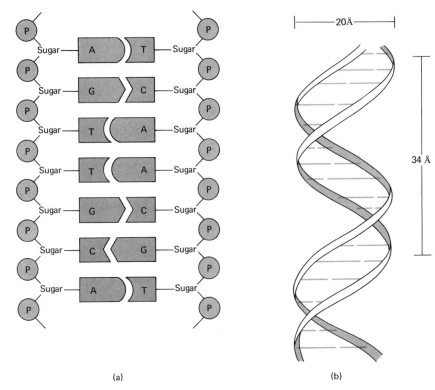

(a)

(b)

(a) The two strands of the DNA molecule connect by hydrogen bridges. Adenine always pairs with thymine of the opposite strand and cytosine always pairs with guanine. In (b) the double helical structure can be seen as a three dimensional structure with the strands wound around one another. The horizontal lines represent base pairs connecting the two strands.

figure 2-13

THE WATSON-
CRICK MODEL
FOR DNA
REPLICATION

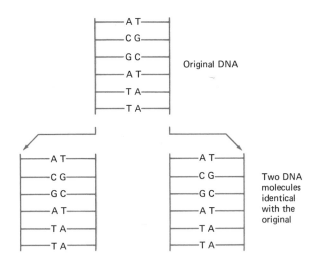

synthesis is accomplished by means of molecules of RNA.

MESSENGER RNA The information of the DNA is *transcribed* to an RNA molecule by the synthesis of an RNA molecule as a complement to the DNA; that is, the sequence of bases of the newly formed RNA molecule is dependent on the sequence of bases in the DNA. The newly formed single-stranded RNA contains *uracil* instead of thymine, but other than this difference and its smaller size, the RNA resembles a single strand of DNA. This *messenger RNA (mRNA)* moves out of the nucleus and into the cytoplasm and carries the information embodied in the sequence of bases on the DNA.

TRANSFER RNA The synthesis of proteins takes place on the ribosomes. *Transfer RNA (tRNA)* is a relatively small molecule (about 80 nucleotides), which functions to bring activated amino acids to the ribosome where the proteins will be synthesized. There is at least one transfer RNA for each of the 20 common amino acids, indicating a degree of specificity.

RIBOSOME The mRNA, carrying the information from the DNA, becomes attached to a ribosome that is composed of RNA and protein. The information on the mRNA causes the proper tRNA with its activated amino acid to line up with the mRNA on the ribosome. As the amino acids align, they form a protein chain by the action of enzymes. The total sequence of events is shown in Module 2A.

The Genetic Code

The sequence of bases of the DNA is transcribed onto the mRNA, which then moves out of the nucleus into the cytoplasm. How does this sequence of bases produce a particular sequence of amino acids in a protein? There are 20 common amino acids in proteins, and any code would have to account for at least 20 different "letters" (amino acids) that could be made into many kinds of "words" (proteins). If a single base in the DNA sequence could code for a single amino acid, there would be a code for only four amino acids (4^1), as there are only four bases in DNA. If two bases could code for an amino acid, then there would be 4^2 possibilities or 16. Neither of these possibilities could account for a code for 20 amino acids. However, if three bases could code for a single amino acid, there would be 4^3 or 64 possibilities, enough to code for all the amino acids as well as for signals to start and to stop.

The actual breaking of the code was begun by the brilliant work of Nirenberg, who utilized broken bacterial cells (*Escherichia coli*, a colon bacterium) and a mRNA made in the laboratory. The broken bacteria provided the needed factors for synthesis of proteins except for mRNA. The laboratory-made mRNA added was a polymer of uracil (U-U-U-U-U. . .). Using experiments in which all 20 amino acids were present, but only one of which was radioactive, Nirenberg demonstrated that the protein that was made consisted of a chain of the amino acid, *phenylalanine*. It appeared that the code on the mRNA for phenylalanine was then U-U-U. By varying the bases on the mRNA sequence, the complete code was deciphered.

How does the tRNA recognize a particular sequence on the mRNA and line up on the ribosome? It has been shown that the tRNA has a region where a code complimentary to the code on the mRNA exists.

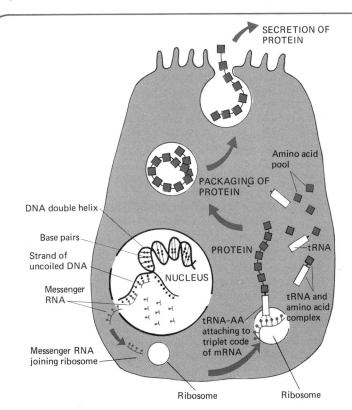

SECRETION OF PROTEIN

PACKAGING OF PROTEIN

Amino acid pool

DNA double helix

Base pairs

Strand of uncoiled DNA

Messenger RNA

PROTEIN

tRNA

NUCLEUS

tRNA and amino acid complex

Messenger RNA joining ribosome

tRNA-AA attaching to triplet code of mRNA

Ribosome

Ribosome

The synthesis of proteins requires information of a precise order and a mechanism for arranging the amino acids into the desired arrangement. A summary of the cellular mechanism involved in the synthesis of proteins can be represented as

$$\text{DNA} \xrightarrow{\text{transcription}} \text{RNA} \xrightarrow{\text{translation}} \text{Proteins}$$

The coded message in DNA is maintained in the sequence of bases and is transcribed to messenger RNA which moves out of the nucleus into the cytoplasm. In the cytoplasm ribosomes become attached to the messenger RNA (mRNA) and begin to translate the information as the mRNA moves past. The mechanism of translation of the RNA code into a specific protein involves reading the three base code (triplet) on the mRNA. This is done by matching up triplet codes in the mRNA with anticodes on the transfer RNA (tRNA) which have attached to them specific amino acids. This is accomplished on the ribosome, and as each triplet code is read, the mRNA moves to present the next triplet code to the ribosome to be matched with a new tRNA and its attached amino acid. The amino acids are bound together by the formation of the peptide bond, and when the entire message of the mRNA has been translated, the completed protein is detached from the ribosome.

For phenylalanine, where the code is U-U-U, an "anticode" was found on the phenylalanine tRNA. Anticodes have been found on a number of tRNA's that are complementary to the codes for specific amino acids. Two tRNA's with their activated amino acids are lined up on a ribosome according to the code on the mRNA, and a peptide bond is formed by the action of the enzymes. The mRNA now moves over to the next amino acid code, and the proper amino acid is lined up and bonded. This procedure goes on until the protein is completed. Usually more than one ribosome moves along the mRNA at one time, so that several proteins are being formed simultaneously (Module 2A).

energy conversion

energy flow

The cell requires energy in order to support such functions as the synthesis of new molecules, active transport of materials across the cell membrane, and the contractile process. The ultimate source of all energy for living things is the sun's light energy which is converted into chemical energy (food) through photosynthesis. Chemical energy, in the form of food, is taken into the body and transformed into usable energy through a series of chemical reactions.

energy storage— ATP

The power system of a cell is intimately involved with the formation and utilization of a stable, energy-rich molecule that could be called upon when a cell has to do work. Although all molecules have certain energy levels, *adenosine triphosphate* (ATP) is *the* primary high-energy compound because of the total amount of usable energy it releases when broken down by the addition of a water molecule (hydrolysis). The molecule as seen in Figure 2-10 is composed of adenosine, ribose, and three phosphates. When the terminal phosphate is released from a mole of ATP by the enzymatic addition of water, about 7000 calories are made available to do work. A calorie is the amount of heat required to raise the temperature of 1 g of water 1°C. The latter energy unit is termed the *small calorie;* a *large Calorie* is the amount of heat required to raise the temperature of 1000 g of water 1°C. The large Calorie is also called the *kilocalorie (kcal),* and it is the unit of measurement applied to food energy.

The 7 kcal released on hydrolysis of ATP compares with 2 or 3 kcal when 1 mole of almost any other kind of bond is broken. Sometimes ATP is spoken of as having a high-energy "bond," but it is more correct to think of ATP as a high-energy compound that releases more than the usual amount of energy when its terminal phosphate is hydrolyzed. The end product of this splitting is *adenosine diphosphate* (ADP) plus phosphate (often written Pi for inorganic phosphate). It takes at least 7 kcal per mole to make an ATP from ADP and Pi.

How is ATP used? In a chemical reaction such as

$$A \rightleftharpoons B$$

the changes in energy levels of the reaction in each direction, that is, $A \longrightarrow B$ and $B \longrightarrow A$, can be measured and expressed in terms of

figure 2-14
_____
ENDERGONIC AND
EXERGONIC
REACTIONS

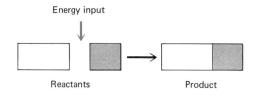

Energy input

Reactants   Product

The upper diagram represents an endergonic reaction, and the lower diagram represents an exergonic reaction.

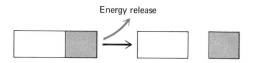

Energy release

free energy (the energy capable of doing work). Reactions occurring spontaneously – that is, requiring no energy input – have a decrease in free energy. These reactions are termed *exergonic* (ex = out, gonic = work). If we assume that the reaction of A ⟶ B is exergonic, then the reaction will proceed spontaneously, and energy will be given off. The reaction B ⟶ A, however, would not be a spontaneous one, and in order for this reaction to occur, energy must be put into the system – an *endergonic* reaction (en = within) (Figure 2-14).

In the synthesis of molecules by the cell, many of the reactions are:

figure 2-15
_____
THE COUPLING
OF ATP TO DRIVE
A REACTION

Glucose + phosphate → glucose 6-phosphate + 3000 calories endergonic

ATP + water → ADP + phosphate − 7000 calories exergonic

coupling of reactions

Glucose + ATP → glucose 6-phosphate + ADP 3000 + (−7000) =
−4000 calories
exergonic

NH_2

CH_2—O—$\overset{\overset{O}{\|}}{P}$—O—$\overset{\overset{O}{\|}}{P}$—O—$\overset{\overset{O}{\|}}{P}$—OH
                OH   OH   OH

OH OH

Adenosine triphosphate (ATP) structure

endergonic. These reactions require energy, which may be obtained from the exergonic splitting of ATP and coupling that reaction to the desired endergonic synthesis reaction (Figure 2-15).

ATP is not the only source of energy for a cell; there are other energy systems. However, ATP is the main storage molecule for energy, and its stability makes it well suited for this purpose.

metabolism   The sum total of chemical reactions in the body is termed *metabolism*. In general, metabolic activities consist of (a) the breakdown of molecules so that their component parts may be utilized in the formation of new molecules needed by the organism, (b) the capture of energy released during the molecular breakdown, and (c) the synthesis of new molecules (biosynthesis). Metabolism is sometimes characterized as consisting of *catabolism* (breakdown activities) and *anabolism* (synthetic activities). An example would be the ingestion of bread (flour is a plant polysaccharide or starch composed of chains of glucose units). The starch is broken down into individual glucose molecules, some of which are further broken down to carbon dioxide and water with the release of energy trapped in the form of ATP. Those glucose molecules not degraded can be synthesized into glycogen, a form of animal starch but with a different total molecular structure from the original plant starch.

The Metabolism of Glucose   The breakdown of 1 mole of glucose to carbon dioxide and water makes available approximately 690,000 calories of energy, and the sum of the reactions is given in the equation

$$C_6H_{12}O_6 + 6O_2 \longrightarrow 6CO_2 + 6H_2O + 690,000 \text{ calories}$$
$$\text{glucose} \quad \text{oxygen} \qquad \text{carbon} \quad \text{water}$$
$$\text{dioxide}$$

The equation shows only that energy is released and not what happens to the energy. Unless trapped by some reaction, the energy is not available to the cell but simply dissipates as heat. Neither does the equation show the many reactions taking place between the beginning of the glucose breakdown and its appearance as carbon dioxide and water. It is those reactions that tell us how energy is captured in the form of ATP. In general, the procedure is a stepwise breakdown of glucose with energy released in small portions and coupling of the release with ATP formation.

The process of *glycolysis* (glyco = sweet; lysis = breakdown) is accomplished in the absence of free molecular oxygen, and the final breakdown product of glucose in this pathway is lactic acid.

$$C_6H_{12}O_6 \longrightarrow 2C_3H_6O_3$$
$$\text{glucose} \qquad \text{lactic acid}$$

The breakdown of glucose by this process involves several important steps:

1. The utilization of two molecules of ATP to prime the breakdown process.

2. The splitting of the 6-carbon glucose molecule into two 3-carbon fragments.

3. The use of a cofactor, a small molecule that works cooperatively with an enzyme, to receive or donate hydrogen atoms.

4. The production of four molecules of ATP from each glucose molecule.

5. The production of pyruvic acid that can be converted to lactic acid in the absence of oxygen, or further broken down to carbon dioxide and water in the presence of oxygen.

ATP is produced by arranging phosphate groups on the 3-carbon fragments of glucose in such a way that they acquire high energy, and then transferring the high-energy phosphates to ADP ($\sim$ = high energy)

$$C_3 \sim P + ADP \longrightarrow C_3 + ATP$$

This occurs at two steps, and as there are two 3-carbon molecules resulting from each glucose molecule, the total ATP production is four.

Oxidation and Reduction

An important reaction during glycolysis, as well as in many other processes, is that of *oxidation-reduction.*

Oxidation is defined as the *loss* of electrons, and reduction is defined as the *gain* of electrons.

$$\text{(oxidation)} \quad Fe^{2+} \longrightarrow Fe^{3+} + 1 \text{ electron}$$

The iron ion has lost one electron and is therefore oxidized.

$$\text{(reduction)} \quad Fe^{3+} + 1 \text{ electron} \longrightarrow Fe^{2+}$$

The iron ion has gained an electron and is now reduced.

This simplified example does not illustrate one important point concerning oxidation-reduction reactions. Whenever oxidation takes place, there must be some acceptor for the electron that comes off the oxidized substance.

$$2Na + Cu^{2+} \longrightarrow 2Na^+ + Cu$$

sodium + ionized copper   ionized + copper sodium

In this reaction note that sodium is *oxidized* (loses electrons) and copper is *reduced* (gains electrons).

In biological systems loss of electrons is often accompanied by the loss of the proton in hydrogen; that is, oxidation is the loss of a hydrogen atom. In fact, usually two hydrogens are lost. An example is seen in the glucose breakdown cycle.

$$\begin{array}{ccc}
CH_3 & & CH_3 \\
| & & | \\
\boxed{H-C-OH} \rightleftharpoons \boxed{C=O} & + & 2H \\
| & & | \\
COOH & & COOH \\
\text{lactic acid} & & \text{pyruvic acid}
\end{array}$$

In the glucose breakdown sequence, a specific acceptor called *nico-tinamide adenine dinucleotide* (NAD) combines with the liberated hydrogens in the presence of specific enzymes. After accepting the hydrogens, the NAD is reduced to $NADH_2$.

$$
\begin{array}{cc}
CH_3 & CH_3 \\
| & | \\
H—C—OH + NAD \longrightarrow & C\!\!=\!\!O + NADH_2 \\
| & | \\
COOH & COOH \\
\text{lactic acid} & \text{pyruvic acid} \\
\text{NAD oxidized form} & \text{NAD reduced form}
\end{array}
$$

Even though oxidation-reduction reactions take place in the above series of reactions, there is no involvement of free molecular oxygen. The reactions that lead to pyruvic acid (and lactic acid) are therefore termed *anaerobic* (an = without; aer = air).

Pyruvic acid is a key intermediate that results from the breakdown of glucose by glycolysis. It can be reduced to lactic acid by the addition of hydrogens from $NADH_2$ (the reverse of the above reaction), or it can be broken down further in the presence of oxygen.

The *net* production of ATP resulting from glycolysis is

$$
\begin{array}{ll}
\text{moles of ATP used} & 2 \\
\text{moles of ATP synthesized} & \underline{4} \\
& 2 \quad \text{(net)}
\end{array}
$$

As each mole of ATP has a free energy of about 7 kcal, the total energy captured from 1 mole of glucose is about 14 kcal. The energy captured with respect to the total energy available (690) can be calculated as

$$
\frac{\text{amount of energy captured}}{\text{amount of energy available}} \times 100 = \text{percent efficiency}
$$

$$
\frac{14}{690} \times 100 = 2 \text{ percent efficiency}
$$

If we consider the energy captured with respect to the *total* energy of glucose, then the efficiency is approximately 2 percent.

The Krebs Cycle   Where oxygen is available, lactic acid is not an end point in the breakdown of glucose. Rather, pyruvic acid is broken down in a stepwise fashion with the subsequent release of carbon dioxide and hydrogens. The latter combine with oxygen to form water. Figure 2-16 shows the steps involved in this process. Significant points to be noted are (a) the release of single carbons as carbon dioxide, (b) the release of pairs of hydrogens (electrons) which reduce NAD, and (c) the cyclic nature of the process made possible by regeneration of one of the early compounds in the cycle.

After the release of carbon dioxide and the reduction of NAD in the breakdown of pyruvic acid, a 2-carbon compound, *acetate*, remains. With the aid of *coenzyme A*, acetate combines with a 4-carbon compound, *oxaloacetate*. It is by this means that the 2-carbon fragment

figure 2-16

REACTION
SEQUENCE IN THE
KREBS CYCLE

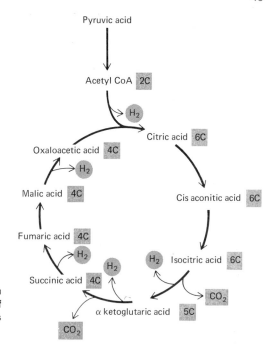

Note that the two carbon dioxide molecules given off account for the two carbons from acetyl CoA.

enters the *Krebs cycle* (so-called after Hans Krebs, who contributed greatly to our knowledge of this metabolic phase) to be broken down to carbon dioxide with the remaining hydrogens used to reduce NAD. Figure 2-16 shows that oxaloacetate combined with the acetate makes a 6-carbon fragment, *citrate*. The atoms of the citrate molecule are rearranged to make *isocitrate* which is oxidized. Carbon dioxide is released from the resultant molecule to form *α-ketoglutarate*. Between isocitrate and succinate, two NAD are reduced, and carbon dioxide is released. An ATP is also made in much the same way as described in anaerobic respiration. At this point, the 2 carbon atoms that have entered the cycle have been released as carbon dioxide. Hydrogens reduce FAD (flavin adenine dinucleotide), a hydrogen acceptor similar to NAD, in the succinate to fumarate reaction, and NAD in the malate to oxaloacetate reaction, making a total of four sites within the cycle where reducing hydrogens are trapped.

The cycle is started by addition of the 2-carbon acetate to oxaloacetate, and the 2-carbon fragment is eventually broken down with the regeneration of oxaloacetate. The cyclic nature of this process has many advantages. Not only does it serve in glucose metabolism, but it also plays a major role in the metabolism of fats, carbohydrates, amino acids and nucleic acids.

Mitochondria and the Formation of ATP

The Krebs cycle reactions take place in the mitochondria and require the presence of oxygen as the final electron acceptor with the resultant formation of water. The overall reaction is

$$NADH_2 + \tfrac{1}{2}O_2 \longrightarrow H_2O + NAD$$

The energy of 1 mole of $NADH_2$ is about 52 kcal. The electrons from this compound are passed along a series of electron transport molecules, each having a slightly lower energy level than the one before (Figure 2-17). The advantage of this cascade system is that the energy available in $NADH_2$ is released in steps rather than all at once. At *three* places along the way, sufficient energy is released to convert $ADP + Pi$ into ATP (Figure 2-17). In order for the reactions to proceed to completion, oxygen must be available. If oxygen were absent, the electrons would remain on each of the electron acceptors, for there would be no available acceptors for electrons and the greatest part of the NAD would be in the reduced form. This situation means that the electrons coming from the Krebs cycle reactions would have nowhere to go, and those reactions would stop, leading to an increase in lactic acid concentration. Cyanide poisoning is a result of the blocking of electron transport function of one of the *cytochromes* (an electron transport molecule) in the electron transport system. This blockage means that the electrons cannot be passed to oxygen and the whole system is shut down with the resultant lack of ATP production. Without ATP to support the energy needs of the sensitive nerve cells, as well as all the other cells, the organism begins to approach death.

figure 2-17

ELECTRON CASCADE AND ENERGY CAPTURE IN THE FORM OF NEW ATP

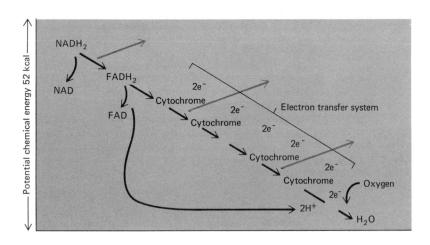

Figure 2-16 shows four sites where $NADH_2$ is made and one site where $FADH_2$ is produced. One mole of glucose is broken into 2 moles of pyruvic acid, so there must be a doubling of all the $NADH_2$ and $FADH_2$. The $FADH_2$ has a slightly lower energy level than $NADH_2$ and is responsible for the production of only *two* ATP, as shown in Figure 2-17. Thus we have

$$
\begin{array}{lll}
8NADH_2 \times 3 & = & 24ATP \\
2FADH_2 \times 2 & = & 4ATP \\
\text{Krebs cycle ATP} & = & 2ATP \\
2NADH_2 \text{ (glycolysis)} \times 2 & = & \underline{4ATP} \\
& & 34ATP
\end{array}
$$

Anaerobic respiration:

$$\text{Total} \quad \frac{2\text{ATP}}{36\text{ATP}}$$

The efficiency of energy captured from glucose breakdown is

$$36 \times 7 = \frac{252}{690} = 37 \text{ percent efficiency (approx.)}$$

The energy that is not captured appears in the form of heat. This heat can be used to maintain body temperature; however, in a warm environment, energy may be spent in order to dissipate the heat. There is also some feeling that some of the energy that is not trapped as ATP may, in fact, be utilized for other biological purposes such as movement of ions across membranes. Not only is there an increase in efficiency over anaerobic respiration but the energy still present in pyruvic acid is made available by breaking it down to carbon dioxide and water.

movement of materials through the cell membrane

The cell or plasma membrane has been characterized as a trilaminar structure – that is, a layer of lipid between two layers of protein. Although this concept has great support, it does not account for all the properties of cell membranes. Investigations have indicated that pores with an average diameter of 8 to 10 Å might exist in membranes. These pores have been visualized as being (a) dynamic (that is, they are not fixed sites, but appear and disappear), (b) tortuous rather than straight through channels, and (c) electrically charged (Figure 2-18). They are thought to be large enough to allow water and some small molecules to flow freely through the membrane. Potassium ions permeate the cell membrane more rapidly than sodium ions, which is in keeping with the reported diameters of these two ions, 4 Å as opposed to 5 Å.

The pores are only one way in which molecules can pass the cell membrane. If patches of membrane lipid are exposed on the outer surface of a cell membrane, large lipid-soluble material can "dissolve" and thus pass through the membrane into the cell.

The cell continually takes in molecules needed for synthesis and gives off waste molecules. It must also regulate the kinds and concentration of salt ions inside the cell. At first glance it appears as if transport across

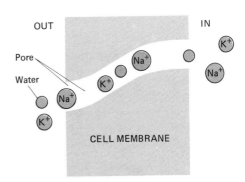

figure 2-18

HYPOTHETICAL PORE IN THE CELL MEMBRANE

Differences in size could account for some of the variations in the rate of movement of molecules and ions through the cell membrane. Tortuosity of the channel and electrical charges along the pore could also affect the movement of substances across the membrane.

figure 2-19

DIFFUSION OF
MOLECULES IN
SOLUTION

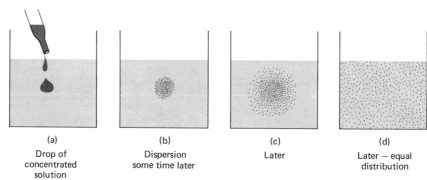

(a)

Drop of
concentrated
solution

(b)

Dispersion
some time later

(c)

Later

(d)

Later — equal
distribution

the membrane were handled by simple diffusion; that is, as the cell utilizes its glucose, new sugar moves from the higher (outside the cell) concentration to the lower (inside the cell) concentration. Based upon knowledge of membrane structure and observing rates of exchange, it is known that most diffusion occurs with "some help."

diffusion

Free Diffusion

At normal temperatures, molecules are in constant random motion. If the molecules are in a confined space, this random motion leads to collisions of molecules with one another and with the vessel walls until the molecules are distributed evenly in the closed space (Figure 2-19). If a drop of concentrated solution is placed in a large volume of additional solvent, the individual solute molecules will move until they are equally distributed in the new space. This process of movement from an area of higher concentration to an area of lower concentration is termed *diffusion*. This concept is important, since such processes as oxygen passage into the blood from the lungs depend on diffusion.

When a membrane is placed between a solution of distilled water and salt, sodium chloride (the sodium chloride ionizes to $Na^+ + Cl^-$), simple diffusion will occur if the membrane is freely permeable to the Na^+ and Cl^- ions. The movement of salt ions in one direction eventually will equal the movement of salt ions in the other direction. Actually, the same situation exists for the water molecules, since they are initially concentrated on one side and must become equally distributed across the membrane (Figure 2-20).

figure 2-20

DIFFUSION OF
SALT ION ACROSS
A MEMBRANE

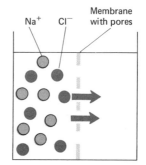
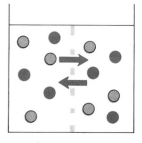

OSMOSIS In a system where the membrane separating the two solutions is *semipermeable* (with pores that allow only the passage of water but not large proteins), within a period of time the fluid level on one side is greater than that on the other. This result is due to *osmosis*. Osmosis is the movement of water from an area of higher concentration to an area of lower concentration; it is, in fact, a case of "water diffusion." In the situation above, the large protein molecules cannot move through the membrane, which means that the concentration of water in the side with the protein is lower than the side without. Water moves across the membrane from both sides, but since more water molecules are present in one side than the other, there is a net movement of water from one side to the other. Of course, because one side contains *only* water, it would appear that all the water would move to the other side in an attempt to equalize the concentrations. However, as the solution rises, pressure is exerted which, at some point (depending on the concentration of undiffusible protein molecules), is equal to the pressure exerted by the movement of water molecules from the side without protein. This pressure is known as the *osmotic pressure*. If the protein solution were in a closed but stretchable container, that container would increase in volume.

If red blood cells are placed in distilled water, the osmotic pressure is sufficient to drive enough water into the cell to cause disruption (Figure 2-21). Such a solution is said to be *hypotonic*. If the red blood cell were placed in a 0.9 percent solution of sodium chloride, it would retain its shape, since this solution matches the osmotic pressure of the red blood cell; the solution is termed *isotonic*. A *hypertonic* solution contains higher salt concentrations than normal, and water molecules move out of the cell, thereby causing *crenation* (shrinking).

figure 2-21

THE EFFECT OF
CHANGES IN
OSMOTIC
PRESSURE ON
RED BLOOD
CELLS

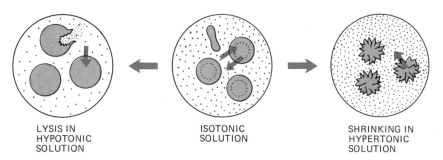

LYSIS IN
HYPOTONIC
SOLUTION

ISOTONIC
SOLUTION

SHRINKING IN
HYPERTONIC
SOLUTION

Facilitated
Diffusion

In some cases, increasing the external concentration of a molecule leads to a *slower* increase in movement of molecules into the cell than would be predicted from free diffusion. The interpretation of these results is that for the molecules to cross the membrane they must become attached to some molecule in the membrane, much like an enzyme-substrate reaction, and be released to the inside. Diffusion is "facilitated" by this carrier system and therefore the name, *facilitated diffusion*. The membrane complex involved in this type of transport is called a *carrier* molecule. Because the number of carrier molecules in a membrane is limited, the number of diffusing molecules attached to them is also lim-

figure 2-22

MODEL OF A
CARRIER SYSTEM
IN FACILITATED
DIFFUSION

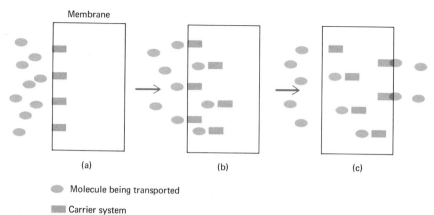

(a)   (b)   (c)

⬭ Molecule being transported

▨ Carrier system

ited. The carrier system therefore can be saturated. Facilitated diffusion does not change the equilibrium established (the internal concentration is determined by the concentration gradient), and no energy is expended by the cell.

The carrier system is a theoretical interpretation based on the results of experiments. Membrane molecules which bind material being transported have been isolated, and there are indications that it might be possible to isolate and identify all the components of the system. A model of facilitated diffusion is shown in Figure 2-22.

active transport   Both free and facilitated diffusions produce molecular distributions based on concentration gradients. However, a look at the actual concentration on either side of the cell membrane indicates that the distribution of molecules cannot always be accounted for on the basis of diffusion (Table 2-2).

Experimentation with radioactively labeled ions clearly show that Na^+, K^+, and Cl^- are freely diffusible across the membrane, and yet they are unequally concentrated inside the cell. It was also demonstrated just as clearly that if the cell's energy-producing machinery is shut down in any way, the concentration of ions will tend to become equal on both sides of the membrane. Obviously energy is required for maintaining the unequal concentrations seen in the normal cell.

If Na^+ can diffuse freely across the membrane, why is there such a low concentration of Na^+ *inside* the cell? The membrane contains an energy mechanism for moving Na^+ out of the cell *against* a concentration gradient. A similar situation exists for K^+; in fact, the movement of some of the K^+ inward appears to be coupled to the movement of Na^+

table 2-2

APPROXIMATE
CONCENTRATION
OF IONS ON
EITHER SIDE OF
CELL MEMBRANE
(IN MILLIMOLAR)

TYPE OF ION	EXTRACELLULAR	INTRACELLULAR
Sodium	140	10
Potassium	5	140
Chloride	100	4

figure 2-23

VARIOUS
METHODS OF
MOVEMENT OF
MATERIALS
ACROSS THE
CELL MEMBRANE

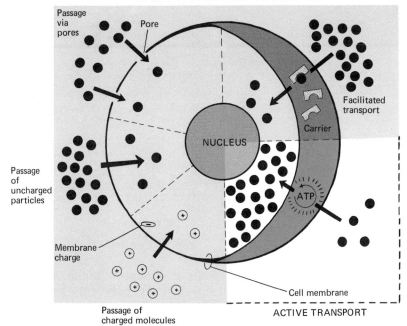

TYPES OF DIFFUSION BASED ON GRADIENT

outward. A system in which energy is expended to transport molecules against a concentration gradient is termed *active transport* (Figure 2-23). Models of active transport (Figure 2-24) have been developed, generally with the inclusion of a carrier or a chain of carrier molecules, but no clear picture of the molecular mechanism has been shown thus far.

The ions Na^+ and K^+ are two examples of actively transported molecules of which there are many more. Some sugars, amino acids, and many other compounds are known to be actively transported across certain cell membranes.

pinocytosis   *Pinocytosis* (Figure 2-25) is the process by which small vesicles are formed that incorporate materials adsorbed on the membrane. The vesicles move into the cytoplasm and their contents are released. This mechanism gives the cell another method for transporting molecules across the cell membrane. The vesicle formation and movement are energy dependent; pinocytosis might thus be thought of as active transport. However, the molecules passing into the cytoplasm by this process may or may not be moving against a concentration gradient. Many types of cells utilize pinocytosis, including white blood cells, kidney cells, and cells lining blood vessels.

cell division   Growth results from an increase in individual cell volume and an increase in the total number of cells. Individual cell volume is limited by the ability of diffusion to move molecules into and out of the cell at rates needed by the cell. Since the cell volume increases at a faster rate than the cell surface area, the surface-to-volume ratio decreases until it

figure 2-24

MODEL OF ACTIVE
TRANSPORT

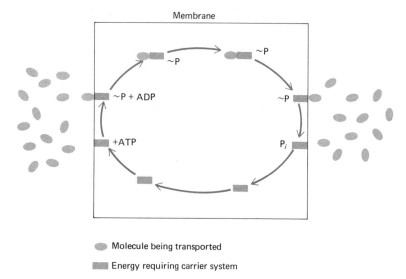

Molecule being transported

Energy requiring carrier system

reaches the point at which exchange of materials across the surface
membrane is insufficient to handle the metabolic needs of the cell. Division of the cell leads to a more manageable surface-to-volume ratio. This
relationship is not to imply that such ratios are the only influence on cell
division, but it is difficult to deny their importance.

The rate of cellular division varies, being high during early growth and
healing as well as during the normal replacement of certain cells such
as red blood cells. It can be low in some tissues, and in the case of
nervous tissue, nonexistent after full growth of nervous organs has
taken place.

figure 2-25

PINOCYTOSIS

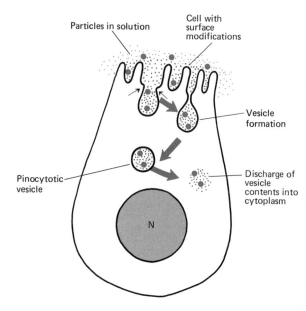

mitosis   *Mitosis* is the process by which the nuclear material is divided into two equal portions (*karyokinesis*), and the portions are parceled out to the divided cytoplasm. In some cases, the cytoplasm does not divide, leading to a cell with several complements of genetic material. The important generality that can be made is that the genetic material (DNA) that was duplicated prior to division, and is located in the chromosomes, is parceled out, a set to each new daughter cell.

The threadlike chromosomes are visible during cell division, but not usually during the *interphase* (nondividing phase). The DNA is apparently tightly coiled in the chromosome (Figure 2-26) during division, and thereby makes the chromosome easy to see. Replication of DNA takes place during the interphase.

The process of cell division is continuous once it begins, but for convenience it is separated into arbitrary stages: *interphase, prophase, metaphase, anaphase,* and *telophase* (Module 2B). In human as well as most animal cells, a pair of *centrioles* is present near the nucleus and begins the formation of the *mitotic spindle*, a structure composed of spindle fibers. The centrioles move to opposite ends of the cell and establish the poles to which the chromosomes move. Extending from the poles are spindle fibers, composed of bundles of microtubules. Some fibers attach to the *centromere* or *kinetochore,* a constriction of the chromosome specialized for fiber attachment, and others run from pole to pole. Each chromosome, composed of the two *chromatids,* lines up on the equator of the spindle and splits. After separation, each chromatid, now called a *chromosome,* moves toward one pole by a process not understood but known to involve the microtubules making up the spindle

figure 2-26

THE MITOTIC
APPARATUS

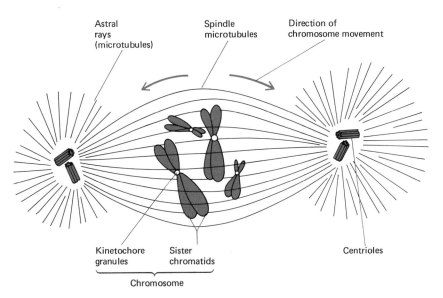

Astral
rays
(microtubules)

Spindle
microtubules

Direction of
chromosome movement

Kinetochore
granules

Sister
chromatids

Centrioles

Chromosome

Spindle fibers can be seen running from centriole to centriole. They also attach to the chromosomes at the kinetochore. Contraction of spindle microtubules pulls the chromosomes to the poles during anaphase and telophase.

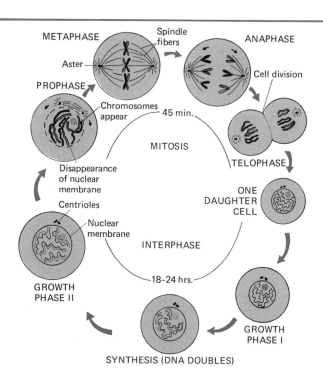

Approximately 10^{14} cells which make up the adult human develop from the single fertilized egg. This is accomplished by the process of cell division, or mitosis. For convenience mitosis is divided into the stages of interphase, prophase, metaphase, and telophase, but it must be made clear that mitosis is a continuous process.

INTERPHASE   Chromosomes are not usually visible by light microscopy during interphase, and electron microscopy shows only dense patches of chromosome material in the nucleus. However, it is at this period that the amount of DNA in the cell is doubled—evidence that a new set of genetic material is being prepared for the next cell division. Interphase is essentially a growth and energy storage phase, as mitosis depends on stored energy rather than energy made available at the time of division.

PROPHASE   At prophase the centrioles have begun to move to establish the poles of the spindle while chromosomes become more easily visible. The chromosomes can now be seen as a pair of chromatids joined by the kinetochore.

METAPHASE   The chromosomes become lined up on the equatorial plane and the spindle fibers are seen to be attached to the kinetochores of the chromosomes.

ANAPHASE   The chromatid pair in a chromosome separate and move toward the opposite poles. The fibers of the spindle shorten and the chromosomes seem to be pulled toward the poles.

TELOPHASE   The chromosomes, clustered at the poles and now beginning to lose their identity, are enclosed in a new nuclear membrane. The division of the cytoplasm takes place (cytokinesis) and the process of mitosis is complete.

figure 2-27
CILIARY ACTION

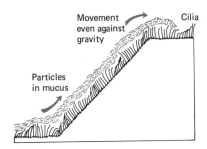

Movement even against gravity

Cilia

Particles in mucus

fibers. At the end of telophase, the cytoplasm usually cleaves to form the new daughter cells.

motility   We tend to think of cell motility in terms of muscle cell contraction or the movement of white blood cells engaged in phagocytosis. However, during embryological development, there is a constant reorganization of the cells as new anatomical features are formed. Examination of the cells of the fully formed body reveals that all cells, in fact, contain contractile-like proteins for intracellular movement (the movement of granules or the release of secretions), with those cells specialized for contraction (muscle cells) containing a high percentage of this type of protein.

ameboid movement   *Ameboid movement* is so called because it is exemplified by a slow movement over surfaces as is seen in the unicellular *Ameba*. It is an energy-dependent process that appears to involve changing parts of the cell from a gel to a sol and back again.

cila   *Cilia* are cell organelles that project from the cell's surface and by their motion move materials across the surface. Cilia are found on the surface epithelial cells lining the trachea, and the coordinated movement of the cilia in the trachea moves foreign materials trapped in mucus up and out of the lungs (Figure 2-27). Another motile process, structurally similar to cilia, is the *flagellum* that produces movement for an entire cell, for example, sperm.

muscle   Muscle cells are highly specialized for the function of contraction. Chapter 5 explains, in detail, the process of muscle cell contraction.

common factors in motility   Requirements for all motile systems are the presence of ATP to serve as an energy source and an enzyme that will catalyze the breakdown of ATP in order to make the energy available. In some cases, the enzyme also serves as part of the contractile system.

homeostasis   At all levels of organization of the human body there are mechanisms concerned with maintaining an optimal (relatively constant) internal environment. The importance of the maintenance of the internal environment was first recognized by the great French physiologist Claude

(a) *General concept of homeostasis and feedback control*

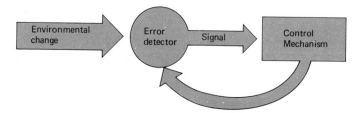

Environmental change → Error detector → Signal → Control Mechanism

Controlled compensatory response (FEEDBACK LOOP)

(b) Example of *Cellular Homeostasis*

Environmental change

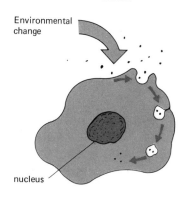

nucleus

Specific material needed by cell becomes absorbed on to cell membrane. Cell "detects" material, and "signals" control mechanism to respond by pinocytosis, which brings material into cell. Feedback signal turns off pinocytosis when sufficient material in cell.

(c) Example of *Body Homeostasis*

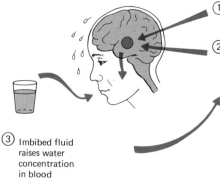

① Decrease in water concentration in blood through loss by sweating

② Brain center detects decreased water concentration and initiates thrist sensation and drinking

Feedback signal turns off thirst center

③ Imbibed fluid raises water concentration in blood

Bernard, who found that the blood sugar concentration and indeed all substances dissolved in the fluid that bathes the cells of the body are regulated within narrow limits. The self-regulatory activities carried out by the multitude of cells, tissues, and organs that make up the body were further elaborated by the American physiologist Walter Cannon. Cannon coined the term *homeostasis* to describe the operation of coordinated physiological processes which maintain stability. Homeostasis in its simplest form requires the detection of environmental change, which in turn automatically initiates a reaction that will compensate for the change and restores function to its normal state (see Module 2C). Such self-regulating life processes involve a *feedback* control; thus in the diagram two quantities are interdependent, that is, the environmental change and the controlled compensatory response. Each is a cause and each an effect on one another. Physiology is a science which is in large part concerned with homeostatic mechanism at all levels of organization.

The homeostatic mechanism operates at all levels. In Module 2C, homeostasis at the cellular level and at the organismic level are illustrated. In the following chapters of this book many other homeostatic mechanisms will be discussed in considerable detail.

summary
molecules
and
compounds

1. Atoms: combine to form compounds, the smallest unit of which is a molecule
2. Molecular weight: the sum of the atomic weights of the atom in a compound; gram molecular weight (mole) is the molecular weight in grams

biological
compounds

1. Water
   (a) water makes up about 70 percent of body mass; it is the best-known solvent; causes ionization of many compounds; has a high specific heat; acts as a lubricating medium and a vehicle to transport nutrients, wastes, and dissolved gases
   (b) true solutions: single-phase systems in which the solute is a crystalloid (capable of being crystallized)
   (c) colloidal solutions: contain larger particles that are generally charged on the surface
   (d) acids: donate protons (hydrogen ions)
   (e) bases: accept protons
   (f) pH: the negative logarithm of the hydrogen ion concentration; many pH values fall between 6 and 8 in biological systems
   (g) buffers: compounds that tend to neutralize acids or bases
2. Elements in biological systems
   (a) only a limited number of the 105 elements are found in the body; carbon, hydrogen, oxygen, and nitrogen are the most abundant
   (b) carbohydrates: generally have water-to-carbon ratio of 1:1; glucose is a 6-carbon sugar (monosaccharide), which can combine with other monosaccharides to form disaccharides, or it can form long-chained branched polymers (polysaccharides) such as glycogen, a starch

(c) lipids: substances soluble in lipid solvents; common fats (triglycerides) contain glycerol and fatty acids; fatty acids can be saturated or unsaturated. Lipids have a higher energy content than carbohydrates and proteins; phospholipids, diglycerides containing phosphate, are found in high concentration in membranes

(d) proteins: composed of the 20 common amino acids in various combinations, producing a highly diversified group of compounds

(e) enzymes: proteins that serve as catalysts to speed up reactions; they function by combining with the substrate molecule in a fashion somewhat analogous to that of a lock and key

(f) nucleic acids: nitrogenous compounds that are found in deoxyribonucleic acid (DNA) and in ribonucleic acids (RNA); DNA is found in the chromosome and carries the genetic information (code) in its sequence of nucleic acid bases. The code on the double-stranded DNA is copied on to single-stranded RNA, which combines with the ribosomes in the cytoplasm. Amino acids attached to specific transfer RNA line up according to the code and are incorporated into specific proteins

energy conversion

1. Chemical energy: obtained by the breaking of the chemical bonds in food; some of this energy can be stored in a high-energy substance, adenosine triphosphate (ATP)
2. Free energy: the energy that can be used for doing work
3. Exergonic: reactions that increase free energy
4. Endergonic: reactions that decrease free energy
5. Metabolism: the sum of the chemical reactions involving breakdown of molecules (*catabolism*) and synthesis (*anabolism*); carbohydrate metabolism involves a stepwise breakdown of glucose to carbon dioxide and water produces a net of 36 ATP's

   (a) anaerobic: part of carbohydrate metabolism is known as glycolysis and operates without oxygen
   (b) aerobic process: oxidative breakdown of a 2-carbon fragment by the Krebs cycle; oxidation of some of the intermediates leads to the production of reduced NAD, which in turn donates electrons to the electron transport system in mitochondria, whereby ATP is formed

movement of materials through cell membrane

1. Pores: membranes may have small pores (approximately 8 Å)
2. Osmosis: the movement of water from an area of higher concentration to an area of lower concentration; generally due to the presence of large protein molecules on one side of membrane
3. Carriers: molecule movement can be facilitated by the presence of "carrier" systems in the membrane. Energy is needed to actively transport molecules against a concentration gradient
4. Pinocytosis: the use of energy for the formation of small vesicles to move molecules into the cell

mitosis   1. Chromosomes divide and separate into two daughter cells
            2. Four stages
                 (a) prophase
                 (b) metaphase
                 (c) anaphase
                 (d) telophase

3

tissue, organ, system, and body organization

tissues
definition
epithelium
connective tissue
muscle tissue
nerve tissue

organs
general information
glands
tissue membranes

systems

body organization
directional terms
planes of reference
body cavities

clinical considerations

summary

In the living world there are one-celled organisms which perform all of the tasks that our multicellular bodies perform; they ingest food, break down materials for energy, synthesize new substances, eliminate waste, and reproduce. In contrast, the cells of multicellular organisms such as man are not self-contained; during development they lose or repress many essential and vital activities. The billions of cells in man are not mere images of one another, however. Cells sacrifice many functions to concentrate on one, and in doing so they frequently alter their structure. There are cells specialized for secretion, cells primarily designed for support, and cells that are exclusively for reproduction; each of these cell types is morphologically different.

Cells are described as the structural and functional units of the body, but the body is studied at various levels of organization, with each level being highly specialized for a given function. Groups of cells form *tissues*; tissues in turn unite to form *organs*, which are the components of *systems*, and the sum total of the systems is the *human being* (Module 3A).

tissues

definition

The organization of cells that are similar in structure and function comprise a tissue. There are only four basic tissues in the body. Most organs are composed of *epithelium*, which, with rare exception, lines and covers all parts of the body; *connective tissue*, which supports and binds parts; *muscle tissue*, which produces movement and heat production; and *nerve tissue*, which is specialized for irritability and conductivity. (In some textbooks blood is classified as a separate tissue, but here it will be treated as a type of connective tissue.) The detailed discussion of the structural and functional aspects of muscle and nerve tissues can be handled more meaningfully in their respective chapters (Chapter 6 on muscular system and Chapters 5, 7, 8, and 9 on the nervous system). The treatment in this section is merely to establish the primary tissues of the

epithelium

body and to describe in some detail epithelium and connective tissues.

Location

The lining of the mouth, the outside of the skin, the covering over the eyes, the inside of the nose, the outside of the heart, even the inner wall of blood vessels are composed of epithelium. In addition to "lining and covering," epithelial cells also constitute the major tissue in glands, for example, the liver and organs such as the kidney.

Classification

Epithelial tissue is classified on the basis of cell shape and cell arrangement. There are three basic epithelial cell shapes: an elongated columnar-shaped cell suitably labeled *columnar*, a flatter version adequately termed *cuboidal*, and a flattened type called *squamous* (Figure 3-1). The squamous cells that line closed body cavities with no opening to the outside (for example, the cavity in which the heart resides) are called *mesothelium*. The squamous cells lining the blood vessels are called *endothelium*. These special terms are not exclusively anatomical, but refer to the origins of the cells (Chapter 21). Classifications also include the specialty of the epithelial cell, for example, *secretory cuboidal epithelium* or *ciliated columnar epithelium* (Figure 3-1).

When the cells are arranged in a single layer, the tissue is called *simple*

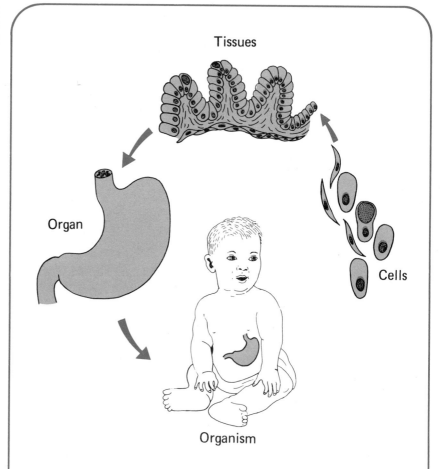

The human body contains 60 trillion cells all functioning in an integrated fashion. The cell is the smallest independent unit of biological activity, but a multitude of cell types exist, each type specialized to fulfill a given special function. Thus cells which form the component parts of man undergo a series of interactions with other cells which are genetically programmed to undergo development along specific lines. Thus primitive cells differentiate (specialize) to form aggregates of cells to carry out a specific function. Such functional aggregates are called tissues and may be made up of several cell types. Aggregates of tissues are highly organized to form various parts of the body. Thus a functional stomach obviously requires more than one tissue type, that is, structural connective tissues, contractile muscular tissue, secretory epithelial tissues, all arranged or organized in proper position to maximize efficient function. Finally, a number of organs, organ systems, and specialized tissues form the human organism, the most awesomely complex aggregation of functional parts ever to be found on this planet.

figure 3-1

EPITHELIAL
CLASSIFICATION

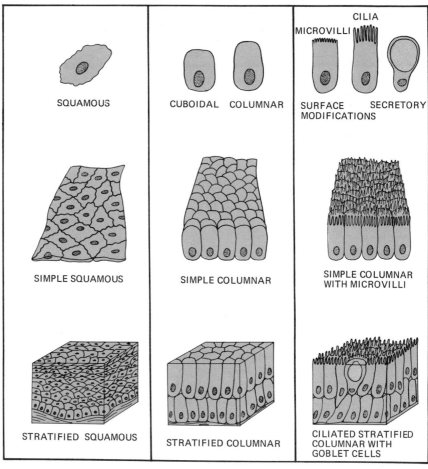

CILIA
MICROVILLI

SQUAMOUS

CUBOIDAL   COLUMNAR

SURFACE   SECRETORY
MODIFICATIONS

SIMPLE SQUAMOUS

SIMPLE COLUMNAR

SIMPLE COLUMNAR
WITH MICROVILLI

STRATIFIED SQUAMOUS

STRATIFIED COLUMNAR

CILIATED STRATIFIED
COLUMNAR WITH
GOBLET CELLS

The flat squamous cells exist in a single (simple) layer or in many layers (strati-fied). Cuboidal and columnar cells have similar layer arrangements. Epithelium may be further characterized by specializations, for example, secretory activity or surface modifications.

epithelium. If the cells are cuboidal, the layer is called *simple cuboidal epithelium.* Simple cuboidal epithelium is found in the kidney tubules; *simple squamous epithelium (endothelium)* lines the blood vessels; and *simple columnar epithelium* is located in the stomach and in the intestines.

When the cells are arranged in distinct layers, the tissue is called *stratified epithelium.* This type of epithelium takes on the name of the *surface cell;* if the top cell is squamous, the tissue is *stratified squamous epithelium.* The outermost part of the skin is an excellent example of stratified squamous epithelium.

In addition there are several immediate types between simple and stratified. For example, *transitional epithelium* is found in the bladder. When the bladder is empty, the lining appears to be stratified, but as the

table 3-1

TYPES OF
EPITHELIUM AND
LOCATION

DIVISION	CELL AND MODIFICATION	LOCATION
Simple	Squamous	Blood vessels, membranes
	Cuboidal	Kidney ducts, liver, glands
	Columnar, ciliated	Oviduct
	Columnar, nonciliated	Gall bladder
Stratified	Squamous, keratinized	Skin
	Squamous, nonkeratinized	Mouth, anus, vagina
	Cuboidal	Sweat glands
	Columnar	Urethra
	Transitional columnar	Bladder
Other types	Pseudostratified: columnar, ciliated	Trachea
	Transitional	Bladder

bladder fills and the walls stretch, the cells slip over one another and the lining becomes a simple layer, hence the name *transitional.*

General
Characteristics

CELLULAR Epithelial cells are close together and little intercellular material exists between them. That part of an epithelial cell exposed to the air or the liquid environment is termed the *apical surface,* and the end of the epithelial cell that is attached to an underlayer of tissue is called the *basal surface.*

VASCULARITY Epithelial tissues in the strictest sense are *avascular,* without blood supply, and are nourished by the blood vessels of the adjacent connective tissue. In spite of avascularity, the epithelial cells survive quite well, because they are never too far away from the connective tissue vessels.

NERVE SUPPLY Epithelium, because of its general location, is a strategic tissue. The skin, for example, is in contact with the external environment and locally it has a good nerve supply. Epithelium that forms linings or organs generally has a poor nerve supply.

REPAIR AND REGENERATION Epithelial cells generally are mitotically active, a process that provides the tissue with excellent regenerative and repair capabilities. This characteristic is especially true for the skin and digestive tract lining. (No cell functions in the stomach lining for more than 48 hours.) However, exceptions do exist, and certain epithelial cells (for example, liver) have the very slow turnover rate of about 45 days.

Function

The roles that epithelial tissues play are a reflection of their organization and location. We would expect that a lining or covering would contain cells placed close together. Likewise an avascular condition is advantageous, since a slight injury does not produce bleeding. A group of cells in contact with the environment must immediately respond to changes in the environment, and this function is reflected in the excellent nerve supply of epithelial tissue. Finally, since these cells are subjected to many types of irritations and injuries, efficient repair and regeneration are essential. Listed below are examples of the tissue's functions.

PROTECTION Epithelium provides a barrier against the invasion of microorganisms and minimizes trauma. The outer layer of dead epithelial cells of the skin forms a cocoon around the body and protects the internal tissues against drying out. The remarkable capacity of the skin to form new cells is another aspect of protection.

RECEPTION Certain epithelial cells are specialized to pick up stimuli from the environment that would not affect ordinary cells. These super-sensitive cells are connected to nerves, which relay the signals to the spinal cord and the brain.

SECRETION Epithelial cells can manufacture materials utilized by adjacent cells or by cells elsewhere in the body, and this material is termed a *secretion.* An example would be acid-secreting cells of the stomach. Some secretions are enzymes, whereas others are simply used for lubrication.

EXCRETION If the metabolic products of the cell are not utilized by other cells, they are removed from the body and are called *excretions.* The epithelial cells in parts of the kidney remove unwanted materials from the blood, which then pass from the kidney cells into excretory ducts and are removed from the body.

ABSORPTION The ability to take in materials that reach the epithelial surface varies, but it is most highly developed in cells of the kidney, gut lining, and the glands.

REPRODUCTION The epithelial cells of the testes and ovaries are unique in that when they divide, the chromosome number is halved, and they undergo morphological and genetic changes to form the mature egg (*ovum*) or *spermatozoan.*

connective tissue
Location

Connective tissue is widely distributed in the body. It fills spaces and organs, binds the tissues into organs, connects organs, serves as a major supportive tissue of the entire body, and provides the formed elements of the blood. Its ubiquitous distribution is equaled only by the large number of functions it performs.

Classification

Connective tissue is composed of a large variety of cells (Figure 3-2) and a mass of intercellular (between cells) material called the *matrix* secreted by some of its cells. Notwithstanding the number of cell types, the

figure 3-2

CONNECTIVE
TISSUE
CLASSIFICATION

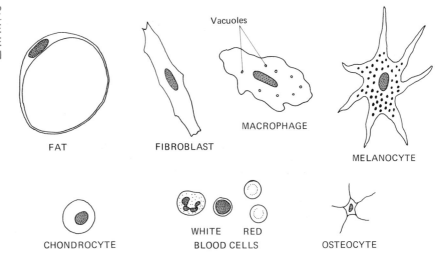

FAT   FIBROBLAST   Vacuoles   MACROPHAGE   MELANOCYTE

CHONDROCYTE   WHITE   RED
BLOOD CELLS   OSTEOCYTE

nonliving matrix that exists between the cells is more abundant, and the classification of connective tissue is usually based on the intercellular component that dominates the tissue. For example, *elastic tissue* contains a large amount of intercellular *elastic fibers.* Exceptions would be cartilage and bony tissues, so named because of their cells and not their intercellular substances.

Cell Types (Figure 3-2)

FIBROBLAST (blast = embryonic or primitive.) Fibroblasts are embryonic connective tissue cells that produce intercellular material, for example, *fibers* and the *amorphous* (without shape) matrix. In adult tissue, the fibroblasts are called *fibrocytes;* however, some fibroblasts persist even in adult tissues.

FAT CELLS Storage units characterized primarily by the large accumulation of fat droplets are called fat cells; the cytoplasm is pushed toward the cell membrane to form a ring.

PIGMENT CELLS Pigment cells contribute to the color of skin and other organs.

MACROPHAGES Scattered throughout the connective tissue are specialized cells, called *macrophages,* that act as defense units by their ability to scavenge.

CHONDROCYTE The principal cell of cartilage connective tissue is called the *chondrocyte.* It secretes the unique matrix that gives this tissue its tensile strength.

OSTEOCYTE The principal cell of bone connective tissue is the osteocyte, which in many ways is similar to the chondrocyte. The similarities are detailed in the section on new bone formation.

MAST CELL Mast cells store *heparin* (anticoagulant) and *histamine* (constricts blood vessels), and they are frequently located adjacent to the small blood vessels.

BLOOD CELLS A variety of blood cells is scattered throughout the connective tissue and serves in defense of the body (Figure 3-3). The functions of the red and white cells are discussed in Chapter 11.

RETICULAR CELLS Reticular cells are also part of the phagocytic defense system of the body. They also are part of the internal framework of many organs.

Fibers

COLLAGEN Collagen fibers are part of the intercellular matrix.

ELASTIC FIBERS Elastic fibers are found in most intercellular material.

RETICULAR FIBERS More delicate fibers than collagen and elastic, reticular fibers are the third fibrous component.

Amorphous Substance or Matrix

GROUND SUBSTANCE A semisolid, jellylike material in which the cells and fibers are embedded forms the base of connective tissue. The matrix is composed of a combination of proteins and carbohydrates, and in certain tissues (for example, bone) the deposition of salts transforms the gel-like material into a firm, hardened mass.

TISSUE FLUID The fluid and dissolved materials that escape from the blood vessels constitute the *internal environment.* Tissue fluid bathes the cells and provides nutrients, gases, and other vital materials; it is also involved in removing metabolic end products and waste.

figure 3-3

DEVELOPMENT OF
BLOOD CELLS

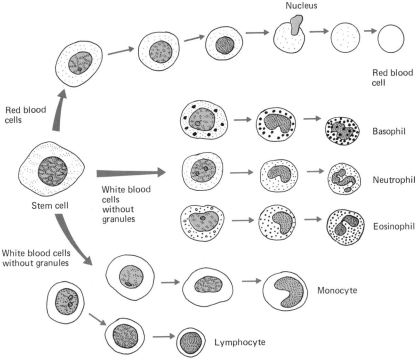

Types of blood cells, as they would appear in an idealized stained blood smear, are shown. A single cell is theorized as being the stem cell for all types. Note that the red blood cell and the platelet have no nuclei. Each cell type passes through a series of stages before reaching maturity. In certain blood diseases immature stages of the different cell types are found circulating in the blood, and this information helps to characterize the disease.

Tissue Types   AREOLAR The most abundant connective tissue of the body is the areolar type. It contains fibroblasts, fibrocytes, and other connective tissue cell types. The fibers are either collagenous or elastic. Areolar tissue is used as a "road bed" for blood vessels (to sit on and to keep them in place) and for "packing" so that virtually no spaces exist within the tissues of an organ.

RETICULAR The delicate network of reticular fibers characterizes reticular tissue. It frequently serves as the "skeleton" of such soft organs as the liver, spleen, and lymph nodes.

FIBROUS TISSUE Fibrous tissue functions as an anchor for lacing muscles together (*fascia*), attaching muscles to bone (*tendons*), or holding bones in place at joints (*ligaments*).

ADIPOSE TISSUE The fat cells appear (Figure 3-4) as the dominant unit in adipose tissue, because as they become engorged with fat droplets, they push the other cellular and noncellular elements aside. The stored fat material is used when needed for energy. Most mature individuals know where fat is stored, for example, the waist and lower abdomen. In addition to the latter anatomical areas, fat covers most of the organs as

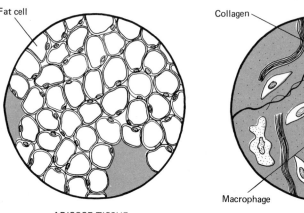

figure 3-4

ADIPOSE AND
AREOLAR TISSUES

Fat cell   Collagen   Elastic fiber

Macrophage   Fibroblast

ADIPOSE TISSUE   AREOLAR CONNECTIVE TISSUE

**A thin spread of adipose tissue is shown. The lipid droplets have been extracted
by the preparation of the tissue leaving a thin rim of cytoplasm and a flat nucleus.
The areolar tissue is an example of loose connective tissue.**

a protective padding, particularly around the heart and kidney.

HEMOPOIETIC TISSUE Blood-forming tissue (*hemopoietic*) is discussed
in detail in Chapter 10 "Blood."

CARTILAGE Also called *chondrium* (*gristle*), cartilage is located in the
nose, ears, and around the ends of bones, and it is the principal skeletal
tissue of the embryo until replaced by bone.

BONE *Bony* or *osseous* tissue is much the same as cartilage except that
the intracellular matrix becomes hard through the deposition of calcium
salts. Practically all of a *bone organ* is composed of osseous tissue.

General
Characteristics

PRIMARILY INTERCELLULAR The amount of ground substance or tissue
fluid far exceeds the total amount of connective tissue cells.

VASCULARITY Excellent blood supply is characteristic of connective tissue, and the capillaries provide materials for this tissue as well as for
the adjacent epithelial layer. (Exception is cartilage.)

NERVE SUPPLY Connective tissue has an excellent nerve supply with
receptors for sensations of deep pressure and pain.

REGENERATION AND REPAIR The fibroblast acts as a stem cell and provides new connective tissue cells for repair and replacement.

Functions

SUPPORT AND CONNECTION The functions of support and connection are
primary. The skeleton is composed almost entirely of connective tissue
that supports the gross elements of the body. Most soft organs have some
type of internal scaffolding of reticular fibers for support. Binding parts
or groups of organs into a single unit to provide for greater functional
efficiency is due to areolar and fibrous connective tissue.

DEFENSE In addition to mechanical functions, connective tissue is involved in the defense of the body. Through the action of phagocytic cells
and the consistency of the ground substance that acts as a barrier, most
harmful materials are removed or isolated from the general circulation.

Defense capabilities also include the laying down of new fibers by fibroblasts during wound healing.

TRANSPORT Most metabolites will pass through connective tissue enroute to their site of action, and the elements of connective tissue in all probability have an effect on the transport of the material.

muscle tissue

All movements of the body, except those resulting from gravity, are the result of muscle contraction. In muscle cells, most of the properties of cytoplasm are minimized in favor of two specializations, *contraction* and *conduction*. (A detailed treatment of muscle cell structure function is provided in Chapter 6.) When discussing muscle tissue, the term *muscle fiber* is used as a synonym for a muscle cell (to be distinguished from connective tissue fiber, which is noncellular and nonliving). There are three types of muscle cells, each forming a specific muscle tissue. The distinction between the types of muscle tissue is based upon either the cells' structure or function. Muscles are either voluntary (usually attached to the skeleton) or involuntary (form parts of organs).

Classification

SMOOTH MUSCLE Sometimes smooth muscle tissue is referred to as *visceral muscle* (Figure 3-5). The cells are generally arranged in sheets and the cells show great extensibility and elasticity. In the skin isolated smooth muscle fibers are found in connection with the hair follicles and are called *erector pili muscle fibers*. The cells microscopically appear homogeneous, hence the term *smooth muscle*. As a general rule, smooth muscle is involuntary. The length of the smooth muscle fibers varies from as little as 0.02 mm (found in blood vessels) to 0.5 mm (found in the uterus). Smooth muscle is found as a layer in all hollow organs (except the heart), the outside covering of the spleen, as part of the blood vessels and ducts, and in the skin.

STRIATED MUSCLE Sometimes striated muscle tissue is referred to as *skeletal muscle* (Figure 3-5). Striated muscle is voluntary (nerves ending in the muscle come directly from the brain or spinal cord, Chapter 11) and is associated with the muscle organs. The cells have alternating bands that give them a striped appearance; they also are multinucleated. The importance of these bands in the physiology of skeletal muscle is described at length in Chapter 6. The individual fibers are quite long, measuring as much as 50 mm (2 inches) as seen in the *sartorius muscle*. A simple organ such as the *biceps* contains 50,000 muscle fibers. The

figure 3-5

ARRANGEMENT
OF MUSCLE
TISSUE IN
LONGITUDINAL
AND TRANSVERSE
SECTIONS

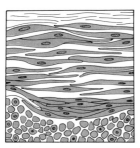 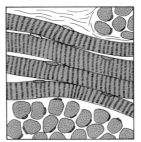 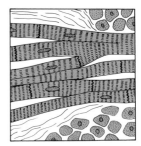

SMOOTH   STRIATED   CARDIAC

skeletal muscle tissue accounts for about 40 percent of the total body weight and is truly the *meat* of any vertebrate.

CARDIAC MUSCLE The cells comprising cardiac muscle are also striated in appearance and look like skeletal muscle, but they are *involuntary*. The cardiac muscle cells have a smaller diameter, shorter length, and fewer nuclei than skeletal muscle. This tissue is restricted to the heart and to a layer in the wall of the great vessels that emerge from the heart.

General Characteristics

CONTRACTILITY This general characteristic of cytoplasm reaches its greatest development in muscle tissue. The mechanism for contractility has been studied intensively and will be described in greater detail in Chapter 6. As a counterfunction, muscles also show great extensibility.

CONDUCTIVITY Along with contractility, conductivity has developed to a greater extent in muscle cells than in all other cells, with the exception of the nerve cells. The *Purkinje fibers* of the heart are muscle cells specialized to carry impulses, and they serve as an example of conductivity being a more important adaptation of muscle cells than contractility.

VASCULARITY All muscle tissues have excellent blood supplies. Except for a few endocrine organs and the lung, probably no tissue in the body has more blood vessels per volume than muscle tissue. In skeletal muscle, each cell is supplied with its own capillary to assure that these very active cells are properly nourished (Figure 3-6).

NERVE SUPPLY A good nerve supply is also a characteristic of muscle tissue; in fact, the two major divisions of the nervous system are classified on the type of muscle under stimulation. If smooth or cardiac muscle is involved, both of which are involuntary, the *autonomic division* of the nervous system carries the impulse. Impulses to skeletal or voluntary muscles are carried by the *somatic division* of the nervous system.

TONUS Muscle tissues are normally under partial contraction, called *muscle tonus*. Not only does this semicontracted state provide stability to the body, but it also produces heat as a by-product of the contraction. It is this heat that provides most of the normal temperature of the body.

REGENERATION AND REPAIR The regenerative capacity of muscle tissue is extremely limited. There are conditions when new smooth muscle fibers can form in the adult under proper conditions, but skeletal muscle fibers cannot regenerate unless the injury is minimal. In most instances, the traumatized area is replaced not with muscle tissue, but with *scar tissue* composed of fibrous connective tissue. Cardiac damage is especially serious, because scar tissue in the heart is more debilitating than scar tissue in the other types of muscle tissues. As a general rule, a man is born with the number of fibers that he will have during life, and he can only lose muscle fibers with aging, by trauma, and by disease.

Functions

With the exception of movement by gravity, all body motion depends upon muscle contraction.

nerve tissue

Location and Classification

Nerve tissue is composed of two elements: the *neuron*, which is the structural and functional unit of the nervous system involved in the processing of information and the *neuroglia*, which provides support, insulation, and nutrition to the neurons. The neuroglia or *glia* is tissue that is composed of cells unique to the nervous system; however, regular connective tissue also supports and connects parts of the organs compos-

figure 3-6

MUSCLE TISSUE
VASCULARITY

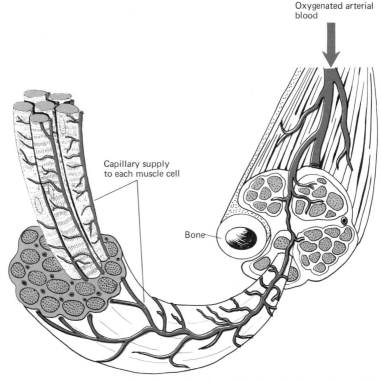

Oxygenated arterial
blood

Capillary supply
to each muscle cell

Bone

**A large muscle, for example, biceps, is schematically subdivided to illustrate the
extent that individual muscle fibers (cells) have their own blood supply.**

ing the nervous system (Figure 3-7). Part of a neuron is also covered by
a sheath of cells called the *neurilemma.* Several types of neurons and
glial cells are described in Chapter 5, which is solely devoted to their
anatomy and physiology.

For the purpose of clarifying anatomical divisions, nerve tissue is
subdivided into *white* or *gray matter,* which are the major components
of the tissue in a given area. Fibers of certain neurons are covered with
a white fatty material (myelin), and therefore "white" matter refers to
large aggregations of these types of fibers, whereas those areas composed mainly of cell bodies of neurons that have no fatty covering (as
well as fibers without myelin) are referred to as "gray" matter.

The bulk of the neurons and glial cells is found in the central *nervous
system* (brain and spinal cord), but elements of nerve tissue penetrate
almost everywhere in the body. Outside the central nervous system the
largest aggregation of nerve tissue is found in the *ganglia* and *nerves,*
which transmit impulses to and from the central nervous system (brain
and spinal cord). A *ganglion,* by definition, is a group of nerve cell bodies
located outside the central nervous system. A *nerve,* by definition, is an
aggregation of fibers leading to or from the central nervous system.

The term *fiber* has appeared now for the third time: (a) in connective
tissue, fibers are nonliving and noncellular; (b) in muscle tissue, the

figure 3-7
NEURON AND
NEUROGLIA

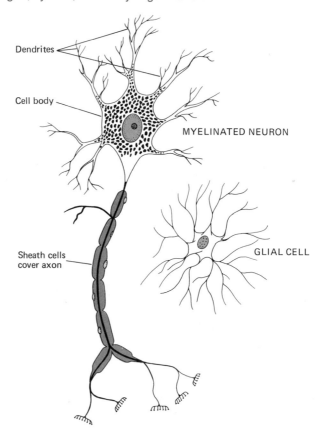

Dendrites

Cell body

MYELINATED NEURON

Sheath cells
cover axon

GLIAL CELL

fibers are the cells and, of course, they are living; and (c) in nerve tissue, the fibers represent extensions of the living cell, for example, *axons* and *dendrites* (Figure 3-7).

General
Characteristics

CELLULAR Some of the largest and longest cells of the body are found in nerve tissue. Although the nerve cell bodies are restricted to relatively small masses of the brain and spinal cord, their fibrous extensions spread out to form the bulk of these organs.

VASCULARITY Nerve tissue has a moderate blood supply, but the blood vessels are located in the connective tissue surrounding the nerve organs and do not penetrate the tissue per se.

NERVE SUPPLY Paradoxically, the nervous system has no nerves of its own. The brain can be handled without the brain recognizing the pressure (that it is being touched).

REPAIR AND REGENERATION Neurons, like muscle cells, do not divide once they pass through their early period of development. Repair is therefore almost negligible. In rare instances, if conditions are extremely favorable, there may be some regeneration of the axon.

Functions

IRRITABILITY AND CONDUCTIVITY The properties of irritability and conductivity reach their highest development in nerve tissue. Stimuli are

figure 3-8

TISSUES OF A
MULTILAYERED
ORGAN

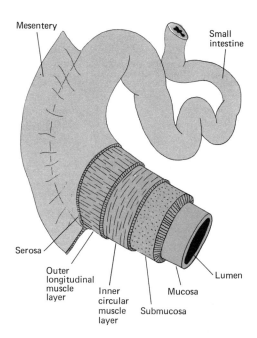

received by nerve endings and conducted at great speed to and from the central nervous system.

INTEGRATION The external and internal environments are connected to the integrating centers of the spinal cord and brain via the nerves, and this interaction permits the multicellular organism to function as a single unit.

organs

general
information

The combination of any two or more tissues forms an organ, and the tissues of an organ are integrated to perform certain functions. Generally, all the basic tissues are present, with one type dominant by virtue of its quantity or by its activity. The kidney is composed primarily of epithelial tissue, whereas in bone, connective tissue predominates. The intestine is a multilayered organ composed of a simple cuboidal epithelial lining that rests on a network of fibrous connective tissue (Figure 3-8). Next to the connective tissue layer are three layers of smooth muscle, and surrounding all these is the usual mesothelium coat. Blood vessels nurture all layers, with the exception of the epithelial, and nerve elements permeate them all. The intestinal epithelial lining, with its secretory cells producing digestive enzymes, provides the characteristics that primarily identify the intestine. The other tissues provide secondary functions; for example, the muscles churn the food, thereby aiding digestion. This organ has therefore all the general characteristics of its component tissues plus the specialization of the epithelial lining.

glands

Specialized organs for secretion are called *glands.* The active part of a gland is composed of the epithelial cells, which are supported and nourished by a base of areolar connective tissue (Figure 3-9).

figure 3-9
GLANDULAR
TISSUES

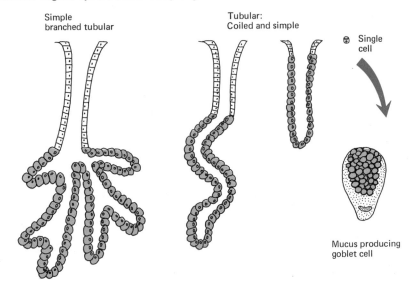

Simple
branched tubular

Tubular:
Coiled and simple

Single
cell

Mucus producing
goblet cell

Several types of simple tubular glands are shown in longitudinal view. The secretory epithelial cell is generally large and cuboidal shaped, with the nucleus located at the base of the cell. The excretory duct of the gland is composed of columnar type cells which are continuous with the surface epithelium. A single cell specialized into a glandular cell is also shown (goblet cell). A compound gland as opposed to a simple gland would be composed of several simple glands emptying into a single excretory duct.

The lining of the digestive, reproductive, and respiratory systems contains single secretory *(goblet)* cells that are termed "unicellular glands." Technically these are not glands, since by definition a gland is multicellular.

Glands can be classified by the type of secretion, formation of the secretion, or how the secretion is transported.

Type of Secretion   MUCUS Mucus is a thick, viscous material, found in the digestive, respiratory, and reproductive systems.
SEROUS Serous secretions are thin and watery, and are characteristic of the salivary glands and covering of the lungs.
CELLULAR The testes and ovaries, thymus, and spleen secrete cells.
OIL Wax glands of the ear are an example of oil-secreting organs.

Formation of
Secretion
(Figure 3-10)   HOLOCRINE The entire cell is discharged with the accumulated secretions, for example, sebaceous glands.
APOCRINE A small part of the cell is released along with the secretory granules, for example mammary glands.
MEROCRINE The cell releases the secretory material, and the cell stays intact, for example, endocrine glands.

Transport   EXOCRINE Exocrine secretions leave the gland by a duct that goes to a specific site (Figure 3-10). For example, the digestive enzymes secreted by the pancreas are carried to the small intestine by a pancreatic duct.

figure 3-10

COMPARISON OF
ENDOCRINE AND
EXOCRINE
SECRETIONS

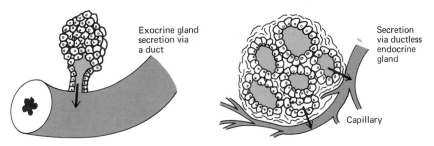

Exocrine gland
secretion via
a duct

Secretion
via ductless
endocrine
gland

Capillary

In most instances, exocrine secretions eventually reach the outside of the body (skin glands, salivary glands). Exocrine glands may also be further subdivided on the basis of their microanatomy (not discussed here).

ENDOCRINE In the endocrine glands the blood vessels are in direct contact with the secretory cells, and the secretion directly enters the bloodstream to be conveyed to some other part of the body (Figure 3-10). Further descriptions of the endocrine glands are discussed in the chapter on endocrinology (Chapter 18).

tissue
membranes

A membrane (at the tissue level as opposed to the cell) is a sheet of epithelial cells which rests on a base of fibrous connective tissue and serves to bind groups of organs and to line cavities. The basis for classifying membranes depends on the nature of the secretion. *Serous mem-*

figure 3-11

SEROUS AND
MUCOUS
MEMBRANES

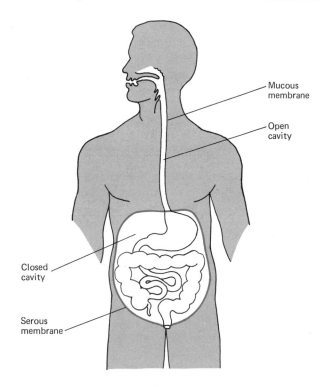

Mucous
membrane

Open
cavity

Closed
cavity

Serous
membrane

branes secrete a thin, watery secretion as opposed to *mucous membranes,* which secrete a more viscous fluid. Serous membranes line cavities that have no structural exit to the exterior–the pleural (lung) and pericardial (heart) cavities. Mucous membranes mostly line cavities that eventually open to the exterior–respiratory, digestive, reproductive, and urinary systems (Figure 3-11).

Unfortunately, the term *membrane* is also used to describe the lining of joints (the area in which bones articulate). Structurally these membranes are different in that they have no epithelial layer and the connective tissue cells provide the secretion. A common type of membrane of this nature is the *synovial membrane,* whose secretion protects the joint and the articulating bones by lubricating the area and minimizing friction (Figure 3-12).

figure 3-12

SYNOVIAL
MEMBRANE AND
JOINT

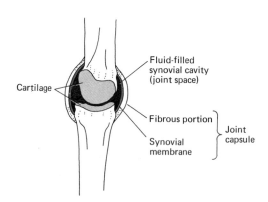

Cartilage

Fluid-filled
synovial cavity
(joint space)

Fibrous portion ⎫
⎬ Joint
⎭ capsule

Synovial
membrane

systems   The combination of organs with related or similar functions constitutes a *system.* In a system each organ performs a different function, but all of them are adapted to an overall end point. For example, the digestive system is composed of a myriad of organs that function in an integrated fashion to provide nutrients for the organism. In the case of the digestive system, both nerve and chemical control are essential to this integrated activity.

SKELETAL Bones, cartilages, and joints form the skeletal system.

MUSCULAR The muscular system is restricted arbitrarily to voluntary muscles, and each muscle, for example, biceps, is an organ.

CIRCULATORY The heart, blood vessels, and lymphatics comprise the circulatory system.

NERVOUS The brain, spinal cord, ganglia, and nerves are the subunits of the nervous system. The *special sense organs,* eye, ear, nose, mouth (taste), as well as the more *general receptors* of pressure, pain, temperature, and knowledge of motion and position are frequently included in this division. Technically, the general receptors are not organs, but units of cells performing a specialized function.

ENDOCRINE The endocrine system contains all the glands that pour their secretions (hormones) directly into the blood stream. The endocrine or ductless glands include the pituitary, thyroid, parathyroid, and adrenals, and parts of the pancreas, ovary, and testes.

DIGESTIVE The major organs of the digestive system are the mouth, esophagus, stomach, small intestine, colon, and rectum. Associated with these major organs are the accessory glands: the salivary glands, pancreas, gall bladder, and liver.

RESPIRATORY The respiratory system includes the nose, pharynx, larynx, bronchi, and lungs.

URINARY The kidneys, ureters, bladder, and urethra form the urinary system.

INTEGUMENTARY The skin can be thought of as a continuity of organs, for the skin is different structurally — and to a lesser extent functionally — in various locations of the body. The integument also has specialized derivatives in the presence of hair and nails.

REPRODUCTIVE In the female, the reproductive system consists of the ovaries, oviducts, uterus, vagina, and vulva. In the male, the testes, ductus deferens, ejaculatory duct, seminal vesicles, prostate, urethra, urethral glands, and penis constitute the system. The ovary and the testes are the true reproductive organs of the male and female systems, respectively, the other structures being classified as secondary or accessory organs.

body organization
For descriptive purposes the anatomic position of the body is an upright figure, facing forward, arms at the side with the thumbs pointing outward (Module 3B).

directional terms
SUPERIOR Toward the head is termed superior. For example, the elbow is located on the *superior* appendage.

INFERIOR Inferior is away from the head. For example, the knee is located on the *inferior* appendage.

MEDIAL Medial means structured near the midline. For example, the navel is at the *medial* line.

LATERAL Lateral is farther from the midline. For example, the ears are *lateral* to the nose.

POSTERIOR The posterior is the back of the body (*dorsal* also used as a synonym). For example, the shoulder blades are on the *posterior* surface.

ANTERIOR The front of the body is anterior (*ventral* also used as a synonym). For example, the collar bone is on the *anterior* surface.

PROXIMAL Proximal indicates near the point of origin or nearer the main part of the body. For example, the *proximal* end of the arm is attached to the shoulder.

DISTAL Distal is farther from the point of origin. For example, fingers are at the *distal* end of the hand.

planes of reference (Figure 3-13)
TRANSVERSE Transverse divides the body or any part of the body into upper and lower segments. It is also called the *horizontal* plane.

FRONTAL Frontal passes through the body or any part of the body from top to bottom, dividing the section into posterior and anterior (dorsal and ventral) parts. It is also called the *coronal* plane.

MIDSAGITTAL Midsagittal divides the body or any of its parts into equal right and left halves. Any other lengthwise plane that does not run through the midline is called a *sagittal cut* and divides the body or the part into left and right unequal segments.

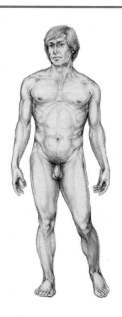
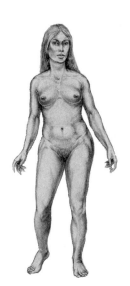

The structure which sets man aside from other vertebrates is his unique internal framework. This skeleton makes up about 20 percent of the body weight and is composed of more than 200 bones. Molded over this framework are the soft tissues that give the body its form. Size, relative amounts of musculature, and distribution of fat are determined not only by one's genetic makeup but also by diet and amount of physical work done. Thus heavy physical work can cause an increase in both bone and muscle growth. There is a great variability in body structure. One system of classifying body structure is based on basic forms: ectomorph (thin), mesomorph (heavy muscular build), and endomorph (plump, stocky). There are, as can be seen, basic structural differences in the two sexes. The bone structure in man is heavier and the adult male has a prominent ridge over the eyes, which is lacking in children and females. The males have about 20 percent more muscle and there are very obvious differences in fat distribution between the sexes (see Chapters 19 and 20).

Facial features, skin pigmentation, and hair distribution are distinctive for the various races of man. The dark-skinned peoples have greater concentrations of the dark brown pigment, melanin. Those peoples whose racial origins were in tropical lands have more melanin than those from higher latitudes. Melanin quantity in fair-skinned peoples is the lowest in blond-haired, blue-eyed races, and may be concentrated in localized spots or freckles. Regardless of race some individuals may lack the capacity to form melanin; such a person is an albino.

The external anatomy also changes with age as connective tissues stretch, skin wrinkles and tissues in general atrophy. Humans also transmit a great deal of nonverbal information by changes in facial expression, muscle tone, and posture. In summary, much can be learned about man from viewing his external anatomy; unfortunately sometimes too much attention is paid to racial features and skin color; for we all belong to the same genus and species, *Homo sapiens.*

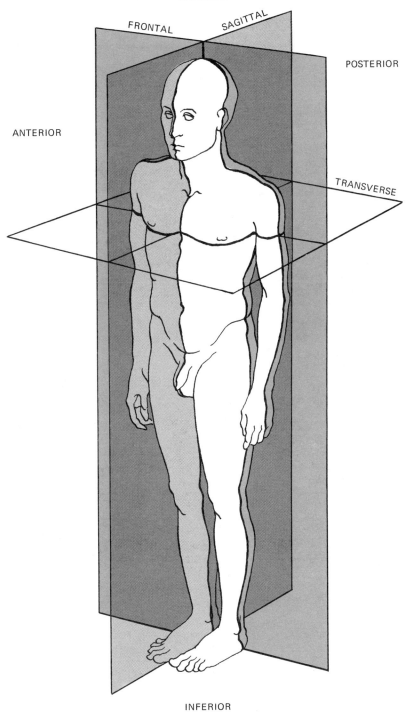

figure 3-13

PLANES OF
REFERENCE

body cavities   The body has two major cavities: the *posterior cavity*, which houses the brain and the spinal cord, and the *anterior cavity*, which is further subdivided and contains the following cavities (Figure 3-14).

THORACIC The thoracic cavity is a large space subdivided into three cavities. The *pericardial* cavity in the middle surrounds the heart and major blood vessels and, by doing so, forms the two *pleural* cavities, one on each side of the heart, each pleural cavity enclosing a lung. The pericardial membrane is part of a larger membrane that runs through the middle of the thoracic cavity and is called the *mediastinum*. The mediastinum also contains the upper ends of the digestive and respiratory systems, the thymus glands, and the major blood vessels.

ABDOMINAL-PELVIC The diaphragm separates the thoracic from the abdominal cavity. The upper abdominal part is an arbitrary area containing the stomach, small and large intestines, pancreas, liver, gall bladder,

figure 3-14

MAJOR BODY
CAVITIES

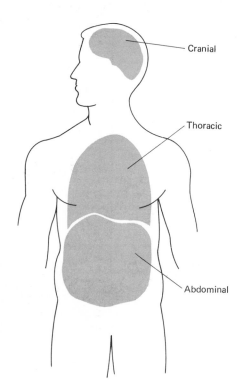

BODY CAVITIES

Only the cranial part of the posterior cavity is shown in the diagram. The subdivisions of the anterior cavity are the thoracic and abdominal-pelvic cavities, which are further subdivided for more accurate descriptions.

and spleen. The pelvic portion contains the distal end of the large intestine, the rectum, the urinary bladder, and the reproductive organs.

The lining of the abdominal pelvic cavity is called the *peritoneum* (a serous membrane), and occasionally this cavity is referred to as the *peritoneal cavity*. The peritoneum is a double membrane; one layer separates and covers the organs, and the other layer lines the cavity. That portion of the peritoneum that covers organs is called the *visceral peritoneum*, and that part that lines the cavity is called the *parietal peritoneum*. A large free fold of the visceral peritoneum called the *greater omentum* forms a blanketlike covering over most of the abdominal viscera. A similar double membrane arrangement is true for the pericardial and pleural cavities; namely, there is a visceral membrane attached to the organ and a parietal layer lining the cavity.

The pelvic cavity is further divided into *true and false areas*. The boundaries of these divisions are discussed in the section on pelvic bones.

clinical considerations

In the periods of development before birth, all the tissues are mitotically active and result in growth. At birth the capacity of cell division by muscle and nervous tissue is minimal, so that in life the degree of repair by tissues varies from almost zero to excellent. As illustrated in Figure 3-15 following a cut or break in the skin there is a rapid cell proliferation of the epithelial tissue along the cut edges, causing some new cells to push up from the basement layer of epithelial cells in the skin. If the wound is deep and involves the connective tissue, fibroblasts will begin to make new fibers and matrix. The blood clot, which contains many trapped cellular elements including primitive fibroblasts, helps to bridge the gap produced by the injury. The damaged blood vessels will soon repair and form new capillary sprouts to revascularize the regenerating areas. If the wound is very extensive, then the damaged areas fill with *granulation tissue*, a fibrous connective tissue that surrounds many small blood vessels and scar tissue.

The epithelial cells of the liver, digestive tube, blood, and skin are mitotically active and regeneration and repair here are excellent. The repair of connective tissue is also good, but slower than that of epithelial cells and, unlike the latter, connective tissue repair is restricted to only a few cell types. Most muscle tissue does not regenerate, and repair is limited to replacement with scar tissue. Although scar tissue fills the gaps made by the trauma, it does not have the contractile activity of muscle tissue; hence the repair area and the organ will work less efficiently. Likewise nerve cells are generally not replaced when they are destroyed, and there is a subsequent loss of conductivity and integration of impulses.

One theory on "why we age" focuses on collagen. It is believed that with time collagen increases and individual collagen fibers cross-link; this condition may create a barrier, thus preventing materials from diffusing through the connective tissue. Since the latter tissue is found in all organs, any hindrance to the movement of material will affect the

figure 3-15
WOUND HEALING

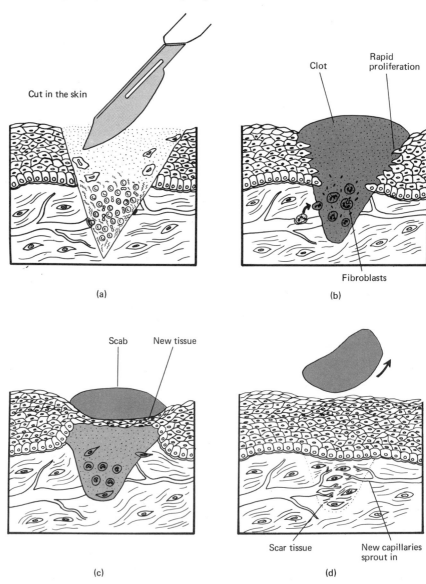

(a)

(b)

(c)

(d)

(a) A break in the skin results in a rupture of blood vessels and bleeding. Eventually a blood clot forms that fills the gap between the cut edges. (b) Following the cessation of bleeding, epithelial cells rapidly proliferate along the margins of the wound. If the wound is deep, connective tissue fibroblasts will also form new fibers and matrix. Dead cells, blood cells, and the clot comprise the scab along the free surface. (c) New tissue and rapid repair of damaged vessels occurs beneath the scab. The capillaries begin to form new branches. (d) The scab sloughs off, the newly formed tissue is revascularized by new capillary sprouts, and the repair is completed.

functioning of the organs, which in turn affects the general condition of the body (see Chapter 23).

summary

epithelium

1. Cell types
   (a) squamous
   (b) cuboidal
   (c) columnar
2. Organization and classification
   (a) simple
   (b) stratified
   (c) pseudostratified (transitional)
   (d) specialized, for example, ciliated
3. General characteristics
   (a) primary cellular
   (b) avascular
   (c) good to poor nerve supply
   (d) mitosis, excellent repair and regeneration
4. Function
   (a) protection
   (b) reception
   (c) secretion
   (d) excretion
   (e) absorption
   (f) reproduction

connective tissues

1. Cell types
   (a) fibroblasts (fibrocytes)
   (b) reticular cells
   (c) fat cells
   (d) phagocytes
   (e) mast cells
   (f) blood cells
   (g) chondrocytes
   (h) osteocytes
2. Intracellular material (matrix)
   (a) collagen fibers
   (b) elastic fibers
   (c) reticular fibers
   (d) amorphous ground substance
   (e) tissue fluid
3. Classification
   (a) areolar
   (b) reticular
   (c) adipose
   (d) tendons
   (e) cartilage
   (f) bone
   (g) hemopoietic (see Chapter 10)

4. General characteristics
   (a) primarily intracellular
   (b) vascularity excellent (except in cartilage)
   (c) excellent nerve supply
   (d) mitosis, excellent repair and regeneration
5. Function
   (a) support
   (b) connection
   (c) defense

muscle tissue
(see
Chapter 6)

1. Cell types
   (a) nonstriated or smooth (involuntary)
   (b) striated (voluntary)
   (c) striated (involuntary)
2. Classification
   (a) visceral
   (b) skeletal
   (c) cardiac
3. General characteristics
   (a) large, elongated cells
   (b) excellent blood and nerve supply
   (c) little or no mitosis with minimal regeneration

4. Functions
   (a) contractility
   (b) conductivity
   (c) elasticity
   (d) heat production

nerve tissue
(see
Chapter 5)

1. Cell types
   (a) neurons
   (b) sheath cells (neurilemma)
   (c) neuroglia
2. Classification
   (a) white matter: predominantly myelinated fibers
   (b) gray matter: predominantly nerve cell bodies and nonmyelinated fibers
   (c) ganglion: an aggregation of nerve cell bodies outside of the brain and spinal cord
3. General characteristics
   (a) glial cells more numerous than neurons
   (b) moderate blood supply
   (c) no nerve supply
   (d) little or no mitosis, very limited repair and regeneration
4. Functions
   (a) irritability
   (b) conductivity
   (c) integration

skeletal system

4

gross anatomy
general characteristics
landmarks
classification: the axial
 skeleton
classification: appendicular
 skeleton

**cellular and tissue special-
 izations**
chondrocytes
osteoblasts and osteocytes
osteoclast
mast cells
cartilage
bone

physiology of bone
calcium and calcification
organogenesis of bone
regeneration and repair
support and protection
articulations

control
hormones
vitamins

factors influencing function
aging
calcium requirements of
 the body

clinical considerations
osteoporosis
osteomalacia
osteomyelitis
neoplasms
storage of toxic minerals
arthritis
slipped disc

teeth
general information
structure
physiology
clinical considerations

The human skeleton is generally viewed as a passive rigid scaffold solely for protection and support (Figures 4-1, 4-2, and 4-3). These two functions of bones are important, but bones also provide for growth, leverage for movement, housing for the blood-forming marrow tissue, and a reservoir for calcium. The significance of the skeletal system is highlighted by the fact that the major group to which man belongs, the *vertebrates*, is a term derived from the system. By merely observing a skeleton or its parts, we can obtain a good idea of the entire body form, and even how it functions. Paleontologists are capable of reconstructing the soft tissue that surrounds the skeleton into remarkable likenesses of early man sometimes on the basis of a mere fragment of a fossil jaw.

Many features of the skeletal system reflect the early history of man. For example, the upright position provides man with a significant advantage over other animals. Just being taller than most animals enhances what we see, hear, and smell. Couple this increased sensitivity with speed (man is one of the fastest animals) and strength, and some of man's superiority is explained. However, the most significant result of the upright position is that it freed the hands, and because of the opposable thumb, the hand is the most versatile and most manipulative organ (instrument) that ever existed on earth.

In addition to its importance as a system in itself, the skeleton has value in that it can be utilized as a map to pinpoint other organs or areas. For example, spinal anesthetic is injected between vertebrae *just* below the end of the spinal cord. If the needle is inserted too high, the spinal cord may be irreparably damaged. The anesthesiologist knows that the spinal cord ends at the level of the second lumbar vertebra. He also knows that an imaginary line drawn from the crest of the hips to the backbone approximately bisects the fourth lumbar vertebra; the rest of the procedure is obvious.

For the physiologist the skeletal system has great importance also because of its intimate association with the metabolism of vital minerals. The predominant tissue of the skeleton organs is connective tissue; however, by weight 65 percent of bone is in some form of a calcium salt. The need for calcium by the body is a continuous phenomenon, which means that calcium uptake and release from bone are never ending.

The skeletal system consists of 206 bones (the number of bones varies slightly, for with development into adulthood, the separate bones fuse into single units, particularly in the skull, the backbone, and the joints) that form two major divisions:

Axial – skull, vertebrae, and thorax
Appendicular – girdles, limbs, hands, and feet.

gross anatomy

general characteristics

The general classification of bones is based primarily on shape – *long, short*, and *flat*. Long bones are divided into a shaft or *diaphysis* (Figure 4-4) and two ends, the *epiphyses*. The shaft of the bone is hollow and forms the *medullary* canal, which contains the marrow (blood-forming tissue described in Chapter 10). Long bones are found in the extremities, and short bones are found in the hands and feet. Short bones are irregular in shape and have a spongy interior that houses the marrow, and a tough outer coat. The vertebral bones and the three bones (ossicles) of the middle ear are examples of *irregular* short bones (Figure 4-4). The

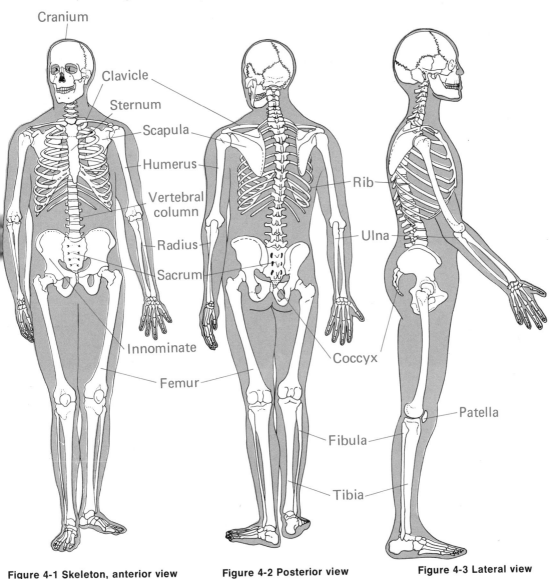

Cranium

Clavicle

Sternum

Scapula

Humerus

Vertebral
column

Radius

Sacrum

Innominate

Femur

Rib

Ulna

Coccyx

Fibula

Tibia

Patella

Figure 4-1 Skeleton, anterior view   **Figure 4-2 Posterior view**   **Figure 4-3 Lateral view**

third type of bone, *flat bone*, is found in the upper part of the skull (Figure 4-7).

landmarks   Living bones are a blue-white-pink color and have unique landmarks. They usually take on the forms of bumps and ridges for muscle and ligament attachments, and for channels that act as "road beds" for nerves. These landmarks, which scar the surfaces of the bone, make up most of the identifying characteristics of an organ. In Figure 4-5 the detailed surface anatomy of the humerus illustrates the depth to which a bone can be studied. In most of the illustrations in this chapter fewer landmarks are represented. However, the reader should be aware that

figure 4-4
TYPES OF BONES

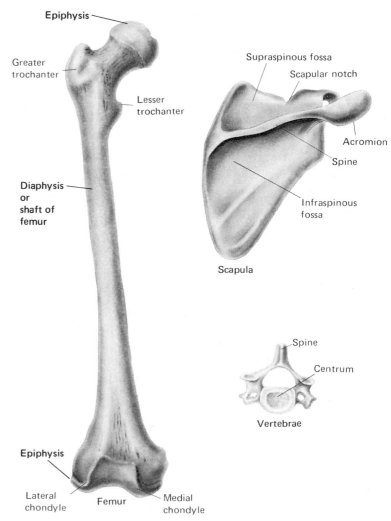

Epiphysis

Greater
trochanter

Lesser
trochanter

Diaphysis
or
shaft of
femur

Epiphysis

Lateral
chondyle

Femur

Medial
chondyle

Supraspinous fossa

Scapular notch

Acromion

Spine

Infraspinous
fossa

Scapula

Spine

Centrum

Vertebrae

the greater the detail of anatomy, the easier the identification becomes. For example, by merely mentioning the term *greater trochanter*, every student of anatomy knows specifically not only the name of the bone (femur) but also the specific area where the protuberance is located. This system of nomenclature is much more practical than a reference to a "large bump on the lateral side at one end of an inferior long bone which supports the body." The various types of landmarks are defined in Table 4-1.

classification:
the axial skeleton

Skull

The skull consists of cranial, facial, hyoid bones, and the ear ossicles (Figures 4-6, 4-7, and 4-8). Eight bones (frontal, occipital, sphenoid, ethmoid, two parietals, and two temporals) collectively form the *neurocranium*, the part of the skull that houses and protects the brain. Even a casual study of the skull shows how beautifully adapted these bones are for protecting the delicate tissues of the brain. The lateral bones are sloped, minimizing the impact of a blow to the area; there are no edges

figure 4-5

LANDMARKS OF
THE RIGHT
HUMERUS

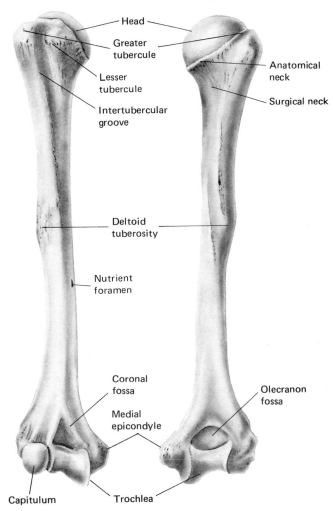

table 4-1
BONE
LANDMARKS

ANATOMIC STRUCTURE	DESCRIPTION
Condyle	Knuckle, small round process
Crest	Ridge on surface of a bone
Fissure	Cleft or slit
Fontanel	Membrane-covered opening
Foramen	Opening
Fossa	Ditch or depression
Fovea	Pit or small depression
Meatus	Channel or passageway
Ridge	Elongated crest
Sinus	Bay, hollow area, or cavity
Spine	Sharp pointed process
Suture	Line of union between bones
Tubercle	Small knoblike process
Tuberosity	Large knoblike process. Tuberosity on the femur called a trochanter

figure 4-6

figure 4-6

SKULL, ANTERIOR
VIEW

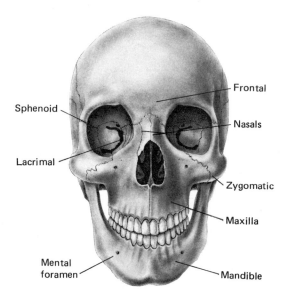

Sphenoid

Frontal

Nasals

Lacrimal

Zygomatic

Maxilla

Mental
foramen

Mandible

figure 4-7

SKULL, LATERAL
VIEW

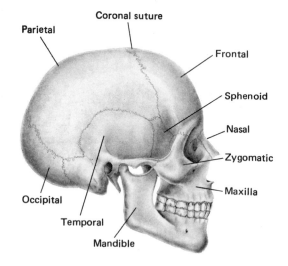

Parietal

Coronal suture

Frontal

Sphenoid

Nasal

Zygomatic

Maxilla

Occipital

Temporal

Mandible

figure 4-8

LATERAL VIEW,
SKULL, MID-
SAGITTAL
SECTION

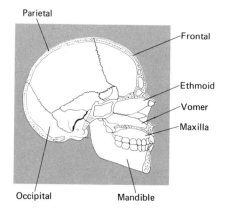

Parietal

Frontal

Ethmoid

Vomer

Maxilla

Occipital

Mandible

figure 4-9

SKULL,
POSTERIOR VIEW

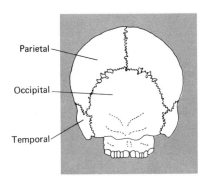

to chip, and each bone fits the neighboring bone, like jigsaw pieces, to form a more rigid union (Figures 4-7 and 4-9). These interlocking surfaces are called *sutures*. The floor of the cranium is formed by the *occipital, sphenoid,* and *ethmoid* bones. The lateral aspects are formed by the paired *temporal* and *parietal* bones, and the front of the skull is composed of the large, unpaired, *frontal* bone.

The occipital bone (Figures 4-9 and 4-10) articulates with the first cervical vertebra by two *condyles* (small rounded processes), and the bone is easily identified by the large opening (*foramen magnum*) through which the spinal cord travels to join the brain. Two rough *ridges*, the *nuchal* lines, allow for the insertion of neck muscles and prevent the head from drooping.

The sphenoid (Figure 4-11) is a bird-shaped (wings stretched, legs facing downward), complicated bone that forms the center part of the cranial floor and also contributes to the walls of the orbit. The sphenoid is characterized by many small openings and by a relatively large depression or *fossa*, the *sella turcica*, where the pituitary gland is located.

The ethmoid bone is small and contributes slightly to the front of the cranial floor and to the nasal septum. This bone also contains many surfaces and helps to make up the orbits of the face; its overall function can best be seen in Figure 4-12. One unique marking of the ethmoid bone is

figure 4-10

OCCIPITAL BONE
AS SEEN
FROM BELOW

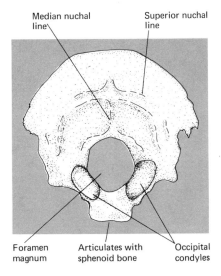

figure 4-11

SPHENOID BONE
—DETACHED

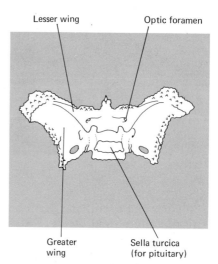

Lesser wing

Optic foramen

Greater
wing

Sella turcica
(for pituitary)

the *cribiform* plate, which is perforated with many minute canals through which the olfactory nerves pass.

Temporal bones (Figure 4-7) form the lower lateral aspects of the skull. Each temporal bone contains the *external auditory meatus,* a canal leading to a membrane at the middle ear. Within the temporal bone are

figure 4-12

ETHMOID BONE—
DETACHED AND
IN SITU

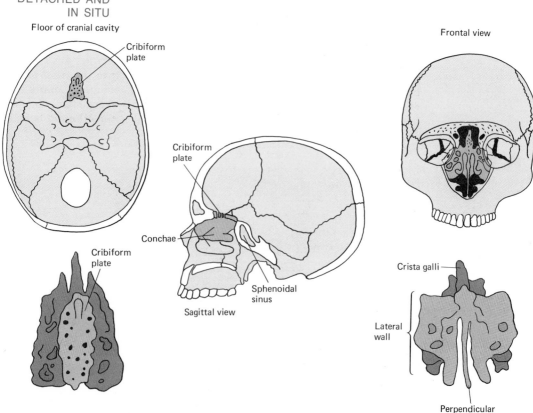

Floor of cranial cavity

Cribiform
plate

Frontal view

Cribiform
plate

Conchae

Cribiform
plate

Sphenoidal
sinus

Sagittal view

Crista galli

Lateral
wall

Perpendicular
plate

the three small bones associated with hearing: the *malleus, incus,* and *stapes.* The function of these bones is discussed in a separate section. Located directly behind the earlobe is another conspicuous temporal landmark, the *mastoid process.*

The frontal bone (Figures 4-6 and 4-7) forms the forehead. This bone contains two very important sinuses or spaces that connect with the nasal passage.

The parietal bones (Figure 4-7), which are square-shaped and convex, form the bulk of the lateral aspects of the skull. The articulating area with the frontal bone is called the *coronal* suture.

FACE The remaining skull bones, excluding the hyoid bone (Figure 4-6), form the face. In general the facial bones are somewhat more specialized, as evidenced by the variety of shapes, and they tend to be more delicate in construction.

MANDIBLE The lower jaw is a single bone and forms the chin and also contains the sockets for the teeth. The broad surfaces of the mandibles (Figures 4-6 and 4-7) are called *rami,* and they articulate with the temporal bones.

VOMER The vomer (Figure 4-8) is the only other unpaired bone in the face, and it forms the lower segment of the nasal septum.

NASAL The small nasal bones (Figures 4-6 and 4-7) form the bridge of the nose and are frequently damaged because of their vulnerable position.

LACRIMAL The smallest bones of the face are found in the medial aspects of the orbit, and they contain the *tear* or *lacrimal* sacs (Figure 4-6).

ZYGOMATIC The zygomatic bones form the cheeks and also contribute to the walls of the orbit (Figures 4-6 and 4-7).

MAXILLA Two of the maxillae bones constitute the upper jaw (Figures 4-6 and 4-7). The formation of the face evolves around the development of the maxillae and nasal bones.

PALATINE The hard palate is formed by the palatines and the maxillae (Figure 4-13); the palatine bones also contribute to the orbit.

HYOID Technically this bone is not part of the face. The horseshoe-shaped hyoid is located above the thyroid cartilage, which also labors under the name of the "Adam's apple."

FONTANELS The development of the skull is not complete at birth, and

figure 4-13

SKULL, INFERIOR
VIEW OF BASE

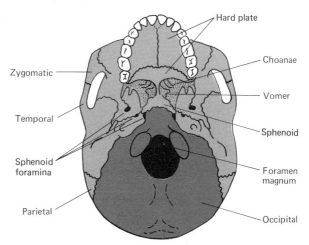

Hard plate
Choanae
Vomer
Sphenoid
Foramen magnum
Occipital
Zygomatic
Temporal
Sphenoid foramina
Parietal

the sutures are separated by spaces covered with membranes called *fontanels* (Figure 4-14). The infant has six fontanels which *close* (the membranes become hardened into bone) within 24 months. The value of the fontanels is apparent in childbirth, for as the fetus passes through the narrow birth canal, the bones can slip over one another because the membranes are yielding. In this manner the head adapts itself to the diameter of the canal without causing undue pressure on the brain.

SINUSES In Figure 4-15 the four major air sinuses are diagrammed in communication with each nasal cavity. The mucous membrane which lines the nose also lines the sinuses. Generally any infection of the nasal mucosa will also produce a corresponding inflammation to the sinus membranes. Technically the sinuses are not part of the skeletal system.

figure 4-14

FETAL SKULL

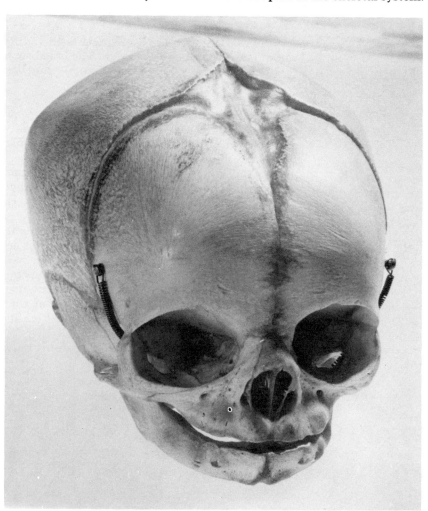

Note that the face is essentially formed around the eyes and nose. The characteristic jigsaw, interlocking articulation of the flat bones of the skull has not formed. The large triangular membrane between the frontal and parietal bones is the anterior fontanelle (soft spot) that has not achieved full ossification at this stage.

figure 4-15

figure 4-15

SINUSES

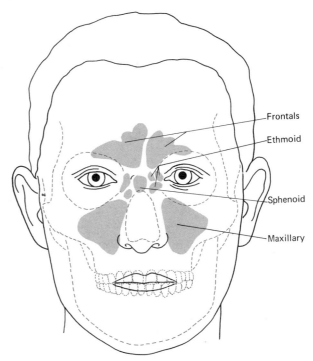

Frontals

Ethmoid

Sphenoid

Maxillary

Vertebral Column   Thirty-three bones form the vertebral column or backbone (Figures 4-16
and 4-17) and include the 7 *cervicals,* 12 *thoracics,* 5 *lumbars,* 5 *sacrals,*
and 4 *coccyxes.* As an abbreviation only the number and first letter are
used; thus the fourth thoracic becomes *T4,* the second lumbar *L2;* and so
forth. In the adult, sacrals and coccygeal bones fuse into a single sacrum
and coccyx, respectively. Collectively the column protects the spinal
cord, supports the viscera, and provides surfaces for muscle attachment.

  Each group of vertebrae shows some variations, indicating a division
of function. For example, the thoracic vertebrae have regions for attachment of the ribs (Figure 4-18); the sacrals lose their individuality by
fusion and thus achieve greater strength; and the atlas is modified for
support and articulation with the occipital condyles (Figure 4-17). These
bones illustrate the high degree of specialization in the seemingly
homogeneous unit called the *backbone.*

  Each vertebra is built around a core or *centrum.* On the centrum are
the articulating surfaces for movement with adjacent vertebrae and in
the thoracic area for articulation with the ribs. Stemming from the
centrum is the neural arch, which encloses the *vertebral foramen.*
Collectively the vertebral foramina form the *neural canal* that contains
the spinal cord. At the junction of the centrum and the neural arch on
either side is a notch, and the notches from adjacent vertebrae join to
form canals for the passage of the spinal nerves emerging from the
spinal cord (Figure 4-19). On the superior and inferior surfaces of each
vertebra are processes for articulation with adjacent bones. The thoracic
vertebrae, in addition, have articulating surfaces for interaction with
the ribs.

figure 4-16

VERTEBRAL
COLUMN

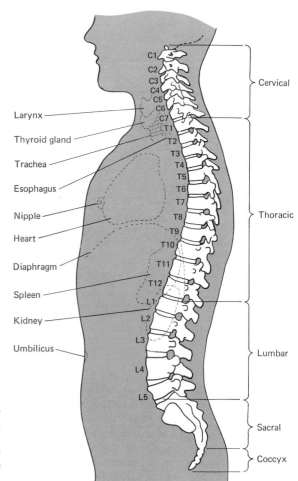

figure 4-16

VERTEBRAL COLUMN

Larynx
Thyroid gland
Trachea
Esophagus
Nipple
Heart
Diaphragm
Spleen
Kidney
Umbilicus

C1
C2
C3
C4
C5
C6
C7
T1
T2
T3
T4
T5
T6
T7
T8
T9
T10
T11
T12
L1
L2
L3
L4
L5

Cervical

Thoracic

Lumbar

Sacral

Coccyx

**Note that the verte-
brae, because of their
fixed position, can be
used as landmarks to lo-
cate certain viscera, the
kidney runs from T12 to
L3.**

The spine is neither straight nor bent, but is distinguished by four curves: *cervical, thoracic, lumbar,* and *sacral* (Figure 4-16). The infant is born with a "C-shaped" vertebral column, similar to that seen in most four-legged animals. In infancy the spine changes to an "S-shaped" structure because of the development of the curvatures. These curvatures, which provide greater support, are associated with two early developmental events: The first curvature appears when the infant supports his head, and the second curvature occurs when the infant begins to sit upright unassisted.

The first two vertebrae, the *atlas* and *axis*, are unique, and the nomenclature aptly describes their function. The atlas is modified to a mere ring with two large facets upon which the occipital condyles of the occipital bone rest. The axis is likewise reduced and has a conspicuous promontory, the *odontoid process.* The odontoid is a stabilizing structure for the articulating skull-atlas-axis unit that is adapted to perform the very simple motions of moving the head in a *yes* and *no* fashion.

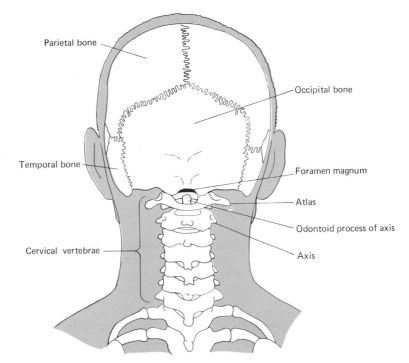

figure 4-17

ARTICULATION OF
SKULL WITH
VERTEBRAL
COLUMN

The vertebrae are not joined in the same fashion as are the skull bone sutures; rather they are laced together by ligaments and muscles. Separating each vertebral segment is a connective tissue disc, and these intervertebral discs are used to cushion the vertebrae against the large number of daily shocks from walking, running, jumping, or even sitting.

figure 4-18

RIB ATTACHMENT
TO A THORACIC
VERTEBRA

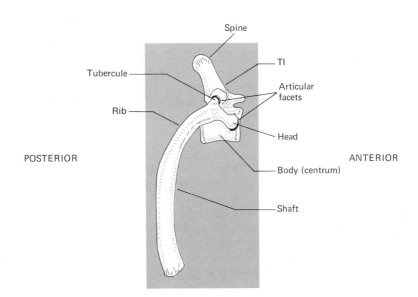

figure 4-19

THORACIC
VERTEBRAE AND
SPINAL NERVES

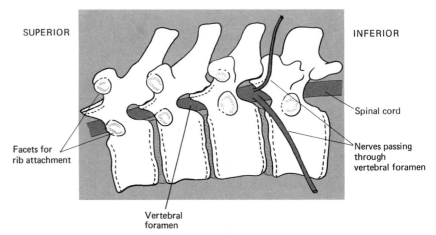

SUPERIOR

INFERIOR

Spinal cord

Facets for
rib attachment

Nerves passing
through
vertebral foramen

Vertebral
foramen

The foramina through which the spinal nerves emerge from the spinal cord are formed by notches on the same plane from adjacent vertebrae. Separating the vertebrae are intervertebral discs.

One of the oddities of man is that he is taller in the morning than in the evening, because during the course of the day the weight of a body compresses the connective tissue discs and the vertebral column may shrink as much as an inch.

The vertebral column (Figure 4-16) is an excellent guide line for locating various internal structures, and the following are a few examples:

1. The first hard promontory felt below the skull is the second cervical vertebral spine.

2. An imaginary line drawn from the shoulder top to the vertebral column will hit the first thoracic *(T1)* spine.

3. *C7* marks the beginning of the trachea.

4. *T8* marks the lower end of the heart.

5. *T12* is at the level of the upper part of the kidney.

Thoracic Cavity   This area is enclosed by the 12 thoracic vertebrae, 12 ribs, the sternum, and by the dome-shaped muscular diaphragm on the lower border. The thoracic cavity protects the heart, lungs, and great vessels as well as providing attachment for those muscles that play an important role in respiration.

STERNUM The middle part of the ventral chest wall is composed of the sternum (Figure 4-1) which consists of three parts – an upper *manubrium,* a middle *body,* and a lower portion called the *xiphoid process.* Because of its accessible location (directly beneath the skin), the sternum is frequently a site for bone punctures to obtain marrow.

RIBS There are 12 ribs (Figures 4-1 and 4-2), and 7 are called *true ribs,* because they attach directly to the cartilage that is attached to the sternum, whereas the lower 5 *(false ribs)* are attached to a strip of cartilage that joins with the cartilage of the true ribs. The last two ribs are also called *floating ribs*, because they are "free" on the anterior surface. The conical shape of the thoracic cavity in part is the result of the position of the ribs and their unequal size. The ribs also slope, which means that the point of attachment of the sixth rib is several centimeters higher in the back than in the front.

classification: appendicular skeleton

The appendicular skeleton consists of the arms, legs, hands, feet, and the upper and lower *girdles* (shoulders and hips). The basic structure of the appendages is quite similar, but the anatomy of the girdle differs considerably.

Upper Extremity and Girdle

SCAPULA AND CLAVICLE The bones of the scapula and clavicle (Figure 4-20) are also called the *shoulder blade* and *collar bone*, respectively, and form the pectoral girdle (shoulder). The scapula contains a socket *(glenoid fossa)*, which is the articulating surface of the upper arm. The union is a ball and socket, which allows for great freedom of motion. Since the upper arms are not used for locomotion or support in man, this mobility provides him with many fringe benefits such as writing, making and using instruments, as well as turning pages. The clavicle *fixes* the scapula in place and allows for efficient lateral movements of the arm. Because the clavicle is so close to the surface and because it receives the full force of a fall when the arms are outstretched, it is one of the most frequently broken large bones in the body.

HUMERUS The humerus (Figure 4-5) is the bone of the upper arm; it articulates with the scapula at its upper end and with the radius and ulna at its lower point. Because the nerves leading into the arm are in intimate contact with the humerus, injuries to this bone frequently result in nerve damage, especially to the radial nerve.

RADIUS AND ULNA The radius and the ulna (Figure 4-21) form the *fore-arm*. The radius is easily identified by holding the arms outstretched

figure 4-20

PECTORAL GIRDLE AND HUMERUS

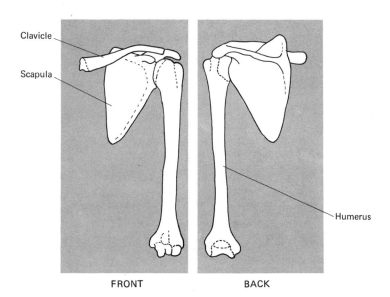

Clavicle

Scapula

Humerus

FRONT   BACK

palm side up and turning the palms over—the bone crossing over is the radius. When taking pulse at the wrist, the radial artery is compressed slightly against the hard tissue of the radius bone. The ulna is the longer of the two bones, and it is easily identified by the semilunar notch, which also constitutes the elbow. No "funny bone" exists; the sensation received following a blow on the elbow is due to the stimulation of the ulnar nerve. The ulna is also distinguished by the fact that the shaft can be palpated along its entire length.

HANDS The hands (Figure 4-21) are composed of 8 *carpal* bones, 5 *metacarpals*, and 14 *phalanges.* Together these bones form a most amazing unit. The dexterity, versatility, and the uniqueness of the hands have been extolled by poets as well as scientists. To paraphrase one scientist's remark, "Without hands we would have remained apes, and not the angels we are." Such a simple act as the ability to touch each of the fingers with the thumb provides man with the physical ability to

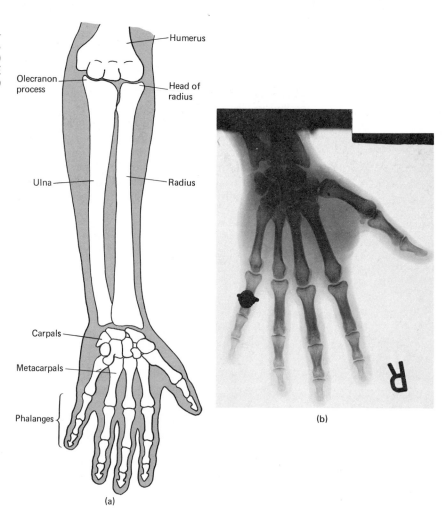

figure 4-21

(a) RADIUS, ULNA, AND HAND AND (b) X-RAY PICTURE OF THE HAND

figure 4-22

MALE AND
FEMALE PELVES

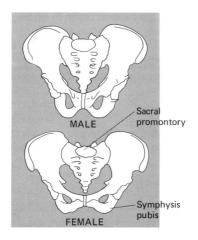

Sacral
promontory

MALE

Symphysis
pubis

FEMALE

If an imaginary line is drawn from
the symphysis pubis to the sacral
promontory, the pelvic cavity is
divided into an upper major or
false pelvis and a lower minor or
true pelvis.

Lower Extremity
and Girdle

achieve enormous technological skill. (Try writing, eating, buttoning, sewing, picking up objects, and so forth, without using the thumb.)

In contrast to the shoulder region, the lower pelvic girdle is quite immobile. This rigidity is obvious when we realize that the functions of the pelvis are to (a) support the trunk and transmit the weight to the lower limbs and (b) protect and support the abdominal and pelvic viscera. The basinlike pelvis is composed of two large bones, the *innominates* (Figure 4-22), which meet anteriorly at the joint called the *symphysis pubis* and connect posteriorly to the sacrum. The innominate bone actually is composed of three bones that fuse together: *ilium, ischium,* and *pubis.*

The ilium (Figures 4-22 and 4-23) is the broad superior bone that forms almost half the *acetabulum* (a deep socket that is the articulating surface for the head of the femur). The *crests* of the ilia are commonly called the *hips.* The two ilia meet at the sacrum and form the very im-

figure 4-23

INNOMINATE
BONE, INTERNAL
SURFACE

ANTERIOR   POSTERIOR

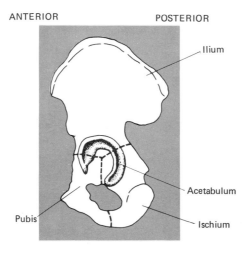

Ilium

Acetabulum

Pubis

Ischium

The innominate is composed of
three bones fused together during
growth: illium, ischium, and pubis.
The two innominates form the
pelvis.

portant *sacroiliac* joints. The lowermost bone is the ischium, and the pubis joins with its counterpart to form the arch of the pelvis.

The interior of the pelvis is divided into two major areas: the *major or false pelvis*, an area that is above an imaginary line drawn from the symphysis pubis to the sacral promontory, and the *minor or true pelvis*, the cavity inferior to this imaginary line (Figure 4-22). To eliminate the possibility of complications during birth, the following measurements of the birth canal can be made: (a) the *anterior-posterior*, which runs from the upper border of the pubis to the sacral promontory; (b) the *transverse*, which measures the widest and narrowest openings (inlet and outlet); and (c) the *oblique*, which extends from the front to the back.

At least three features differentiate the male from the female pelvis (Figure 4-22). (a) The pubic arch in the male is narrow and pointed, whereas the female arch is more wide and round; (b) the superior aperture is heart-shaped in the male and oval in the female; (c) the ilia are more vertical in the male than in the female.

FEMUR The thigh bone or femur (Figure 4-4) is the longest (45 cm) and strongest bone in the body. At its superior end the large knoblike *head* fits into the socket (*acetabulum*). Supporting the head is the *neck*, which forms an obtuse angle with the remainder of the bone. This arrangement is an excellent adaptation related to the upright position of man, for if the angle were less—for example, 90 degrees—there would be an overburdening strain on the neck (Figure 4-4). Two large protuberances, the *greater and lesser trochanter*, are for muscle attachment. On the shaft the most conspicuous landmarks are a *ridge (linea aspera)* and a *nutrient foramen*; the latter marks the entrance of blood vessels and nerves into the bony tissue. The inferior end is marked by the *condyles*, which articulate with the *tibia* of the lower leg.

PATELLA The patella (Figure 4-1) is a small bone that forms the knee cap and is a *sesamoid* bone. Sesamoid bones are specialized structures found in tendons and serve to minimize the strain and friction of a tendon passing over a bony prominence.

figure 4-24

TIBIA AND FIBULA —ANTERIOR VIEW

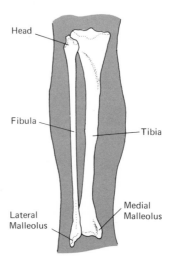

Head

Fibula

Tibia

Lateral Malleolus

Medial Malleolus

figure 4-25

BONES OF THE
LEFT FOOT—
SUPERIOR VIEW

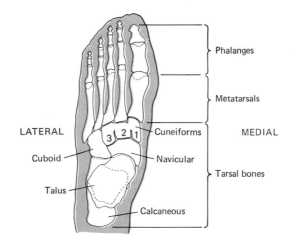

Phalanges

Metatarsals

LATERAL   Cuneiforms   MEDIAL

Cuboid   Navicular

Tarsal bones

Talus

Calcaneous

TIBIA The tibia (Figure 4-24) or *shin* bone is quite easily felt by lightly passing the hand over the front surface of the lower leg or limb. The tibia is located on the medial side of the leg and articulates by its flat condyles with the femur superiorly and with the foot inferiorly. One distinguishing landmark is its *medial malleolus* that forms part of the *ankle.*

FIBULA The smaller and thinner lower leg bone buried in the muscle is the fibula (Figure 4-24). The lower end contains the *lateral malleolus,* which forms the remaining part of the ankle joint.

FOOT Similar to the hand, the foot (Figure 4-25) is composed of a series of bones: seven *tarsal* bones and the large *calcaneous,* and the uppermost bone, the *talus,* articulates with the tibia. The five metatarsals make up the remainder of the arch of the foot, and the 14 phalanges comprise the toes. If *versatile* is the adjective for the hand, *stable* best describes the anatomy of the foot.

cellular and tissue specializations

In the history of the skeletal organs (both embryological as well as evolutionary), two tissues play a key role: One is cartilage and the second is bone. Each tissue has a distinct cell, the *chondrocyte* and *osteocyte,* respectively. They are morphologically quite similar during development, and it is only when the cells mature and group into their specific tissues that the morphological and functional aspects become distinct.

chondrocytes

Cartilage cells as viewed by the light microscope are spheroid, with or without processes, and show the usual cell organelles and inclusions. Even when magnified by electron microscopy, the chondrocytes have no distinguishing features beyond those of a moderately active cell (for example, fair amount of rough endoplasmic reticulum).

osteoblasts and osteocytes

The osteoblasts and the osteocytes, representing two different stages of maturation, are quite similar; the osteoblast forms the matrix, and the osteocyte is the mature bone cell; both have the general appearance of cells involved in protein synthesis: mitochondria, rough endoplasmic reticulum, and granules. At lower magnification, cytochemical techniques demonstrate the cytoplasm to be *rich in RNA*, which indicates protein synthesis, and *PAS positive*, the chemical test for polysaccharides, which indicates that the complex sugar is present in the cytoplasm.

osteoclasts   Osteoclasts supposedly resorb bone during growth and remodeling stages. Evidence for this reabsorption function is indirectly demonstrated by the presence of cytoplasmic mineral deposits and vacuoles containing crystals within the cells. The cells also show *acid phosphatase activity.* This activity is of interest because of a theory that states that cells involved in *building* bone have a high *alkaline phosphatase* level and cells that contain acid phosphatase are involved in the *resorption* process (Figure 4-26).

All bone cell types have a common ancestor, and during active growth (in the fetus and in disease), much transformation from one type to another takes place. There is good evidence that a *mesenchyme cell* (refers to the embryonic origin of the cell, Chapter 21) is the ancestor to all bone cell types; the relationship is diagrammed below.

mesenchymal cell ⟶ osteoblast ⟷ osteocyte
↘ ↗
osteoclast

mast cells   Technically speaking the mast cells are not found in bone per se except under stressful or disease conditions, but are found in large numbers in the marrow. In the discussion on connective tissue, the ubiquitous mast cell was described as storing histamine and heparin, and probably this cell is also involved in the production of the bone matrix.

cartilage   One of the general characteristics listed for connective tissue is that it is primarily intercellular; both cartilage and bony tissues are excellent examples of this tissue. As the stem mesenchymal cells divide to form cartilage cells, they lose most of their processes and orient into layers. Usually, the cells are grouped in twos or fours and sometimes even multiples of four. Simultaneously, the chondrocytes secrete a relatively homogeneous and amorphous matrix that is reinforced by minute collagen fibers. Chemically, the intercellular substance is composed of

figure 4-26

OSTEOBLAST
AND OSTEOCLAST
ACTIVITY

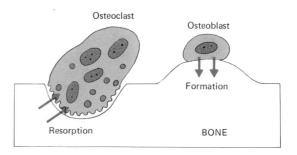

simple proteins (gelatin and albumin) and a great deal of water. The intercellular ground substance might be called a "solid glue." The maturing cells continue to produce this matrix until the cells are engulfed in their own secretion, thus limiting cellular division. The entire process is called *chondrification.*

Cartilage is a relatively inert (nonactive) tissue and does not contain the usual complement of arteries and veins, lymphatic vessels and nerves. The absence of efficient circulatory elements within cartilage proper means that waste materials or nutrients leaving or entering the cells diffuse slowly across the relatively dense matrix.

Since mitosis is limited by the hardening of the matrix, most new growth occurs from a layer of connective tissue, the *perichondrium,* which is wrapped around the cartilage mass. Growth proceeds in much the same manner as a tree grows—by the *perichondrial "bark"* providing the new cells.

bone   The primary formation of bone is almost the same as that outlined for cartilage. The mesenchyme produces osteoblasts that orient in layers as they secrete their matrix. The differences that do occur are related to the fact that the mineralization of the intercellular material produces exceptionally hard matrix. This hardening negates the possibility that the osteocytes could obtain enough nutrition via diffusion through the matrix. Even if it were possible, this incompetent manner of moving materials from one area to another would not meet the needs of the metabolically active osteocytes.

During *ossification* (hardening of the matrix), the branching fibers of osteocytes are not immediately lost. Thus as the matrix is being deposited one cell is "tied" to its neighbors by these *anastomosing* fibers; eventually, the cytoplasmic processes are withdrawn, leaving a minute channel (Figure 4-27). These *canaliculi,* as they are called, are small, but molecules are able to traverse the bony tissue by this system.

Another difference between cartilage and bone is that bony layers are deposited around a capillary, lymphatics, and nerves. The channels thus formed are called *Haversian canals,* and they measure as much as 0.15 mm in diameter (Figure 4-27). These canals are frequently joined by cross canals (*Volkmann*). Canaliculi also open into the Haversian canals. Materials that seep out of a capillary into a Haversian canal can travel by these channels to the adjacent bone cells. Because there is no capillary meshwork within the matrix, this system serves quite adequately to transport materials from bone cell to bone cell, and from bone cells to the bloodstream.

physiology of bone   To a large extent the physiology of bone is involved with the metabolism of calcium, since bone is composed primarily of tricalcium phosphate $[Ca_3(PO_4)]_2$ and calcium carbonate ($CaCO_3$), 80 and 14 percent, respectively. The other minerals that contribute to bone are magnesium phosphate $[Mg(PO_4)]_2$, 4 percent, and small amounts of sodium and potassium. Collectively these minerals form a calcium salt, which in turn forms crystals that vary from 50 to 100 Å. These crystals become the noncellular building material of bone.

calcium and calcification

figure 4-27

THE HAVERSIAN
SYSTEM

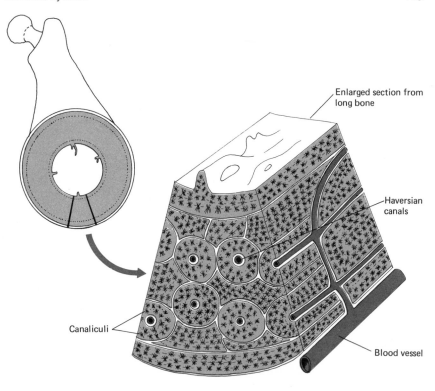

Enlarged section from
long bone

Haversian
canals

Canaliculi

Blood vessel

How bone is hardened by calcium salts is still uncertain, but it is believed that microfibers in the matrix of bony tissue provide specific sites
for the deposition of the calcium and that collagen also initiates or *seeds*
crystal formation. If the concentration of calcium and phosphates in the
blood, or in any other extracellular fluid, is extraordinarily high, calcium
may be precipitated anywhere in the body.

organogenesis
of bone

Bone, like any other organ, is composed of a combination of primary tissues. What distinguishes this organ from an organ of the digestive system, for example, is that the mass of the organ is primarily a single tissue, *osseous tissue.* About the fifth week of embryonic development, the
skeletal system starts by forming miniaturizations of mature bone, using
cartilage as the primary tissue. This development is called *cartilage
replacement bone formation* or *endochondral formation,* and it is characteristic of all the bones of the skeletal system with the exception of the
flat bones of the skull, the bones of the face, hyoid and clavicle. The latter
bones are formed by a process called *membrane bone formation,* which
will be discussed subsequently.

In Module 4A, the changes that take place in the conversion of a cartilage embryonic bone to a mature organ are diagrammed. Briefly, cartilage destruction and replacement by bony tissue are progressive and
spread in all directions from the initial zone. Later in the development
of the bone both ends undergo a similar process of cartilage replacement,

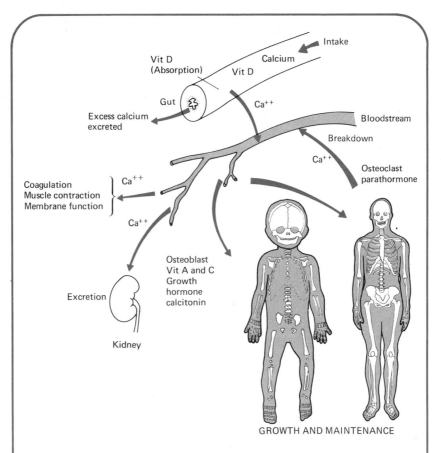

GROWTH AND MAINTENANCE

All during life, bones are continually undergoing breakdown, repair, and re-modeling, and the physiological mechanism of these processes is basically similar to the mechanism of bone development in the fetus. Calcium (Ca) metabolism plays a major role in all of these pre- and postnatal stages of development. Calcium is absorbed into the bloodstream from the intestine; Vitamin D plays a key role in increasing the rate of Ca absorption. Carried by the blood the Ca will be used at many sites, but the majority of the available Ca will be utilized for the formation of new bone. Excess Ca is excreted by the kidneys and bowel. The deposition of new bone is influenced by vitamin A, Vitamin C, and several hormones. Any decrease in blood Ca triggers the secretion of parathormone. This hormone restores blood Ca levels by breaking down bone.

A comparison of a newborn and an adult skeletal system illustrates the changes that occur during maturation. As can be seen, the head of the infant constitutes about 25 percent of the body length, whereas in the adult the head represents slightly more than 10 percent of total length. During prenatal development the arms have a headstart over the legs, but this pattern is reversed during postnatal development. The trunk length remains proportionately constant through all stages of development.

which aids in the bone remodeling. Eventually all of the primary cartilage is destroyed, removed, and replaced by osseous tissue except for the
coverings on the articulating surfaces and for a plate at each end of the
shaft. These cartilaginous centers are called the *epiphyseal plates* and
are necessary for bone growth in the long axis. As long as cartilage forms
on one surface of the plate and new osteocytes can enter at the other
surface, the cartilage formation-replacement mechanism will continue
and there will be growth of the bone in the long axis. The new osteocytes
that arrive at the epiphyseal plate migrate into the shaft and increase
the length of bone. However, once cartilage destruction exceeds its formation, the plate will disappear and this process of bone formation will
also disappear. It is important to remember that the cartilage replacement method of bone formation necessitates first the destruction and
removal of cartilage before ossification will occur.

Membrane bone formation has a similar process of ossification except
that a cartilage model is not a prerequisite, and there is no intervening
destruction of cartilage tissue and replacement by osteocytes. Instead,
the primitive embryonic connective tissue differentiates directly into
bone by the formation of osteocytes and crystals of salts. Most small
bones form in this fashion.

At this point the reader might rightly inquire why it is necessary to
describe the two types of bone formation if the end point, the mature
bone, is indistinguishable. The answer is manifold.

1. Many abnormalities of the bones are congenital (existing at birth)
and are associated with the failure of cartilage removal and subsequent
replacement by bone. For example, rickets could develop from this defect
during the development of long bones.

2. When a bone is fractured, the repair mechanism mirrors the cartilage replacement bone mechanism.

3. In nature, many examples of redundancy are found, and this dual
bone formation is an illustration how a final product, bone, is achieved
by two different procedures.

4. Many specializations seen on bone surfaces form as a result of cartilage replacement activity, especially the custom-fitted articulating surfaces. Exterior growth is minimized in favor of the interior development.

regeneration and repair   During prenatal and postnatal life, the skeleton undergoes remodeling —
microscopic areas of the bone are continuously broken down and ab-
sorbed, and the area is then reconstructed. The cells responsible for the
controlled erosion of bone are the osteoclasts (Figure 4-26 and Module
4B), which produce enzymes that break down the matrix, but leave the
collagen fibers to serve as a framework for the deposition of new bone
tissue. The newly formed bone is essentially a recapitulation of the osteo-
genic process seen in prenatal development. Continual bone breakdown
and reconstruction have several important adaptive features.

1. The destruction of the old bone releases stored calcium to be used
by other parts of the body.

THE
OSSIFICATION
AND GROWTH OF
A LONG BONE

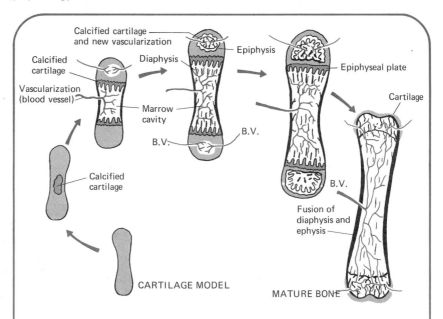

A cartilage model with the same general shape of the future mature bone precedes the development of the mature bone. A peculiarity of this type of development is that the cartilage must first be destroyed and removed before
ossification (new bone formation) will occur. The first signs of cartilage breakdown or calcification occur in the center of the cartilage. Paralleling destruction of cartilage is the formation and the invasion of blood vessels that not
only remove the cartilage debris but also bring in new bone cells (osteoblasts).
The center cavity of the developing bone never fills in with bony tissue and
remains as the primary marrow cavity. New ossification centers occur at different parts of the bone and proceed in a similar manner with calcification
and subsequent ossification. Finally, all of the original cartilage is replaced
except for a thin layer that remains along the articulating surfaces and a plate
in either end of the long bone. These plates are called the *epiphyseal plates,*
and as long as they remain viable, growth in the long bone will occur. Eventually the plates are absorbed and growth ceases.

2. The deposition of new bone brings the cells in closer approximation
to blood vessels as the new Haversian unit forms (no osteocyte is more
than 0.05 mm from its source of nourishment).

3. The process also prevents bones from becoming too massive.

4. The continual deposition of bone allows for a degree of *osseous drift*
—as an individual bone matures, new stresses are forced on it, and the
bone accommodates to these forces by twisting and reforming. This remodeling is what gives each bone the adaptive shape it needs to perform

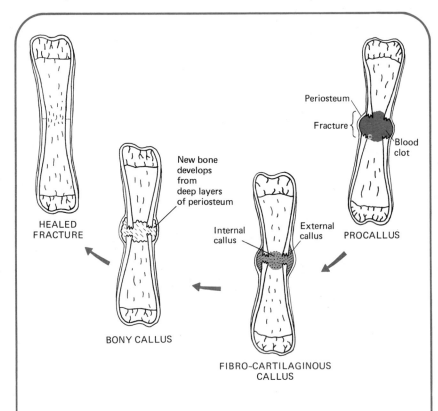

Bone repair in essence is a recapitulation of the process described for bone
formation (Module 4B). The gap that is created between the fractured end of
the bones is initially filled by the blood clot that forms when the blood vessels
are torn. The clot is transformed into a callus by the invasion and migration
of progenitor connective tissue cells. The callus cartilage then calcifies and
is replaced by new bone tissue brought in by the new sprouting capillaries.
Eventually the callus is replaced by bone tissue and the repair is completed.

a very specialized function. The rate of bone deposition is also directly
related to the work load or the force placed on bone. This response explains why a leg in a cast becomes thinner—not only do the muscles
shrink but the bone becomes demineralized. Mitosis is rare to the cells
trapped in a calcified matrix; most regeneration occurs from the periosteal membrane.

support and   So far we have seen that bone is dynamically involved in mineral stor-
protection   age, crystal formation, enzyme activity, and numerous interrelated

figure 4-28

SYNOVIAL JOINT
ARTICULATION

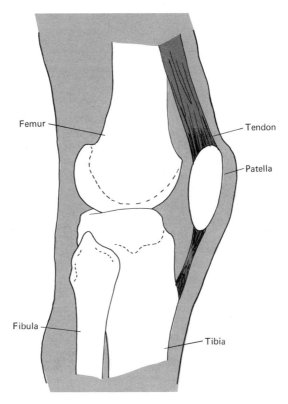

Femur

Tendon

Patella

Fibula

Tibia

growth activities. It would be easy to conclude the functions at this point, yet to do so would eliminate two essential functions: *support and protection.*

It is almost unbelievable, but the center of a vertebra can withstand over 2000 pounds of crushing stress before deformation occurs. Bones are capable of withstanding great forces as well as being able to support tremendous weights. There is little disagreement in the thinking of most paleontologists that the evolution of bone was directly related to the needs for protection. The bony protection of the brain and spinal cord was explained in the introduction to the section on the axial skeleton.

articulations   The *joints* or *articulations* are the sites where bones connect; the specific study of these connections is called *arthrology*, although the term is rarely used. A schematic presentation of a movable knee joint is presented in Figure 4-28. This is a *synovial* joint, and it is characterized by a secretory membrane that produces a synovial fluid to minimize friction. The joint is encapsulated by a tough fibrous sheath, whose connective tissue fibers intermesh with the fibers of the periosteum to create a strong union. Ligaments provide additional support for the joint.

The classification of joints is based primarily on their degree of movement; immovable joints or joints with limited movement are called *synarthrotic* joints, and joints that have great movement are called *diarthrotic*. The types of movement found in movable joints are listed below.

FLEXION A flexion joint decreases the angle between two bones and brings them closer together, for example, bending of the elbow or knee.

EXTENSION An extension joint increases the angle between the articulating bones, for example, straightening the arm and elbow.

ABDUCTION A movement away from the midline of the body is by abduction, for example, moving the arm laterally.

ADDUCTION A movement toward the midline of the body is adduction, for example, bringing the arms back to the sides.

ROTATION The movement of a bone around its own axis or the axis of an adjacent bone is rotation, for example, moving the head as if to say "No."

SUPINATION Supination is the lateral rotation of the forearm, for example, bringing the palm up.

PRONATION Pronation is the opposite of supination, for example, the back of the hand now faces forward.

EVERSION An example of eversion would be rotation of the sole of the foot outward.

INVERSION An example of inversion would be rotation of the sole of the foot inward.

CIRCUMDUCTION Moving the arm so that the hand describes a circle would be circumduction, or moving the head from the chest, to the shoulder, to the back, and thus describing a circle.

control The control of bone absorption and deposition depends primarily on hormones from the thyroid and parathyroid glands, but other hormones and vitamins also function in the regulation of calcium and phosphate metabolism and are, therefore, described in this section.

hormones The *parathyroid* hormones stimulate *osteoclast* activity, which demineralizes bone and frees calcium into the circulation. The level of calcium is increased in blood and produces a fleeting *hypercalcemia* (higher than normal levels of calcium). The calcium is available for blood clotting, cell membrane activity, and so forth. The mechanism of bone reabsorption by the osteoclast is not known. Some believe that osteoclasts act as phagocytes; others presume that osteoclasts secrete an enzyme that demineralizes the bone or a chemical that can tie up calcium. When parathyroid hormone levels are low, osteoblast activity takes over and bone resorption halts; concomitantly, bone deposition increases, and *hypocalcemia* or a low level of circulating calcium results. Part of the regulatory mechanism is under control of *calcitonin*, which can rapidly lower the calcium ion concentration of the blood. Calcitonin is secreted by the thyroid and parathyroid glands. The levels of circulating calcium control the secretion of the parathyroid hormone and calcitonin (Module 4A), and it is quite evident that this feedback mechanism between the hormones and the circulating free calcium is quite sensitive, since the levels of calcium in the extracellular fluids vary very slightly at any given moment.

The hormone *thyroxine* stimulates the metabolism of all body cells; therefore in this fashion it also affects the growth processes of bone.

The *pituitary* gland produces a *growth hormone* that acts directly upon the epiphyseal cartilage to stimulate growth of bones in the long axis. The sex hormones from the testes and ovaries also indirectly influence the final shaping of mature bones (the shape of the male and female pelvis) as well as stimulate general bone growth.

vitamins

The intestinal absorption of calcium from the digestive tract (primarily milk products) would be insignificant without vitamin D, which apparently acts on the calcium-binding capabilities of the gastrointestinal lining. Vitamin D also has some regulatory effect in calcium deposition. Vitamins A and C exert a specific action on osteoblast activity and fiber formation, and thus contribute to the hardening of the bone.

factors
influencing
function

aging

The effects of aging are very evident in the skeletal system. Cartilage is the predominant tissue in the fetus, and it is almost completely replaced by bony tissue by childhood. By the end of the first year the vertebral column shows two major curves: the fontanels close within 20 to 24 months, and by the twentieth year the epiphyseal cartilage is gone, ending growth longitudinally. During the maturation process from birth to old age, the body grows at unequal rates.

The maximum extent of bone growth is achieved at about 20 to 21 years, and from this period on, the skeleton goes into a negative balance with a gradual bone loss equal to almost 30 percent by the time old age is reached. This major loss is seen in the brittle bones and in the very thin facial bones and loss of the surface landmarks associated with old age. The loss of skeletal material is due to a combination of factors, presumably the most important being a nutritional imbalance and a failure of the circulatory system to deliver materials properly.

calcium require-
ments of the body

It was pointed out previously that calcium is needed for many vital functions. In fact, calcium is ubiquitous and is needed for such a fundamental function as maintaining the soundness of the cell plasma membrane.

Calcium needs vary, and since the blood calcium levels are limited (about 10 mg percent), the ultimate source is the reserve found in the bone matrix; for example, if the calcium requirement is increased because of a unique demand, as would occur in pregnancy and insufficient calcium intake, the bone would increase osteoclast activity and release calcium. Conversely, a diet rich in calcium might increase, at least temporarily, osteoblast activity.

clinical
considerations

osteoporosis

Osteoporosis is a nonspecific term that refers to a group of diseases with a common denominator — bones demineralized and are softer than normal. Osteoporosis is frequently the result of a hormonal imbalance or to prolonged disuse, and the net result is a bone that is very vulnerable to stress. It is a disease of the aged.

osteomalacia   *Osteomalacia* is a disease that is also distinguished by a demineralization of the bony tissue, but is usually accompanied with a bending of a
bone, for example, *rickets* (Figure 4-29). It may be due to a lack of vitamin D or an inadequate diet of calcium and phosporus, or to both.

Rickets is mainly a disease of children that results from a nutritional
deficiency of calcium or phosphates. The deficiency is a prolonged one,
and the bones become progressively weaker, producing deformities and
increasing the probability of breaks.

osteomyelitis   Any type of infection in a bone, periosteum, or marrow that produces
inflammation is called *osteomyelitis.* Children are more susceptible
than adults to bone inflammation, and the site of infection is usually
restricted to the long bones of the arms and legs. Before the use of antibiotics, the occurrence and danger of osteomyelitis were much greater
than it is today, because the infections were almost impossible to localize
and difficult to remove. However, among infectious diseases osteomyelitis is one of the least susceptible to antibiotic therapy.

neoplasms   Over 20 different types of benign (mild) and malignant (tend to produce
death) tumors have been identified and associated with the skeleton.
The names of these diseases depend on the types of tissues making up
the tumor. For example, a tumor on the epiphyseal cartilage would be
called a *chondrosarcoma* (*chondro,* referring to cartilage, and *sarcoma,*
a malignant tumor of connective tissue origin). If the tumor were fibrous
in nature, it would be called a *fibrosarcoma,* and if the tumor were benign and nonmalignant, it would be labeled a *fibroma.* A malignant
tumor of epithelial origin is a *carcinoma.*

storage of   The specific affinity of calcium for bone is shared by other minerals and
toxic minerals   in certain situations can lead to pathological states. For example, lead

figure 4-29

RICKETS—X-RAY
PHOTOGRAPH

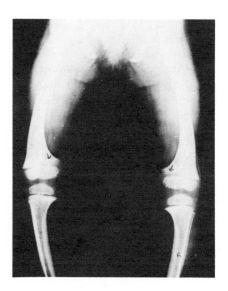

is taken up and released by bone in a manner similar to that described for calcium. The lead enters bone as a lead salt and competes with calcium for mineralization. Since the turnover for lead is slower than for calcium, lead is a poison to bone. Radioactive strontium (found in certain milk) is also taken up by bone, and the radioactivity may cause bone degeneration or tumor formation.

arthritis   The term *arthritis* is merely a catchall referring to inflammatory diseases of the articulating areas. Usually some adjective phrase is added to explain either the cause or a characteristic of the disease, for example, arthritis associated with tuberculosis. Some causes of arthritis are *rheumatic fever, trauma* (when a joint is twisted or injured by falling), or changes in the body chemistry (*gout*). One painful and crippling form of the disease is *rheumatoid arthritis*, the cause of which is unknown (Figure 4-30).

figure 4-30
ARTHRITIS—
X-RAY
PHOTOGRAPH

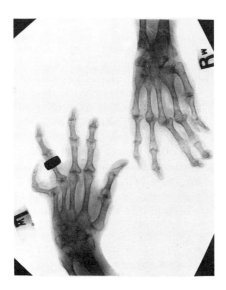

slipped disc   The discs (Figure 4-31) between vertebrae are composed of an outer ring of tough fibrous connective tissue and an inner pulpy core that is also called the *nucleus pulposus*. Because of a variety of causes, the ring portion may give and produce an outward protrusion of the pulposus (*nucleus prolapse*). This condition is conveniently referred to as a "slipped disc," although the actual dislodgment is not of the entire disc but the herniation or protrusion of the core portion. The pain is due to the pressure exerted by the protruded portion directly or indirectly on the adjacent nerves.

teeth   The discussion of teeth is included in this chapter because of their anatomical relationship to bone (Figure 4-32) and because of their mineral
general   metabolism which is comparable to that of bone.
information   During a person's life span, two sets of teeth appear. The *baby, milk,*

figure 4-31
SLIPPED DISC

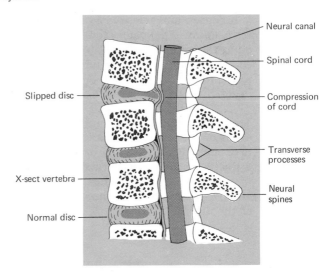

Neural canal

Spinal cord

Compression
of cord

Transverse
processes

Neural
spines

Slipped disc

X-sect vertebra

Normal disc

or *deciduous* teeth begin to appear at 6 months of age. The milk set generally disappears by the twelfth to fourteenth year, with the permanent or second set of teeth appearing gradually between the ages of 6 and 25 years. Two new molars are added to the permanent set of teeth. Sometimes the back molars or *wisdom teeth* do not appear, so some adults may have 28, not 32, teeth.

structure   A tooth consists of two parts (Figure 4-33). The *crown* is the exposed portion above the gum line and is covered with enamel (epithelial in origin, it is 1 percent protein and 99 percent inorganic salts) and is a very tough, hard substance; the lower part of the tooth forms the *roots*, which fit into the sockets found in the mandibles and maxillae. The bulk

figure 4-32
PERMANENT
TEETH

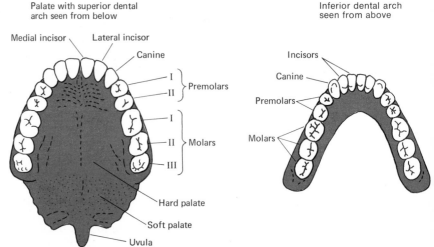

Palate with superior dental
arch seen from below

Inferior dental arch
seen from above

Medial incisor   Lateral incisor

Canine

I
II   Premolars

I
II   Molars
III

Hard palate

Soft palate

Uvula

Incisors

Canine

Premolars

Molars

figure 4-33

LONGITUDINAL
SECTION OF A
TOOTH

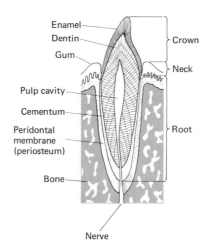

of the tooth is dentin, similar in structure to bone matrix but even harder. Covering the dentin is a layer called cementum that is histologically similar to bone. In the core of the tooth is a pulp cavity filled with loose connective tissue, blood vessels, and nerves. The intermeshing of the fibrous membrane covering of the tooth with the fibers of the periosteal lining of the tooth sockets provides the firm attachment of teeth to bone.

physiology   The groups of teeth are modified for specific functions. Starting at the middle of one jaw, there are two *incisors* for cutting food, one *canine* for tearing, and two *premolars* and three *molars* for grinding (Figure 4-34).

The mechanism for reabsorbing and depositing calcium salts in teeth is unknown, but most investigators believe that the mechanism would be comparable to bone metabolism. The greatest metabolic turnover takes place in the dentin and cementum, and very little in the enamel.

figure 4-34

TYPES OF TEETH

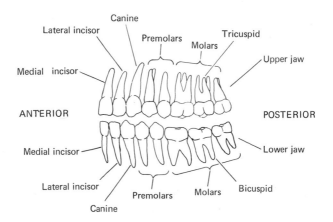

figure 4-35
DEVELOPMENT OF
CARIES

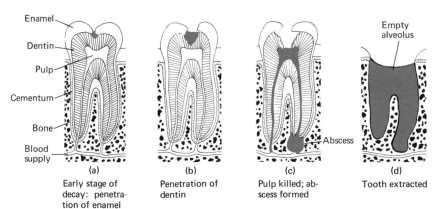

Enamel

Dentin

Pulp

Cementum

Bone

Blood
supply

Empty
alveolus

Abscess

(a)   (b)   (c)   (d)

Early stage of   Penetration of   Pulp killed; ab-   Tooth extracted
decay: penetra-   dentin   scess formed
tion of enamel

clinical
considerations

Caries (Figure 4-35)

A common abnormality of the teeth is *caries* or *erosions* of the enamel. One theory is that trapped food (especially carbohydrates) undergoes degradation producing lactic acid, and the acid erodes the enamel. Another theory is that bacteria trapped in the crevices of the teeth directly produce proteolytic enzymes that destroy the enamel protein. Fluoride is known to make enamel resistant to caries when the chemical is administered in water and toothpaste (Figure 4-35).

Peridontal Disease

Dental statistics indicate that *peridontal* disease may very well be the most widespread of all human diseases, with an incidence as high as 90 percent in the mature adult (over 35 years of age). *Peridontitis* (Figure 4-36) is a syndrome that includes a series of changes beginning with an inflammation of the gums (*gingivitis*) that may produce a separation of the gingiva from the teeth. The inflammation will spread to the tooth-bone juncture, destroying ligaments, cement, and even the bony socket (Figure 4-36); the tooth loosens and eventually it is lost.

figure 4-36
PERIDONTAL
DISEASE

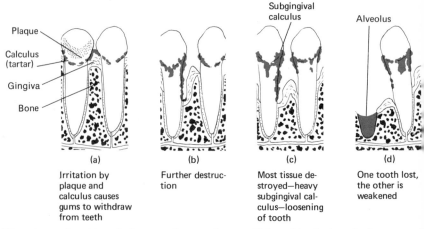

Plaque

Calculus
(tartar)

Gingiva

Bone

Subgingival
calculus

Alveolus

(a)   (b)   (c)   (d)

Irritation by   Further destruc-   Most tissue de-   One tooth lost,
plaque and   tion   stroyed—heavy   the other is
calculus causes   subgingival cal-   weakened
gums to withdraw   culus—loosening
from teeth   of tooth

*Plaque is a coating of bacteria that normally cannot be seen. With special stains it can be demonstrated as a thin layer.

A variety of irritants produces the inflammation of peridontitis. The most common cause is *bacterial plaque,* an accumulation of bacteria whose toxins are believed to be the agent producing inflammation. Food particles trapped on and between teeth are a fine media for plaque to form. The second major factor in producing irritation is *calculus* – a combination of food, bacteria, and mucus that is hardened into scale-like deposits by the calcium salts that are present.

summary

gross anatomy

1. Consists of 206 bones divided into
   (a) axial: skull, vertebrae, thorax
   (b) appendicular: girdles, limbs, hands and feet
2. Types of bones
   (a) long: shaft (diaphysis) and two extremities (epiphyses)
   (b) short: regularly shaped, such as vertebral bones and middle ear bones
   (c) flat: skull bones, which have a compact bone covering for protection
3. Landmarks (Table 4-1)
4. Classification
   (a) Skull (neurocranium)
      frontal   temporal (2)
      occipital   stapes (2)
      sphenoid   malleus (2)
      ethmoid   incus (2)
      parietal (2)
   (b) Skull (face)
      mandible   zygomatic (2)
      maxilla (2)   palatine (2)
      vomer   hyoid
      nasal (2)   inferior nasal conchae (2)
      lacrimal (2)
   (c) fontanelles: spaces between fetal bones covered by membranes that eventually are converted to bone as the infant matures
   (d) sinuses: technically not part of the skeletal system; four major air spaces that communicate with each nasal cavity (frontal, sphenoid, ethmoid, and maxillary)
   (e) vertebral column
      cervical (7)   sacral (4)
      thoracic (12)   coccyx (4)
      lumbar (5)
   (f) thorax
      rib (12)
      vertebrae (12)
      sternum
   (g) pectoral girdle
      scapula (2)   ulna (2)
      clavicle (2)   carpal (16)
      humerus (2)   metacarpal (10)
      radius (2)   phalange (28)

(h) pectoral girdle

illium (2)	fibula (2)
ischium (2)	patella (2)
pubis (2)	tarsal (14)
femur (2)	metatarsal (10)
tibia (2)	phalange (28)

cellular and tissue specialization

1. The principal cells of the skeletal system are chondrocytes (cartilage cells) and osteocytes (bone cells)
2. Osteoclasts: unique cells that secrete enzymes that help to break down the noncellular material or matrix of bone
3. Chondrocytes and osteocytes secrete a matrix that is hardened in a manner not yet explained by the deposition of minerals; process called chondrification for cartilage and ossification for bone
4. Haversian system: bony tissue develops in layers around blood vessels and lacteals and forms minute canals

physiology

1. Mineral metabolism: function of bone closely related with the metabolism of calcium and phosphate, since the bulk of bone is composed principally of tricalcium phosphate, calcium carbonate, and magnesium phosphate, which form crystals that become the matrix of the bone.
2. Organogenesis
    (a) fifth week of embryonic development a cartilage miniturization of the mature bone begins
    (b) endochondral or cartilage replacement bone formation: cartilage bone grows for a period, and then it dies, and the tissue is removed and replaced by osteocytes that form the adult bone
    (c) membrane bone formation: some adult bones form directly by ossification of connective tissue membranes.
3. Regeneration and repair
    (a) bony tissue is continually broken down to prevent excessive thickness, to bring new cells in close approximation to the blood vessel and to release calcium for metabolic needs (blood clotting, muscle contraction)
    (b) when a bone breaks, it is called a fracture, and the process of repair is similar to endochondral bone formation
4. Support and protection are the other major functions of bone

articulation

1. Synarthroses: no movement; joint is held fixed by connective tissue fibers or cartilage as seen in a suture of the skull
2. Amphiarthroses: slight movement as seen in the joints between successive vertebrae
3. Diarthroses: free movement, such as arm and shoulder
    (a) synovial membrane: forms a capsule and secretes a viscous material that lubricates the joint
    (b) ligaments: stabilize and limit joint movement

(c) Types

ball and socket	pivot
hinge	gliding
saddle	

(d) movement

flexion	supination
extension	pronation
abduction	eversion
adduction	inversion
rotation	circumduction

(e) bursae: closed sacs with a synovial membrane lining, found close to joints, especially where movement is over a bony prominence

control

1. Hormones
   (a) parathyroid hormone: stimulates osteoclast activity, thus making calcium available to the body
   (b) calcitonin: lowers blood calcium concentration
   (c) thyroxin: stimulates metabolism of bone cells
   (d) pituitary growth hormone: also stimulates cellular metabolism and has a specific affinity for stimulating the cells of the epiphyseal plates, the cartilage plates found in the epiphysis of long bone which contribute to growth on the long axis as long as the cartilage remains mitotically active
2. Vitamins
   (a) A and C: stimulate osteoblast activity and the deposition of fibers
   (b) D: has a regulatory effect on calcium deposition and apparently speeds up calcium-binding capabilities of the gastrointestinal lining

factors influencing function

1. Aging
   (a) cartilage the predominant tissue in the fetus, almost completely replaced by bony tissue by childhood
   (b) by the end of the first year, the vertebral column shows two major curves
   (c) the fontanelles close within 20 to 24 months
   (d) the epiphyseal cartilages are gone by the twentieth year when maximum extent of bone growth is achieved
   (e) skeleton growth goes into a negative balance after the twenty-first year with gradual bone loss equal to almost 30 percent by the time of old age
2. Calcium requirements
   (a) the ultimate source of calcium is a reserve found in the bone matrix
   (b) at certain periods such as in pregnancy, calcium requirements are altered
   (c) calcium is needed for many vital functions including such fundamental activities as maintaining the soundness of the plasma membrane

clinical considerations

1. Osteoporosis: nonspecific term referring to a group of diseases with a common denominator in that the bones are softer than normal
2. Osteomalacia: distinguished by a demineralization or softening of bony tissue; example would be rickets, which is caused by a lack of vitamin D or an inadequate diet of calcium and phosphorus, or both
3. Osteomyelitis: an infection in a bone or in the marrow that produces inflammation
4. Storage of toxic materials: minerals other than calcium have a specific affinity for bone; lead is an example of a mineral that is taken up and released by bone in a manner similar to that described for calcium; since lead is not metabolized and the turnover is slower than for calcium, lead eventually accumulates and becomes poisonous to bone
5. Arthritis: a general term referring to inflammation of the articulating areas
6. Slip disc: an outward protrusion of the connective tissue discs that are found between adjacent vertebrae

teeth

1. Structure
   (a) crown: that portion of a tooth above the gum line; covered with enamel
   (b) roots: lower part of the tooth that fits into the socket of the jaw
   (c) dentin: bulk of the tooth; similar in structure to bone matrix, but harder
   (d) pulp cavity: center of tooth, filled with loose connective tissue, blood vessels, and nerves

physiology

The groups of teeth are modified for specific functions:
1. Incisors: cutting
2. Canines: tearing
3. Molars: grinding

clinical considerations

1. Caries: erosion of the protein in enamel by proteolytic enzymes, formed by the decomposition of trapped food and bacteria
2. Periodontal disease: possibly the most widespread of all human diseases; a syndrome that includes inflammation of the gums and destruction of the tooth-bone junction, which eventually will loosen the tooth
   (a) plaque: an accumulation of bacteria that supposedly causes inflammation
   (b) calculus: a combination of food and bacteria that is hardened into scalelike deposits by calcium salts

nerve
cells

5

cellular specializations
cell body
dendrites
axons
synapse
neurofibrils and
   microtubules

physiology
membrane potentials
generation of the nerve
   impulse
propagation of an impulse
synaptic events

control
inhibition of transmission
integration
receptor neurons
adaptation
reflex arc

factors influencing function
metabolism

clinical considerations
myasthenia gravis
botulism
tetanus

One of the primary problems of multicellular organisms is communication among their varied cells. Two types of communication systems have evolved for the distribution of information to appropriate cells so that the activities of the billions of cells are integrated. One of these systems is made up of specialized glands whose secretions – chemical messengers called hormones – are released into the circulatory system and then transported to target cells programmed to respond. Such chemical communication is relatively slow, since the common pathway (blood flow) is rather long. This system, the *endocrine system*, will be discussed in Chapter 18. The second system, the *nervous system*, also involves the release of chemical messengers; however, the distance traveled to the target cell is usually short, thereby producing a rapid response. The nervous system is also more specific in that the chemical transmitter released from one cell can elicit a response from only a limited number of cells. This specificity occurs because the chemical is not usually released into the general circulation, but rather between two cells. The chemical messenger is short-lived, since it is rapidly made inactive. Once stimulated, cells of the nervous system conduct information to connecting cells extremely rapidly, at rates upward of 100 yards/sec. (Module 5A)

cellular specializations

The nerve cell, or *neuron*, is the basic unit of the nervous system. Cell types range from simple spherical-shaped structures with as few as two extensions to elongated cylindrical-shaped structures with as many as a thousand extensions (Figure 5-1). The component parts of a generalized nerve cell are shown in Module 5A and described in detail in the following section.

cell body

The *cell body*, or *soma*, is that portion of the cell containing the nucleus. Since the mature nerve cell does not divide, the sole function of the nucleus is to direct the activities of the cell. The cell body usually has within it structures, called *chromophilic substances* or *Nissl bodies*, that stain with basic dyes. Electron microscopy has revealed these bodies to be aggregates of flattened membranes to which ribosomes containing RNA are attached. Some investigators have suggested that the Nissl substance is involved in protein synthesis related to the coding of information within the nerve cell ("memory"), but at this stage of the research such a conclusion appears to be premature. In diseased conditions the Nissl bodies may undergo *chromatolysis* (breakdown and disappearance).

Among the many inclusions found within the nerve cell body, granules containing the brown pigment *lipofuscin* are of special interest. They are believed to be by-products of neuron metabolism, and no special function has yet been ascribed to them. What makes these inclusions noteworthy is that they accumulate with age (frequently filling the cell body in a manner resembling fat accumulation in cells of adipose tissue); therefore, the possibility exists that these pigment granules may be involved in a pathological metabolism related to aging.

dendrites

Extensive branching of the cell body gives rise to the *dendrites*. They carry signals from other neurons or receptors toward the cell body. Since

module 5A

THE NEURON—
THE STRUCTURAL
AND FUNCTIONAL
UNIT OF NEURAL
INFORMATION
PROCESSING

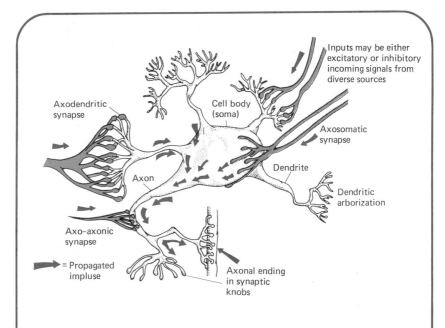

Inputs may be either
excitatory or inhibitory
incoming signals from
diverse sources

Axodendritic
synapse

Cell body
(soma)

Axosomatic
synapse

Dendrite

Dendritic
arborization

Axon

Axo-axonic
synapse

= Propagated
impluse

Axonal ending
in synaptic
knobs

The nerve cell, or neuron, exists in many configurations, but its basic structure generally includes the *dendrite,* the *cell body* or *soma,* and the *axon.* The dendrites are extensions from the cell body, which are modified for reception of incoming signals and transmission of the signals toward the cell body. The cell body contains the nucleus and is the main synthesizing center of the neuron. The axons are extensions that carry impulses away from the cell body, Both dendrites and axons often end in fine terminals.

Inputs to the neuron can be by way of *axodendritic synapses,* where axon terminals of one neuron synapse with dendrites of another neuron; by way of *axosomatic synapses,* where axon terminals of one neuron synapse with the cell body of another neuron; or by way of *axo-axonic synapses,* where the axon terminals of one axon synapse with the axon of another neuron.

there can be multiple dendrites (*arborizations*), it is possible for a nerve cell to receive signals from literally hundreds to tens of thousands of other cells. It has been estimated that there may be up to 250,000 *synaptic terminals* (nerve endings) located on the dendrites of a single cell in the cerebellum.

axons   The *axon* carries signals away from the cell body toward other neurons, gland cells, or muscle cells. Unlike dendrite branching, only one axon is associated with each nerve cell body; however, there can be branches directly from the axon (*collaterals*). The cytoplasm within the axon proper is sometimes referred to as an *axoplasm.*

figure 5-1

SOME
REPRESENTATIVE
TYPES OF
NEURONS

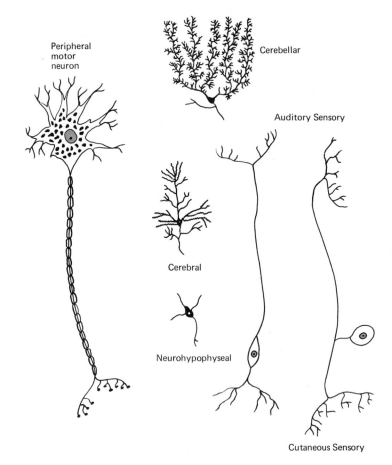

Peripheral
motor
neuron

Cerebellar

Auditory Sensory

Cerebral

Neurohypophyseal

Cutaneous Sensory

figure 5-2

SYNAPTIC
KNOBS

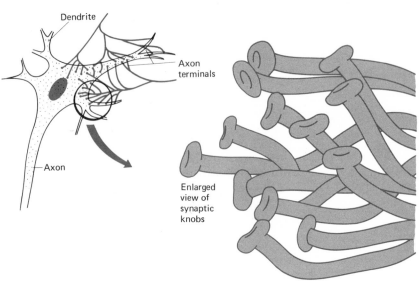

Dendrite

Axon
terminals

Axon

Enlarged
view of
synaptic
knobs

Axons can be less than 1 mm in length or as long as 1 m and they are covered by a *neurilemma*. Beneath the neurilemma may or may not be a thick *myelin* sheath, a structure formed by the *Schwann cells* that are also responsible for the presence of the neurilemma. Where myelin is present the Schwann cell actually wraps around the axon many times (Figure 5-3), and the sparse amount of cytoplasm between the membranes makes it appear that the myelin sheath is composed of a lamination of plasma membranes. The fatty myelin serves as insulation for the axon and, as will be explained later, allows for greater speed in carrying impulses along the axon. Schwann cells are lined up adjacent to one another and produce a continuous myelin sheath except where the Schwann cells articulate. These breaks are known as the *nodes of Ranvier* (Figure 5-3). The myelin sheath, if present, ends at the terminal branches of the axon.

synapse   The synapse involves the axon terminal, the synaptic cleft, and the closely apposed membrane of the cell which the nerve is synapsing. Synapses can occur between nerves, between a nerve and gland, and between a nerve and a muscle. The latter is usually called a *neuromuscular*

figure 5-3

MYELIN SHEATH

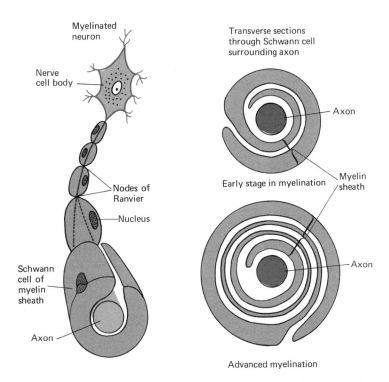

The myelin sheath develops by a wrapping of one end of the Schwann cell around the other, resulting in a squeezing out of the cytoplasm and the appearance of a laminated structure around the axon.

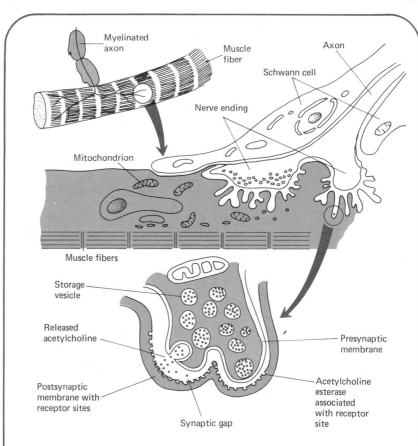

The chemical synapse, which is by far the most common type, consists of the presynaptic and postsynaptic cells and the synaptic space between them. The presynaptic cell generally has vesicles with chemical transmitter agents which are released when an impulse reaches the synaptic area. The chemical transmitter diffuses across the synaptic space and causes the initiation of an impulse on the postsynaptic membrane. A description of the synapse between a neuron and muscle cells follows.

The nerve axon joins the muscle and divides into many fine branches. At the ultrastructural level we see the axon synapsing with the muscle membrane (*neuromuscular junction*). The nerve ending has numerous small vesicles approximately 500 Å in diameter, which contain the neural transmitter *acetylcholine*. When an impulse reaches the nerve ending, some of the acetylcholine is released and diffuses across the synaptic cleft, combining with receptor sites on the folded muscle membrane. The combining of the acetylcholine with the receptor sites on the muscle membrane causes changes in ion permeability to sodium and potassium, and an impulse is established on the muscle membrane. This impulse is similar to the nerve cell impulse, for it can be conducted along the muscle membrane without being diminished. The impulse can cause contraction of the muscle (see Chapter 6). The acetylcholine on the receptor sites is broken down by acetylcholine esterase and the membrane potential is restored to its resting level.

junction. Although these synapses differ somewhat in structure, a generalized description (Module 5B) at the ultrastructural level includes the presence of small membrane-bound granules and numerous mitochondria in the axon terminal (*presynaptic cells*), a synaptic space of 100 to 2000 Å, and the *postsynaptic cell.*

neurofibrils and microtubules

Neurofibrils are long fine fibrils with a diameter of about 60 Å. They are found in the cytoplasm of both axons or dendrites. Microtubules with a diameter of approximately 250 Å are also found in nerve axons and in dendrites. The functions of neurofibrils and microtubules are unclear, but they may be associated with the transport of acetylcholine and norepinephrine (see section on synaptic events).

physiology

membrane potentials

Methods of Measuring Potential

The fact that a *potential difference* or *electric* charge separation exists across an "unexcited" nerve cell axon was established by placing electrodes on the outside and inside of the membrane and measuring the difference in potential. Since the electrodes available to early workers were larger in diameter than the axon, the procedure used was to crush or cut the nerve and place an electrode on the crushed or cut end. This electrode was then considered as the "inside" electrode and a potential difference could be recorded between it and an electrode on the outside. This system was not ideal, since a certain amount of leakage occurred across the surface of the membrane through the salt solution that is present on the membrane. With the development of microelectrodes with tip diameters of less than 1 μ, it became possible to record *directly* electric charges across the membranes of many cells.

Cause of a Potential

When electrodes are arranged so as to measure the electric potential difference across the membrane of a nonexcited or resting neuron, a difference (inside negative with respect to the outside) of about -90 mv (millivolts) is noted (Figure 5-4). There is strong evidence that this po-

figure 5-4

THE MEMBRANE OR 'RESTING' POTENTIAL

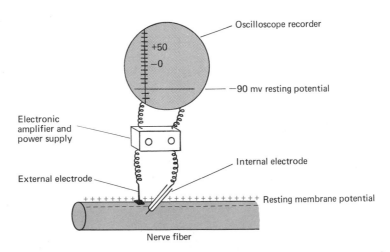

Electrodes measure the difference in potential across the neuron membrane.

tential difference is due to the unequal distribution of ions on either side of the membrane resulting in a high rate of potassium ion leakage inward. Potassium ions leak in faster than sodium ions leak out, because potassium ions have a smaller total diameter. The potential developed across the membrane of a resting neuron is termed the *membrane* or *resting* potential.

The nerve cell membrane is a semipermeable membrane capable of letting certain molecules and ions pass and keeping certain others (for example, large protein molecules) from passing. Although the sodium ion, in its hydrated form, is larger than the potassium and chloride ions and therefore moves through the membrane more slowly, this slower sodium movement should not account for unequal distribution of ions as seen in Figure 5-5. The ions are free to flow across the membrane and, with time, should obey the laws of diffusion and be distributed equally on both sides of the membrane.

The major contribution to the disproportionate distribution of ions is a "pump" which, by the expenditure of metabolic energy, extrudes sodium ions from the nerve cell to the exterior and concomitantly moves potassium ions into the interior. The machinery for the movement of sodium ions appears to be built into the membrane itself and the energy is supplied by ATP. This active transport of sodium operates at a sufficient rate to keep the sodium ion concentration on the outside of the membrane some 10 to 15 times the concentration of sodium on the inside in spite of the fact that sodium is diffusing through the membrane all the time.

The high concentration of potassium ions on the inside of the membrane is primarily accounted for by coupling of the movement of potassium ions inward to the active extrusion of sodium ions outward and also by the attraction of the many negatively charged internal ions. Since sodium ions are actively pumped from the inside of the neuron, potassium is the major positive ion inside the cell. Chloride ions are distributed passively.

If the production of energy by the nerve cell is poisoned or inhibited in any way, the sodium and potassium ions begin to become equally concen-

figure 5-5

DISTRIBUTION OF
IONS ACROSS
THE AXON
MEMBRANE

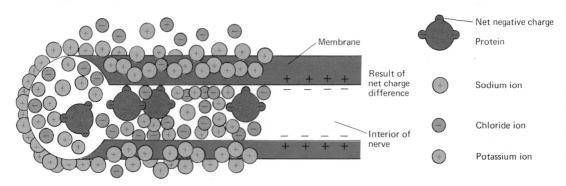

trated on both sides of the membrane. This equilibrium is reflected in the membrane potential that now moves toward zero. If this metabolic block is released in sufficient time and energy becomes available again, the potential will return to its normal resting level, indicating the reestablishment of a difference in the distribution of ions across the membrane.

generation of the nerve impulse

The existence of a potential across the membrane is not unique to the nerve cell, for such potentials are found across the membrane of a wide variety of animal and plant cells. What is unique about the nerve (and muscle) cell membrane is that it has the capacity to generate an impulse (action potential) in response to some stimulus and to propagate the impulse down the full length of the membrane (sometimes a distance of over a meter) without any decrease in the strength of the impulse.

Characteristics of a Nerve Impulse

The *action potential* is a *transient reversal of the resting potential*. When a nerve is stimulated, the membrane is *depolarized* and the membrane potential, which is normally somewhere near −90 mv, moves toward a less negative potential. If the stimulus is below the *threshold* or triggering level, the membrane will move back to its original *resting potential* (become *polarized* again). When the potential reaches the threshold, however, there is an explosive reversal of the membrane potential, and at the height of this impulse the reversal may be as much as +50 mv (Figure 5-6).

The action potential is often referred to as an *all-or-none* event; that is, once threshold is reached, a full action potential is generated. If the stimulus is below threshold, no action potential develops.

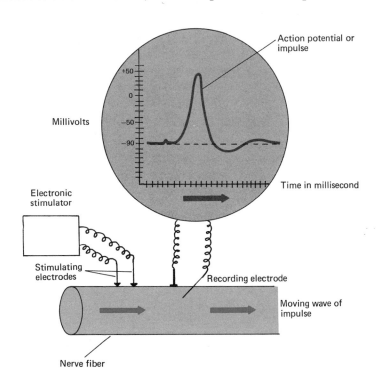

figure 5-6

NERVE ACTION POTENTIAL OR IMPULSE

Recording with an
Oscilloscope

The instrument of choice for recording changing potentials such as those generated from nerve and muscle fibers is the oscilloscope (Figure 5-7). The heart of the instrument is a cathode-ray tube somewhat similar to a television tube. An electron beam can be made to sweep across the inside face of this vacuum tube and excite phosphorescent material, thus producing a lighted replica of its path. A pair of plates or electrodes controls the horizontal beam movement. By adjusting the potential on these plates, the beam can be made to move across the face with varying speeds. Another pair of plates regulates the movement of the beam in the vertical direction. As long as the potential on these plates is constant, the beam will move horizontally in a straight line. If, however, a pair of electrodes is placed across an axon membrane as shown in Figure 5-7 and a nerve is stimulated sufficiently to produce an action potential, with proper amplification the signal or potential arriving at the vertical plates will change the horizontal beam in a way that will duplicate the electric

figure 5-7

ELECTRONIC
RECORDING

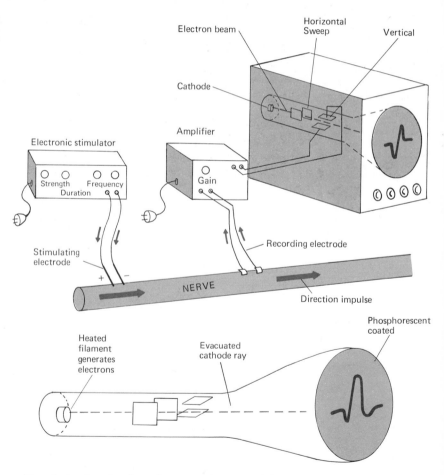

The electronic recording of nerve action potentials using the cathode ray oscilloscope.

changes involved in the action potential of the nerve; the pattern will be reproduced on the screen.

Cause of an
Impulse

The action potential, as do all membrane potentials, reflects the distribution of ions across the membrane. What is believed to happen when a stimulus is applied to a nerve is that there is some redistribution of ions in a very selective pattern. The initial event triggered by a threshold stimulus is a selective increase in the permeability of the membrane to sodium ions. Because there is a higher concentration of sodium ions on the outside, there is an influx of sodium to the inside of the membrane. This drives the membrane potential in the positive direction. Shortly afterward the permeability to sodium ions is shut down and permeability to potassium ions increases, allowing potassium ions to go out and thereby drive the potential back toward the resting potential (Figure 5-8).

The key to the action potential is the change in permeability to sodium ions. The movement of sodium ions inward in response to the change in permeability is what reverses the membrane potential from negative to positive. Which mechanism in the membrane is responsible for the sudden change in potential is not known, nor is it known which membrane mechanism is operative in shutting down sodium permeability. When the sodium permeability is shut down and the potassium permeability is increased, no new action potential can be induced. This stage is the so-called *refractory period.* Since the action potential depends on the change in sodium permeability, it is obvious that no new action potential can be generated as long as the sodium permeability is shut down.

It should be noted that each impulse involves the passage of only a small number of the total ion population. It is estimated that a nerve fiber 0.5 μ in diameter would lose less than one-thousandth of its potassium ions with an impulse. This minor loss means that even with the sodium pump shut off, such a fiber could generate many impulses before it would run down. The usual pattern of activity of neurons is the occurrence of bursts of action potentials followed by periods of quiescence. It is during these quiescent periods that the sodium pump is able to redistribute the ions across the membrane.

propagation of
an impulse

Comparison of
Nerve with Cable

One analogy often used to describe the nerve axon is to compare it to an electric cable. The analogy consists of relating the nerve membrane to the insulation around the cable and axoplasm to the interior of the cable. The interior of the nerve axon is, in fact, a poor conductor when compared to the cable, and the membrane is not a particularly efficient insulating medium. This comparison is also faulty in that the cable interior conducts the current, whereas the nerve depends on the movement of ions across the membrane. However, the analogy has been a great help in understanding how the impulse, once generated, can spread along the entire length of the axon.

Because the nerve axon has cablelike properties, it is possible for an impulse to produce changes in potential in adjoining areas of the axon membrane due to the movement of ions for short distances internally, externally, and across the membrane. The ion exchange produces lines

figure 5-8

ION FLOW DURING
NERVE ACTION
POTENTIAL

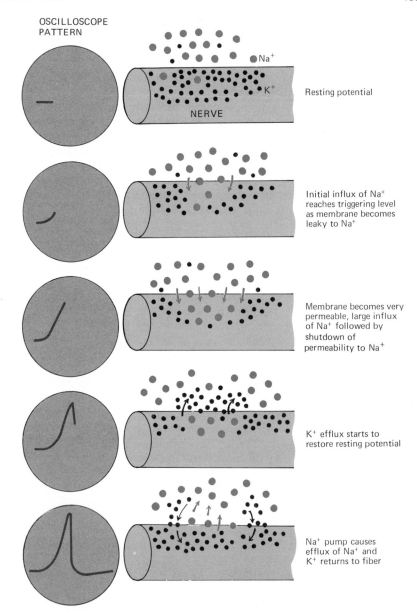

OSCILLOSCOPE
PATTERN

Na$^+$

NERVE

K$^+$

Resting potential

Initial influx of Na$^+$
reaches triggering level
as membrane becomes
leaky to Na$^+$

Membrane becomes very
permeable, large influx
of Na$^+$ followed by
shutdown of
permeability to Na$^+$

K$^+$ efflux starts to
restore resting potential

Na$^+$ pump causes
efflux of Na$^+$ and
K$^+$ returns to fiber

of current flow that form loops and are therefore known as *local circuits*
(Figure 5-9). Since the cable properties of the membrane are poor, this
spread of current does not extend far from the point of origin of the impulse, perhaps 1 or 2 mm. The potential changes at those points nearest
the origin of the impulse are of *suprathreshold* quality and can generate
an impulse. New local circuits are established further from the point of
origin, and in this way there is a sequential spread of the impulse along
the membrane.

figure 5-9
LOCAL CIRCUITS

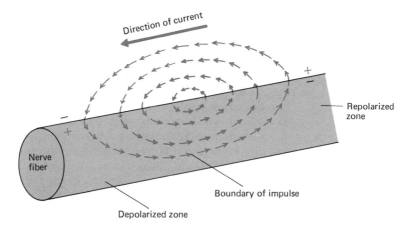

Local circuits during excitation cause depolarization at the leading edge of the circuit, producing a continuous wave of depolarization along the axon.

The impulse or action potential spreads along the membrane in a wavelike fashion much as a wave moving across water. The analogy here is a good one, since the wave is a reflection of the movement of ions across the membrane rather than a continuous movement of ions along the length of the membrane.

Conduction in an Axon
Under experimental conditions the initiation of the impulse at a particular point on the axon gives rise to a spread of the impulse in both directions, since current changes of sufficient magnitude occur on both sides of the point of application of the stimulus. In the normal physiological situation, the nerve is stimulated at the dendrite end, and the impulse travels the length of the axon culminating in a particular event at the axon terminals.

Although great emphasis has been placed on the events at the membrane of the nerve axon, as pointed out, the interior plays a significant role in the functioning of the neuron. First, the metabolic processes of a neuron cytoplasm are the prime source of energy for the sodium pump. Second, the spread of the impulse is dependent on circuits that are generated in localized areas of the membrane and axoplasm. This latter property is a function of the *conductance* of the axoplasm. In this case the conductance can be defined as *the ability of the axoplasm to allow movement of ions.* The conductance, although rather poor, is still capable of supporting the small spread of current. For one thing the conductance of the axoplasm is dependent on the thickness of the axon. The larger the diameter of the axon, the greater the conductance. In practical terms the impulse is spread more rapidly down the length of an axon with a larger diameter than one with a smaller diameter. In general, nerves leading to muscles that must react rapidly (those involved with escape movements) have axons with larger diameters than those leading to muscles whose functions are more vegetative (muscles of the digestive tract).

Myelin and
Saltatory
Conduction

What has been stated above about axon diameter and rate of conduction is generally true, except that evolution has gone one step further. A special system has evolved that allows for more rapid conduction without an extremely large increase in axon diameter. The adaptation involves laying down as a sheath of lipoprotein, called myelin (see Figure 5-3), about the axon; the sheath develops as a result of the wrapping of a pseudopodial-like extension of the adjacent Schwann cell in a spiral fashion. This wrapping leads to an arrangement in which there are a number of closely apposed membranes covering a nerve axon and acting as an efficient insulating layer. Such a layer, if continuous along the length of the axon, would prevent the propagation of an impulse. The actual arrangement is one in which there are regular breaks (nodes of Ranvier) in the sheath; the nodes actually allow for a more rapid conduction of the impulse, since the impulse is regenerated at each of the nodes in sequential fashion and does not have to spread continuously along the membrane. That this jumping, or saltatory spread of the impulse, allows for more rapid conduction is readily seen from a comparison of the *conduction velocities* (that is, the rate of passage of the action potential) of an axon that utilizes the saltatory system and one that does not. A selected nonmyelinated squid axon has a diameter of 700 μ and a conduction velocity of 25 m/sec, whereas the myelinated A-type axons of the frog have a conduction velocity of about 50 m/sec with a diameter of only 18 μ!

There is a further advantage of myelination besides that of reducing the diameter of the axon required for a particular conduction velocity. Ions cross the membrane as a result of the impulse propagated along the membrane. In order for the membrane to be completely restored to its resting state, ions in equivalent number and kind must reenter. In the case of sodium ions, this transit takes energy. Since ions only cross the membrane at the nodes in myelinated nerves, it has been estimated that only about $1/300$ of the ions crossing an unmyelinated nerve passes the membrane of a myelinated membrane. This observation means that rearranging the ions across myelinated nerves requires only $1/300$ of the metabolic energy as that in unmyelinated nerves.

synaptic events

We have commented earlier that we might call the nerve cell a *secretory* cell with special membrane properties related to electrochemical phenomena. Evidence obtained from histochemical, physiological, and biochemical studies indicates that the arrival of the impulse at the axon terminal causes a release of a chemical transmitter that diffuses across the synaptic space and induces permeability changes in the postsynaptic membrane. This release leads to a generation of a new action potential on the postsynaptic membrane, which can then be propagated along the membrane of the postsynaptic cell. (Figure 5-10)

Release of
Acetylcholine

A close look at a synaptic area reveals that within the axon terminal small membrane-bound structures that are called *vesicles* are localized (Figure 5-10, Module 5B). These vesicles have a diameter of about 400 to 500 Å. Within the brain, spinal cord, and peripheral nervous system,

figure 5-10

SYNAPTIC
TRANSMISSION

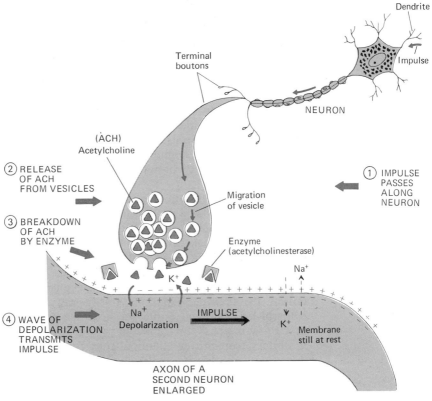

there are neurons with synaptic vesicles containing the transmitter substance, *acetylcholine*, which is synthesized from acetic acid and choline.

$$CH_3COOH + (CH_3)_3N^+CH_2CH_2OH \rightleftharpoons CH_3COOCH_2CH_2N^+(CH_3)_3 + H_2O$$

acetic acid   choline   acetylcholine

This compound is released when the impulse arrives. Although the mechanism of release of acetylcholine from these vesicles is not known, a possible mechanism is one in which the vesicles move to the plasma membrane, open in some way, and allow the acetylcholine to escape into the synaptic space. The presence of calcium ions is necessary in order for release to occur. The acetylcholine then moves across the space by simple diffusion and combines with special receptor sites on the postsynaptic membrane. This interaction of transmitter material with receptor site leads to permeability changes in the postsynaptic membrane, and ions cross causing a depolarization of the membrane. The sequence of events associated with the synapse is shown in Module 5B.

Breakdown of   The degree of depolarization is dependent on the amount of acetyl-
Acetylcholine   choline that arrives at the postsynaptic receptor sites. Sufficient amounts
                 of transmitter substance can cause a level of depolarization that is above
                 threshold and an action potential can develop on the postsynaptic mem-

brane. If acetylcholine were allowed to remain on the receptor sites, the membrane would remain depolarized. An enzyme, *acetylcholine esterase*, is present in the postsynaptic membrane and rapidly breaks down the acetylcholine to acetic acid and choline. The membrane is then returned to its normal resting potential.

The class of neurons that secretes acetylcholine has been chosen for discussion as this class is by far the best known. Those nerve cells having acetylcholine as a chemical transmitter are called *cholinergic*. Another class includes those nerve cells that secrete *norepinephrine* at their synaptic terminals. These cells are called *adrenergic*: that is, they have vesicles that somehow release norepinephrine into a synaptic space which causes changes in the postsynaptic membrane potential.

control

inhibition of transmission

Thus far only excitation, or generation of an action potential, in the postsynaptic cell has been discussed. There are many cases known in which the stimulation of a presynaptic cell leads to *inhibition* in the postsynaptic cell. The usual case is that in which stimulation of the one produces a higher degree of polarization in the other (Figure 5-11). The action of the *inhibitory chemical transmitter* causes the potential of the postsynaptic membrane to move even further away from zero potential, for example, from −70 to −75 mv. If an amount of excitatory transmitter chemical sufficient to cause membrane depolarization to just 1 or 2 mv past the threshold voltage arrives simultaneously with an inhibitory transmitter chemical that can cause a hyperpolarization of 5 mv, a depolarization will occur, but it will not have sufficient magnitude to trigger an action potential.

The increase in negative potential caused by an inhibitory transmitter is thought to be due to an increase in permeability of the membrane to potassium or chloride ions, or to both. Because there is a greater concen-

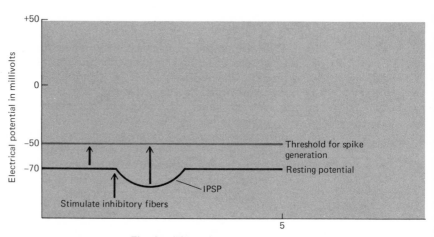

figure 5-11

NEURAL INHIBITION

Stimulation of an inhibitory neuron causes the generation of an inhibitory postsynaptic potential (IPSP) on the postsynaptic neuron.

tration of potassium on the inside, any selective increase in permeability would allow potassium ions to flow outward, thereby increasing the negative internal potential.

In some cases acetylcholine and norepinephrine act as excitatory agents or transmitters; in other cases they act as inhibitory transmitters. (A description of several examples of this type of action is given in Chapter 10.) The action of the transmitter apparently depends on the nature of the receptor sites on the postsynaptic membrane.

integration   Thus far, with the exception of the discussion on inhibition, the relationships inferred have been on a one-to-one basis – that is, one presynaptic nerve cell and one postsynaptic cell. In many cases, if not most, the general picture is one in which several to several hundred cells impinge on another. These, of course, may be excitory or inhibitory. If simultaneous or closely following signals arrive at the membrane of a single nerve cell, then those signals produce an action which is a result of the integration of the postsynaptic activities.

Summation   Summation is one type of integration. It is the sum of the changes in the postsynaptic membrane caused by two or more presynaptic events. These changes in postsynaptic potentials are usually changes in local (subthreshold) potentials which, if sufficient, could lead to a full-blown action potential. Summation may be either spatial or temporal. In Figure 5-12, the sum of two presynaptic potentials from a single neuron arriving at close intervals causes temporal summation on the postsynaptic membrane. In Figure 5-11, spatial summation, the effect of two presynaptic inputs from two neurons arriving at close intervals at the postsynaptic

figure 5-12

SUMMATION OF
STIMULI

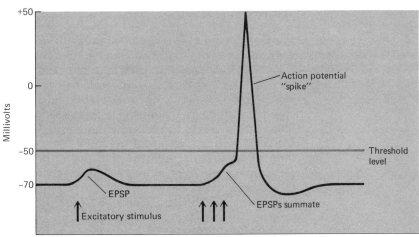

Summation is the result of the nearly simultaneous arrival of more than one subthreshold stimuli at a postsynaptic neuron; EPSP, excitatory postsynaptic potential. The shape of the action potential is distorted in order to show the effect.

figure 5-13
FACILITATION

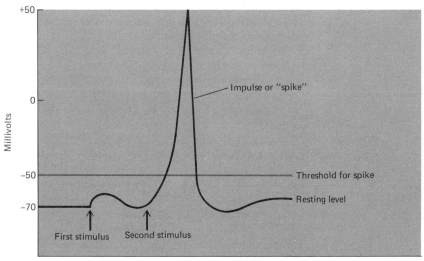

membrane, is illustrated. The example figure shows the effect of two pre-synaptic events – one excitatory and one inhibitory.

Facilitation, another type of integration, is characterized by a greater than normal response at the postsynaptic membrane to one or more presynaptic inputs. An example of facilitation is seen in Figure 5-13, where the initial response to a presynaptic input by the postsynaptic membrane is a small change in excitability. A second identical presynaptic input, following closely after the first, however, produces a greater change in excitability in the postsynaptic membrane. Other examples of integration will be given in the chapters dealing with specific neural pathways.

Facilitation

NEURONAL POOLS The dendritic areas of cell bodies of neurons in the gray matter of the spinal cord and in the brain have synapses from many cells. Many of those synapses may come from a single presynaptic cell, in which case the presynaptic cell has great influence over the postsynaptic. Conversely, if the presynaptic cell has only one or two synaptic endings on the postsynaptic cell, its influence is less. The first situation illustrates a cell in the center of a neuronal pool; the second illustrates when the cell is at the pool's edge. These conditions can be translated into information transfer. If cells A and B (Figure 5-14) represent the presynaptic cells, and cells 1, 2, 3, and 4 represent the postsynaptic cells, then stimulation of cell *A* would fire cell 1, which is in the center of its neuronal pool. This is a reasonable expectation, since cell *A* has seven synaptic endings on cell 1 and only three on cell 2. The same situation exists with cell *B* and cell 3. In each case, cell 2 is facilitated; that is, its membrane potential is made slightly more positive and is more excitable, *more easily fired.* Now if *A* and *B* were stimulated simultaneously, then there would be six synaptic endings discharging on cell 2, sufficient to reach threshold and fire an impulse.

Synaptic Arrangements

figure 5-14

DIAGRAM OF A
NEURONAL POOL

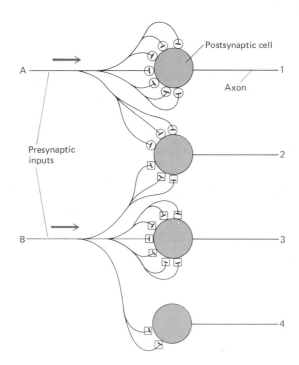

RECIPROCAL INNERVATION In many instances it is important to inhibit
the muscle activity that acts in the opposite direction to a desired action,
for example, flexion of the arm by the contraction of the biceps with
inhibition of the triceps. This effect can be accomplished through the
intervention of an inhibitory interneuron as seen in Figure 5-15. A collateral from the excitatory cell stimulates an inhibitory neuron which
synapses with the motor neuron and inhibits its firing.

DIVERGENCE AND CONVERGENCE Neuronal output can be made more diffuse by the process of divergence (Figure 5-16). A single signal can cause
the discharge of many cells, for example, the large skeletal muscles. This
pattern is essentially a biological amplifier, since a very small input is
multiplied many times before it reaches its end point. An example of this
is the small amount of light needed to stimulate a single light receptor
cell in the retina. With a divergent pattern, this input is magnified many
times.

Conversely, a large input can produce a very particular response by a
convergent pattern, where a single neuron is the end point in the pathway of a number of neurons (Figure 5-16). Obviously, there are many
variations in these basic patterns.

REVERBERATING AND PARALLEL CIRCUITS A single input can sometimes
produce sustained firing of a postsynaptic cell, sometimes known as
after discharge. This effect is accomplished as shown in Figure 5-17. In
a parallel circuit, pathways of varying lengths from the same presynaptic cells can cause continued discharge until the longest pathway
has fired. An oscillating circuit requires the feedback of a signal from

figure 5-15

INHIBITION OF
ANTAGONIST
MUSCLE DURING
EXCITATION

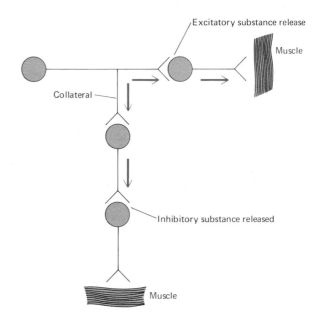

another cell which is discharged by the first (Figure 5-17). Having once started, such a circuit is essentially self-stimulating; however, it is possible for it to run down from *synaptic fatigue.*

receptor neurons   Receptor impulses are dependent on the generation of potentials (generator potentials) on the dendritic endings of the receptor neuron.

figure 5-16

DIVERGENT AND
CONVERGENT
NEURONAL
PATHWAYS

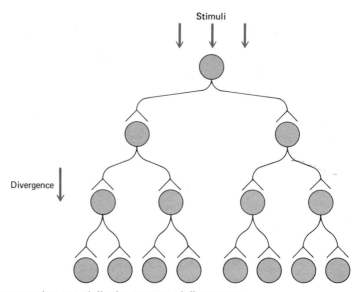

Convergence is essentially the reverse of divergence.

figure 5-17

PARALLEL AND
REVERBERATING
NEURONAL
CIRCUITS

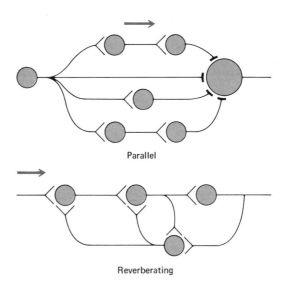

Parallel

Reverberating

Generator
Potentials

The generator potentials are produced by various kinds of stimuli (light, pressure, chemical, and so on). The mechanism by which this potential is produced is not completely known, but work on the *Pacinian corpuscle*, a specialized receptor ending found deep in the skin and mesentery and stimulated by pressure, has given some clues to the mechanism. The Pacinian corpuscle is a laminated structure in which the axon is encased by layers of connective tissue giving an onionlike appearance (Figure 5-18). The axonlike process is myelinated except for a small region in the center of the corpuscle. It is in this region that distortion by pressure is able to produce a change from the resting potential (the *generator potential*) which spreads over a small area. This potential is not propagated, but if it is sufficiently high, an action potential will be produced at the first node. The number of impulses is almost directly proportional to the strength of the generator potential (Figure 5-18). The advantage of the latter system is the wide range of *stimulus strengths* that can be interpreted by the brain.

Adaptation

The fact of adaptation to certain stimuli is well known. When we touch something, we are conscious of the object because of the impulses from the touch receptors. If we leave our hand on the object for a period of time, we are no longer conscious of touching the object. We tend to respond to a *change* in stimulus, but not to a continuous nonvarying stimulus. The sense of touch depends on the number of impulses generated on the receptor, and the loss of the consciousness of touch is due to a decrease in the number of impulses coming from the receptor neuron which had adapted. Some receptors adapt extremely rapidly, whereas others, like muscle spindles, adapt only a very little. This difference is of great value, for in the case of the light receptors in the eye where adaptation occurs quite rapidly, the process allows the individual to operate efficiently in light of changing intensity, while in the case of

figure 5-18
_____

PACINIAN
CORPUSCLE

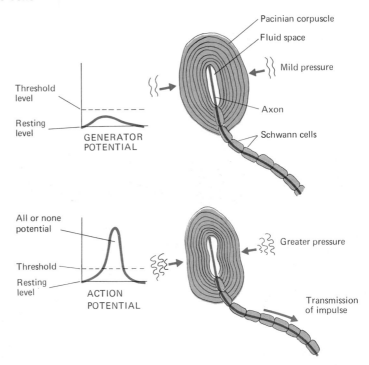

The generation potential is produced by applying pressure to the bulblike ending
of the nerve. Generator potentials of sufficient magnitude produce action potentials
at the first node of Ranvier.

the minimally adapting muscle spindle, it allows the brain to know the
state of the body position with respect to its external environment.

reflex arc   Although we shall have occasion to concern ourselves in more detail
with the subject of the reflex arc in Chapter 8, it is appropriate to introduce this simple but rapid form of integration at this point. If you inad-
vertently touch a hot surface, your hand is withdrawn immediately. You
do not have to go through the process of thinking your hand will be
burned if it is not removed because the surface is hot. Withdrawal of your
hand is involuntary and involves a _reflex arc_ (Figure 5-19). The simplest
of the reflex arcs utilizes only two neurons, a sensory one that carries
information to the spinal cord where it synapses with a motor neuron
that carries an impulse from the spinal cord to the effector organ, generally a muscle. The reflex arc that controls withdrawal of the hand
from a hot surface is a three-neuron arc. This allows for rapid response,
as it does not involve decision making by the higher centers of the brain
and consequently a large number of neurons. The number of neurons in
a pathway affects the rate at which a signal moves in the pathway. This
is so because the time it takes for an impulse to cross a synapse is more
than a thousand times than the rate at which the impulse is conducted
along the axon. The reason for this _synaptic delay_ is the time needed for

figure 5-19
A MONOSYNAPTIC
REFLEX ARC

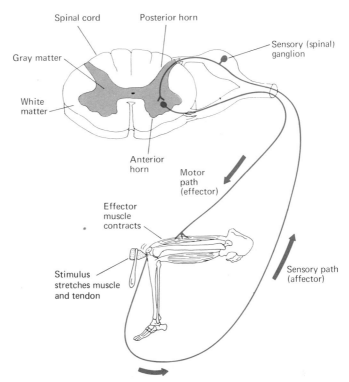

Spinal cord   Posterior horn

Sensory (spinal) ganglion

Gray matter

White matter

Anterior horn   Motor path (effector)

Effector muscle contracts

Stimulus stretches muscle and tendon

Sensory path (affector)

This is the simplest arrangement for a reflex arc. The addition of one or more interneurons between the sensory and motor neuron is seen in other reflex arcs.

release of the chemical transmitter, its diffusion across the synaptic cleft, and the establishment of a new impulse on the postsynaptic neuron. Thus, in neural pathways of equivalent length, the one with the least neurons would conduct the signal the fastest. It is obvious that reflex arcs that tend to protect the individual would have only a few neurons. There are connections between the neurons in the reflex arc and the brain, and in the case of the reflex withdrawal of the hand from a hot surface, the sensation of being burned would actually follow *after* the withdrawal of the hand. This lag is due to the long neural pathway containing many neurons that is required for the brain to integrate the signal and produce the sensation of pain.

factors
influencing
function

metabolism

Oxygen
Requirements

Nerve tissues, as do all tissues in the body, require a source of energy to do work and oxygen in order to utilize that energy. The oxygen requirements for nerve tissue can be judged from studies on the metabolism of the brain that reveal that the brain of an average adult consumes 20 percent of the total oxygen utilized by the body. Since the brain weight for such an individual is somewhere in the vicinity of 2 percent of the total body weight, this relationship indicates that the rate of oxygen utilization by the brain is 10 times greater than the rate in the rest of the tissues of the body. In children where the brain weight is greater than in adults, up to 50 percent of the total oxygen utilized can be consumed by the brain. Obviously, such high requirements must be met by an unusually large supply of blood to the brain cells. The brain of a resting adult receives about 17 percent of the blood pumped from the heart. Not only does the brain require large amounts of oxygen, but it cannot get along without it for even short periods. An interruption of the blood flow to the brain for as little as 10 seconds can cause loss of consciousness. Whereas we can do with periods of anoxia, that is, lack of O_2 in many of our tissues (for example, muscles), the lack of oxygen to the nerve cells for as little as 3 to 5 minutes causes irreversible changes that can be shown by alteration in or by loss of brain wave patterns (electroencephalogram, Chapter 8) and a lack of response by the affected individual even though other organs such as the heart or lungs are functioning.

Glucose Requirements

It appears that the main source of energy for nerve cells, especially those of the brain, is glucose. If blood glucose levels fall, ATP levels fall, which leads to changes in the mental state, including possibly coma.

clinical considerations

There are, of course, numerous disorders of the nervous system. Our knowledge of the basic mechanisms of the physiology of the nerve cell is often extremely important in understanding these disorders.

myasthenia gravis

Myasthenia gravis, a disease that affects the transmission of the impulse from the presynaptic cell to the muscle membrane, leads to a loss of strength that may be mild or sufficiently severe to lead to incapacitation or even death. The condition is caused by a block in the transmission of the impulse from the nerve to the muscle, and some investigators believe that this block results from an inability of the nerve cell to synthesize enough *cholineacetylase* (an enzyme that makes acetylcholine from acetic acid and choline). In the absence of sufficient cholineacetylase, levels of acetylcholine are below normal.

Certain pharmacological agents, which inhibit the breakdown of acetylcholine by suppressing the action of *acetylcholinesterase* (the enzyme that breaks down acetylcholine to acetic acid and choline), are able to give temporary relief to some patients. The inability of the nerve cell to make the enzyme might be genetically determined, but this is only one possibility.

botulism

Although not a common disorder, botulism has a mortality rate of 65 percent. As little as 0.12 μg of botulism toxin can kill an adult, and it is considered the most potent poison known. The toxin is a protein substance produced and released by the bacterium *Clostridium botulinum*. The toxin produces paralysis of the muscles, and in cases where death occurs, it is due to paralysis of respiratory muscles or cardiovascular collapse. The toxin does not act directly on the muscles, but prevents contraction by blocking synaptic transmission at the neuromuscular junction.

tetanus

The bacterium *Clostridium tetani*, which can be picked up from the soil, produces a toxin that depresses the inhibitory synapse (similar to the action of *strychnine*). This results in an uncoordinated excitability leading to muscle spasms. Because spasms of the jaw muscle occur early in this disease, the condition is often called lockjaw.

summary

cellular speciali- zations

1. Nerve cell: the basic unit of the nervous system; also called the neuron, consists of the cell body (soma), dendrites which carry signals toward the cell body, and the axon which carries signals away from the cell body

2. Synapse: the presynaptic cell with vesicles, the synaptic space, and the postsynaptic cell

physiology

1. Membrane or resting potential: the net negative charge of a membrane due to unequal concentrations of ions on either side of the membrane and the leakage of potassium ions into the cell; the large concentration difference in sodium and potassium ions across the membrane due mainly to the active transport of these ions

2. Action potential: a transient reversal of the resting potential, caused by a selective change in permeability of the membrane to, first, sodium ions and then potassium ions; movement of sodium ions causes the membrane potential to reverse polarity; potassium movement out brings the potential back to resting level

3. All or none: when threshold is reached, a full-blown action potential occurs

4. Conduction of the action potential along the axon membrane depends on the depolarization of areas adjacent to the impulse so that threshold is reached

5. Saltatory conduction: more rapid than normal conduction; possible because of the myelin sheaths around axons; added advantage of saltatory conduction is the lower amount of energy needed to maintain the ion concentration difference

6. Chemical transmitter: impulse triggers the axon terminals to release a chemical transmitter, which diffuses across the synaptic space and causes a depolarization of the postsynaptic membrane; in some cases, the chemical transmitter causes a hyperpolarization of the postsynaptic membrane, serving as a form of inhibition

control

1. Summation: the sum of changes in postsynaptic membrane potential caused by two or more presynaptic events

2. Facilitation: a greater than normal response of a postsynaptic membrane to the second of two inputs

3. Neuronal pools: neurons synapse with a number of other neurons and often have more than one synapse with the same cell; the firing of one cell in a pool will influence the cells it synapses with in different ways

4. Reciprocal innervation: inhibition of one activity by way of a collateral neuron which synapses with a pathway for excitation of another activity

5. Divergence and convergence: neuronal patterns for spreading (amplifying) a signal, or for narrowing many signals to a single input

6. Parallel and reverberating circuits: neuronal patterns providing for a series of sequential discharges from a single input or for a self-stimulating oscillatory circuit

7. Generator potentials: produced on dendritic areas of receptor (sensory) neurons by various stimuli; many receptor neurons adapt to stimuli

8. Reflex arc: a neuronal pattern consisting of a small number of neurons; allows rapid action without involvement of the higher nervous centers

9. Nervous tissue has a high metabolic rate and requires a good supply of glucose and oxygen

clinical considerations

1. Myasthenia gravis: disease which affects the transmission of the impulse from the nerve to the muscle

2. Botulism: the inhibition of muscle contraction by bacterial toxin that blocks synaptic transmission

3. Tetanus: the depression of inhibitory synaptic activity by toxin from *Clostridium tetani* produces muscle spasms

muscular system

6

gross anatomy
parts of a muscle
blood supply
nerve supply
major muscles of the
  head-neck region
major muscles of the
  thorax
major muscles of the
  abdomen
major muscles of the
  upper arm
major muscles of the
  lower arm
major muscles of the thigh
major muscles of the
  lower leg

cellular and tissue specializations
skeletal muscle
cardiac muscle
smooth muscle

physiology
skeletal muscle
smooth muscle

control

factors influencing function

clinical considerations
muscular dystrophy
glycogen storage disease
denervation
fibrillation

"If science is the art of measuring, then, muscle has no equal as a material in the study of life, for there is no other tissue whose function is connected with equally extensive changes in chemistry, physical state, energy, and dimensions. That is why physiology, up to the turn of the century, was mainly muscle physiology. . . . The function of muscle is to create motion. There are many sorts of motion, thus there are many sorts of muscle, even if the basic principles on which they are built may be identical. A muscle cell or fiber is a very complex system, and the unit of its function, the *twitch*, is a very complex cycle."

The above remarks were made by Albert Szent-Györgyi, the Nobel laureate, and in a nutshell the eminent scientist described the importance of muscle.

figure 6-1

EXTERNAL VIEW OF MUSCULATURE OF AN ADULT MALE

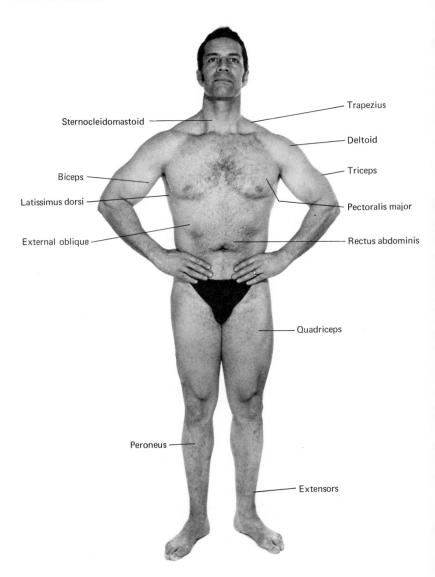

In this chapter the gross anatomy of representative skeletal muscles from each area of the body is described primarily to stimulate the reader's appreciation of the variety and adaptation of individual muscles as seen in the life photographs in Figures 6-1 and 6-2.

Since muscles are the machines of the body, directly converting chemical energy into a vectorial (directed) force, the emphasis in this chapter will be related to functions of muscle at the cellular and organ level.

gross anatomy　Muscles can only contract (pull), and some other force including gravity must be exerted to return the muscle to its relaxed state. For example,

figure 6-2

EXTERNAL VIEW OF THE MUSCULATURE OF AN ADULT FEMALE

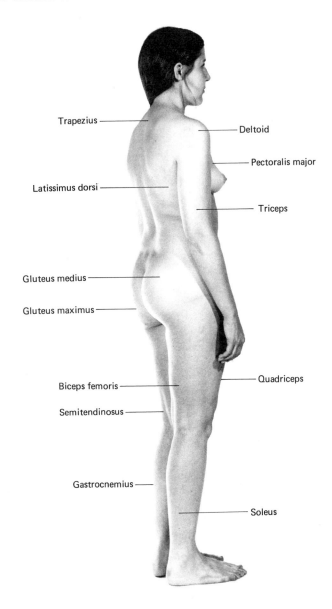

Trapezius

Deltoid

Pectoralis major

Latissimus dorsi

Triceps

Gluteus medius

Gluteus maximus

Quadriceps

Biceps femoris

Semitendinosus

Gastrocnemius

Soleus

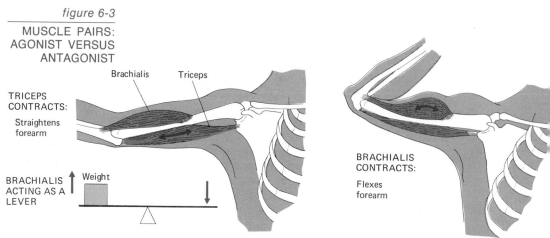

figure 6-3

MUSCLE PAIRS:
AGONIST VERSUS
ANTAGONIST

Brachialis   Triceps

TRICEPS
CONTRACTS:

Straightens
forearm

BRACHIALIS
CONTRACTS:

Flexes
forearm

BRACHIALIS ↑ Weight
ACTING AS A ↓
LEVER

the arrangement of muscles is usually in pairs, with *agonist* and *antagonist* groups; the biceps (agonist) will raise the forearm, but the triceps (antagonistic) must contract to pull the forearm back into place and also to stretch the bicep muscles (Figure 6-3). Resting muscles are never truly relaxed. It probably would be better to use the terms "contraction-decontraction" than the present terms of contraction and relaxation, for although we speak of muscle fatigue, it is doubtful, except in experimental situations, that a muscle is ever truly fatigued. It is possible to contract the muscle and keep the length constant. Since no work will be performed, all the energy is released as heat. This type of action is called *isometric contraction.** Opposed to isometric contraction is the more common *isotonic contraction*, in which the muscle shortens, and work is performed in addition to releasing heat.

The classification of muscles generally follows the skeletal classifications (muscles of the thorax, muscles of the vertebral column, and pelvic muscles). No single criterion is used in naming a muscle, which is somewhat unfortunate for there is thus no uniformity in the nomenclature; size, location, mode of action, plus many other variables are all utilized in naming a muscle. Most voluntary muscles are attached to the skeleton and thus form a system of levers with bones (Figure 6-3).

With rare exception, movement requires the contraction of a group of muscles as well as the relaxation of adjacent muscles. This group action requires neurological control that not only relaxes or contracts muscles, but does so with a variety of graded stimuli. This subtle interdependence of muscles is easily demonstrated by the following exercise. If one lightly presses his forefinger against the ball of the thumb, the freedom of action of the other three fingers of the same hand is only slightly restricted. When the pressure is increased between the forefinger and thumb, the action of the free fingers becomes stiffer.

---

* Work is equal to mass (grams) times distance (centimeters). Work also equals energy (unit of energy is the calorie). If no work is performed in isometric contraction, the energy is released as heat.

Energy = work = mass × distance

figure 6-4

COMPONENT
PARTS OF A
MUSCLE

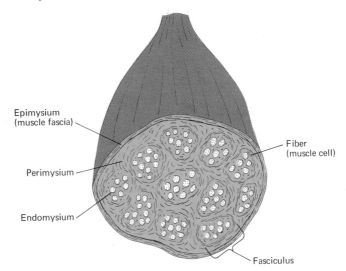

Epimysium
(muscle fascia)

Fiber
(muscle cell)

Perimysium

Endomysium

Fasciculus

Figure 6-4 is a breakdown of a muscle organ into its component parts. The details of the individual fibers are discussed in a later section. It can be seen that each muscle fiber is joined with other parallel muscle fibers into bundles by the intertwining of connective tissue surrounding each cell. These bundles of *fascicles* in turn are integrated into larger units, and the muscle organ is finally formed from these units. Practically all of this development takes place during prenatal life, and the postnatal growth of a muscle with age and by exercise occurs by the enlarging of the individual cells and not by mitosis.

parts of a
muscle

The larger muscles are spindle-shaped and divided into three parts. One end is called the *origin;* the opposite end is the *insertion;* and the bulk of the muscle in between is termed the *body* or *belly.* The origin refers to the end of the muscle that remains fixed during contraction; the insertion is the movable portion.

The fibrous connective tissue that surrounds individual fibers, as well as bundles of fibers, forms the connection between muscles and their attachments. Muscles attach to the skin or membranes by a broad connection, which frequently runs along the entire margin of the muscle. Muscles that perform a great amount of work generally converge on a small insertion point (Figure 6-5). In this situation, the connective tissue extends beyond the limits of the individual muscle fibers as a band of fibers (tendon). The tendon fibers are intermeshed with the connective tissue fibers of the bone (periosteum) to effect a remarkably strong union.

blood supply

Because muscles are always performing some degree of work, the higher rates of metabolism often stimulate the development of an extensive vascular bed. Every muscle cell is nourished by a capillary, but during the muscle's less active phase, 90 percent of the muscle capillary bed is closed down. With stimulation the large blood vessels open up and fill the smallest capillaries (Figure 3-7). (The regulation of the muscular

figure 6-5

MUSCLE
ATTACHMENT TO
BONE

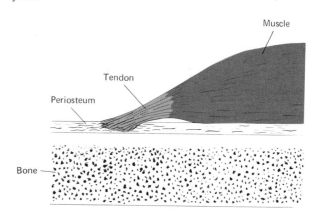

blood flow is described in Chapter 12.) The lymphatic supply to muscles is not as extensive as the blood supply, and most of the lymphatic vessels are associated with bundles of fibers rather than with the individual fibers.

nerve supply

It has been estimated that a large skeletal muscle receives as many as 200 impulses per second. A nerve fiber enters a muscle tissue and breaks up into many subdivisions; each muscle fiber will receive one of these smaller branches. The junction of the nerve with the muscle fiber is quite specialized and is discussed in Chapter 5 and Module 5B.

Two types of nerve stimulation occur in skeletal muscle. One is a direct stimulation of the muscle fiber that results in a rapid and complete contraction of the muscle, and most muscles have this type of motor stimulation. A second type of stimulation excites only parts of a muscle and utilizes a complex feedback system to obtain partial contraction to a predetermined length. This type not only produces graded contractions, but movement is slower and more prolonged. The muscles responsible for maintaining posture are examples of the second type of innervation. Muscles via the nerves also relay a great deal of information to the brain. For example, if a man extends his arm outright, even with closed eyes, there is an awareness of position of the arm. This knowledge about the orientation of the body in space is due to sensory information picked up by specialized nerve endings in muscles called *proprioceptors* that relay the information to nerves informing the brain of the state of the muscle. The proprioceptors are sensitive to the stretching or contracting of muscles, and they play a significant role in movement, coordination, and posture.

**major muscles of
the head-neck
region**

Masseter

The major muscle for chewing is a *superficial* (immediately beneath the skin) muscle that extends from the zygomatic arch to the mandible (Figures 6-6 and 6-7). When the muscle contracts, the lower jaw or mandible is lifted. This muscle can be felt by clenching the teeth.

Platysma

The platysma is a broad, flat, superficial muscle of both the head and neck. It runs from the fascia of the upper chest and shoulder (pectoral and deltoid muscles) and inserts on the mandible. When contracted, it will depress the lower jaw.

figure 6-6
MAJOR MUSCLES
OF THE HEAD

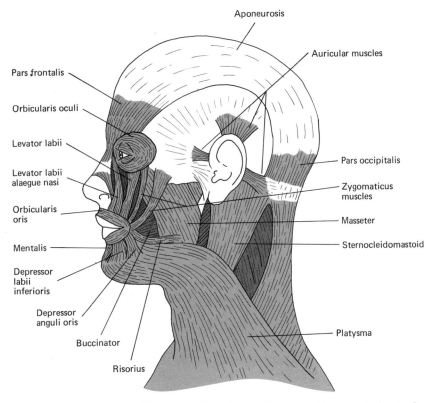

Sternoclavo-
mastoid
(Sternocleido-
mastoid)

The sternoclavomastoid, a superficial muscle, is well named, for it describes the double origin, sternum and clavicle, and the single insertion
on the mastoid process. By placing the chin on the fist *(The Thinker)*,
resistance is added, and the muscle is easily felt. When contracted on one
side only, the muscle helps to turn the head toward the right or left
shoulder. When both muscles contract simultaneously, the chin is elevated (Figure 6-7).

figure 6-7
MAJOR MUSCLES
OF THE JAWS

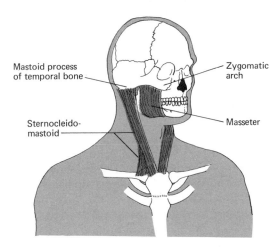

**Major muscles used in clos-
ing and opening the jaws
showing origins and insertions.**

figure 6-8

MAJOR MUSCLES
OF THE THORAX

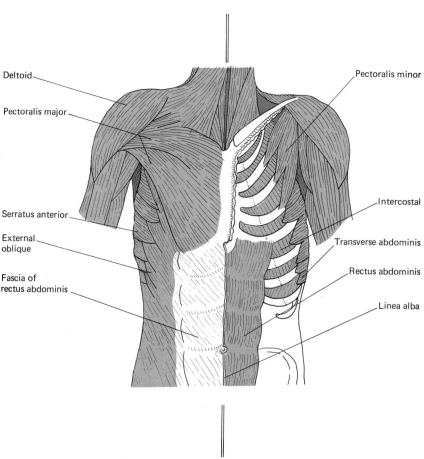

Deltoid

Pectoralis major

Serratus anterior

External
oblique

Fascia of
rectus abdominis

Pectoralis minor

Intercostal

Transverse abdominis

Rectus abdominis

Linea alba

major muscles of
the thorax

Most of the muscles in the area of the thorax are superficial and associated with movement of the appendages and with breathing (Figure
6-8). The chest muscles involved with breathing are generally smaller
and lie deep along the rib cage and vertebral column.

Pectorals

The bulk of the chest musculature is formed by the superficial pectoral
muscles. They have multiorigins: clavicle, sternum, cartilages of the
upper ribs, and fascia covering the abdomen. However, the fibers all
converge on a single tendon inserted on the humerus. When these muscles contract, they exert a powerful force for pulling the arm down and
over the chest (Figure 6-8).

Latissimus
Dorsi

The latissimus dorsi is a large fan-shaped muscle covering most of the
lower back (Figure 6-9) that works opposite to the pectoral muscles on
the same side. It stems from all of the lower vertebral spines starting
with T6 and the hipbone iliac crest and inserts on the humerus. Contraction of the latissimus draws the arm backward, downward, and
inward. These muscles are especially well developed in excellent swim-
mers.

figure 6-9
LATISSIMUS
DORSI

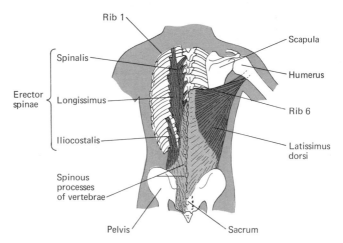

Rib 1

Scapula

Humerus

Spinalis

Erector
spinae

Longissimus

Rib 6

Latissimus
dorsi

Iliocostalis

Spinous
processes
of vertebrae

Pelvis   Sacrum

Sacrospinalis
: The sacrospinalis is an example of a long deep muscle. It originates from the sacrum, lumbar, and lower thoracic vertebrae and inserts on the upper thoracic vertebrae, ribs, and clavicle. The overlapping insertions help to straighten the vertebral column to give an erect position when the muscles contract on both sides. By contracting either the left or right sacrospinalis, the body will bend toward the contracting side.

Intercostals
: Numerous small muscles that originate on the lower surfaces of ribs and insert on the upper borders of the ribs below the origins are called intercostals. Collectively, they form two layers, *external* and *internal*.

Diaphragm
: The separation between the thoracic and abdominal cavities is formed by the dome-shaped diaphragm, which is composed of muscle except for the tendon in the central portion. The tendon marks the insertion of the converging muscle fibers originating from the tip of the sternum, lower ribs, and lumbar vertebrae. The tendon is pierced by three openings for the passage of the *esophagus* and *vagus nerves*, the *inferior vena cava*, and the *aorta* and *thoracic duct*. (The latter three structures are a major vein, artery, and lymph vessel, respectively.) When the diaphragm contracts, the central portion of the muscle is pulled down, enlarging the thoracic cavity. The diaphragm thus becomes the principal muscle for respiration. The abdominal muscles and the intraabdominal pressure (from the compression of the organs during inspiration) aid in the return of the diaphragm to its noncontracted convex shape, which occurs with exhalation (Figure 6-10).

major muscles of
the abdomen

External Oblique
Muscle
: The external oblique is a thin broad muscle that runs down from the lower eight ribs to the linea alba and the iliac crest. In Figure 6-11, the broad triangular fascia (aponeuroses) that forms the oblique's lower attachment is readily visible and represents an important supporting element of the abdominal wall. When the external obliques contract, they aid in expiration, defecation, urination, and help support the viscera in this region. The latter is a particularly important function of the abdominal musculature, because in the abdominal region, there is no direct skeletal protection or support.

figure 6-10
THE
DIAPHRAGM

figure 6-10
THE
DIAPHRAGM

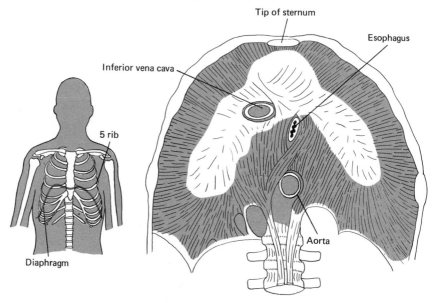

Internal Oblique
Muscle

The internal oblique is a flat broad muscle that lies obliquely beneath the external oblique muscle (Figure 6-12). It has its origin from the lumbar fascia and iliac crest. The fibers run upward and insert on the linea alba and the cartilages of the seventh to the ninth ribs. These muscles function similarly to those of the external obliques.

The obliques and the *transverse abdominis,* which run circumferentially and girdles the abdominal region, are oriented in three distinct layers, and their fibers run in three different directions. This arrangement is like plywood that is structured from thin slabs of wood super-

figure 6-11
THE ABDOMINAL
MUSCULATURE—
ORIGINS AND
INSERTIONS

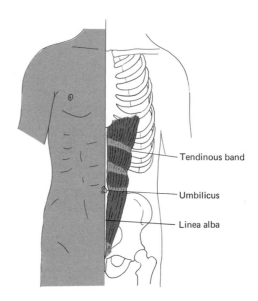

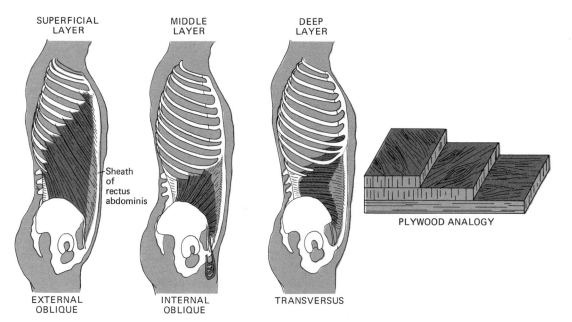

figure 6-12

THE PLYWOOD
ANALOGY FOR
THE ABDOMINAL
MUSCULATURE

SUPERFICIAL
LAYER

MIDDLE
LAYER

DEEP
LAYER

Sheath
of
rectus
abdominis

PLYWOOD ANALOGY

EXTERNAL
OBLIQUE

INTERNAL
OBLIQUE

TRANSVERSUS

imposed one upon another and compressed under great pressure; the wood fibers run at an angle to the adjacent layers (Figure 6-12).

Rectus Abdominis
Another muscle that compresses the abdominal wall, the rectus abdominis, runs from the pubic crest to the cartilages of the fifth to seventh ribs.

major muscles of the upper arm
The primary function of the upper arm involves flexion, extension, and adduction of the forearm. There are five muscles in this region, with the biceps and triceps making up the greatest mass.

Biceps Brachii
This muscle has two points of origin or two *heads*. The *long head* originates from the upper margin of the glenoid fossa (scapula), and the *short head* originates at the coracoid process. The muscle has a single insertion on the tuberosity of the radius.

Triceps Brachii
The general origins of the three heads (*long, lateral,* and *medial*) are the axillary border of the scapula and the posterior and lateral surfaces of the humerus, respectively. All heads insert on and in the olecranon of the ulna.

major muscles of the lower arm
There are many muscles in the forearm. For convenience, they may be subdivided into two major groups. The muscles in the front of the arm are called *palmar* or *flexor* muscles, and the muscles on the back of the arm are *posterior* or *extensor* muscles. With few exceptions, these mus-

figure 6-13

MUSCLES OF THE
FOREARM AND
HAND

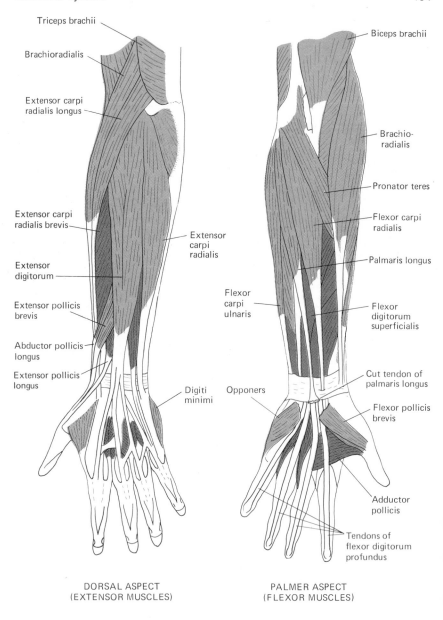

Triceps brachii

Brachioradialis

Extensor carpi
radialis longus

Extensor carpi
radialis brevis

Extensor
digitorum

Extensor pollicis
brevis

Abductor pollicis
longus

Extensor pollicis
longus

Extensor
carpi
radialis

Digiti
minimi

Biceps brachii

Brachio-
radialis

Pronator teres

Flexor carpi
radialis

Palmaris longus

Flexor
digitorum
superficialis

Flexor
carpi
ulnaris

Opponers

Cut tendon of
palmaris longus

Flexor pollicis
brevis

Adductor
pollicis

Tendons of
flexor digitorum
profundus

DORSAL ASPECT
(EXTENSOR MUSCLES)

PALMER ASPECT
(FLEXOR MUSCLES)

cles arise on the distal end of the humerus and insert by tendons into parts of the hand.

| Extensor Digitorum | The extensor digitorum produces an extension of the wrist and fingers. It runs from the epicondyle of the humerus to the middle phalanges of the fingers (see Figure 6-13). |

| Flexor Digitorum Superficialis | The flexor digitorum superficialis is a muscle antagonistic to the extensor digitorum and runs from the epicondyle of the humerus to the |

figure 6-14

MAJOR MUSCLES
OF THE THIGH

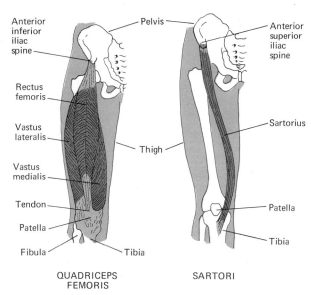

Anterior inferior iliac spine

Pelvis

Anterior superior iliac spine

Rectus femoris

Vastus lateralis

Thigh

Sartorius

Vastus medialis

Tendon

Patella

Patella

Fibula

Tibia

Tibia

QUADRICEPS FEMORIS

SARTORI

middle phalanges of the fingers, but on the opposite side of the arm; it
serves to flex the fingers and the wrist (Figure 6-13).

major muscles of the thigh

Quadriceps Femoris

The bulk of the anterior part of the thigh is composed of four muscles,
the quadriceps, which have different origins but a common insertion.
These muscles contracting together provide a powerful muscular action, the extension of the leg, as seen in kicking. They originate on the
femur and iliac and converge on a single tendon which inserts on the
tibia (Figure 6-14).

Sartorius

The longest muscle of the body, the sartorius, originates on the ilium and
crosses over the thigh to insert on the medial side of the tibia (Figure
6-14). The sartorius thus crosses two joints, hip and knee, and as would
be expected, performs several functions. Its most common action is a
reflection of its name ("sartor" in Latin means tailor), for when an individual sits in a "tailor's position," the sartorius is the principal muscle
utilized in crossing the legs.

major muscles of the lower leg

Gastrocnemius

The principal calf muscle or gastrocnemius runs from its origin on the
femur to its insertion on the calcaneus (tarsal) bone. The insertion is by
way of the *Achilles tendon*. The gastrocnemius extends the foot and
flexes the lower leg.

Soleus

The soleus is located under the gastrocnemius and has multiple origins
on the tibia and fibula and inserts on the calcaneus. It works with the
gastrocnemius to extend the foot.

Extensors

These are a group of muscles (*peroneus* and *tibialis*) that originate at
several locations on the tibia and fibula and insert on the foot. Collectively these muscles extend or evert the foot.

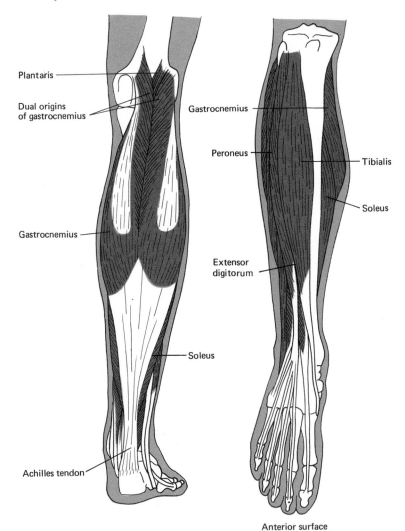

figure 6-15
MUSCLES OF
THE CALF

Plantaris

Dual origins
of gastrocnemius

Gastrocnemius

Gastrocnemius

Peroneus

Tibialis

Soleus

Extensor
digitorum

Soleus

Achilles tendon

Anterior surface

cellular and
tissue
specializations

Contraction of muscles depends on shortening of the muscle cells. The mechanism for shortening is generally associated with an organized system of fibrous elements within the cells. The contraction itself must be initiated by some signal to the muscle cells, generally from the nerve cells, and must be paid for in energy provided by the cell's metabolism.

Examination of the microanatomy of muscle reveals three basic types: *skeletal, cardiac,* and *smooth.*

skeletal muscle

A skeletal muscle fiber is composed of smaller units, the *myofibrils* (Figure 6-16). The myofibrils have repeating areas of dark and light bands that give skeletal muscle its striated appearance. A close examination of the myofibrils reveals repeating structural units that are called *sarcomeres.*

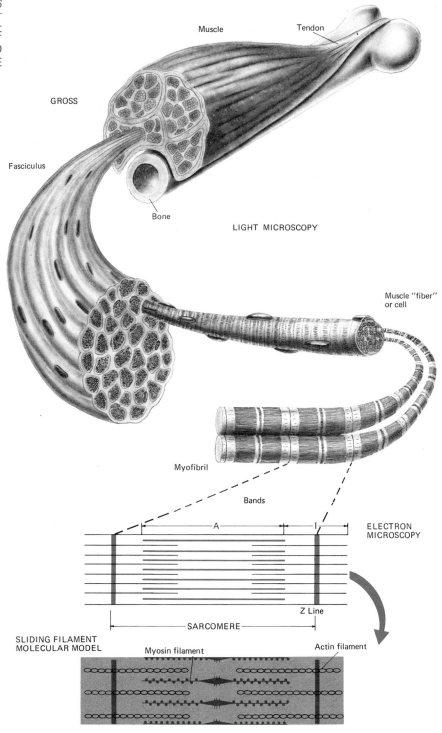

figure 6-16

STRUCTURAL
COMPONENTS OF
STRIATED
MUSCLE

GROSS

Muscle

Tendon

Fasciculus

Bone

LIGHT MICROSCOPY

Muscle "fiber"
or cell

Myofibril

Bands

A   I

ELECTRON
MICROSCOPY

Z Line

SARCOMERE

SLIDING FILAMENT
MOLECULAR MODEL

Myosin filament

Actin filament

The sarcomere (Figure 6-16) is delineated by the so-called Z *lines*, dense lines to which *thin filaments (actin)* are attached. *Thick filaments (myosin)* between the thin filaments are centrally located. The so-called I *band* consists of regions of thin filaments only, whereas the A *band* encompasses the region of overlap of thick and thin filaments. There is a lighter region in the center of the A band (H *zone*), because there is no thin filament overlap with the thick filaments. Regularly spaced projections (crossbridges) are associated with the thick filaments, extending toward the thin filaments.

Two important properties of muscle proteins had been developed quite early.

1. That actin and myosin extracted from muscle combined to form a single structure, *actomyosin*, and that the presence of ATP would cause the actomyosin to split apart to actin and myosin.

2. That myosin acted as an enzyme to break down ATP to ADP with the release of energy. These reactions are summarized below.

$$\text{(a)}\quad \text{actomyosin} + \text{ATP} \longrightarrow \text{actin} + \text{myosin} + \text{ADP} + \text{P}i$$
$$\text{(b)}\quad \text{ATP} + \text{myosin} \longrightarrow \text{ADP} + \text{P}i$$

It was later proposed in what has become known as the *sliding filament hypothesis* that the thin filaments move over the thick filaments by a rachetlike arrangement that involves the making and breaking of chemical bonds between the crossbridges of the myosin and sites on the actin (Figure 6-17). During this process ATP is broken down and supplies the energy needed to make new bonds between the crossbridges of myosin and actin.

Why muscle does not contract continually is directly related to the *availability* of calcium, which like ATP is needed for contraction. Calcium is found in the muscle cell, but an internal membrane, the *sarcoplasmic reticulum*, can isolate and store the calcium. When a muscle cell is stimulated by the arrival of a nerve impulse, the permeability of the sarcoplasmic reticulum is also affected, and calcium ions are released and diffuse into the sarcomeres to activate the contractile mechanism. When the nerve stimulus is past, the calcium is actively transported back into the sarcoplasmic reticulum, thereby shutting down the contractile mechanism. Because of this activity, the microsomes of the sarcoplasmic reticulum are frequently called the *relaxing factor.*

There is a system of tubules that are continuations of openings in the outer membrane of the muscle fiber. These tubules are called *transverse tubules*, because they run transversely across the muscle fiber in the region of the Z lines (Figure 6-18). The tubules are actually extensions of the muscle fiber membrane, the sarcolemma. The impulse that appears on the outer part of the muscle fiber is conducted to the myofibrillar area by the transverse tubule. This system allows for practically simultaneous contraction of all the muscle fiber myofibrils. If there were no transverse tubules and sarcoplasmic reticulum and calcium had to

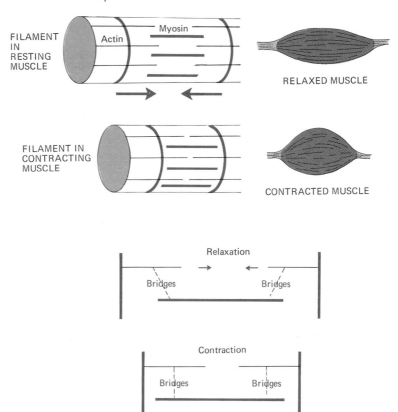

figure 6-17

SLIDING
FILAMENT
HYPOTHESIS OF
SKELETAL
MUSCLE
CONTRACTION

Cross bridges from the thick filament move the thin filaments toward the center of the sarcomere, resulting in contraction (shortening of the muscle).

diffuse in from the outside of the 100-μ muscle fiber, the rate of diffusion would allow only about 2 percent of the needed calcium to move in during the duration of a normal contraction. The transverse tubules and sarcoplasmic reticulum allow for rapid dissemination of the stimulus and release of calcium at a site usually no further away than 1 μ from the contracting elements (Module 6).

Early measurements showed that ATP did not decrease during muscle contraction as might be expected, but, rather, the levels of *phosphocreatine* decreased. Phosphocreatine, also a high-energy compound, is able to transfer its high-energy phosphate to ADP to make ATP.

$$\text{phosphocreatine} + \text{ADP} \longrightarrow \text{creatine} + \text{ATP}$$

The ATP levels stay sufficiently high for contraction, because as soon as ATP is broken down to ADP, the ADP is rephosphorylated by phosphocreatine.

cardiac muscle   Cardiac muscle is discussed in Chapter 11.

figure 6-18

THE
SARCOPLASMIC
RETICULUM AND
TRANSVERSE
TUBULE SYSTEM

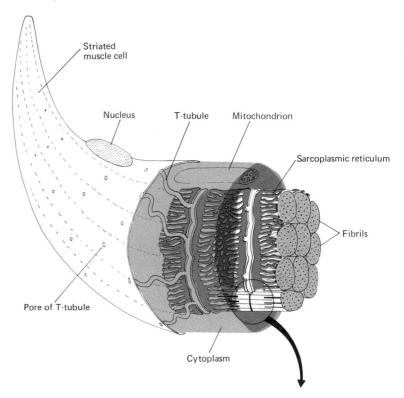

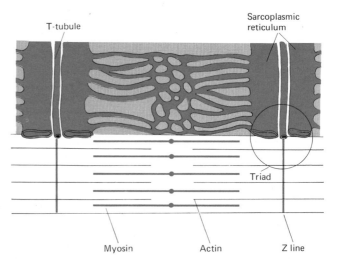

The transverse tubular (T-tubule) system. The impulse can reach the region of the individual sarcomere by way of the T-tubule system, thereby allowing for practically simultaneous contraction of myofibrils. Calcium is stored in the sarcoplasmic reticulum and released at the arrival of a nerve impulse which depolarizes the muscle membrane.

MUSCLE
CONTRACTION

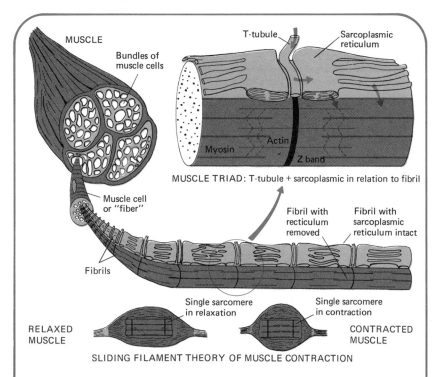

MUSCLE TRIAD: T-tubule + sarcoplasmic in relation to fibril

SLIDING FILAMENT THEORY OF MUSCLE CONTRACTION

Contraction of muscles depends on shortening of muscle cells. The mechanism for shortening of skeletal muscles is associated with fibrous elements within the cells. The contract is initiated by some signal and is paid for in energy provided by the cells' metabolism.

The skeletal muscle bundle is composed of muscle cells, or "fibers", and the fibers are composed of myofibrils. The unit of contraction is the sarcomere which is delineated by the Z-lines. The sarcomere has within it a set of thick filaments containing the protein myosin and a set of thin filaments containing the protein actin. In the presence of ATP and Ca^{2+} actin and myosin are able to bind with each other, while in the presence of ATP but absence of Ca^{2+} they remain separate. According to the sliding filament theory of muscle contraction, cross bridges on the myosin filaments move the thin filaments past them by a rachetlike arrangement utilizing ATP for an energy source. This is accomplished by making a chemical bond between the cross bridge of myosin and a molecule of actin, the subsequent movement of the cross bridge with movement of the actin filament, the breaking of the chemical bond and establishment of a new bond between the cross bridge and actin.

Continuous contraction does not occur because Ca^{2+} is stored in the sarcoplasmic reticulum and only released when an impulse arrives. Near simultaneous contraction of the individual sarcomeres is possible because of the transverse tubule (T-tubule) system which extends from the outer membrane to the region of individual sarcomeres. Arrival of an impulse via the T-tubule triggers the release of Ca^{2+} from the adjacent sarcoplasmic reticulum and contraction results. Calcium is then actively moved back into the sarcoplasmic reticulum and contraction ceases.

smooth muscle

On the basis of cellular specializations, smooth muscle cells are the least specialized of the three types of muscle tissue. The sarcoplasm contains myofilaments that may or may not be organized into loose bundles resembling the myofibril structure. Actin and myosin are also found in smooth muscle, and calcium and ATP are required for contraction, but unlike striated muscles a longer time is needed for contraction and relaxation of smooth muscle.

physiology

skeletal muscle

Muscle Twitch

If a muscle such as the frog gastrocnemius is isolated and attached in such a way as to record its degree of contraction, a stimulus to either the nerve leading to the muscle or to the muscle itself will produce a record such as that seen in Figure 6-19. An examination of the *muscle twitch* reveals three principal events: (a) the *latent period*, which is the period between the stimulus and the beginning of contraction, usually about 10 msec, and which is probably due more to the properties of the recording arrangement rather than to the muscle; (b) the *contraction period*, which is about 40 msec; and (c) the *relaxation period*, which is about 50 msec. The time for the total contraction of this particular muscle is then about 100 msec (0.1 second). The time course for the twitch of various muscle types is different.

The extent of the twitch depends on the stimulus applied. The stimulus must reach some *threshold* value before the muscle responds at all. Increased stimulus increases the extent of contraction until some maximum is obtained, the reason being that weak stimuli, above threshold, may cause the contraction of only a portion of the fibers that compose the muscle. As the stimulus is increased, more fibers are brought into play until all of them are contracting in response to the stimulus. Increasing the stimulus beyond the strength required for maximum contraction has no additional effect.

Thus the individual fibers are said to obey the *all-or-none* law; for example, when threshold for the fiber is reached, it contracts maximally. The response of a muscle to a stimulus, in fact, varies, depending on the state of the fiber (whether it is fatigued or just recovering from a contraction). However, the all-or-none effect does apply to the fiber and the particular state it is in.

figure 6-19

THE MUSCLE
TWITCH

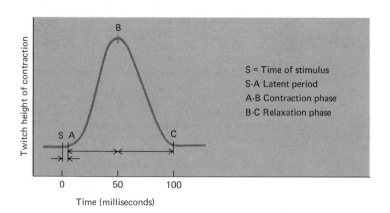

Twitch height of contraction

B

S = Time of stimulus
S-A Latent period
A-B Contraction phase
B-C Relaxation phase

S A   C

0   50   100

Time (milliseconds)

Summation

Summation of contraction can occur when stimuli follow closely on one another. The stimulated muscle fiber is initially in an excited state, but for a short time afterward it enters into a short *refractory state* during which time the muscle fiber is unresponsive to any more stimuli. However, the refractory period is over before the fiber is fully relaxed, and a stimulus equal to the initial stimulus, arriving after the refractory period and before the muscle is fully relaxed, will cause a contraction of greater magnitude than the first stimulus (Figure 6-20). Summation is the recruiting of additional muscle fibers in response to stimuli that follow closely on one another. Additional fibers are activated, because the stimulus is above threshold for those fibers. When the stimulus frequency is high, it is possible for the maximum number of fibers to be contracted, in which case increasing the stimulus frequency does not result in any increase in contraction. This state is known as *tetanus*. Muscles in the intact body generally operate between the state of individual twitches and complete tetany; the latter state is seen in muscles handling heavy loads.

Isotonic versus
Isometric
Contraction

The activity of an isolated muscle is measured in several different ways. *Isotonic* contractions are those in which the muscle shortens, but the tension remains the same (Figure 6-21). This kind of contraction takes place when an individual uses the biceps muscle to lift a load. *Isometric*

figure 6-20

THE SUMMATION
OF
CONTRACTIONS
AND TETANIC
CONTRACTION

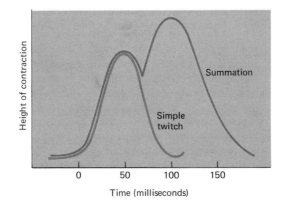

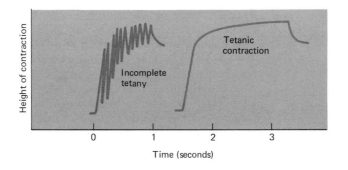

figure 6-21

RECORDING
(a) ISOTONIC AND
(b) ISOMETRIC
CONTRACTIONS

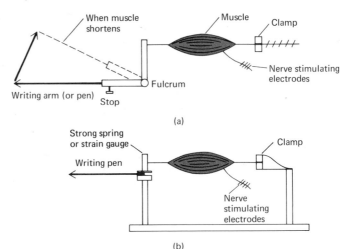

contractions are those in which the muscle length remains essentially constant and tension changes. An example is the contraction of quadricep muscles of the leg when an individual is in a standing position. Tension increases without shortening of the muscle by an increase in the number of crossbridges made between the actin and the myosin filaments in the sarcomeres.

Velocity and Load   The *velocity* of muscle shortening will vary with *load increase* so that with greater loads producing lower velocities. When there is no load, a muscle can reach maximum contraction in about 0.05 second, and as the load increases, the velocity decreases. Again referring to the sliding-filament theory, this result could be explained by the possibility of increasing the number of crossbridges between actin and myosin with increasing load. Since each reaction requires a finite time, a large number of reactions would take greater time, and the net effect would be a decrease in the velocity of contraction.

If we calculate the amount of work (mass times distance) that is done in lifting a weight, at some weight the muscle does maximal work. This optimum occurs when the force and velocity are about one-third of their maximum value. For most efficient work, the muscle load would have to be arranged to fit the above conditions.

Length-Tension   Strong support for the sliding-filament theory comes from studies on the
Studies   effect of fiber length on *tension*. Tension of a stimulated muscle fiber is maximum near resting length and falls off on either side (Figure 6-22). The *overlap* that can occur between the actin and the myosin filaments may be decreased, with a corresponding decrease in the number of possible crossbridges. On the one hand, tension falls to zero when the fiber is stretched so that no overlap occurs. On the other hand, tension also falls to zero when crossbridge formation is extensively interfered with, as when the actin filaments overlap one another in shortened fibers.

Muscle Tone   The term *muscle tone* is generally used to define the resistance of muscle to passive stretch. Many muscles, especially the muscles con-

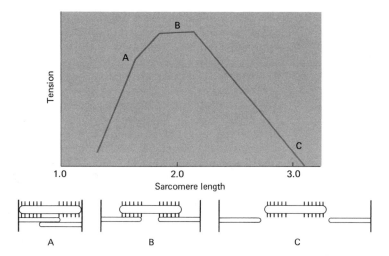

figure 6-22

TENSION VERSUS
LOAD

Metabolism in
Skeletal Muscle

cerned with posture, react to stretch by contracting (see Chapter 8 for mechanism), producing a general tautness in the muscle. This tone or tonus is produced by the contraction of a limited number of fibers within the muscle bundle. Where the muscles are not being stretched, as in the case of the postural muscles during sleep or in pathological conditions where the stretch response is lost, muscle is termed *flaccid*. The opposite of this situation is when the muscles are hyperstimulated and become abnormally contracted, in which case they are termed *spastic*.

There is a general belief that muscles are continually stimulated to remain in a mildly contracted state even when that muscle or muscle group is not in use. This conclusion, however, is not borne out by recordings of completely resting muscles, which, in fact, demonstrate quite clearly that resting muscle is not being stimulated.

The energy for the contraction of muscle is related to the availability of ATP. Muscle cells produce ATP in a manner identical to all other cells; they break down energy-rich molecules like glycogen to glucose and produce ATP in the mitochondria in the presence of oxygen. The levels of ATP in muscle are relatively low, enough to support probably less than ten twitches in most muscles, but the ADP can be rephosphorylated by the phosphocreatine that is present in muscle. During extended contractions, phosphocreatine levels also fall. They, as well as the levels of ATP, must be built up again by the metabolism of the cell. When energy is no longer available, as in the case of permanent cutoff of circulation or death, the muscle will become stiff for a period of time. That state is termed *rigor*. Rigor is most likely a result of an increase in the number of *fixed* crossbridges being formed between actin and myosin filaments, since no ATP is present to keep actin and myosin separate.

When an isolated muscle is continually contracted in the presence of an oxygen-containing atmosphere, the muscle will eventually fatigue and no longer contract. Given a period of rest, however, contraction can take place again. If the same experiment is carried out in an atmosphere of nitrogen, the muscle contracts and fatigues, but does not recover from the fatigue. During contraction in the oxygen-containing atmosphere, oxygen and glycogen are consumed, and carbon dioxide is produced; the amount of energy produced is equal to the work accomplished by the muscle plus the heat generated. In the case of the muscle contracting in a nitrogen-containing atmosphere, glycogen is consumed and lactic acid is produced.

We have seen that the breakdown of glucose to pyruvic acid is an anaerobic process (does not require oxygen) and that ATP is produced in this sequence of reactions (Chapter 2). In the absence of oxygen, pyruvic acid cannot be broken down further by the mitochondria. Instead, the pyruvic acid is reduced to lactic acid, the accumulation of which leads to a shutdown of the *Krebs citric acid cycle*. When oxygen is available, some of the excess lactic acid is oxidized back to pyruvic acid and metabolized in the Krebs cycle, mainly in the liver and heart muscle. The remainder of the excess lactic acid is converted into glycogen by the liver.

Two methods by which energy can be supplied for contracting muscles are *anaerobic* and *aerobic*. The anaerobic method involves the metabolism of phosphocreatine and the breakdown of glycogen to lactic acid. Both of these compounds, as well as the mechanism for their breakdown, are present in the muscle, which means that energy can be supplied at a high rate, and contraction can go on until phosphocreatine and glycogen are depleted. However, the amount of energy derived from the metabolism of phosphocreatine or from the breakdown of glycogen to lactic acid is limited. The principal aerobic method involves the breakdown of carbohydrates and fats, with the utilization of oxygen, all of which are brought to the muscle by the circulatory system. The reader is reminded that the term "oxidation" includes three types of chemical reactions: (a) combination with oxygen, (b) removal of hydrogen, and (c) removal of electrons. In aerobic metabolism, the rate of supplying energy is lower because of the oxidative reactions that must occur and the limited ability of the circulatory system to deliver the carbohydrates, fats, and oxygen, but the limitation is compensated for by the large amount of energy available. (One estimate is that an individual can bicycle 2000 miles on a gallon of fat, an amount most adult bodies contain.)

The sprinter running the 100-meter dash can run on the energy supplied by the anaerobic pathway with its concomitant buildup of lactic acid. After the race, the sprinter must "pay" for this buildup by increased oxygen consumption ("oxygen debt") which is utilized to break the lactic acid down to carbon dioxide and water, the aerobic pathway. The marathon runner can go long distances at slower rates without getting into extreme oxygen debt by burning energy supplied by the aerobic pathway.

smooth muscle   Smooth muscle is classified into two types, *multiunit* or *single unit*, depending primarily on the type of innervation. Multiunit smooth muscle is characterized by discrete, individually innervated muscle cells (Figure 6-23). This type of muscle is found in blood vessels and in the iris of the eye. Single-unit smooth muscle occurs in groups in which the cells lie adjacent and the cell membranes of adjoining cells come in contact

figure 6-23
SMOOTH MUSCLE
TYPES

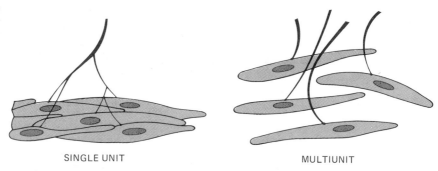

SINGLE UNIT   MULTIUNIT

with one another (Figure 6-23). Each muscle fiber need not be inner-vated, since the stimulus can pass from one cell to the next through the areas of close contact where there is *low electrical resistance.* In fact, the contraction may be *self-regenerating* as in cardiac muscle, so that single-unit smooth muscle may have its own *pacemaker* activity and only need innervation for regulation. Single-unit smooth muscle is found in the gut, in the ureter, in the bile duct, and in other tubular structures. The wave of contraction that is generated along these tubular structures moves materials along in the direction of the wave.

control   The control of muscle activity is by way of nerves, and this mechanism is discussed in Chapters 6, 8, 9, and 10.

factors influencing function   The *all-or-none* law previously referred to must not be taken to mean that all responses obeying this law are of the same magnitude. In the case of muscle, the response depends on the contractile state of the fibers, for example, whether they have been very recently stimulated and are "warmed," whether they are fatigued, or any number of other fac-tors. Once threshold is reached, the contraction is explosive. It is this kind of explosive event, as occurs in nerve and muscle, that comes under the all-or-none law.

Muscle contraction is dependent on the supply of oxygen, and muscles do store some oxygen in combination with *myoglobin,* a molecule found in muscle that is similar to hemoglobin. Myoglobin is iron rich and gives muscle its characteristic red color. Of course, the major source of oxygen is supplied by the red cell hemoglobin. When muscles are active, circula-tion to the muscles is increased with a concomitant decrease in blood flow to less active organs such as in the digestive viscera. This shunt of blood along with an increased cardiac output of up to 10 times pro-duces a net rise in arterial pressure. Increased ventilation at the lungs increases the oxygen supply. In spite of these compensatory changes that occur with muscle contraction, however, when work is being done at extreme rates, the circulatory system cannot supply sufficient oxygen. If contraction continues for extended periods, the muscles fatigue. Al-though there is no clear picture as to the cause of muscle fatigue, there is evidence that synaptic function apparently is not impaired, and meta-bolic disruption may be the major factor.

clinical
considerations

muscular
dystrophy

Muscular dystrophy is a general name given to several disorders that produce a progressive weakness in skeletal (and sometimes cardiac) muscle without any obvious inflammation of the muscle tissue. A degeneration and loss of muscle occur with no loss of function to the nervous system. It is a genetic disease that may be due to some breakdown in metabolic or hormonal function.

glycogen storage
disease

Glycogen storage disease is a condition in which the deposition of large amounts of glycogen results in the progressive destruction of the sarcoplasmic reticulum.

denervation

Although denervation of muscle is in itself not a disease, it can result from diseases like *poliomyelitis* in which the nerves are damaged. When denervation continues for a period of time, the muscle begins to atrophy and may become useless even if reinnervation occurs. One method of helping the denervated muscle is to stimulate it electrically while it is under load.

fibrillation

The state of the motor unit (nerve, synapse, muscles) can be determined by use of electrodes placed in the muscle bundle (electromyography). Normal muscle activity recorded in this manner produces potentials of about 4 mv lasting approximately 5 msec. If disease or accident causes a denervation of the muscle, after approximately one week, small spontaneous potentials of 10 to 200 mv lasting 1 to 2 msec occur. These potentials have an intrinsic rhythmicity of up to 10 per second. This latter condition is known as *fibrillation* and is the result of spontaneous contractions of *single* muscle fibers. Fibrillation disappears when reinnervation takes place or atrophy of the muscle occurs. Because fibrillation is reduced by curare (a drug which blocks acetylcholine) or enhanced by prostigmine (a drug which blocks the breakdown of acetylcholine by acetylcholinesterase), it is thought that the spontaneous discharges are produced by circulating acetylcholine.

muscle spasm
and muscle
cramps

Debilitating painful muscle spasms, particularly in the back and neck, affect over a half million individuals in the United States yearly. In most cases prolonged muscle spasm of skeletal muscles is due to a pinched spinal nerve often associated with disc disease. Lack of activity causing atrophy of skeletal muscle and nervous tension are predisposing factors in 80 percent of cases of muscle spasm. For muscle spasm, it is necessary first to relieve the pain and then as quickly as possible to begin gentle movements aimed at returning the muscles to their normal length and tension.

Localized, sustained, and painful cramps that cause a single muscle to go into vigorous involuntary contraction (sometimes after exercise but occurring even during sleep) cannot be explained at present. Stretching the cramped muscle usually relieves the pain, possibly due to inhibitory signals from the tendon stretch receptors feeding back to the motor neurons innervating the cramped muscle.

summary

gross anatomy
(list of major
muscles only)

GENERAL REGION	MUSCLE	GENERAL ORIGIN	GENERAL INSERTION	FUNCTION
Head and face	Frontalis	Galea aponeurotica	Muscles around eye, for example, orbicularis oculi	Raises skin of brow (frowning) and raises eyebrows
	Occipitalis	Occipital	Galea aponeurotica	Draws scalp backward
	Orbicularis oculi	Maxillary and frontal bones	Eyelid and cheek	Closes eyelids, winking
	Masseter	Zygomatic arch	Mandible	Closes jaw
	Temporalis	Temporal	Mandible	Closes jaw
	Pterygoid	Sphenoid	Mandible	Closes jaw
	Zygomaticus	Zygomatic	Angle of mouth and upper lip	Opens mouth; lifts upper lip
	Buccinator	Mandible and maxilla	Corner of mouth	Compresses cheek
	Mentalis	Mandible	Cheek	Raises and pushes lower lip forward
	Levator labii	Eye orbit	Orbicular oris	Elevates upper lip
	Orbicularis ori	Surrounds mouth	Corner of mouth	Closes lips, kissing
Eye	Superior rectus	Apex of orbit	Upper eyeball	Moves eye upward
	Inferior rectus	Apex of orbit	Lower eyeball	Moves eye downward
	Medial rectus	Apex of orbit	Medial aspect of eyeball	Moves eye medially
	Lateral rectus	Apex of orbit	Lateral aspect of eyeball	Moves eye laterally
	Superior oblique	Apex of orbit	Between superior and lateral recti	Rotates eyeball
	Inferior oblique	Anterior margin of orbit	Between lateral and inferior recti	Rotates eyeball
Tongue	Styloglossus	Temporal	Inferior surface of tongue	Moves tongue upward and backward
	Hyoglossus	Hyoid	Side of tongue	Depresses tongue
	Genioglossus	Mandible	Hyoid	Pushes tongue down and forward
Neck	Sternocleidomastoid	Sternum and clavicle	Temporal	Rotates head, flex cervicle vertebrae, elevate chin
	Sternohyoid	Sternum	Hyoid	Depresses hyoid and larynx
	Sternothyroid	Sternum	Thyroid cartilages	Depresses larynx
	Omohyoid	Scapula	Hyoid	Depresses hyoid and larynx
	Splenius capitis	Upper cervical	Temporal	Moves head laterally
Vertebral column	Longissimus (several muscles)	Transverse processes of thoracic vertebrae	Temporal; thoracic vertebrae	Bends and rotates head; extends and rotates upper vertebrae
	Scalenus	Transverse processes of cervical vertebrae	Upper ribs	Elevates first two ribs; bends vertebral column to one side; breathing
	Iliocostal (several muscles)	Iliac crest and ribs	Bridges ribs	Extends spine
	Sacrospinal complex	Lower thoracic and lumbar vertebrae; ilium	Lower ribs, spine of thoracic vertebrae	Extends spine
	Psoas	Last thoracic and lumbar vertebrae	Femur and ilium	Flexes and bends lumbar spine; flexes thigh
	Quadratus lumbarum	Ilium	Upper lumbar vertebrae	Moves spine laterally
	Rectus abdominis	Pubis	Middle ribs	Flexes spine
Shoulder and chest	Trapezius	Occipital, thoracic vertebrae	Clavicle and scapula	Lifts and pulls back scapula (straightening shoulders)
	Deltoid	Clavicle and scapula	Humerus	Abducts, extends, and flexes humerus
	Serratus	Upper ribs	Scapula	Moves scapula away from spine and inward

GENERAL REGION	MUSCLE	GENERAL ORIGIN	GENERAL INSERTION	FUNCTION
	Rhomboid	Thoracic vertebrae	Scapula	Elevates and retracts scapula
	Levator scapulae	Cervical vertebrae	Scapula	Elevates scapula; if scapula fixed, rotates neck
	Sufraspinatus	Scapula	Humerus	Abducts arm
	Infraspinatus	Scapula	Humerus	Abducts arm
	Pectoralis major	Clavicle, sternum costal cartilages	Humerus	Pulls arm forward, downward
	Pectoralis minor	Upper ribs	Scapula	Draws scapula forward, downward
	Teres major/minor	Scapula	Humerus	Adducts and rotates arm
	Subscapularis	Scapula	Humerus	Adducts arm
	Coracobrachialis	Scapula	Humerus	Adducts arm
	Latissimus dorsi	Ilium, lower ribs, thoracolumbar fascia	Humerus	Draws shoulder down; extends, rotates arm medially (used in swimming)
	Diaphragm	Sternum tip, intercostal cartilages, and lumbar vertebrae	Central tendon	Increases thorax by pulling down on central tendon, respiration
	External intercostals	Lower edge of ribs	Upper edge of rib below	Pulls ribs toward one another
	Internal intercostals	Inner surface of rib	Upper edge of rib below	Pulls ribs toward one another
Upper arm across elbow	Triceps brachii	Scapula, humerus	Ulna	Extends lower arm
	Anconeus	Humerus	Ulna	Extends lower arm
	Biceps brachii	Scapula	Radius	Flexes lower arm
	Brochialis	Humerus	Ulna	Flexes lower arm
	Pronator teres	Humerus and ulna	Radius	Flexes and pronates lower arm
Lower arm	Flexor carpi (several muscles)	Humerus and ulna	Metacarpals	Flexes, abducts, adducts wrist
	Palmaris	Humerus	Fascia and carpal ligaments	Flexes wrist
	Extensor carpi (several muscles)	Humerus	Metacarpals	Extends, abducts, and adducts wrist
	Extensor digitorum communis	Humerus	Tendons on fingers	Pull on digits and extends wrist
	Supinator	Humerus and ulna	Radius	Supinates hand
Hand	Flexor pollicis	Radius and carpals	Thumb	Flexes thumb
	Flexor digitorum	Ulna and carpals	Phalanges	Flexes fingers
	Extensor pollicis	Ulna	Phalanges	Extends thumb
	Extensor indicis	Ulna	Phalanges	Extends index finger
	Abductor pollicis	Radius, ulna, carpals	Metacarpals and thumb	Abducts thumb
	Adductor pollicis	Metacarpals	Thumb	Adducts thumb
Abdomen	External oblique	Lower ribs	Linea alba, pubis, ilium	Compresses abdomen and flexes spine
	Internal oblique	Ilium and thoracolumbar fascia	Tip of sternum, and lower ribs, linea alba	Compresses abdomen and flexes spine
	Rectus abdominis	Pubis	Rib cartilages	Compresses abdomen and flexes spine
	Transverse abdominis	Ilium, lower rib cartilages thoracolumbar fascia	Tip of sternum, pubis, linea alba	Constricts abdomen
Hip	Gluteal muscles	Ilium, sacrum, coccyx	Femur	Extends, rotates, and abducts thigh
	Iliopsoas	Lumbar vertebrae	Femur	Flexes and rotates thigh; flexes spine
	Tensor fasciae latae	Ilium	Iliotibial fascia	Flexes thigh
	Obturator	Ischium and pubis	Femur	Rotates thigh
	Pectineus	Pubis and pectineal line	Femur	Adducts, flexes thigh
	Adductors (several muscles)	Pubis and ischium	Femur	Adducts, flexes, rotates, extends thigh
Thigh	Biceps femoris	Ischium	Tibia and fibula	Flexes and rotates leg
	Semimembranosus	Ischium	Tibia	Flexes leg and rotates thigh
	Popliteus	Femur	Tibia	Flexes and rotates leg
	Quadriceps	Femur	Patella and tibia	Extends leg and flexes thigh
	Sartorius	Ilium	Tibia	Flexes thigh and rotates leg
	Gracilis	Pubis	Tibia	Flexes leg and adducts thigh

GENERAL REGION	MUSCLE	GENERAL ORIGIN	GENERAL INSERTION	FUNCTION
Lower leg	Gastrocnemius	Femur	Calcaneous (tarsal)	Flexes leg and plantar flexion of foot
	Soleus	Tibia and fibula	Calcaneous	Plantar flexion of foot
	Tibialis	Tibia and fibula	Tarsals and metatarsals	Plantar and dorsally flexes foot
	Peroneus (several muscles)	Tibia and fibula	Metatarsals	Dorsally flexes and pronates foot
	Plantaris	Femur	Calcaneous	Plantar flexion of foot and flexes leg
Foot	Flexors (several muscles)	Tarsals	Phalanges	Flexes toes
	Extensors (several muscles)	Tibia and fibula	Phalanges	Extends toes and dorsally flexes and pronates foot
	Abductor hallucis	Calcaneous	Phalanges	Abducts and flexes toes

cellular and tissue specializations

1. Skeletal muscle
   (a) fibers: equivalent to cell, myofibrils with sarcomeres

Z line	I band (thin filaments only)
thin filaments (actin)	A band (overlap of thick and
thick filaments (myosin)	thin filaments)
	H zone

   (b) actomyosin: actin and myosin bonded together
   (c) myosin has ATPase activity
   (d) sliding filament hypothesis: thin filaments slide over thick filaments producing contraction; ATP supplies energy; calcium needed for contraction
   (e) sarcoplasmic reticulum: specialized endoplasmic reticulum which stores calcium; when stimulated, releases calcium, allowing muscle to contract
   (f) transverse tubules: tubular invagination of muscle membrane; brings stimulus to sarcoplasmic reticulum; allows rapid contraction
   (g) phosphocreatine: high-energy compound which can donate high-energy phosphate to ADP to form ATP
2. Cardiac muscle: specialized striated muscle in heart (see Chapter 11)
3. Smooth muscle: nonstriated; contains loosely organized actin and myosin, also ATP; requires calcium for contraction; contraction is slow

physiology

1. Skeletal muscle
   (a) muscle twitch
      latent period
      contraction period
      relaxation period
      all-or-none law: individual fibers obey all-or-none law; muscle bundle contains numerous fibers; increasing stimulus can increase contraction of muscle bundle by recruiting more fibers
   (b) summation: stimulating muscle following refractory state, but before it is fully relaxed, produces greater contraction than initial equal stimulus; when maximum number of fibers is contracting in response to high-frequency stimulus, tetanus develops

(c) isotonic: muscle shortens, tension remains constant

(d) isometric: muscle length constant, tension changes

(e) velocity and load: velocity of muscle shortening decreases with greater loads

(f) length versus tension: tension is related to the number of cross-bridges that can be formed between thick and thin filaments; tension is greatest near resting length and falls off when muscle is stretched or begins to shorten markedly

(g) muscle tone: state of contraction of muscles produced by reflex activity, generally related to posture

(h) metabolism: energy supplied by anaerobic and aerobic respiration; short periods of anaerobic respiration possible with buildup of lactic acid leading to oxygen debt

2. Smooth muscle

(a) multiunit: discrete, individually innervated cells

(b) single unit: groups of cells, may have pacemaker; stimulus conducted via low-resistance junctions between cells

control   Generally via nervous system

factors influencing function   1. All-or-none law: magnitude of all-or-none response depends on state of muscle

2. Circulation may be a limiting factor during heavy work; synaptic fatigue likely to occur before muscle fatigue

clinical considerations   1. Muscular dystrophy: diseases causing muscle degeneration; genetic

2. Glycogen storage disease: excess glycogen storage breaks down sarcoplasmic reticulum

3. Denervation: loss of nerve input causes atrophy of muscle

4. Fibrillation: spontaneous, uncoordinated rapid muscle activity, generally seen when innervation is lost

the central nervous system

7

gross anatomy
brain
spinal cord
meninges
ventricles of brain and
   cerebrospinal fluid

cellular and tissue specializations
cerebrum (telencephalon)
diencephalon
mesencephalon
metencephalon
myelencephalon
spinal cord

physiology
telencephalon
diencephalon
mesencephalon
metencephalon
  (cerebellum and pons)
myelencephalon
  (medulla oblongata)

spinal cord
motor pathways
limbic system or visceral
  brain

factors influencing function
environment
physicochemical factors
biological

clinical considerations
epilepsy
syncope and coma
cerebral palsy and other
  palsies
demyelinating diseases
aphasias and ataxia
stroke
headaches
bacterial and viral
  infections
drugs and brain chemistry
other chemical factors
  affecting the brain

Homo sapiens is endowed with an awesomely complex nervous system. The network of neurons (about 10 billion) that form in the brain makes man unique among all creatures, for only he has learned to control his environment and to enculturate. With this brain, man carries on a dazzling array of tasks simultaneously. The brain is the seat of *consciousness, remembering, perceiving, evaluating,* and *deciding;* it is the home of *emotions* and *feelings;* it is the *mind.* The brain integrates sensory signals and coordinates muscle movements in a purposeful way and regulates basic drives necessary for species survival (thirst, hunger, fight, and flight). The brain is the center of pleasure and pain, hate and love, selfishness and selflessness. Yet, of all the parts of the body intensively studied, the brain has been the slowest to yield its secrets.

The brain is a rather gelatinous mass of neurons and glial cells, which, in the adult, weighs about 3 pounds. The brain is well protected by the skull, and the vascularity of the enveloping tissues makes the brain the best-nourished organ in the body. As an additional protection (and perhaps some nutritive value), a circulating fluid acts as a shock absorber surrounding and cushioning the brain and spinal cord (Figure 7-1). On opening the cranium and removing the membranes, the brain is seen to fill the entire cavity. The dominant structures are the two large cerebral hemispheres (Figure 7-2). The hemispheres are but one division of the

figure 7-1

OVERVIEW—
CENTRAL
NERVOUS SYSTEM

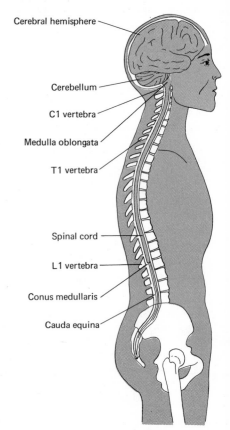

Cerebral hemisphere

Cerebellum

C1 vertebra

Medulla oblongata

T1 vertebra

Spinal cord

L1 vertebra

Conus medullaris

Cauda equina

An overview of the central nervous system (CNS) showing relationships of some major components of the brain and spinal cord to the rest of the body.

figure 7-2

BRAIN IN SITU

THE BRAIN IN THE CENTRAL CAVITY

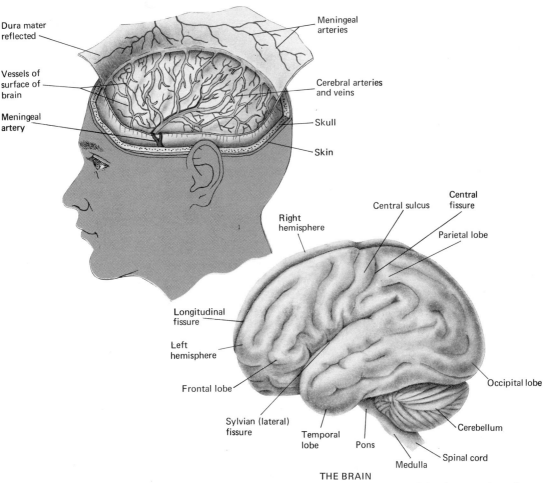

THE BRAIN

The upper drawing shows the brain in situ with the overlying bone and meninges removed. Note the extensive supply of blood vessels on the brain's exposed surface. The lower drawing shows a surface view of the left cerebral hemisphere showing some of the major anatomical landmarks.

brain, but they overlap and partially hide the remaining parts. The brain divisions and the nomenclature are given in Table 7-1.

The brain and the spinal cord are also called the *central nervous system* (CNS), and the nerves constitute the *peripheral nervous system*.

gross anatomy
brain
Telencephalon

Two hemispheres make up the cerebrum. They are separated into right and left halves by a deep furrow, the *longitudinal fissure* (Figure 7-2). If the lobes are gently pulled apart, a broad band of fibers, the *corpus callosum*, bridging the two hemispheres is seen (Figure 7-2). The surface

table 7-1
DIVISIONS OF
THE BRAIN^a

EMBRYOLOGICAL DIVISION	SECONDARY DIVISIONS	DEVELOPED SUBDIVISIONS	NERVES	CAVITIES
Prosencephalon	Telencephalon	Cerebral cortex	I, II	Lateral ventricles[b]
		Basal ganglia		
		Olfactory brain		
	Diencephalon	Thalamus		Third ventricle
		Epithalamus		
		Hypothalamus		
		Pituitary stalk and posterior lobe		
		Optic stalk and retina		
Mesencephalon	Mesencephalon	Corpora quadrigemina	III, IV	Cerebral aqueduct
Rhombencephalon	Metencephalon	Cerebellum, pons	V to VIII	Fourth ventricle
	Myelencephalon	Medulla oblongata	IX to XII	
		Spinal cord	Spinal	Central canal

^a Adapted from Arey, *Developmental Anatomy*, 6th ed. Phila., Pa.: Saunders, 1954.
^b First and second lateral ventricles.

of each hemisphere is marked by many furrows called *sulci*, and the bulging ridges between the sulci are called *gyri* (singular, *gyrus*) (Figure 7-2). This folding of the outer surfaces of the cerebrum greatly increases its surface area.

The brain's ridges and grooves can be used as fixed landmarks for identifying gross anatomical areas. The *lateral fissure* separates the *temporal* lobe; the *central fissure* separates the *frontal* and *parietal* lobes; the *parietooccipital fissure*, as the name implies, separates the *parietal* from the *occipital* lobe. The lobes derive their names from the overlying bony structures (Figure 7-3).

If a cross section is made through the telencephalon, we can see that the mass of tissue is organized into two major layers—a thin outer region, grayish in color called the *cortex* and an inner, large *white area* (Figure 7-4). Scattered within the white matter are islands of gray matter, and they are referred to as *nuclei*. These areas are discussed at length in the next section. Internal landmarks are the fairly large cavities, the *first* and *second* or *lateral* ventricles (Figure 7-5). These structures are also treated separately. Finally, the I and II cranial nerves emerge from the base of the cerebrum.

Diencephalon   The *diencephalon*, partially hidden by the cerebrum, forms the area around the third ventricle (Figure 7-6). The floor of the ventricle is the *hypothalmus;* the roof is the *epithalmus;* and the lateral walls constitute the *thalmus.* Each section is composed of gray and white matter. Embryologically, the diencephalon gives rise to some important structures: *pineal gland,* posterior lobe of the *pituitary gland*, and the *retina-optic stalk.* Although these structures are not part of the CNS per se, with the exception of the pineal, they are still anatomically tied to the diencephalon.

figure 7-3

CROSS AREAS OF
BRAIN SURFACE

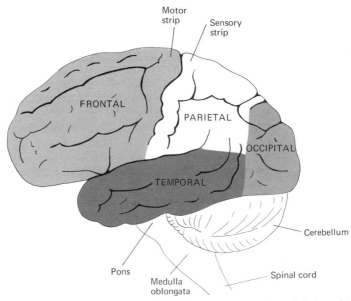

Motor strip

Sensory strip

FRONTAL

PARIETAL

OCCIPITAL

TEMPORAL

Cerebellum

Pons

Medulla oblongata

Spinal cord

Gross anatomical areas of the brain. The frontal, parietal, occipital, and temporal lobes derive their name from the overlying bony structure.

Mesencephalon

The section of the brain called the *mesencephalon* or *midbrain* is the smallest region, barely measuring 1 inch in length, yet it has several important subdivisions recognizable at a gross level. On its upper surface, four knoblike elevations contain centers for sight and hearing called the *superior and inferior colliculi*, respectively. The colliculi are also referred to as the *corpora quadrigemina*. The superficial origins of the *III and IV cranial nerves* are also found here. The midbrain surrounds a narrow canal (*cerebral aqueduct*) that links the third ventricle to the fourth ventricle below. Likewise, the mass of fibers of the midbrain links the diencephalon with the remainder of the brain stem (Figure 7-7).

Metencephalon (Cerebellum and Pons)

The *metencephalon* (Figure 7-8) is part of the brain stem covering part of the fourth ventricle. The larger segment is the cerebellum, which is divided into three major lobes: *anterior, posterior,* and *middle* (also called the *vermis*). The cerebellar surface is convuluted and quite similar to the cerebrum in that it has an outer gray area, *cerebellar cortex,** and an inner white region (all other areas of the CNS have an outer white area and an inner gray). The *pons* is a conspicuous enlargement of the posterior surface adjacent to the cerebellum. The superficial origins of *IV to VIII cranial nerves* emerge from this region.

Myelencephalon (Medulla Oblongata)

The *myelencephalon* is the lowest segment of the brain and connects with the spinal cord. The medulla is a triangular structure, broad at the top, surrounding the fourth ventricle (Figure 7-9). The inferior surface

* Although the cerebrum and cerebellum both have a cortex, when the term is used alone, for example, brain cortex, the reference is usually restricted to the cerebral cortex.

has two large bulges that contain major fiber pathways. The *IX to XII cranial nerves* have their superficial origins at the medulla.

spinal cord   The spinal cord is a tapering tube, about 18 inches in length and 0.5 inch thick, that passes through the protective bony canal formed by the vertebrae. The lumen of the cord is called the *central canal,* and it is continuous with the fourth ventricle of the medulla. The taper of the cord is not uniform in that two enlargements are formed due to the concentration of nerves passing to the muscles of the arms and legs (Figure 7-10). The *cervical enlargement* is located between *C*3 and *T*2, and the lower *lumbar enlargement* is found between *T*9 and *T*12. Except for a brief period during fetal development, the cord does not run the entire length of the neural canal but ends at the second lumbar vertebra.

At regular intervals with the vertebrae, the cord gives off spinal nerves, and the areas of emergence of these nerves are classified similarly to the divisions of the backbone: *cervical, thoracic, lumbar,* and *sacral-coccygeal.*

the meninges   The brain and spinal cord are enveloped by three membranes, collectively called the *meninges.* The outer covering, *dura mater,* is primarily

figure 7-4

CROSS SECTION
OF THE
CEREBRUM

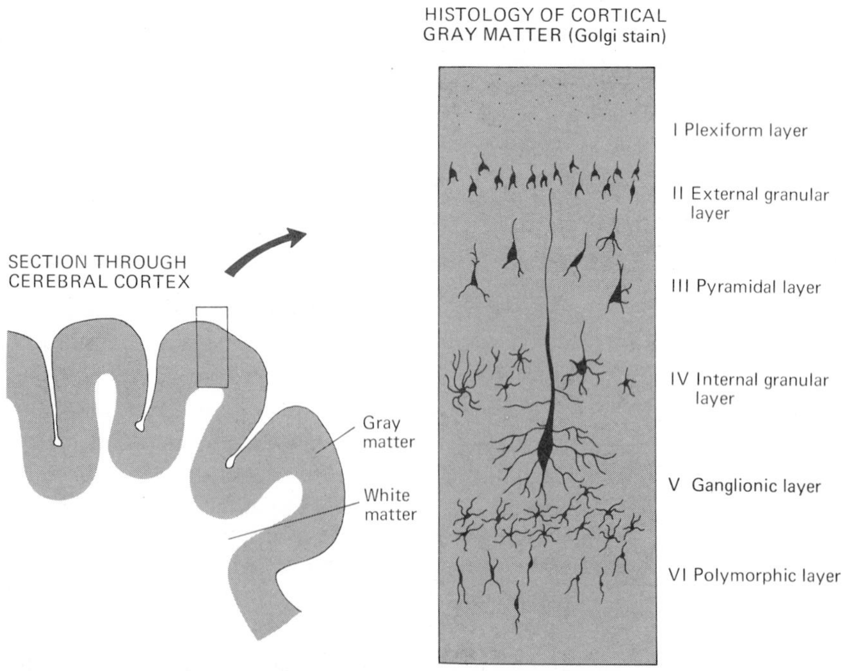

HISTOLOGY OF CORTICAL
GRAY MATTER (Golgi stain)

SECTION THROUGH
CEREBRAL CORTEX

Gray matter

White matter

I Plexiform layer

II External granular layer

III Pyramidal layer

IV Internal granular layer

V Ganglionic layer

VI Polymorphic layer

Cross section through the cerebrum shows an outer bark or cortex. Note that the cortex is actually made up of six discrete layers of interconnecting neurons. Below the gray matter the brain appears white due to the massive collection of myelinated fibers, hence the name white matter. Approximately 90 percent of all neurons are in the cerebral cortex.

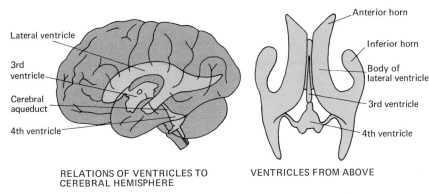

figure 7-5

INTERNAL BRAIN
SPACES

RELATIONS OF VENTRICLES TO
CEREBRAL HEMISPHERE

VENTRICLES FROM ABOVE

The internal spaces of the brain, the ventricles.

made up of tough fibrous connective tissue. The layer closest to the brain, and actually adhering to it, is the *pia mater*, a delicate connective tissue membrane. Sandwiched between the dura and pia mater is the *arachnoid* layer, a fine double-layered vascular membrane composed of connective tissue and flattened cuboidal mesothelium. The relationships of the membranes and their associated spaces are shown diagrammatically in Figures 7-10 and 7-11.

ventricles of brain and cerebrospinal fluid

Enclosed within the brain are four fluid-filled supporting spaces, the ventricles, which communicate with one another by connecting channels. Each cerebral hemisphere contains a large *lateral ventricle (first and second ventricles)* communicating with each other, and the lateral ventricles communicate with the third ventricle of the diencephalon via the *foramen of Monro*. The third ventricle drains into the *fourth ventricle* in the medulla oblongata by way of the *cerebral aqueduct (aqueduct of Sylvius)*. Posteriorly, the fourth ventricle connects with the *central canal* of the spinal cord (Figure 7-5).

The roof of the third and fourth ventricles contains a network of capillary vessels, the *choroid plexus*, which produce about 500 ml of *cerebrospinal fluid* (CSF) each day; production and resorption are continuous processes. The secretory processes are regulated so that the cerebrospinal fluid volume and pressure can change to meet the needs of maintaining the *intracranial pressure* (normally 10 to 20 mm/Hg). At the level of the fourth ventricle, the cerebrospinal fluid escapes into the subarachnoid space through two small openings and circulates around the surface of the brain and cord within the subarachnoid space. Ultimately the cerebrospinal fluid is absorbed by the highly vascularized *arachnoid villi*, where the resorbed constituents return to the venous cerebral circulation (Figure 7-11).

cellular and tissue specializations

Since the neuron was discussed at length in Chapter 5, the focus in this section is primarily on the spatial orientation of neurons and their aggregation into definitive and functional centers.

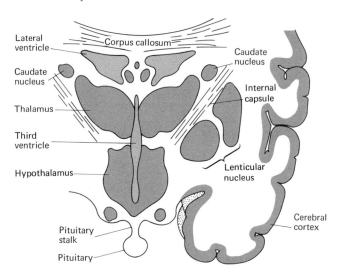

figure 7-6

CROSS SECTION—
DIENCEPHALON

Lateral
ventricle
Corpus callosum
Caudate
nucleus
Caudate
nucleus
Internal
capsule
Thalamus
Third
ventricle
Hypothalamus
Lenticular
nucleus
Cerebral
cortex
Pituitary
stalk
Pituitary

Cross section of the diencephalon showing major functional and anatomical aggregations of subcortical gray matter. Note the great collection of fibers connecting right and left cerebral hemispheres, the corpus callosum. This diagram sets only the boundaries of major structures, but in actuality each major structure may be made up of several well defined nuclei.

As would be expected not all neurons are alike, and their cytoarchitecture is a reflection of their functional diversity. Some neurons are relatively large and may have synaptic connections with over 100,000 other neurons. Others are small and may have only one or two synaptic connections.

In addition to neurons, the CNS contains a large number of *neuroglia* (also called *glia*). There are perhaps 10 times as many glial cells as neurons, occupying about 10 percent of the brain volume. These glia, unlike neurons, maintain their ability to divide throughout the life of the individual. These cells fill the spaces between neurons and form an intimate sheath around individual nerve cells and smaller blood vessels in the brain. There are two main classes of glia: the *oligodendrocytes* and the *astrocytes.* The more numerous (75 percent of all glia) oligodendrocytes make the myelin which surrounds most axons, while the function of larger astrocytes is a matter of controversy. It was thought that these cells provide a supportive and nutritive role, but recent studies have suggested that their main function may be regulation of ions (particularly potassium) in synaptic regions. A third cell type, the *microglia*, which is thought to be transformed monocytes from the blood, is a mobile phagocytic cell which acts as brain macrophages.

cerebrum
(telencephalon)

Cortex

The cortex (gray matter) constitutes an outer region of the cerebrum about 1 mm thick. Within this strip are six layers of nerve cell bodies (and small segments of their dendrites and axons). The basic cell of the cerebral cortex is the *pyramidal cell*, and its distinctive feature is the radiating dendritic complex and a prominent axon. The cortical gray matter can be subdivided on the basis of the microanatomy (Figure 7-4) or on the basis of function (see *Broca's areas,* Figure 7-12).

Beneath the cortex, the white matter is oriented into three major types of fibrous pathways: (a) *projection tracts,* in which the fibers go to and from the diencephalon and parts of the brain stem; (b) *association tracts,* in which fibers connect different parts of the cortex, but on the same hemisphere; and (c) *transverse* or *commissural tracts,* in which fibers run from one hemisphere to another (Figure 7-6). The *corpus callosum* mentioned previously is the largest commissural tract; two other important pathways are the *hippocampus* and *anterior commissural.*

Within the *subcortical* area are nuclei. Sometimes the subcortical nuclei are called *basal ganglia* (this label is not quite correct, for the term *ganglia* should be reserved for aggregations of nerve cell bodies outside of the CNS). These masses of nerve cell bodies lie adjacent to the thalamus. As we shall see in the section on physiology, they are important *relay* and *integrating stations* between the higher centers in the cortex and the remainder of the brain. Three important pairs of subcortical nuclei are the *caudate, putamen,* and *globus pallidus.* On each

figure 7-7

CROSS SECTION —
MIDBRAIN

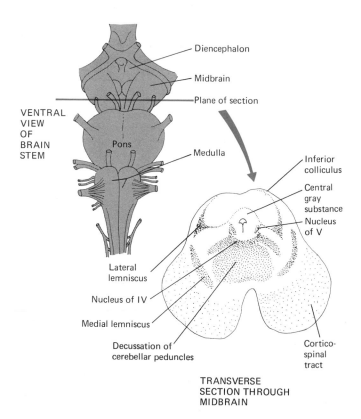

Cross section and ventral view of the midbrain or mesencephalon showing major anatomical landmarks.

side together with another gray area, the *internal capsule*, they form what is also known as the *corpus striatum* (Figure 7-13).

diencephalon   Most of the diencephalon is composed of gray areas similar to the sub-cortical nuclei (some textbooks include the thalamus and hypothalamus as part of the subcortical nuclei, although the centers of the diencephalon are functionally quite different). Essentially, these aggregations of gray matter relay or associate stimuli. For example, every sensory impulse of the body, with the exception of the olfactory nerves, must pass over a synapse in the thalamus before being relayed to the cerebral cortex.

The epithalamus is different from the other regions of the diencephalon in that it is primarily secretory in function (cerebrospinal fluid).

mesencephalon   The midbrain contains an important network of neurons that form part of the *reticular formation* (Figure 7-18)—a linking network of neurons that runs from the diencephalon through the brain stem. Within the reticular formation are the nuclei of the III and IV cranial nerves, special nuclei associated with the transmission of light and hearing. The base of the midbrain is composed primarily of myelinated fibers forming cerebral motor tracts.

figure 7-8

PONS-
CEREBELLUM,
GROSS ANATOMY,
AND CYTO
ARCHITECTURE

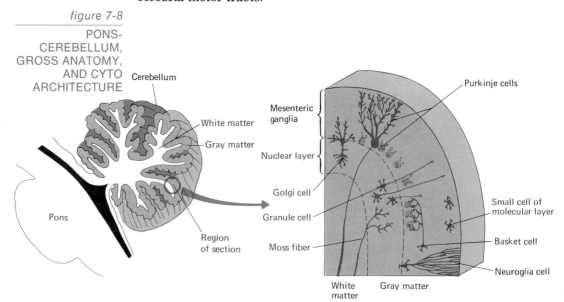

In the upper left can be seen the anatomical relationship of the pons and cerebellum after the cerebral hemispheres have been removed. Usually the cerebellum is partially hidden by the cerebrum (see Figure 7-3). Like the cerebrum the cerebellum is composed of an outer bark of gray matter and an inner mass of white matter. Seventy-five percent of the surface area of the cerebellum is not visible from the surface since much of the cortex is convoluted or folded. The cellular arrangement of the cerebellar cortex shows layering and several discrete neuronal types dominated by the large Purkinje cells and layers of granule cells. The circuitry in the cerebellum suggests feedback loops within feedback loops, an anatomical arrangement expected in this motor coordination center.

metencephalon   The arrangement of the nerve cell bodies in the cerebellar cortex is generally similar to that seen in the cerebrum except that only two anatomical layers are present. The extraordinary branching of dendrites is indicative of the wide range of space covered by a single cell (Figure 7-8).

The neuron arrangement in the pons forms an outer white matter region surrounding an inner gray. The centers for the V and VIII cranial nerves are located within the pons, but the bulk of this part of the brain is comprised of numerous fiber tracts joining the medulla to the cerebellum and upper regions of the brain.

myelencephalon   In cross section (Figure 7-9) the medulla is seen to be composed of a vast number of ascending and descending fibers. Almost the entire anterolateral area is made up of these fibrous tracts. The roof of the medulla is thin-walled and highly vascularized, and the blood vessels in this area secrete cerebrospinal fluid. Internally the gray matter is organized into a variety of vital centers involved in the control of respiration, blood pressure, and heart rate. Other aggregations of neurons in the medulla regulate lesser functions, such as swallowing, hiccuping, and vomiting. The starting points (nerve cell bodies) of the fibers constituting the IX to XII cranial nerves are also located in the medulla.

spinal cord   The white and gray matter are well delineated in the spinal cord. The reader will note that the central gray matter roughly forms the letter H, and the parts of the letter (called *horns*) divide each half of the cord into

figure 7-9

MYELENCEPHALON

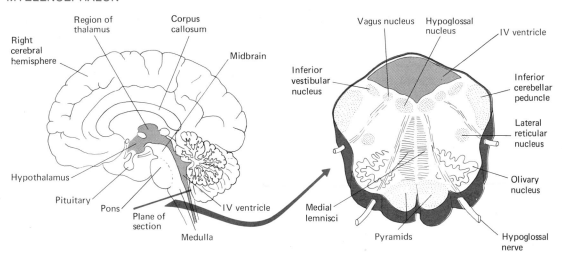

MEDULLA CROSS SECTION

The gross anatomy of the myelencephalon (medulla oblongata) is shown in sagittal section through the brain (left), and at the right is seen the anatomical relationships of the medulla in cross section. Note the large IV ventricle on the dorsal aspect of the medulla and the large pyramids (collections of motor fibers) on the ventral side.

figure 7-10

SPINAL CORD IN
THREE
DIMENSIONS

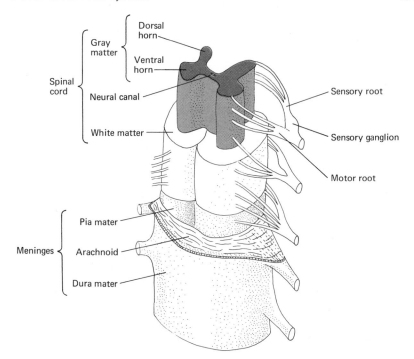

The spinal cord shown in an exploded three-dimensional diagram. Like the rest of the CNS the cord is encased in bone and meninges and has a hollow canal which is continuous with the ventricles of the brain. Sensory fibers enter into the sensory ganglion (dorsal root ganglion), and motor fibers form the ventral root. Both sensory and motor roots fuse to form the segmental spinal nerves.

three regions: *posterior, median,* and *anterior* (Figure 7-10). Each gray matter horn (also called *column*) contains dendrites and nerve cell bodies. Usually, the axons or dendrites remain on the side on which they enter the cord, but some will cross over. The fibers of the white area are not randomly distributed but form groups that are functionally related. Figure 7-14 gives the anatomical locations of major ascending and descending tracts. The cord is symmetrical, and motor and sensory tracts exist in both halves. The significance of these pathways will be treated further in the section on physiology.

physiology

telencephalon

Although all parts of the cerebral cortex may interact, it is nevertheless possible to ascribe specific functions to a number of well-defined cortical regions. This localization of function has been determined in humans by a number of methods, for example, electric stimulation of specific brain loci, recording brain electric responses, and surgical or traumatic destruction of specific parts of the brain. From studies in rats, cats, lower primates, and man, several sensory, association, and motor areas have been mapped. This localization is seen in Figure 7-10, which is a simplified version only showing major areas. It is convenient to deal with each major functional area separately, though it must be stressed that

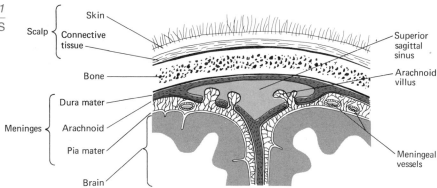

figure 7-11
MENINGES

The meninges or protective membranes which enveolp the CNS (see also Figure 7-10) and provide both protective and secretory functions. In the latter case the cerebrospinal fluid (CSF) is elaborated by the choroid plexus and reabsorbed in the arachnoid villi.

The Motor Cortex

such a separation is arbitrary and simplistic. In reality all functions are interconnected.

The motor cortex controls the highly refined precise voluntary movement of the skeletal muscles. In experimental animals (both anesthetized and unanesthetized), electric stimulation of various parts of the motor area can evoke several hundred distinguishable movements. The areas controlling each set of muscles are represented topographically in the *motor projection* areas of the cerebral cortex. A systematic analysis of the motor area reveals a "point-to-point" representation, with those muscle groups needing the most exact control (fingers, lips, voice box) having extensive cerebral representation; this organization would be expected in any precise control system. A cross section through the primary motor

figure 7-12
FUNCTIONAL MAP
OF CORTEX

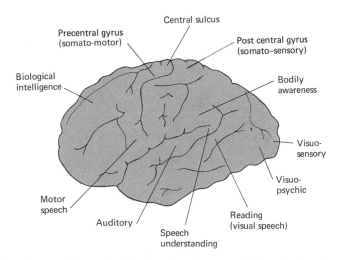

Functional map of the cerebral cortex showing some of the major functional areas.

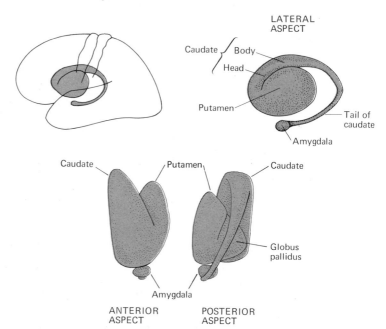

figure 7-13

THE BASAL
GANGLIA

LATERAL
ASPECT

Caudate — Body
Head
Putamen
Tail of
caudate
Amygdala

Caudate   Putamen   Caudate

Globus
pallidus

Amygdala

ANTERIOR   POSTERIOR
ASPECT   ASPECT

The basal ganglia shown in relationship to the cerebrum (upper left) and three anatomical views of these subcortical masses of gray matter as they would appear if removed from the enveloping mass of the cerebrum.

cortex of man permits us to draw a caricature or *motor homunculus* of the neural representation (Figure 7-15).

Sensory Areas
Discrimination or perception of sensory inputs is localized in the cerebrocortical sensory projection areas. These areas are shown in Figure 7-15, where it may be noted that there are separate regions for *somesthesis (body senses), audition, vision, olfaction,* and *taste.* As is the case for motor areas, there is a point-to-point representation in the sensory areas also, so that those peripheral areas having the most receptors (eyes, mouth, hands) have the largest number of cortical neurons.

Association Areas
The *cerebrocortical association areas* give man his unique capacity to accumulate and utilize knowledge, solve problems, and reason logically. The association areas also are responsible for a number of other mental functions such as curiosity, foresight, imagination, speech, emotion, personality, and conscience. Unlike inputs to the purely sensory and motor areas, the same information appears to be diffusely distributed at many points in the *association cortex* of each cerebral hemisphere. Such redundancy means that accumulated information is relatively permanent.

The initial event in *learning* is a sensory input that is then relayed to an association area. The association areas for visual and sound memory are located near these sensory areas, with the major association for other inputs being in front of the motor area (Figure 7-12). The association

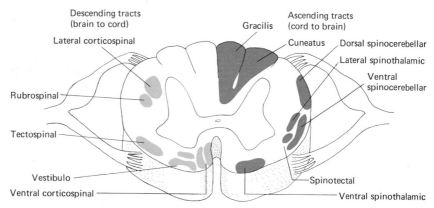

figure 7-14

CROSS SECTION
SPINAL CORD
(FIBER TRACTS)

A cross-sectional view of the spinal cord shows some major ascending fiber tracts on the right and descending fiber tracts on the left. Each tract or major collection of fibers bears an appropriate anatomical designation indicating functional connections as seen in Table 7-2.

areas also send large fiber connections to the motor areas. It is possible to conceptualize the pathways involved in any skilled motor task. When hitting a baseball, for example, the sensory information from the eyes is integrated in the visual sensory area and relayed to an association area. There, past information and immediate sensory information are integrated; the velocity and trajectory of the ball are calculated; and a projection is made as to where that ball will be at the moment it passes over the plate. This information is then relayed to the motor area activating those motor neurons that will cause the proper muscles to contract so that the bat meets the ball at the correct instant in time. In a highly trained and successful player this system is accurate over 33 percent of the time. See Module 7A for a diagrammatic presentation of the structures and pathways described above.

But how does the brain remember (Module 7B)? Most sensory inputs result in only a fragile transient *memory trace*, which will fade into oblivion unless reinforced. Such short-term memories last a few hours. With repetition the sensory inputs may be *consolidated* into semipermanent long-term memories that are recalled on demand by some unknown retrieval system in the association areas. We also know that some bits of memory, particularly vivid ones in our early life, are most stable and persistent, although generally memories tend to decay with the passage of time. Most recent memories are the least firmly fixed. Painful memories are not merely forgotten, they are often actively suppressed. Brain damage sometimes disrupts the memory circuits in the association area and results in memory loss or amnesia. Much remains to be learned about brain mechanisms in memory and learning. Despite our fragmental insight into the underlying anatomy, chemistry, and function of the association cortex, we still learn, think, create, wonder, and imagine.

Basal Ganglia   The basal ganglia within the depths of the cerebrum are essential in coordinating the voluntary muscle movements, but their precise role is not clear.

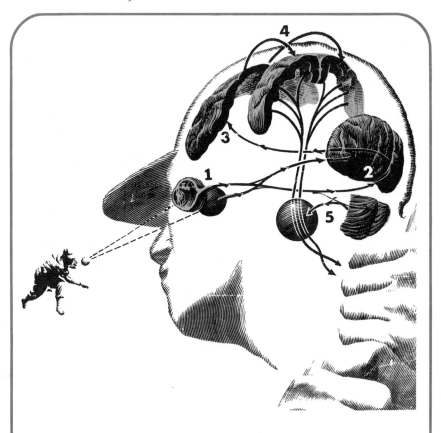

The above drawing depicts how a sensory input is integrated and translated into behavior. In such a behavior as hitting a baseball, up to 75 percent of all CNS neurons may be involved. As the ball leaves the pitcher's hand traveling at 90 miles per hour the batter receives a series of binocular images coded in both space and time (1). These initiate signals which are relayed via the optic pathway (see Chapter 11) to the visual cortex in the occipital lobe (2). This sensory information is then continuously relayed to the frontal association areas (3), where past memories of velocity and trajectory of the ball are integrated and compared with the new sensory signals. Here the decision is made as to where the ball will be at that fraction of a second when it crosses the plate, and the decision is made to swing or not to swing. Information is then relayed to the motor cortex (4) and integrated signals are sent via motor coordinating centers in the cerebellum and basal ganglia (5), and the proper sequence of signals (both excitatory and inhibitory) is sent down the spinal cord and thence out to the appropriate muscles which bring the bat into proper position to hit the ball. A well-trained player is relatively accurate, resulting in an efficiency of 33 to 66 percent. Thus one-third of the time he will hit it where *"they ain't,"* one-third of the time he will hit it where *"they is,"* and one-third of the time he will miss. (Illustration courtesy of Sandoz.)

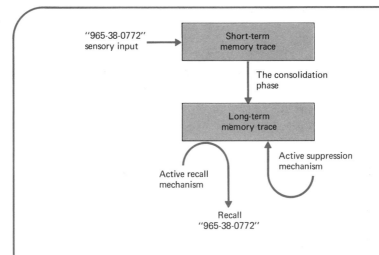

How we form memories, utilize these past bits of stored information, how we recall some memories on demand, and how painful memories are suppressed are still in large part a mystery, but it is possible to construct a hypothetical model from the limited facts available to us. Such a schematic hypothetical model is shown above. All memories start with some sensory input to the brain and result in the formation of a transient, exceptionally fragile, short-term memory trace. Such short-term memories fade rapidly, in minutes to a few hours, unless they are consolidated into permanent long-term memory traces. We know that formation of short-term memory involves the reticular activating system, which is responsible for focused attention, and the motivational brain or limbic system, which provides the needed drive to retain memory. Thus repetition and reinforcement (reward in the case of success, or punishment in event of failure) are known to aid the consolidation phase. Recent work has also suggested that protein synthesis may be needed to convert the short-term memory into a durable, accessible circuit in the brain. Long-term memories may persist throughout the life of the individual. How the recall and suppression systems work is very unclear, but despite our limited understanding we do remember and use past information in an effective manner.

diencephalon

Thalamus

All sensory impulses reach the thalamus via the large _spinothalamic tract_ and are then relayed to the sensory cortex by the _thalamocortical_ tracts. There are also large fiber connections between the motor cortex, thalamus, and basal ganglia, and other fibers from cortex via thalamus to the hypothalamus. Just by looking at these connections, we could deduce thalamic function to be that of the major relay station between the cerebral cortex and many lower parts of the brain. The thalamus relays most sensory inputs to the cortex (except olfactory pathway) and plays a particularly important role in the perception of pain (Module 7C). Other signals relayed through the thalamus via the _limbic system_ (discussed later) affect emotions and motivated behavior. Still other thala-

PAIN PERCEPTION

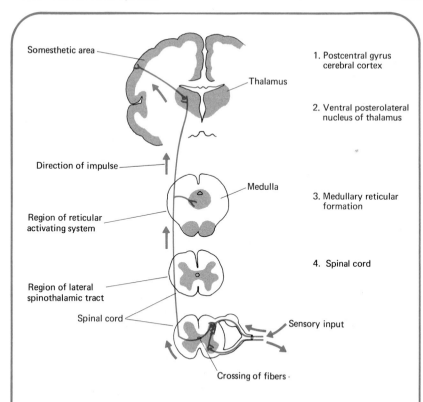

Somesthetic area

Thalamus

1. Postcentral gyrus
   cerebral cortex

2. Ventral posterolateral
   nucleus of thalamus

Direction of impulse

Medulla

3. Medullary reticular
   formation

Region of reticular
activating system

4. Spinal cord

Region of lateral
spinothalamic tract

Spinal cord

Sensory input

Crossing of fibers

Pain is an elusive sensation and as of today there is no acceptable uniform system of experimental measurement of pain in man. Even its definition is difficult since the perception of pain is a private phenomenon and wide differences in pain sensitivity exist. Unlike other sensory modalities (for example, vision, hearing, etc.) the response to a hurtful stimulus is relatively primitive. At the spinal cord level of organization pain does not reach the level of consciousness before a reflex withdrawl response is elicited. At the conscious level the experience of pain depends on a variety of factors which interact in some yet to be explained fashion. These factors include: (a) The extent of the trauma, (b) the individual's history of previous pain exposure, (c) the immediate state of the individual's psychic state (for example, anxiety, etc.), and (d) the individual's cultural background. Previous pain tends to change sensitivity, and as in other functions of the nervous system, afferent (incoming) signals may be enhanced or suppressed. In this way an otherwise mild, painful stimulus could be perceived as a severely painful experience if the subject were anxious (emotional) or was focusing attention on the hurt. On the other hand, severe wounds or injuries have been ignored (unperceived) by people in highly motivated states, such as men in battle or football players during a game. Experimentally it has been shown that nerve fibers in the pain pathway are subject to modification—changes in electrical excitability at several levels in the CNS (see above for schematic of classic pain pathway).

figure 7-15

THE MOTOR AND
SENSORY CORTEX

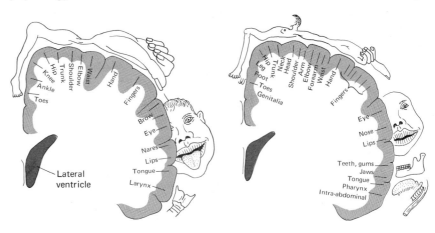

MOTOR HOMUNCULUS   SENSORY HOMUNCULUS

The drawing at the left shows a section through the motor cortex and the proportional point-to-point representation. The caricaturelike figure or motor homunculus shows relative neural representation by depicting in larger dimension those areas with the greatest motor supply. The drawing at the right shows a similar cross section through the somato-sensory area (the post-central gyrus), and the sensory homunculus shows relative sensory representation in the brain. Note that relatively large areas are devoted to the mouth and hands.

mic relays play a role in motor coordination, arousal, and focused attention. For example, if the thalamus of a subject is stimulated electrically, his response may be that he has a feeling of well-being or an aura of fear, but he cannot discretely pinpoint why he feels good or bad.

Hypothalamus   The hypothalamus is a group of 15 or so nuclei forming the floor and lower lateral walls of the third ventricle of the brain (Figure 7-16). Although it only weighs about 4 g, it is of great physiological importance. First, the hypothalamus is the principal *controling and integrating center* for the entire *autonomic nervous system* (involuntary actions). Its afferent fibers bring in messages from the cerebral cortex, thalamus, medulla, and spinal cord. These incoming signals eventually evoke motor signals that evoke behavior appropriate to situations of *approach, avoidance, fight,* and *flight.* Specifically, this small segment of the brain participates in the regulation of (a) body temperature, (b) rage, fear, and anxiety, (c) blood pressure, (d) appetite, (e) sleep, (f) urine volume, (g) salt balance, and (h) control of a number of endocrine activities. The hypothalamus, therefore, is a lower echelon but important center for emotional behavior. Many psychic states manifest themselves in overt body responses, such as rage or tension. The hypothalamus could very well be a critical area for *psychosomatic* phenomena.

The hypothalamus may even be considered an endocrine organ, since *releasing factors* that regulate the hormones of the anterior pituitary are produced in specific brain nuclei and are carried to the anterior pituitary by the blood stream. There are also specialized *neurosecretory cells* in some hypothalamic nuclei that synthesize and transport hormones

figure 7-16
THE
HYPOTHALAMUS

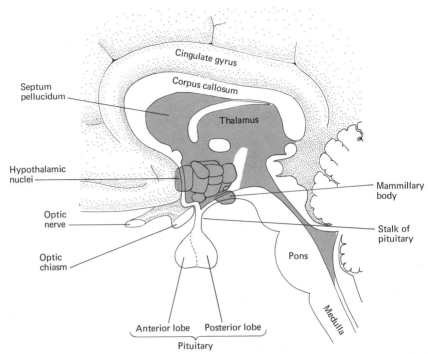

The hypothalamus or head ganglion of the autonomic nervous system is the final common path for a vast array of visceral integrating signals as well as the major controlling influence on pituitary function. The paired hypothalamic nuclei are named according to their anatomical position rather than by their function, for example, supraoptic nuclei, paraventricular nuclei, and so on.

along their axons to the *posterior lobe* of the pituitary (Figure 7-17). Details of hypothalamic activities are discussed in several chapters, such as control of endocrine secretions.

mesencephalon   The midbrain is primarily made up of white matter, great fiber tracts that connect the cerebrum, thalamus, and hypothalamus to the hindbrain and cord. The corpora quadrigemina are involved in visual perception and auditory reflexes. Sometimes the pons is considered as the ventral portion of the midbrain. The pons not only contains pathways conducting information between the spinal cord and other parts of the brain, but also contains a *respiratory reflex center* working in conjunction with respiratory centers in the medulla oblongata to regulate pulmonary ventilation. There are other concentrations of neurons in the depths of the midbrain such as the *red nucleus*, which is involved in motor coordination as well as reflex activity (eye movements and pupillary dilation). Finally, a collection of neurons runs the length of the midbrain and extends anteriorly to the diencephalon. This aggregation of neurons is the so-called brain stem *reticular activating system* (RAS), and it is of such importance that it will be dealt with separately in the following section.

figure 7-17

HYPOTHALAMIC
CONTROL OF
PITUITARY

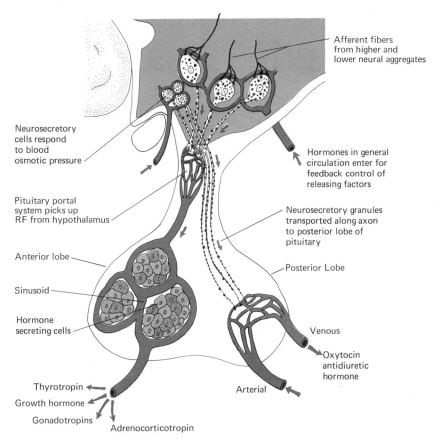

Hypothalamic control of the pituitary gland is mediated via specific releasing factors elaborated by neurosecretory cells in the hypothalamus. The releasing factors are carried to the target cells in the pituitary without being diluted by means of a unique vascular portal system.

The Reticular Activating System

Functionally, the reticular activating system (RAS) integrates responses to a vast number of environmental sensory inputs (Figure 7-18). We are unaware of most of the thousands of sensory signals impinging on our brain each second (for example, pressure of a shoe, ring, watch, saliva in the mouth, and so forth), unless we focus our attention on them. Furthermore, much of our sensory information must be filtered in such a way that only significant inputs are selected to reach the portals of consciousness. It is the job of the reticular activating system to control (a) *arousal*, (b) *sleep*, and (c) *awareness (focus* and *attention)*. Arousal consists of bringing the brain from an asleep to an awake state. Arousal can be seen not only behaviorally but also can be seen in changes in brain electrical activity. Arousal is effected by all sensory inputs via collateral fibers which feed into the reticular activating system; therefore arousal is a nonspecific phenomenon. The brain tends to *habituate*—that is, show diminished responsiveness—to any monotonous or repetitive stimulus. Any novel stimulus will produce arousal or dishabituation.

figure 7-18

RETICULAR
ACTIVATING
SYSTEM

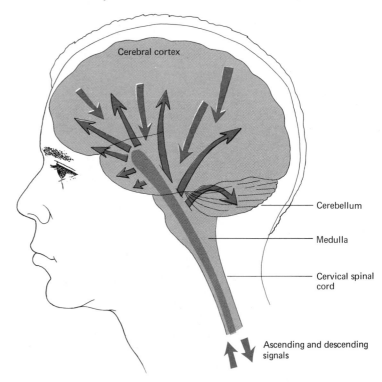

The reticular activating system (RAS) or "waking brain" modulates almost all ongoing activity in the CNS. Any sensory input can cause nonspecific arousal (awakening and alerting), and the RAS is essential in focusing attention as well. The major ascending and descending signals of the RAS are shown by arrows.

There are two pathways involved in nonspecific arousal. (a) Signals from the *ascending reticular activating system* (ARAS) influence excitability of the cerebral cortex, cerebellum, and hypothalamus directly, and these structures, in turn, feed back to the system, as can be seen in Figure 7-18; (b) signals from the *descending reticular activating system* (DRAS) influence the muscle reflexes, which in turn cause an increased sensory input to the ascending reticular activating system indirectly producing arousal.

In addition to producing nonspecific arousal, the reticular activating system is capable of alerting specific or the focused attention that allows us to be conscious of both environment and self. This function is important in detecting differences between two similar inputs and in selective concentration on a subject. To select specific inputs, the reticular activating system usually modulates the vast array of sensory inputs by suppressing irrelevant inputs and enhancing relevant sensory messages.

Damage to the reticular activating system, particularly to the ascending influences, produces a sleeplike state. There is also evidence that a number of narcotics (for example, opium) and hallucinogens (for example, LSD) act selectively on the system. Some drugs such as the amphetamines *(speed)* produce enhanced arousal whereas others produce sleep and dreams (Module 7D).

metencephalon (cerebellum and pons) Anatomically and functionally the cerebellum can be divided into three input circuits and three output circuits. However, these units are structured in such a way that all inputs affect all outputs. The cerebellum is thus organized as a series of feedback loops within feedback loops, and the whole purpose of this organization is postural adjustment and coordination. The motor organization is complex, involving inputs from the cerebrum motor areas, the *vestibular* (balance) organs, vestibular nuclei, proprioceptors, touch receptors, and practically every subcortical center associated with motor activity.

The cerebellar functions can be summarized again here as (a) the *maintenance of equilibrium* by adjusting excitation to the motor neurons innervating the antigravity muscles (extensors); (b) *postural reflexes* which, with appropriate adjustments, regulate the *stretch reflexes* in the extensor muscles—in this way cerebellar influences are superimposed in a patterned fashion over the stretch reflexes, and posture is maintained; and (c) *coordination of purposeful voluntary movement* initiated in the cerebral centers. By adjusting the signals to appropriate muscle groups, it is possible to bring about a synchronous contraction of the proper timing, speed, and force. An example of this sort of act is seen in the response to a command, "Place the tip of your index finger to the tip of your nose."

myelencephalon (medulla oblongata) The medulla oblongata not only conducts information both ways—between the higher centers and the spinal cord—but also contains a number of *vital centers.* Although these centers are influenced by sensory signals from the viscera and body surface, they are also under the influence of higher centers, mainly the hypothalamus and cerebral cortex. This cerebrocortical influence on hypothalamic and medullary function accounts for many of the so-called *psychosomatic symptoms* (for example, high blood pressure and ulcers). The vital centers of the medulla are (a) *cardiac control centers*, both accelerator and depressor; (b) *vasomotor centers*, which integrate vascular reflexes and the shunting of blood to active organs; (c) *gastrointestinal control centers;* (d) *respiratory centers* (others are also found in the pons).

the spinal cord All afferent and efferent signals to and from the brain are carried by large and small fiber tracts in the white matter of the cord. As seen in Figure 7-14, the locations of all major tracts are mapped.

The major tracts and their function are also listed in Table 7-2. All descending motor signals contact the motor neurons in the ventral horn of the gray matter; hence these cells constitute the "final common pathway" to the skeletal muscles. As described earlier the many signals that activate these motor neurons work mainly as part of a reflex to coordinate voluntary motor activity, but higher centers superimpose their influences over local reflexes.

SLEEP

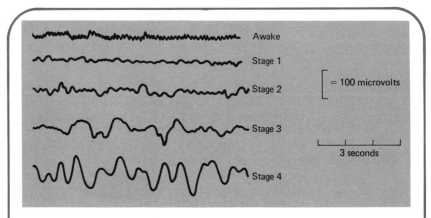

All creatures including man suspend their activity for a prolonged period once every 24 hours. This sleep period is a recurrent 24 hour or circadian rhythm. Deprived of sleep humans lose efficiency, cannot sustain concentration, and become depressed or irritable. Indeed if sleep deprivation is prolonged, the subject's behavior becomes frankly psychotic. Usually the rhythmicity is in concordance with the alteration of dark and light. A sudden change in one's schedule, which is experienced after crossing several time zones in a jet aircraft, causes "jet lag" so that although in a new day-night environment the subject still functions as if he were at home, that is, his biological clock is out of kilter. Sleep consists of a series of undulating cycles, each 90 to 110 minutes long. The subject passes through a series of levels of consciousness, physiological and neural changes. The electroencephalograms (EEG) above depict the electrical changes reflected by the brain waves. In the awake state the EEG shows a low amplitude, fast, asynchronous pattern, but as one starts to doze the muscles relax, the heart slows, the temperature begins to drop, the eyes roll and the EEG pattern starts to show larger, slower synchronized waves (stages 1, 2, 3 and 4 above). Stages 3 and 4 constitute deep sleep and if a person is deprived of stage 4 but permitted all the other stages of sleep, he will be depressed the next day. In the next sleep cycle the Stage 4 deprived individual will exhibit an increase in stage 4 as if trying to rectify the lack. Sleep has been called the "great rejuvenator," and indeed recent research has shown that in stage 4 the release of growth hormone is increased, suggesting that this is a period of regrowth and repair of the day's wear and tear.

In monitoring the EEG changes associated with sleep it was found that there were recurrent periods of rapid eye movements (REM) coinciding with rapid, irregular, low voltage EEGs. If a person is awakened during this period of REM or paradoxical sleep, he will almost always report that he was dreaming, and although dreams occur in other stages of sleep, the best and most emotionally laden dream recall is in REM sleep. Subjects deprived of REM sleep become exceptionally irritable and if given a chance to sleep exhibit an orgy of REM sleep as if compensating for the previous loss. Hence REM seems to play some essential role; it has been postulated that REM sleep is a period of discharge of building excitement in the emotional brain (limbic system). Recent studies with psychotic patients suggest that sleep EEGs and ability to compensate for REM loss may be different from normal individuals. Today there is an enormous amount of sleep research in progress and considerable new understanding should soon be forthcoming.

figure 7-19

THE LOWER
MOTOR NEURON,
THE COMMON
PATH FOR MOTOR
ACTIVITY

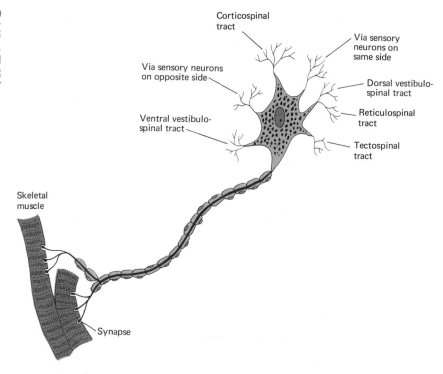

The final common path for motor activity is the lower motor neuron found in the ventral horn of the gray matter of the spinal cord. Some of the major inputs to the lower motor neuron are shown. Such neurons may have over 100,000 synaptic endings terminating on the cell body and dendritic arborization. Temporal and spatial summations of these inputs determine whether or not the lower neuron will discharge its signals via the thick myelinated axons. The axons of these lower motor neurons form the majority of fibers in the ventral root.

motor pathways

The Pyramidal System

The upper motor neurons, the *giant Betz cells* of the cerebral cortex primary motor area, initiate voluntary, precise motor acts, and their fibers form a pathway known as the *pyramidal tract.* This tract also receives fibers from many other parts of the cerebral cortex. The anatomical details of the pyramidal system are shown in Figure 7-20.

The Extrapyramidal System

The extrapyramidal pathways originate from either the motor cortex or various other structures such as the basal ganglia, cerebellum, or reticular activating system, shown in Figure 7-21.

The extrapyramidal system controls large automatic movements and postural adjustments which, along with the precise control of fine movement mediated via the pyramidal tracts, permits coordinated purposeful muscle activity. For example, when inserting a key into a key hole, the pyramidal system regulates precise fine movements of the wrist, hand, and fingers, and the grosser movements of the arms, shoulder, and trunk are extrapyramidal in origin. The extrapyramidal system superimposes its control over the motor organization of the spinal reflexes.

table 7-2
SOME MAJOR
SPINAL TRACTS

SPINAL TRACT	FUNCTION
Funiculus gracilis ⎱ Funiculus cuneatus ⎰	Transmit muscle and joint sensations to brain
Lateral spinothalamic tract	Transmit pain and temperature sensation to brain
Ventral spinothalamic tract	Transmit touch sensation to brain
Ventral spinocerebellar tract	Transmit impulses to cerebellum via pons and medulla
Rubrospinal tract	Transmit coordinating signal from cerebellum via red nucleus
Pyramidal tract	Transmit motor signal from cortex to lower motor neuron
Tectospinal tract	Transmit optic and auditory motor signals

This control is mediated by two types of fibers: those that increase the degree of muscle contraction by facilitating or enhancing the inputs to the motor neurons and those that decrease the degree of muscle contraction by inhibiting or suppressing inputs to the motor neurons. If the motor neurons to the extensor muscles are facilitated, there is a simultaneous reciprocal inhibition of the motor neurons to the flexor muscles. These facilitating and inhibitory fibers, which originate in the brain stem reticular activating system, are in turn controlled by a multitude of inputs from higher motor centers (for example, cerebellum, motor cortex, and basal ganglia). The complex circuitry, while not fully understood, does insure smoothly integrated motor control. Extrapyramidal fibers are also involved in external emotional expression (originating in the limbic system); thus automatic expressions signifying pleasure, anxiety, fear, anger, or disgust are due to extrapyramidal impulses to the facial musculature.

limbic system or
the visceral brain

The cerebral cortex sets man apart from other animals, but the older parts of the brain, particularly those that in earlier evolutionary history had to do with smell (olfaction), play a major role in human behavior. One feature of the evolutionary processes is that old structures are not discarded but are modified and new structures are added. The *rhinencephalon,* the old olfactory brain (part of the forebrain), and its associated structures appear to be involved with the emotional state motivation and experience. Behaviors that have to do with preservation of the species (sex, maternal, and defense of young) or with the preservation of the individual (hunger, thirst, fight, and flight) are part of this system. Because the limbic system coordinates sensory inputs with visceral or bodily reactions and needs, it is sometimes called the *visceral brain.*

Emotion is a state of mental excitement, arousal, heightened awareness, and changes in feeling (affect). The neuroanatomic basis for emotions is a circuit of structure and fiber tracts collectively referred to as

figure 7-20

THE PYRAMIDAL SYSTEM

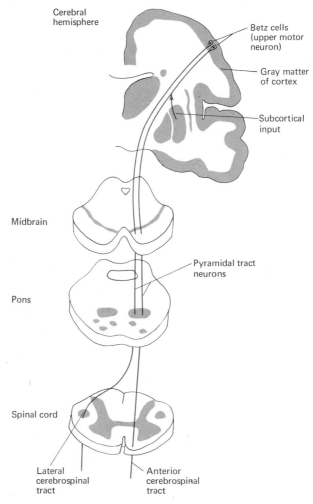

The pyramidal system showing the pathway for precise voluntary motor acts. Note that the fibers crossover or decussate; thus the right motor cortex controls lower motor neurons on the left.

the *limbic system*. It involves neurons of the *cingulate gyrus* of the cortex, the *hippocampus, fornix, amygdaloid nuclei, anterior thalamus, rhinencephalon,* and *hypothalamus* (see Figure 7-22). The limbic system and cerebral cortical association areas interact, and thus the limbic system sets the emotional background for man's intellectual functioning.

The functional localization of emotion is difficult to delineate anatomically. Lesions in any number of points in the pathway—for example, hypothalamus, frontal, or temporal lobes—may produce rage, hypersexuality, a ravenous appetite, and pleasure reactions. Damage to or

figure 7-21

THE EXTRA-
PYRAMIDAL
SYSTEM

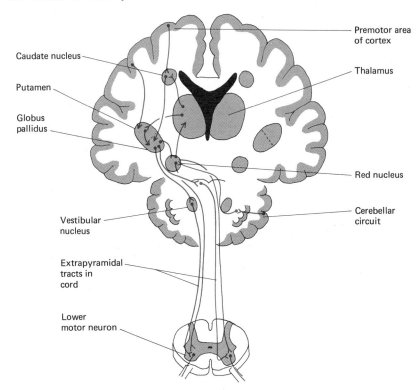

Caudate nucleus

Putamen

Globus
pallidus

Vestibular
nucleus

Extrapyramidal
tracts in
cord

Lower
motor neuron

Premotor area
of cortex

Thalamus

Red nucleus

Cerebellar
circuit

**The extrapyramidal system showing pathway responsible for postural adjust-
ments and less precise movements.**

stimulation of other loci in the limbic circuit may evoke loss of appetite, anxiety, fear, escape behavior, and hyposexuality. The degree of altered emotion is dependent on both site and extent of the lesion. It is thought that many psychoactive drugs, tranquilizers, and energizers have their effect in the limbic system. The final common pathway of this limbic system is the hypothalamus or "head office" of the autonomic nervous system. Together, all these interconnecting structures interact harmoniously "subserving the emotional state."

**factors
influencing
function**

environment

The brain, like other organ systems, is continually affected by the environment, and the effects may not be transient, but etched permanently in the behavioral patterns of the individual. There is, in other words, a continuity of development, and at all stages the brain is affected by a multitude of physiological and psychological inputs. These experiences influence the development of the brain, the establishment of new synapses, learning, memory, emotions, and motivation. There is no functional separation between innate (genetic) and learned (nurtured by environment) behavior. Thus many neural malfunctions, neuroses, and psychoses have both biological and environmental components that are inextricably interwoven.

figure 7-22
THE LIMBIC
SYSTEM

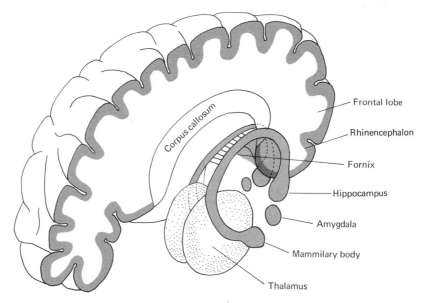

The limbic system in cutaway showing some of the major anatomical components of the primitive visceral bràin. Functional localization is difficult; thus a given behavior such as rage may involve a number of different limbic structures. The final common pathway for many responses controlled by the limbic system is the hypothalamus.

The nervous system may respond to stress (any environmental upset) in a variety of predictable ways referred to as *coping behavior.* Coping behavior involves a number of physiological changes such as the release of adrenalin and corticosterone (a hormone from the adrenal gland); changes in blood sugar, heart rate, blood pressure; gastrointestinal activity; and changes in arousal and motor activity, which appropriately deal with the stress. On the other hand, some stresses are not adequately coped with and result in *psychosomatic* symptoms such as *displacement activity,* transfer of behavior to an inappropriate target, and *neurotic* or *psycho*neurotic behavior. The forms of stress are highly varied. They may be subtle as decision making or severe as sensory deprivation. Depriving the brain of a myriad of normal sensory inputs can produce a severe emotional upset, hallucination, and disorientation. Infants and children raised in sensory-deprived environments may also have stunted growth. Similarly, emotional trauma, sensory overload, noise, overcrowding, frustration, and pain may also precipitate or trigger abnormal behavior and loss of control.

physicochemical factors   A number of physicochemical factors may markedly influence brain function. The brain is particularly sensitive to alteration in carbon dioxide concentration, blood sugar levels, oxygen concentration, pH, and ionic balance. Because of its active metabolism, the brain needs a constant supply of oxygen and sugar. A mild decrease in blood sugar evokes feelings of fatigue. A significant decrease will cause unconsciousness, convulsions, and coma. Oxygen is probably the most critical element for normal brain function, and even a brief decrease of blood flow to the brain causes dizziness (abrupt sitting up in bed or standing after squatting). A further decrease in blood supply to the brain causes *syncope*, that is, loss of consciousness. Depriving the brain of oxygen even for short periods of time may result in extensive death of neurons with severe intellectual, motor, and sensory impairment, leaving the person in a permanent vegetablelike state. Brain anoxia for long periods can result in death.

Carbon dioxide, even in low concentrations, is essential for maintaining normal central nervous system excitability; hence even the oxygen used for resuscitation contains 5 percent carbon dioxide. High concentrations of carbon dioxide disrupt brain function. Carbon dioxide concentration is of particular importance in regulating cardiovascular and respiratory control centers and is also important in the autoregulation of cerebral circulation.

Another factor influencing function is the concentration of ions. Ionic balance is essential to all tissue, but is of particular importance in the neuromuscular system. Any disease that seriously disrupts electrolyte balance of sodium, potassium, calcium, and chloride ions can cause tremors, convulsions, coma, and even death. Certain hypothalamic neurons act as *osmoreceptors* responding to changes in blood and salt concentrations and osmotic pressure.

biological A number of hormones modify the function of the central nervous system. The hypothalamus, in particular, is under feedback control of sex hormones, thyroid hormone, and some adrenal hormones. As the hormone level increases, the production or release (or both) of *hypothalamic releasing factors* is inhibited.

clinical considerations

epilepsy *Epilepsy* is due to a sudden and excessive burst of high-frequency electrical activity in some part of the brain. If motor areas are involved, there can be severe convulsions associated with the seizure. In most seizures there is some variation in the state of consciousness. Of epileptics studied on autopsy, 63 percent reveal a focal brain abnormality and have a history of head injury or inflammation of nerve tissues. Genetic factors apparently are also involved as suggested by the finding that identical twins show a concordance of 60 percent; that is, if one twin has epilepsy, the other will also show the abnormality 60 times out of 100.

syncope and coma *Syncope* or fainting, a brief loss of consciousness, can result from a sudden burst of emotions or an event that causes a transient decrease in brain blood supply. Coma is a prolonged loss of consciousness, and its causes are diverse.

cerebral palsy and other palsies *Cerebral palsy* is characterized by *spastic* shaking movements and loss of motor control. It is usually due to a focal brain damage occurring at birth or in early childhood. A number of other palsies exist, such as *Parkinson's disease*, which are often seen years after recovery from viral encephalitis.

demyelinating
diseases

Any disease that causes a loss of myelin will obviously cause "short circuits" of neural events. The most insidious of the demyelinating diseases is *multiple sclerosis,* a progressive disease possibly of viral origin that produces tremors, palsies, speech disturbances, weakness, and eventually death.

aphasias and
ataxia

Disorders of language function, the ability to comprehend or vocalize, are called *aphasias.* The cause can be any event that damages neurons in a speech motor area or sensory association area. The meanings of words are seen, heard, or spoken in an incomprehensible way; concept is lost. Even deaf mutes reading by braille have suffered aphasias (loss of ability to read with the fingers).

Diseases in the cerebellum or cerebellar tracts result in incoordinated movement called *ataxia.* Part of the problem is because the person cannot predict the extent of his muscular actions or judge distances.

stroke

A cerebral vascular accident or *stroke* is any serious disruption of circulation to the brain, usually from a thrombus or hemorrhage. The loss of circulation results in death of irreplaceable neurons and may cause severe defects depending on the extent of the damage. The symptoms are most severe during the initial stages when inflammation and pressure changes affect nearby undamaged neurons. With the passage of time, as inflammation subsides and the dead tissues are phagocytized, there is often a partial or complete return of function.

headaches

Head pains are frequent in most organic disease states, but the vast majority of headaches are *functional* due to tension or stress. The tension headache pain is constant and often results from fatigue or ischemia of the extracranial head and neck muscles. Such headaches respond well to mild analgesics such as aspirin. *Migraine* headaches are due to intracranial dilation of blood vessels and are characterized by a pulsating pain usually on one side of the head. The symptoms are complex, and the headache is often preceded by some *prodromal sensory change* (a predictive smell or a sound). The headaches tend to be recurrent and often are associated with nausea and other gastrointestinal symptoms, ocular symptoms, or sinus symptoms.

bacterial and
viral infections

A number of bacteria and viruses affect the central nervous system. The so-called *neurotropic viruses,* such as *poliomyelitis virus,* affect spinal cord motor neurons and will produce paralysis of muscles affected by these nerves. Even the cold sore virus, *Herpes simplex,* is a potentially lethal substance in the brain. Thus any virus that causes inflammation of the brain, *encephalitis,* or inflammation of the meninges, *meningitis,* produces a variety of motor and sensory disturbances such as somnolence (drowsiness), coma, convulsions, and death.

drugs and
brain chemistry

In addition to acetylcholine a number of other *synaptic transmitters* (chemical messengers) are found in the brain. Of particular importance are *serotonin* and *norepinephrine,* which are transmitters found in highest concentration in those portions of the brain having to do with

table 7-3
SOME MAJOR
PSYCHOPHARMA-
COLOGIC AGENTS

CHEMICAL NAME AND STRUCTURE	SOURCE	COMMENTS
$CH_2CH_2NH_2$ Mescaline CH_3O CH_3O CH_3O	Tops of dumpling cactus *Andalonium williamsii,* also synthetic	Hallucinatory sensation mostly visual, sometimes restlessness and anxiety, sometimes nausea and vomiting
CH_3 H_2C—C—NH_2 H Amphetamine	A synthetic product	In low-to-moderate doses, a CNS stimulant; enhances alertness, causes euphoria, inhibits appetite and sleep. In very high doses may be hallucinogenic
C_2H_5 CON—C_2H_5 NCH_3 N H LSD (lysergic acid diethylamide)	From fungus ergot, *Claviceps purpurea,* also synthetic	Euphoria, loss of logic, vivid hallucinations, most potent of known hallucinogens; some panic reactions
H N Psilocybin O—$PO(OH)_2$	From mushroom *Psilocybe mexicana,* also synthetic	Sense of unreality, visual and auditory hallucinations, euphoria, depersonalization
CH_3 OH C_5H_{11} C—O CH_3 CH_3 Tetrahydrocannabinol	Leaves and fruiting tops of female hemp plant *Cannabis sativa*	Euphoria, tension release, sometimes drowsiness

TWO NORMAL SYNAPTIC TRANSMITTERS FOUND IN THE CNS

H
HO—C—CH_2NH_3

OH

OH

Norepinephrine

OH—   —$CH_2CH_2NH_2$

N

Serotonin

emotion and attention. Any drug that (a) enhances the release of these transmitters, (b) inhibits the breakdown of these transmitters, or (c) blocks the action of these transmitters will produce alterations in brain function and behavior. Compounds that alter behavior are called *psychopharmacologic drugs* and can be further classified as (a) *tranquilizers* or *ataraxic drugs*, which decrease anxiety; (b) *antidepressants*, which alleviate mood swings; (c) *psychoenergizers*, which produce arousal, euphoria (elation), sleeplessness, and inhibit appetite; (d) *hallucinogens*, which produce sensory imagery and dreamlike distortion of perception; and (e) *narcotics*, which alleviate pain and induce sedation and sleep. Some of the more commonly used psychoactive drugs are shown in Table 7-3 along with their chemical structures. It can be seen that many of these drugs have chemical structures similar to the normal brain transmitters serotonin or norepinephrine, also shown in Table 7-3.

These drugs may be administered many ways: orally, inhaling or sniffing, subcutaneously (*skin popping*), or by intravenous injection (*main lining*). As with most drugs, there is the development of *tolerance* with repeated exposure; that is, the sensation to a given amount of drug is diminished. With the development of tolerance, the user must use increasingly large amounts of the drug to attain the same effect. Many drugs do not cause true addiction — the development of a physiological craving, which if not satisfied will cause severe *withdrawal symptoms*, cramps, nausea, hysteria, and pain. All of the opiates (heroin, morphine, and cocaine) and some barbiturates cause addiction on repeated exposure. However, the nonaddictive drugs, although not causing true addiction, may be habit forming; that is, the user develops a strong psychological dependence on them.

A variety of psychoactive agents used in concert may interact in *synergistic fashion*; that is, in combination the effects of each are multiplied. This enhancing characteristic of drugs in combination may produce extreme responses and even death. For example, both alcohol and barbiturates depress the brain's respiratory centers. If a nonlethal amount of barbiturate and a nonlethal dose of alcohol are taken close together, the result may be fatal.

Ethyl alcohol, probably the oldest and most common psychoactive agent, is a mild central nervous system depressant. In small amounts it can produce euphoria and loss of inhibitions, but in higher concentration it causes loss of motor control, nausea, vomiting, loss of equilibrium, aggressiveness, and unconsciousness.

other chemical factors affecting the brain

A number of metallic organic compounds, such as *methyl mercury*, specifically affect the brain. Recent evidence from Japan, Canada, and Scandinavia has shown cases of severe neurologic defects and death due to repeated ingestion of fish containing methyl mercury in high concentration. Other metallic substances are known to affect mood. For example, *lithium salts* can be beneficial in the treatment of depression.

summary

1. Brain: a gelatinous 3-pound mass of nervous tissue and blood vessels well protected by bone and surrounding membranes; divided into five major anatomical components

gross anatomy

(a) telencephalon: composed of two large cerebral hemispheres divided by the longitudinal fissure; surface is folded into furrows or sulci; two hemispheres are connected to each other by a giant fiber tract, the corpus collosum; each hemisphere has a thin outer bark of nerve cell bodies, the cortex (gray matter), and a mass of white myelinated fibers (white matter); imbedded in the white matter are aggregates of neurons (nuclei); the hemispheres have internal fluid-filled cavities, the ventricles

(b) diencephalon: almost surrounded by the cerebral hemispheres is a hollow structure whose walls surround the third ventricle; composed of epithalamus, thalamus and hypothalamus, below which is attached the pituitary gland

(c) mesencephalon: small region made up of four corpora quadrigemina involved in relaying auditory and visual signals; superficial origin of III and IV cranial nerves

(d) metencephalon: part of the brain stem made up of a large convoluted cerebellum having external gray matter (cortex) and inner white matter; pons, a bulging ventral mass of fiber tracts, makes up the remainder of the metencephalon; superficial origin of the IV to VIII cranial nerves

(e) myelencephalon: the lowest segment of the brain stem, the medulla, connects the rest of the brain to the spinal column; surrounds the fourth ventricle; superficial origin of the IX to XII cranial nerves

2. Spinal cord
   (a) tapering hollow tube composed of fibers and neurons with a bony canal formed by the vertebrae
   (b) two bulges in cord are formed at the level where the nerves to arms and legs emerge from the cord
   (c) at regular intervals, pairs of spinal nerves emerge

3. Meninges: three membranes that surround the cord and brain are:
   (a) dura mater (outermost)
   (b) arachnoid (middle)
   (c) pia mater (innermost)

4. Ventricles and cerebrospinal fluid
   (a) hollow interconnecting spaces within the brain are called ventricles and are filled with cerebrospinal fluid (CSF), which forms continually by the choroid plexus, a vascularized tissue overlying the fourth ventricle.
   (b) fluid maintains an intracranial pressure within the ventricles and around the brain and cord; the arachnoid villi absorb CSF and help maintain intracranial pressure

cellular and tissue specializations

1. Cerebrum (telencephalon)
   (a) cortex composed of six layers of a variety of neuronal types, some with as many as 100,000 interconnections; in addition to neurons, there are 10 times as many neuroglia (glia) which form the insulative material myelin, while other glia play a supportive role for the neurons
   (b) collections of nerve fibers form tracts or pathways carrying neural information from area to area
   (c) many subcortical nuclei made up of nerve cell bodies subserving specific functions

2. Diencephalon: collection of nuclei and fiber tracts whose neurons integrate sensory information, particularly pain (thalamus), and control most autonomic or visceral functions (hypothalamus)

3. Mesencephalon: contains a dense network of neurons and fibers that extend up in the brain stem to the diencephalon and play a major modulatory role in the rest of the nervous system

4. Metencephalon: cerebellar cortex contains certain enormously branching Purkinje cells and several layers of smaller neurons involved in coordinating muscular activities

5. Myelencephalon: not only composed of ascending and descending fiber tracts, but contains concentrations of neurons regulating vital functions such as heart rate, blood flow, and respiration

6. Spinal cord
   (a) inner gray matter forms an H shape
   (b) sensory information is carried in via the dorsal root ganglion, and motor neurons are located in the ventral horn of the gray matter
   (c) association neurons relay and integrate sensory signal, and there are a large number of ascending and descending fiber tracts

physiology

1. Telencephalon
   (a) can be functionally divided into well-defined cortical regions, each subserving a specific function
   (b) motor cortex: controls precise voluntary muscle movements; topographical cortical representation correspond to points on the body; regions have finest motor control (hands, mouth, and lips) have the greatest central representation
   (c) sensory areas: localized areas process incoming sensory signals; somathesis (body sense), hearing, vision, smell, and taste are centrally represented in proportion to peripheral receptor concentrations
   (d) association areas: here resides man's ability to learn, remember, solve problems, and reason logically; incoming sensory information is relayed from sensory areas for integration and perception; association areas exert strong influence over all lower centers of the brain
   (e) basal ganglia: collections of subcortical nuclei essential for coordinating muscle movement

2. Diencephalon
   (a) thalamus: sensory inflow from spinal cord relayed to cortex via thalamocortical tracts; rich fiber connections with hypothalamus and basal ganglia suggest that the thalamus acts as a major selective relay station between upper and lower parts of the central nervous system
   (b) hypothalamus: the 15 or so pairs of nuclei which make up hypothalamus control and integrate the autonomic nervous system and regulate activity of both anterior and posterior pituitary; centers include those for rage-passivity, body temperature, thirst, appetite and satiation, water and electrolyte

balance, and a spectrum of visceral responses associated with approach and avoidance behavior

3. Mesencephalon
    (a) visual perception and auditory reflex information relayed to higher centers; accessory respiratory centers located in the pons, ventral portion of mesencephalon and myelencephalon; red nucleus here involved in motor coordination along with basal ganglia and cerebellum
    (b) the reticular activating system: actually extends into diencephalon and acts to integrate sensory signals and modify activity of other parts of brain selectively enhancing or suppressing sensory inflow; controls sleep-wake states; produces general arousal and focused attention, ascending influences effect hypothalamus cerebral cortex and cerebellum, while descending influences regulate muscle reflexes in spinal cord

4. Metencephalon (cerebellum)
    (a) collection of feedback loops involved in postural adjustments and motor coordination
    (b) major functions include maintenance of equilibrium, postural reflexes, which in turn regulate stretch reflexes in extensor muscles and coordination of purposeful voluntary movements

5. Myelencephalon (medulla oblongata) conducts both ascending and descending information and contains vital centers regulating
    (a) heart
    (b) the blood vessels and blood flow
    (c) gastrointestinal tract and
    (d) respiration (along with centers in the pons)

6. Spinal cord: made up of ascending and descending fiber tracts. Lower motor neurons in ventral horn of the gray matter are final common pathway to skeletal muscle; reflex activity independent of higher centers found here
    (a) motor pathways
    pyramidal system: upper motor neurons in motor cortex control precise motor acts by descending signals in this tract; fibers cross over to opposite side; thus right motor cortex controls the left side.
    extrapyramidal system: a diffuse collection of fibers integrates descending motor activities from cortex to basal ganglia, cerebellum reticular activating system, and red nucleus; controls large automatic movements and postural adjustments by selective enhancing or suppressing inputs
    (b) limbic system: a diffuse collection of structure derived from the old olfactory system (rhinencephalon) involved in primitive behaviors associated with basic drive, aggression, hunger, sex, and other motivated behaviors and emotional states; produces directed behavior patterns and regulates visceral responses. Composed of cingulate gyrus of cortex, hippocampus, fornix, amygdala, thalamus, rhinencephalon, and the hypothalamus, which is the final common pathway for motivated states and visceral responses

factors influencing function

1. Environment: from early development of the brain throughout the organisms' history, the environment molds the brain circuits; a variety of factors such as early experience, dietary protein (first four years), toxins, and viruses can markedly affect later brain function and behavior.

2. Physicochemical factors: the brain is highly sensitive to changes in pH, carbon dioxide concentration, oxygen concentration, and blood sugar levels.

3. Biological: a number of hormones can affect the limbic system and behavior

clinical considerations

1. Epilepsy: abnormal sudden discharge of uncoordinated brain electrical activity usually associated with some type of brain damage; motor epilepsy produces seizures (convulsions) and loss of consciousness

2. Syncope and coma: fainting, loss of consciousness due to drop-in brain blood flow; prolonged deprivation of oxygen and sugar to brain causes prolonged unconsciousness of coma

3. Cerebral palsy and other palsies: loss of voluntary motor control due to localized brain damage induced by drugs, trauma, or viral injection of brain; characterized by spastic discoordinated motor movements

4. Demyelinating diseases: progressive virallike infection, which destroys the myelin insulating material, short-circuits brain pathways, causing tremors, palsy, weakness, sensory disruptions, and eventually death

5. Aphasia and ataxia: disorders in language and motor function associated with localized brain damage

6. Stroke: disruption of brain blood flow usually due to thrombus or hemorrhage; causes localized irreversible brain damage; partial recovery with time in some cases as undamaged neurons take over role of dead neurons

7. Headaches: most frequent organic disease usually associated with stress and lack of blood flow through head and neck muscles; migraine headaches are associated with intracranial dilation of blood vessels

8. Bacterial and viral infections: many viruses (neurotropic viruses), such as poliomyelitis and Herpes simplex, specifically affect neurons, producing inflammation and neuronal death

9. Drugs and brain chemistry: a number of drugs, which either enhance or inhibit synthesis breakdown and release of brain transmitter substances, can alter behavior; sedatives, narcotics, hallucinogens, energizers, antidepressants, and tranquilizers have medicinal uses, but are frequently abused when taken in excessive amounts.

10. Other chemical factors: neurons are particularly sensitive to a number of metals, such as mercury and lead, which cause irreversible brain damage

8

peripheral nervous system and reflex activity

gross anatomy
cranial nerves
spinal nerves
autonomic nervous system

cellular specialization
cell bodies in spinal cord

physiology
autonomic nervous system

control
autonomic control centers

reflex activity
reflex arc
cord reflexes
conditioned reflex
autonomic reflexes

clinical considerations
visceral pain
referred pain

The separation of the nervous system into central and peripheral systems is an artifact and exists only to make this complex subject easier to examine. The reader must have in mind that the nervous system is continuous, which is why integration can take place. The previous chapter has numerous examples of how information is handled by the central nervous system, especially by the higher nervous centers in the brain. In this chapter, the mechanisms involved with handling information in the peripheral nervous system will be discussed and how simple decision making is accomplished by the reflex arc.

The peripheral nervous system encompasses the cranial nerves, the spinal nerves, and the autonomic nervous system. The bundles of nerve fibers that constitute the peripheral nerves can be most easily thought of as an electric cable in which the individual axons may be insulated by a sheath (*neurilemma*) with or without myelin and covered by the connective tissue *endoneurium.* A number of individually "wrapped" axons are then enclosed in the *perineurium,* and one bundle to many bundles are then enclosed in the outermost covering, the *epineurium* (Figure 8-1).

gross anatomy

The term *afferent* or *sensory* is used to describe nerves that carry impulses to the central nervous system, and the term *efferent* or *motor* is used to describe nerves that are carrying impulses away from the central nervous system. Motor nerves excite muscles or glands.

cranial nerves

The cranial nerves originate in the brain and extend to the structure they innervate through the foramina in the skull; the nerves are either sen-

figure 8-1

ARRANGEMENT
OF NERVE AXONS
IN PERIPHERAL
NERVE BUNDLES

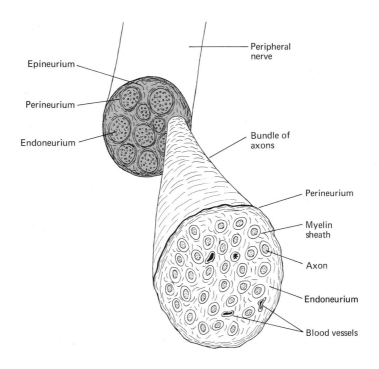

Epineurium

Perineurium

Endoneurium

Peripheral nerve

Bundle of axons

Perineurium

Myelin sheath

Axon

Endoneurium

Blood vessels

table 8-1
CRANIAL NERVES
AND THEIR
FUNCTIONS

NUMBER	NAME	SENSORY FUNCTION	MOTOR FUNCTION
I	Olfactory	Smell	
II	Optic	Vision	
III	Oculomotor	Proprioception	Eye movement, accommodation, regulation of pupil size
IV	Trochlear	Proprioception	Eye movement
V	Trigeminal	Sensations of head	Muscles for chewing
VI	Abducens	Proprioception	Eye movement
VII	Facial	Taste, muscles of facial expression (muscle sense)	Muscles of facial expression, salivary gland secretion
VIII	Acoustic	Equilibrium and hearing	
IX	Glossopharyngeal	Taste, carotid sinus (cardiac reflex)	Swallowing, salivary gland, secretion
X	Vagus	Sensations concerned with heart, peristalsis, respiration	Swallowing, speech, inhibition of heart, constriction of respiratory structures, peristalsis, secretion of digestive glands
XI	Accessory	Shoulder muscles (muscle sense)	Shoulder and head motion, speech
XII	Hypoglossal	Tongue (muscle sense)	Tongue movement

sory, motor, or mixed. As the brain is a highly evolved structure, it is not surprising that the cranial nerves have a somewhat complex arrangement superimposed on the basic pattern. However, the pattern of sensory nerve cell bodies located in peripheral ganglion and motor nerve cell bodies located in the brain is maintained throughout the system of cranial nerves.

There are 12 cranial nerves that are numbered (Roman numerals) as well as named. Table 8-1 summarizes the pertinent information on the cranial nerves, and Figure 8-2 shows their anatomy.

I. Olfactory   The olfactory nerve, responsible for the sense of smell, is a purely sensory nerve. The cell bodies lie outside the brain proper, and the fibers extend to the olfactory epithelium covering part of the nasal septum and most of the superior concha. The fibers form about 20 small bundles that pass through openings in the *cribiform plate* of the *ethmoid* bone and extend to the olfactory bulb. Here they synapse with neurons whose axons constitute the *olfactory tract*, ending in the cerebrum.

II. Optic   The optic nerve too is a purely sensory nerve with cell bodies in the retina of the eye and axons passing through the *optic foramina* to enter the *optic chiasma*. Here fibers from the medial half of the eye cross to the opposite side and the fibers from the lateral side continue on the same side, thus forming the two optic tracts. Most fibers pass to the visual

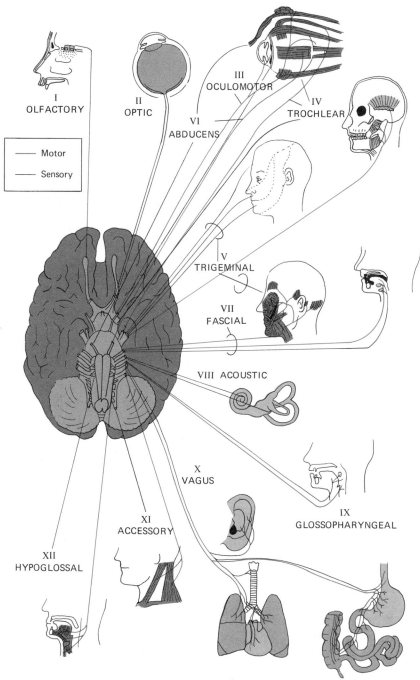

figure 8-2
THE CRANIAL
NERVES

—— Motor

—— Sensory

I
OLFACTORY

II
OPTIC

III
OCULOMOTOR

IV
TROCHLEAR

VI
ABDUCENS

V
TRIGEMINAL

VII
FASCIAL

VIII ACOUSTIC

X
VAGUS

XI
ACCESSORY

IX
GLOSSOPHARYNGEAL

XII
HYPOGLOSSAL

area of the occipital lobe. Some fibers synapse with neurons that control
the eye muscles and with neurons controlling the ciliary muscles that
regulate the amount of light reaching the retina.

III. Oculomotor   The oculomotor nerve controls the movement of all the *extrinsic* muscles of the eye except the *superior oblique* and the *lateral rectus*, which are under the control of the IV and VI cranial nerves, respectively. In addition there are sensory fibers from proprioceptors and fibers that synapse with neurons in the *ciliary ganglion* controlling the muscle responsible for iris constriction and the accommodation of the lens. The nerve emerges from the cerebrum near the pons and courses forward dividing into superior and inferior branches. The superior branch innervates the *superior rectus* and *levator palpebral* muscles; the inferior branch innervates the *medial* and *inferior rectus* and *inferior oblique* muscles.

IV. Trochlear   The trochlear nerve, the smallest of the cranial nerves, arises at the midbrain and innervates the *superior oblique* eye muscles. Sensory fibers from proprioceptors on the muscle are also present in the nerve.

V. Trigeminal   The trigeminal nerve is the largest of the cranial nerves and, as the name implies, has three branches: the *opthalmic, maxillary,* and *mandibular* branches. Its function is mainly sensory, carrying impulses from receptors in various parts of the head for temperature, touch, and pain. Efferent fibers control the mastication (chewing) muscles.

VI. Abducens   Arising from the pons, the abducens nerve supplies motor fibers to the *lateral rectus muscle* of the eye and carries sensory fibers from proprioceptors.

VII. Facial   The facial nerve is a mixed nerve supplying efferent fibers to the facial and scalp muscles as well as to certain glands. There are also afferent fibers from the taste buds on the anterior two-thirds of the tongue. The nerve emerges from the pons through the stylomastoid foramen.

VIII. Acoustic   The acoustic nerve is a purely sensory nerve providing for hearing and equilibrium. There are two main branches. First, the *cochlear nerve* receives impulses from the organ of Corti in the cochlea of the middle ear. The cell bodies of these sensory fibers synapse with neurons whose fibers then run to the medulla. Eventually the sensations pass through the midbrain to the temporal cortex (hearing center).

The second main branch, the *vestibular nerve,* has afferent fibers with endings in the inner ear. Fibers from the ganglion extend to the vestibular nuclei in the medulla. Connections are made with the cerebellum, and equilibrium is maintained by integrating signals from the vestibular area, from the eyes, and from the proprioceptors of the muscles, tendons, and joints.

IX. Glossopharyngeal   The glossopharyngeal nerve is a mixed nerve with efferent fibers that are involved with the control of swallowing and blood pressure. The nerve arises from the side of the medulla and has sensory branches from the pharynx, tonsils, and posterior third of the tongue, as well as from the carotid sinus. The latter structure plays a major role in control of blood pressure.

X. Vagus   The vagus nerve is a mixed nerve extending as far as the large intestine with innervation to many structures, including afferent fibers from mucous membranes of the pharynx, larynx, trachea, and parts of the digestive system. The cell bodies of the afferent fibers are in the jugular ganglion and the nodose ganglion located in and just below the jugular foramen, respectively. Efferent fibers having their origin in the medulla run to the autonomic ganglia and control involuntary activities in the pharynx, larynx, heart, and digestive system.

XI. Accessory   The accessory nerve is a motor nerve with two origins. The *bulbar* portion arises in the medulla and innervates the muscles of the pharynx, larynx, and soft palate. The *spinal* portion arises from the upper five or six segments of the spinal cord and passes up through the foramen magnum, joins with the bulbar portion of the nerve, and exits via the jugular foramen to supply the sternocleidomastoid and the trapezius muscles.

XII. Hypoglossal   The hypoglossal is a motor nerve that arises in the medulla and supplies the tongue muscles.

figure 8-3

SPINAL NERVES

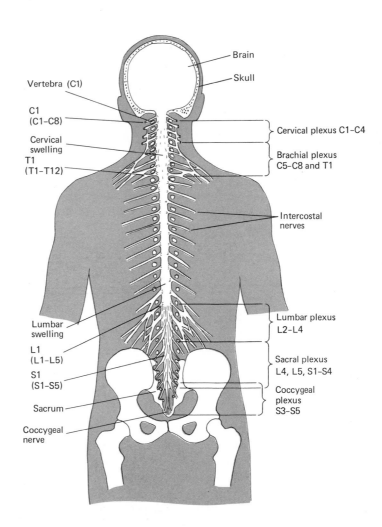

Brain

Skull

Vertebra (C1)

C1
(C1–C8)

Cervical
swelling

T1
(T1–T12)

Cervical plexus C1–C4

Brachial plexus
C5–C8 and T1

Intercostal
nerves

Lumbar
swelling

L1
(L1–L5)

S1
(S1–S5)

Sacrum

Coccygeal
nerve

Lumbar plexus
L2–L4

Sacral plexus
L4, L5, S1–S4

Coccygeal
plexus
S3–S5

spinal nerves The 31 pairs of spinal nerves pass out through the intervertebral foramina and are numbered according to the corresponding vertebrae (Figure 8-3). The first spinal nerve exits between the atlas and the skull and is the first of the cervical nerves (C1). There are eight cervical nerves and seven cervical vertebrae; thus the eighth passes out between the seventh cervical and the first thoracic vertebra. The thoracic (12), lumbar (5), sacral (5), and coccygeal (1) nerves pass out below their corresponding vertebrae.

Spinal nerves are mixed in that they all contain four major components:

1. Somatic afferent – sensory information such as temperature and pressure.
2. Somatic efferent – motor impulses to skeletal muscles.
3. Visceral afferent – sensory information such as blood pressure and heart rate.
4. Visceral efferent – also called *autonomic system;* motor impulses to secretory tissue and to smooth muscle of the viscera.

The spinal nerves arise from the spinal cord by two roots, the *dorsal root,* generally the larger of the two, and the *ventral root* (Figure 8-4). The dorsal root contains only sensory fibers, whereas the ventral contains only motor fibers. Present on the dorsal root is the *dorsal root ganglion,* which is sheathed by the dura mater. The ganglion lies in the vertebral canal except for the ganglia of the first and second cervical nerves, which lie on the arches of their corresponding vertebrae. The fibers of the two roots meet as they pass through the intervertebral foramina to form the spinal nerve, which after a short distance divides into four branches or *rami* (singular, *ramus*). There is a small autonomic branch that joins with a chain of ganglia (see autonomic nervous system); this ramus has two parts: a *white ramus,* which contains myelinated preganglionic neurons, and a *gray ramus,* which consists of postganglionic fibers that return to the spinal nerve to be distributed by way of the major ventral and dorsal rami (Figure 8-4). The ventral rami

figure 8-4

GENERAL
PATTERN OF
SPINAL NERVE
CONNECTIONS

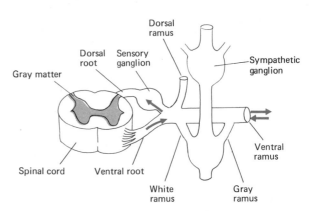

supply the anterior and lateral aspects of the skin and skeletal muscles and are involved in the formation of the large nerve network or plexuses that are present in upper (cervical, brachial) and lower (lumbosacral) regions. The dorsal rami innervate the skin and muscles of the posterior regions of the body. The fourth branch of each spinal nerve is the small *meningeal*, which innervates the meninges.

The cutaneous branches of the dorsal and ventral rami innervate the skin in such a way that it is possible to designate innervated areas as *dermatomes*. The dermatomes overlap, so that injury to one of the spinal nerves leads only to a small loss of sensory area. Not every spinal nerve has cutaneous branches. For example, the ventral rami of the fifth cervical to the first thoracic nerves and from the second lumbar to the second sacral nerves do not supply the skin. Cutaneous branches from other spinal nerves cover the areas not innervated by the nerves mentioned above.

Only in the thoracic region do the spinal nerve rami maintain their segmental nature, since they supply the intercostal muscles. In the other regions of the body, the spinal nerve ventral rami form the large *cervical, brachial,* and *lumbosacral plexuses* (a plexus is network of nerves).

The *cervical plexus* results from the union of the ventral rami of the first four cervical nerves (*C1* through *C4*). The resulting union produces the *lesser occipital,* the *great auricular,* the *transverse, supraclavicular,* and the *phrenic nerves* (Figure 8-3). The first four supply the neck and back of the skull, and the phrenic nerve sends motor fibers to the diaphragm and contains sensory elements from the pericardium and pleura.

The *brachial plexus* is formed from the ventral rami of the fifth, sixth, seventh, and eighth cervical nerves and the first thoracic (*C5* through

figure 8-5

ORGANIZATION OF THE PERIPHERAL NERVES IN THE BRACHIAL PLEXUS

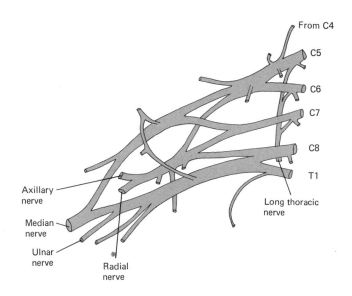

From C4

C5

C6

C7

C8

T1

Axillary nerve

Median nerve

Ulnar nerve

Radial nerve

Long thoracic nerve

C8 and *T1*). The plexus innervates the muscles of the upper part of the body, and the *ulnar, radial, musculocutaneous,* and *median* nerves are the main branches (Figure 8-5).

The *lumbar plexus* is formed from the ventral rami of the first four lumbar nerves and a portion of the twelfth thoracic (*L1* through *L4* and *T12*). The main branches, the *femoral, lateral cutaneous,* and *obdurate* nerves of the lumbar plexus, supply the muscles of the upper leg (Figure 8-6).

The *sacral plexus* is formed from the ventral rami of the first four sacral nerves (*S1* through *S3*), which join to form the *sciatic* nerve, the

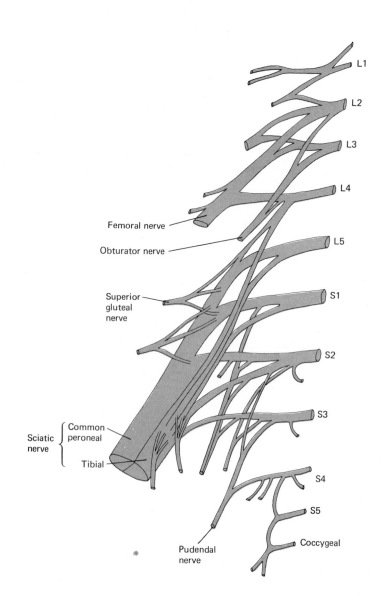

figure 8-6

ORGANIZATION
OF THE
PERIPHERAL
NERVES IN THE
LUMBOSACRAL
PLEXUS

largest of the spinal nerves. The plexus innervates the muscles of the posterior portion of the thigh, leg, and foot (Figure 8-6).

autonomic
nervous
system

The autonomic nervous system controls the *vegetative* or *visceral* functions, such as blood pressure, sweating, body temperature, and other activities that are characterized by lack of conscious control. Sensations of thirst, hunger, sexual feelings, urge to urinate, and sleepiness are examples of *autonomic* sensations. The name autonomic means *due to internal causes or influences.* (Module 8)

The autonomic *efferent* system differs from the nonautonomic (*somatic* or *voluntary*) efferent system in that the latter has a *single neuron running from the central nervous system to an effector organ,* whereas the autonomic nervous system has *more than one neuron outside the central nervous system* innervating an effector organ. The first autonomic neuron runs to a ganglion, where it synapses with a second neuron, which courses to the organ. The first neuron in the pathway is termed *preganglionic* and the second, *postganglionic* (Figure 8-7).

The anatomic pathway of the *afferent* (sensory) division of the autonomic system is similar to those of the nonautonomic afferent system.

Anatomically the efferent portion of the autonomic system can be divided into *sympathetic* and *parasympathetic* divisions. The sympathetic division arises from all of the thoracic and the first two lumbar segments of the spinal cord. For this reason, the sympathetic division is also called the *thoracolumbar* division. The parasympathetic (*craniosacral*) includes the III, VII, IX, and X cranial nerves and the second, third, and fourth sacral spinal nerves. Module 8 gives the structure of the autonomic nervous system.

Sympathetic
Division

The sympathetic division includes: (a) the spinal nerves (*T1* through *T12* and *L1* and *L2*, (b) the pair of long nerve trunks (*paravertebral or sympathetic trunks*) running parallel to the spinal column on which are found a number of ganglia (*paravertebral, sympathetic chain ganglia,* and (c) the collateral ganglia (*superior mesenteric, celiac,* and *inferior mesenteric*). The preganglionic cell bodies, from which the sympathetic division arises, are found in the lateral horns of the spinal cord. Their fibers leave the cord by way of the ventral nerve roots and pass into the sympathetic trunk by way of the white rami. The axons can then (a) synapse with a postganglionic cell in the paravertebral ganglion, (b) pass through the paravertebral ganglion and synapse in a *collateral ganglion* in the gut region, or (c) pass up or down the paravertebral trunks and synapse in a ganglion at a different level. Combinations of the above are also possible. Postganglionic fibers that synapse at a paravertebral ganglion reenter the spinal nerve through the *gray rami* (unmyelineated fibers). This anatomical arrangement would appear to be an economic way of distributing the sympathetic fibers, that is, using the major branches of the spinal nerves rather than establishing a separate distribution system.

Some of the sympathetic branches of the lower thoracic nerves enter the paravertebral ganglia but do not synapse. They emerge from the ganglia as a group of nerves, the splanchnic nerves, and course to the

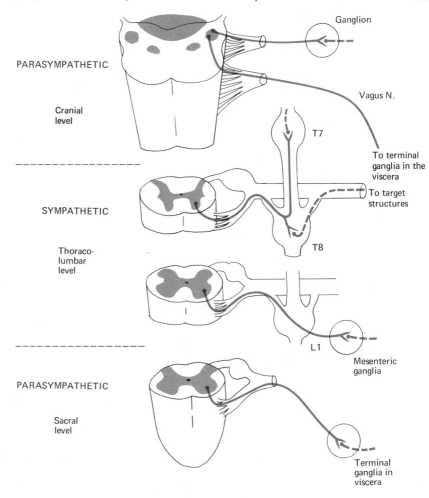

figure 8-7

AUTONOMIC
NERVOUS
SYSTEM
SHOWING THE
RELATIONSHIP
BETWEEN
PREGANGLIONIC
AND
POSTGANGLIONIC
CELLS

collateral ganglia, where they synapse with postganglionic cells that innervate abdominal and pelvic viscera. The so-called solar plexus is formed by the superior mesenteric and celiac ganglia and their associated fibers.

Parasympathetic Division

The parasympathetic preganglionic fibers are long and synapse in *terminal* ganglia that lie on or near the organs they innervate; the postganglionic fibers are therefore very short. The III, VII, and IX nerves regulate the ciliary muscles of the eye, secretory glands, and blood vessels of the head, and the X nerve regulates the heart, lung, kidney, liver, gonads, and most of the stomach and intestines. The sacral portion innervates the lower part of the large intestine and organs of the pelvic region.

cellular
specialization

cell bodies in
the spinal cord

With the exception of the postganglionic neurons, the cell bodies of the neurons forming the peripheral nervous system are located in the central nervous system and therefore need no additional description.

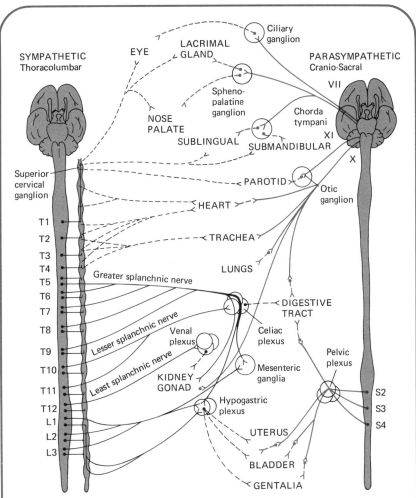

SYMPATHETIC
Thoracolumbar

EYE

LACRIMAL
GLAND

Ciliary
ganglion

PARASYMPATHETIC
Cranio-Sacral

VII

Spheno-
palatine
ganglion

NOSE
PALATE

Chorda
tympani

XI

SUBLINGUAL   SUBMANDIBULAR

X

Superior
cervical
ganglion

PAROTID

Otic
ganglion

HEART

T1

TRACHEA

T2

T3

T4

LUNGS

T5   Greater splanchnic nerve

T6

T7   DIGESTIVE
TRACT

T8   Venal
plexus   Celiac
plexus

T9   Lesser splanchnic nerve   Pelvic
plexus

T10   Mesenteric
ganglia

T11   Least splanchnic nerve   KIDNEY
GONAD

T12   Hypogastric
plexus   S2

L1   S3

L2   S4

L3

UTERUS

BLADDER

GENTALIA

The autonomic nervous system has two divisions, the *sympathetic* and the
parasympathetic. The cell bodies of the sympathetic division arise in the
thoracolumbar region of the spine and send axons to the *sympathetic chains*,
which run parallel to and close to the spinal cord. Most of the axons synapse
with neurons in the ganglia of the sympathetic chain from where postganglionic fibers run to specific organs. In three cases in the sympathetic division
the ganglia are located outside the sympathetic chains. The cell bodies of
the parasympathetic division arise in the brainstem and the sacral region of
the spinal cord, and the axons of these cells synapse with neurons in ganglia
located on or near the organ being innervated.

All the preganglionic fibers secrete *acetylcholine*, while most of the postganglionic fibers of the sympathetic division secrete *norepinephrine*. The
postganglionic fibers of the parasympathetic system secrete acetylcholine.

General stimulation of the sympathetic division produces increased blood
supply to the tissues, increased metabolic rate, and other reactions which
prepare the body for "fight or flight." The function of parasympathetic stimulation is generally that of maintaining the "status quo."

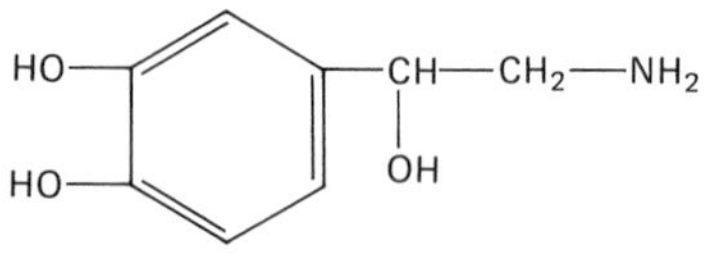

Figure 8-8 Chemical structure of norepinephrine.

physiology

autonomic
nervous
system

Sympathetic
Division

The preganglionic fibers of the autonomic nervous system all liberate the same chemical transmitter, *acetylcholine*. The postganglionic fibers of the sympathetic division release *norepinephrine*, also known as *noradrenaline* (Figure 8-8). Because it was once believed that the sympathetic chemical transmitter was adrenaline (*epinephrine*), sympathetic fibers are called *adrenergic*. Norepinephrine is stored in vesicles in the presynaptic axon terminals much as acetylcholine is (see Chapter 5); however, norepinephrine is inactivated mainly by resorption into the cell rather than enzymatic breakdown as is the case with acetylcholine.

The actions produced by stimulating both the sympathetic and parasympathetic fibers to particular organs are given in Table 8-2; however, we can note here that the general stimulation of the sympathetic division produces a preparation of the body for "fight or flight." Sympathetic stimulation increases the heart rate, diverts blood to the muscles, mobilizes glucose, and causes other activities that are advantageous to an individual in a stress situation.

The adrenal medulla can be considered to be a somewhat modified sympathetic postganglionic structure, for it is a collection of many postganglion fibers which release mainly epinephrine along with a small amount of norepinephrine into the general circulation. The epinephrine secreted by the adrenal medulla acts very much like the norepinephrine secreted by the other sympathetic fibers, although its action may not be as potent. However, it has the advantage of lasting about 10 times as long. The adrenal medulla also serves as a safety factor. If *denervation*

table 8-2
ACTIONS INDUCED
BY STIMULATION
OF AUTONOMIC
NERVOUS SYSTEM

ORGAN	SYMPATHETIC	PARASYMPATHETIC
Heart, cardiac muscle	Increased rate	Decreased rate
Lungs, bronchi	Dilation	Constriction
Gut	Decreased peristalsis	Increased peristalsis
Urinary bladder	Inhibits contraction	Contraction
Urinary bladder sphincters	Constriction	Dilatation
Penis	Ejaculation	Erection
Blood vessels	Generally constricts, some dilation	Dilation
Eye: iris muscle	Contraction of circular fibers, constriction of pupil	Contraction of radial fibers, dilation of pupil
Piloerector muscles	Contraction	None
Salivary glands	Inhibition	Stimulation
Sweat glands	Increased secretion	None
Adrenal medulla	Increased	None

(absence of nerve stimulus) of the other parts of the sympathetic system occurs, the gland constantly releases a small amount of epinephrine. This secretion results in the recovery of tone of most organs that have had their sympathetic innervation severed. The secretions of the adrenal medulla are also known to cause an increase in the metabolism of many cells that are not innervated by the sympathetic system.

One exception to the rule that the sympathetic postganglionic fibers secrete norepinephrine is the postganglionic fibers to the sweat glands where acetylcholine is released.

Parasympathetic Division   The parasympathetic postganglionic fibers secrete acetylcholine. The action of acetylcholine depends on the nature of the target organ; for example, it causes inhibition of the rate of heart muscle contraction and acceleration of the rate of contraction of muscles of the stomach and intestine. Postganglionic fibers that secrete acetylcholine are termed cholinergic. Table 8-2 gives the results of stimulating parasympathetic fibers to various organs.

A *reciprocal action* exists in terms of control of the visceral organs; if one system excites, the other inhibits. An example of this is control of the heart rate. The intrinsic rate of heart muscle contraction is increased by release of norepinephrine from the sympathetic postganglionic fibers of the spinal nerves and is slowed down by the release of acetylcholine from the parasympathetic postganglionic fiber of the vagus nerve. The opposite is true for the intestine; namely, the parasympathetic stimulates and the sympathetic inhibits. However, not all organs have dual innervation. Only the sympathetic division innervates the adrenal medulla, spleen, sweat glands, and pilomotor muscles, whereas the parasympathetic division appears to have control of the ciliary and sphincter muscles of the eye.

If the sympathetic system is classified as the emergency division, then the parasympathetic can be labeled the *conservation* division, and the latter is in operation most of the time. For example, when the heart increases to accommodate for work, such as climbing a flight of stairs, the increased rate is not due to sympathetic stimulation but to a decrease in the amount of vagus inhibition. Only an emergency situation, "fight or flight," would invoke a major sympathetic response.

control

autonomic control centers   Autonomic centers are located mainly in the hypothalamus, pons, and medulla and are treated in detail in chapters dealing with specific control centers (temperature, water regulation, and so forth). Figure 8-9 gives an overall view of the centers, which have been termed the *visceral brain.* There is good evidence for cerebral dominance over the spinal cord reflexes, as when the spinal cord is severed from the higher centers and the motor reflexes become exaggerated and sometimes uncoordinated.

reflex activity   Reflex activity encompasses the involuntary responses to stimuli. Adjusting the position of the body with respect to the pull of gravity, maintenance of a constant internal temperature in response to changes in environmental temperature, and adjusting to changes in blood pressure are examples of reflex activities. There are numerous such adjustments

figure 8-9

AUTONOMIC
CONTROL
CENTERS
IN THE
HYPOTHALAMUS

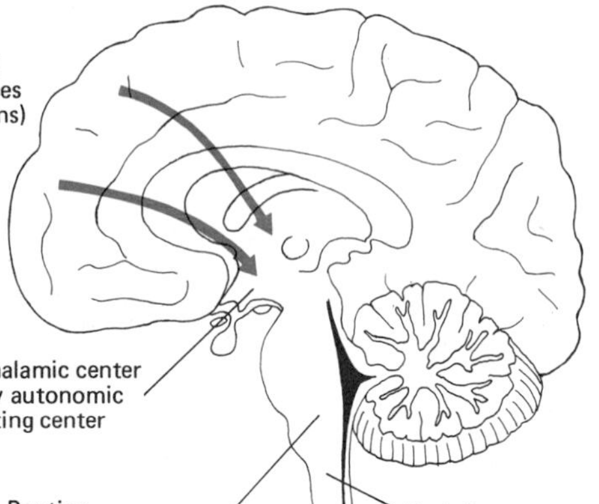

Cerebral
influences
(emotions)

The arrows indicate inputs from the cerebral cortex and limbic system. These inputs play a major role in visceral responses to stress and emotion and are involved in many psychosomatic responses.

Hypothalamic center
Primary autonomic
integrating center

Pontine
Respiratory center

Medullary
control centers
1. cardiac centers
2. vasomotor centers
3. respiratory center
4. emetic center

that have constantly to be made, and if each input, such as change in environmental temperature, had to be accompanied by a voluntary response involving conscious thought, the nervous system would have to be more complex than it is. Homeostasis is thereby maintained mainly by the mechanism of reflex action, which generally involves the nervous system at the level of the spinal cord (*cord reflexes*) or at the cord and visceral brain (*autonomic reflexes*).

reflex arc   The simplest pathway in the nervous system involves two neurons, a *receptor neuron* and an *effector neuron*. This arrangement is seen in the *reflex arc*, where the sequence of actions is: stimulation of the receptor, generation of an impulse on the afferent neuron, synaptic transmission, impulse generation on the effector neuron, and release of transmitter from the affector endings (Figure 5-10). An example of the two-neuron (*monosynaptic*) reflex is seen in the *knee jerk* or *stretch* reflex, commonly employed to test the state of the spinal cord at the level of the lumbosacral plexus. When the tendon of the quadriceps femoris muscle is stretched by tapping on the tendon, proprioceptors in the tendon generate an impulse that travels to the ventral horn of the gray matter. Here the impulse is generated on the effector (motor) neuron, propagated to the endings of the muscle, and produces contraction of the muscle. The time needed for such a process is in the order of 10 msec. Had the message been passed up the cord to the brain, integrated, and a motor impulse passed down again, the time course would have been much longer due to the increased length and the number of synapses in the pathway.

A three-neuron (*polysynaptic*) reflex involves a receptor cell that extends only to the dorsal horn, where it synapses with an interneuron (*internuncial* neuron). The interneuron extends to the ventral horn and synapses with an effector neuron.

figure 8-10
THE MUSCLE
SPINDLE

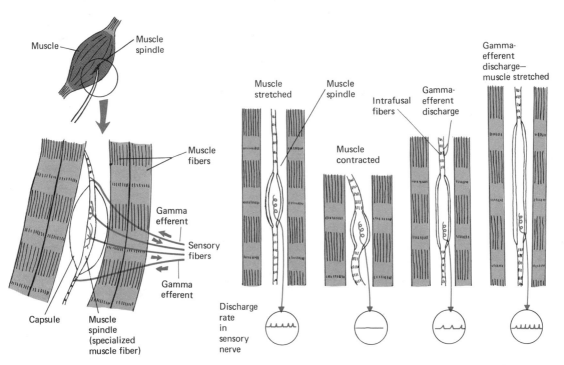

When stretching of muscle occurs, the intrafusal fibers are stretched and the annulospiral receptors are excited. The signals from these receptors travel along a reflex circuit to the cord and cause contraction of the stretched muscle. This system maintains a certain state of contraction in the muscles.

Of course, there may be polysynaptic reflex arcs with more than two synapses. Since position of parts of the body are in constant need of adjustment, it seems an efficient scheme to have many of these pathways as reflex arcs. If this were not so, then the brain would have to integrate the incoming signals and produce some output signal. Thus the cord reflexes leave the brain "free to handle more important business." This is not to say that reflex arcs are isolated from the pathways to the brain. Indeed, signals are sent up the cord so that the brain is cognizant of the position of the various parts of the body. Thus the brain has a reference point when there is a need for voluntary activity.

cord reflexes

Muscle Spindle

The muscle spindle is sensory and provides information on the length of a muscle and the rate of change when that muscle is contracting. This information processing is accomplished through the *annulospiral receptor*, which is wrapped around the *intrafusal fibers*, noncontractile

figure 8-11

GOLGI TENDON
ORGAN AT
MUSCLE-TENDON
JUNCTION

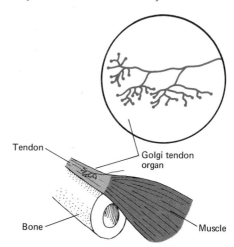

Tendon

Golgi tendon
organ

Bone

Muscle

but stretchable regions of the muscle spindle (Figure 8-10). When stretching of the muscles occurs, the intrafusal fibers are stretched and the annulospiral receptors are excited. The signal proceeds through a reflex arc and causes contraction of the muscle. Thus the action of the system is to maintain the muscle bundle at a certain state of contraction. In addition to the annulospiral receptors, there are also *flower spray receptors* that have a similar function but require greater stimulation to become excitable.

Golgi Tendon   The Golgi tendon organ consists of an end of a receptor neuron located
Reflex   on the tendon near the musculotendinous junction. The Golgi tendon reflex is used to measure muscle load and responds only to high stimulation (overload) by triggering an inhibitory reflex arc (Figure 8-11). The inhibition leads to lengthening of the muscle (lengthening reaction) and protects the muscle from overload and possible tearing. The sudden relaxation of the leg muscle brought on by the Golgi tendon reflex will lead to a sudden folding up of the leg, the so-called *clasped-knife reflex.*

Flexor Reflex   The flexor reflex is elicited whenever pain endings of a limb are stimulated. If a strong stimulus is applied to the tip of a finger, the hand is withdrawn. This flexor reflex is a polysynaptic reflex involving interneurons, as not only does the motor signal produce contraction of the flexor muscles, but the interneurons synapse with inhibitory neurons that produce inhibition of antagonistic muscles (Figure 8-12). Increasing the strength of the stimulus involves more sensory fibers and therefore a larger response. The flexor reflex is seen in animals in which the spinal cord has been severed from the brain, demonstrating that this response is indeed a cord response.

Cross-Extensor   Within a fraction of a second of the flexor reflex start, the opposite limb
Reflex   begins to extend. Such an action tends to push the body away from the pain-producing stimulus. Other reflexes are listed in Table 8-3.

figure 8-12

A POLYSNAPTIC
REFLEX ARC OR
RECIPROCAL
INNERVATION

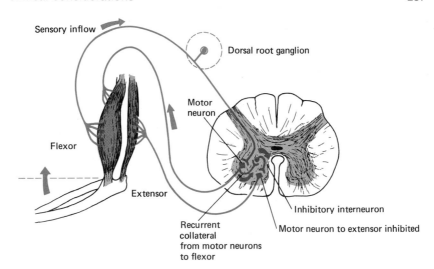

Sensory inflow

Dorsal root ganglion

Motor
neuron

Flexor

Extensor

Inhibitory interneuron

Recurrent
collateral
from motor neurons
to flexor

Motor neuron to extensor inhibited

The flexor reflex is a purposeful response which withdraws a limb from a painful stimulus. The organization of the sensory input is such that signals to the motor neurons of the flexor are excitatory while at the same time signals are sent via inhibitory interneurons to inhibit the motor neurons innervating the antagonistic group of extensor muscles.

conditioned
reflex

The classical work of the Russian physiologist Pavlov established that a conditioned reflex is a *learned* reflex. At the time of his studies, it was well known that a salivation, an *unconditioned* or *natural* reflex, began when a dog was presented with food. Pavlov rang a bell each time he gave the dog food and showed that after a series of such conditionings, the dog salivated when the bell was rung even though no food was given. Unconsciously, the dog learned to associate the bell with food and responded by salivating. Such a process requires that new patterns of association be established within the existing pathways of the nervous system. The same sort of reflexlike conditioned learning occurs in humans.

autonomic
reflexes

The neuron pattern for an autonomic reflex differs from the cord reflexes in that an additional neuron is interposed in the efferent pathway (Figure 8-7). Examples of such reflexes are emptying of the bladder and control of arterial blood pressure. As was stated earlier, centers in the brain have dominance over autonomic reflexes.

clinical
considerations

visceral pain

Despite the fact that the physiology of pain is poorly understood, it is possible to recognize different types of pain. One classification divides pain into *epicritical* pain, which is usually considered as a well-localized, superficial, and sharp sensation, and *protopathic* or visceral pain, which is poorly localized, dull, and pulsating. Such visceral pain is evoked by inflammation, lack of oxygen in the viscera, severe distension, or smooth muscle spasm. Another characteristic of visceral pain is that the sensation is often referred to some other part of the body, for example, damage

table 8-3
SPINAL REFLEXES

TYPE OF REFLEX	LOCATION	MODE OF RESPONSE
Deep reflexes	Patellar reflex (knee jerk)	Extension of leg when tendon of the quadriceps femoris muscle is struck just below the patella
	Achilles reflex (ankle jerk)	Plantar flexion when Achilles tendon is struck
	Biceps reflex	Flexion of forearm when biceps brachii muscle tendon is struck
	Triceps reflex	Extension of forearm when triceps brachii muscle tendon is struck
Superficial reflexes	Plantar reflex	Flexion of toes when sole of foot is stimulated. If instead of normal response, big toe extends upward and other toes spread, there is possible damage to pyramidal tract (Babinski reflex)
	Cremasteric reflex	Contraction of cremaster muscle leading to drawing up of testicle on side stimulated
	Corneal reflex	Closing of eyelid when cornea is touched
Visceral reflexes	Ciliospinal reflex	Dilation of pupil when skin of neck is stimulated
	Pupillary light reflex	Constriction of pupil when a light is shone in the eyes

to heart muscle often causes pain sensations in the left shoulder, left arm, and smallest finger of the left hand, as well as to the throat and lower jaw.

referred pain   Visceral pain is the sum of two events—one a poorly localized dull pain and the other a sharp pain precisely located to an area of the skin that is

figure 8-13
REFERRED PAIN

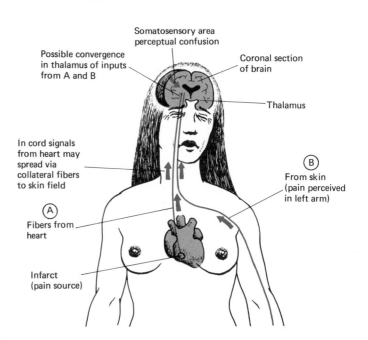

often not associated with the area of the origin of the pain. This type of pain is termed *referred pain.* An example of this is the sharp pain felt in the region of the left axilla (armpit) and left arm when pain impulses originate in the heart, as during a heart attack.

The reason this occurs is due to the position of the heart during early development. The embryological development of the heart occurs in the region of the neck and upper thorax, and the afferent pain fibers from the heart enter the spinal cord in this region. It is postulated that when these pain fibers are highly stimulated, impulses may spread to skin pain neurons in the same spinal segment, and the individual feels referred pain in the skin (Figure 8-13). An alternate hypothesis is that the visceral and skin pain impulses converge in the thalamus, and the brain mistakenly identifies all stimuli as coming from the skin because it has never sensed (no memory) a pain originating from the heart.

summary

gross anatomy

1. Cranial nerves: originate in brain and extend to structure they innervate; nerves either sensory, motor, or mixed; Roman numeral assigned to each nerve
   I. Olfactory
   II. Optic
   III. Oculomotor
   IV. Trochlear
   V. Trigeminal
   VI. Abducens
   VII. Facial
   VIII. Acoustic
   IX. Glossopharyngeal
   X. Vagus
   XI. Accessory
   XII. Hypoglossal
2. Spinal nerves: 31 pairs; pass out through intervertebral foramina
   (a) dorsal root: contains sensory fibers
   (b) dorsal root ganglion: contains sensory cell bodies
   (c) ventral root: contains motor fibers
   (d) rami: branches of the spinal nerve
      white rami; contain myelinated fibers
      gray rami: contain postganglionic fibers that return to spinal cord
      ventral rami: supplies anterior and lateral aspects of skin and skeletal muscles
      dorsal rami: innervate skin and muscle of posterior regions of the body
   (e) cervical plexus: union of ventral rami of first four cervical nerves; innervates neck and back as well as diaphragm
   (f) brachial plexus: union of ventral rami of $C5$ through $C8$, and $T1$; innervates muscles of the upper body
   (g) lumbar plexus: union of ventral rami of $L1$ through $L4$ and $T12$; innervates muscles of upper leg
   (h) sacral plexus: union of ventral rami of $S1$ through $S4$; innervates muscles of posterior portion of thigh, leg, and foot

3. Autonomic nervous system: controls vegetative functions; instead of single neuron running from spinal cord to effector organ, autonomic system utilizes two neurons outside CNS to carry a motor impulse to a target structure

   (a) preganglionic: neuron runs from CNS to autonomic ganglion
   (b) postganglionic: runs from ganglion to effector organ
   (c) sympathetic division: arises from all thoracic and first two lumbar segments
   (d) parasympathetic division: arises from III, VII, IX, and X cranial nerves and S2 through S4 spinal nerves

physiology

1. Autonomic nervous system

   (a) sympathetic division: preganglionic fibers liberate acetylcholine; postganglionic fibers liberate norepinephrine; sympathetic stimulation prepares body for "fight or flight." Adrenal medulla secretes mainly epinephrine into circulation, producing longer-lasting sympathetic effects

2. Parasympathetic division: preganglionic fibers liberate acetylcholine; postganglionic fibers liberate acetylcholine; a conservation or "status quo" system

control

1. Autonomic control centers: mainly in hypothalamus, pons, and medulla (visceral brain)

2. Reflex activity

   (a) reflex arc: involved minimum of receptor neuron and effector neuron; monosynaptic or polysynaptic
   (b) cord reflexes

      muscle spindle: a sensory reflex; provides information on length of muscle; annulospiral receptor responds to stretch by sending impulse through reflex arc that causes contraction of muscle

      Golgi tendon reflex: Golgi tendon organ (sensory) response only to extreme stimulation by triggering inhibitory reflex arc

      flexor reflex: initiated by pain endings in the limb that is stimulated; leads to withdrawal

      cross-extensor reflex: leads to activation of extensor muscles in limbs opposite to those stimulated by flexor reflex

3. Conditioned reflex: a learned reflex involving new patterns of association in nervous pathway

4. Autonomic reflexes: like other reflexes, except for an additional neuron in efferent pathway

clinical considerations

1. Visceral pain: caused by stimulation of pain receptors in viscera over wide area

2. Referred pain: pain located to an area of the skin not associated with the area of the origin of the pain

special sensory organs

9

the eye
anatomy
physiology of vision
clinical considerations

the ear
anatomy
physiology of hearing
clinical considerations

equilibrium

taste

smell

Man has evolved a myriad of highly specialized cells (sensory receptors) remarkably sensitive to certain stimuli such as light, sound, pressure, and chemicals. To evoke a meaningful response, the stimulus must not only be detected, but also processed by the brain. All stimuli have certain characteristics in common: *quality* (physicochemical nature), *frequency, duration,* and *amplitude* (intensity). Each sense organ is most sensitive to only one type of stimulus, although any very strong stimulus can elicit a paradoxical response – for example, a blow to the eye produces a visual response. The sensitivity to specific stimuli is remarkable, for it has been calculated that as little as one molecule can stimulate a single chemical receptor, and as little as one photon of light (which can be thought of as equivalent to a molecule) can stimulate a single light receptor.

the eye

The eye is the mind's major window to the world. A person need only close his eyes and attempt to perform the most routine tasks to appreciate the magnitude of the eye's activities.

anatomy

The eyeball is well padded by fatty tissues and protected by the bony orbits. The anterior coverings, the eyelids, and the lubricating fluid, *tears,* are additional protective devices. The eyeball is essentially spherical and can be thought of as a multilayered structure (Figure 9-1). The outermost layer, the *fibrous tunic,* consists of the *sclera* (the white of the eye) and the transparent *cornea.* The next layer, the *vascular tunic,* consists of the *choroid,* a highly vascular tissue, the *ciliary body,* and *iris.* The ciliary body and iris also contain contractile elements involved in the adjustment of the iris opening, the *pupil,* to changing light intensi-

figure 9-1

ANATOMY OF
THE EYE

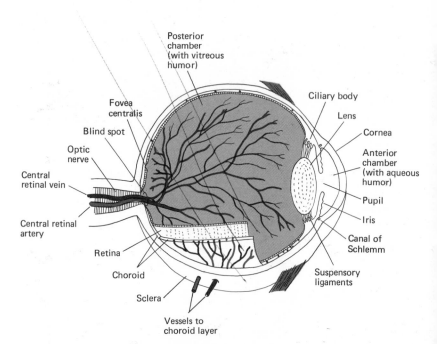

Posterior chamber (with vitreous humor)

Fovea centralis

Blind spot

Optic nerve

Central retinal vein

Central retinal artery

Retina

Choroid

Sclera

Vessels to choroid layer

Ciliary body

Lens

Cornea

Anterior chamber (with aqueous humor)

Pupil

Iris

Canal of Schlemm

Suspensory ligaments

ties and distance. The third and innermost layer, the *nervous tunic*, is composed of the *retina*, containing the light receptor cells, and the epithelial layer, which continues from the retina part way forward. Inside the tunics are the *lens*, the *vitreous body*, and the *aqueous humor*. All of these structures are shown in Figure 9-1.

The Sclera The opaque sclera (the white of the eye) covers the eye except anteriorly where the cornea is present and posteriorly at the point where the optic nerve and retinal blood vessels enter the eye.

The Cornea The cornea is transparent, covering about one-sixth of the eye. It is nonvascular, as the presence of blood vessels would scatter light, but it has a rich supply of sensory nerves as evidenced by rapid closing of the eyelids whenever anything touches the cornea. The cornea bulges slightly from the rest of the eye.

The Ciliary Body The ciliary body is a continuation of the choroid and is triangular in cross section. It is composed of the ciliary processes, the ciliary muscle, the ciliary ring, and the ciliary portion of the retina. The ciliary processes are approximately 80 folds covered by secretory epithelium. The ciliary muscles are of the smooth muscle type and have three orientations— circular, radial, and meridional.

The Iris and the Pupil The iris is a highly vascularized ring of muscular tissue containing pigment. The muscle fibers are circular, and contraction leads to constriction of the pupil. In addition, a set of radial contractile fibers, which are not true muscle fibers, also aids in the constriction of the pupil. Another set of radial fibers is probably responsible for dilation of the pupil. The iris is colored by the presence of melanin pigment granules, the *amount* of pigment determining the color. When only a small amount of pigment is present, the iris appears blue; when a greater amount is present, the iris appears brown. Babies have blue eyes because of the limited amount of pigment present in the iris at birth.

The Lens The lens is immediately posterior to the iris and cornea (Figure 9-1) and is constructed of modified epithelial cells that have elongated to become lens fibers. The cells lose their nuclei and most of the cytoplasmic organelles making the lens transparent. The lens is attached to the ciliary body by means of the *suspensory ligaments* (sometimes termed the *zonula*).

Aqueous Humor The iris separates the eye into two compartments: the *anterior* and the *posterior chambers*. These chambers are filled with aqueous humor, a fluid akin to the plasma, but with significant differences. The protein concentration of the aqueous humor in the anterior chamber is approximately 0.02 percent as compared to 7 percent for the plasma, and the aqueous humor is also hypertonic to plasma. The epithelial cells lining the folds that make up the ciliary processes are highly vascularized and appear to be secretory in character. It is felt that the fluid secreted from these cells constitutes the bulk of the aqueous humor. The fluid supplies the nutritive needs of the lens and cornea and maintains intraocular pressure. Humor moves from the posterior chamber to the anterior chamber by way of the space between the iris and the lens and is removed from the anterior chamber by way of the *canal of Schlemm,* a vessel located at the junction of the cornea and the sclera (Figure 9-1).

The Vitreous Body
The vitreous body is a gelatinous structure filling the bulk of the posterior chamber. It is closed by a membrane, but the cells responsible for the formation of the colloidal material that forms the gel are not known. Through the vitreous body, from the lens region to the retina, runs the *hyaloid canal* containing the degenerated hyaloid artery. The detailed structure of the retina is better understood if described as part of the physiology of vision.

Ocular Muscles
The six ocular muscles that control the movement of the eye are shown in Figure 9-2. Although each muscle can contract separately, it is the coordinated activities of all the muscles that direct the gaze in the desired direction.

The Eyelids
The eyelids function to protect the eyes and to keep the surface of the cornea from drying. A thin connective tissue layer, the conjunctiva, lines the eyelids and continues over the anterior surface of the eyeball. At the inner edge of the eyelid are located the *tarsal glands,* which secrete an oily material that keeps the eyelids from sticking together (Figure 9-3).

The Lacrimal Glands
The lacrimal glands in the upper lateral side of each orbit produce the tears that provide lubrication for the movement of the lids over the eyes (Figure 9-4). The tear fluid collects at the inner edge of the eye and drains into the *lacrimal sac* via the *lacrimal canals;* it then runs to the *nasolacrimal duct* and from there to the inferior meatus of the nose. When the mucous membranes of these passages are swollen as with a cold or hay fever, the tears are not drained into the nasal passages but collect and spill over from the eyes.

physiology of vision
The eye has often been compared with a camera, and in a sense this is a good analogy (Figure 9-5). The camera is enclosed and protected, and it has a lens for focusing the image, an iris diaphragm to adjust the opening, and an image-forming surface, the film. Even the sophisticated

figure 9-2

THE OCULAR MUSCLES

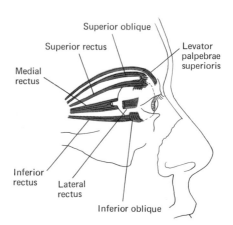

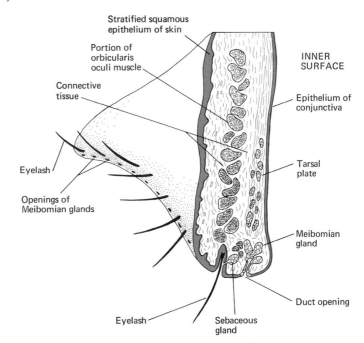

figure 9-3

STRUCTURE OF
THE EYELID

Stratified squamous
epithelium of skin

INNER
SURFACE

Portion of
orbicularis
oculi muscle

Connective
tissue

Epithelium of
conjunctiva

Eyelash

Tarsal
plate

Openings of
Meibomian glands

Meibomian
gland

Duct opening

Eyelash

Sebaceous
gland

cameras of today that automatically adjust the iris diaphragm and
shutter speed for the available amount of light are no match for the
human eye which focuses automatically and continually regenerates
its "film."

The eye is a *dioptric system,* meaning that parts of the eye have refractive powers to focus an image on the retina. To understand how this

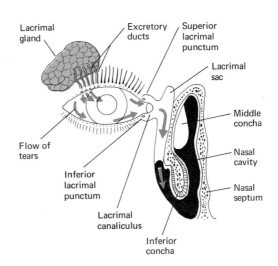

figure 9-4

THE LACRIMAL
GLAND AND
DIRECTION OF
TEAR FLOW

Lacrimal
gland

Excretory
ducts

Superior
lacrimal
punctum

Lacrimal
sac

Middle
concha

Flow of
tears

Nasal
cavity

Inferior
lacrimal
punctum

Nasal
septum

Lacrimal
canaliculus

Inferior
concha

figure 9-5

COMPARISON OF
THE HUMAN EYE
WITH THE
CAMERA

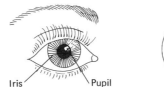

Iris   Pupil

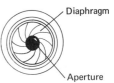

Diaphragm

Aperture

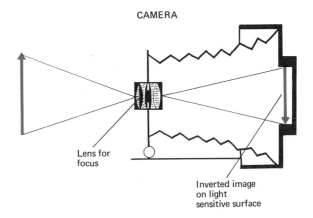

CAMERA

Lens for
focus

Inverted image
on light
sensitive surface

figure 9-5

COMPARISON OF
THE HUMAN EYE
WITH THE
CAMERA

biological system functions, it is necessary to examine some of the fundamentals of optics.

Refraction
Light travels through space at a speed of 186,000 miles per second, but the speed is slowed by passing through solids or liquids. If an angle exists at the junction of two media through which light passes, such as from air to cornea or air to glass, the light is bent at the angle, and the phenomenon is known as *refraction* (Figure 9-6).

With convex glass lenses, the light is bent as it leaves the air and enters the glass and again as it leaves the glass and enters the air. From the figure, we can see that spherical convex lenses will focus the light

figure 9-6

REFRACTION

Air   Glass

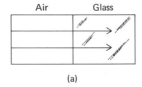

(a)

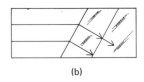

(b)

Refraction depends on the difference in optical density of the two media and the angle at which the light beam strikes the interface. In (a), the light beam strikes the interface at right angles and although the wave front is slowed, it is not bent. In (b), the lower edge of the wave front strikes the interface first and is slowed while the upper edge of the wave front is still moving rapidly through air. When the upper edge of the front strikes, the wave front has assumed a new direction.

figure 9-7

REFRACTION OF
LIGHT BY
CONVEX LENSES

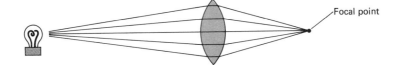

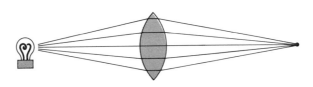

The refraction of light by convex lenses from close and distant point sources of light.

at a given point, the *focal point,* whereas cylindrical lenses will focus the light along a line. The distance from the lens to the focal point is called the *focal length,* which varies with the curvature of the lens. Concave lenses cause the light to diverge rather than converge.

An important aspect of the refraction of light by convex lenses is the source of light. For the above examples, light from a distance is used as the light source so that the light entering the lens would be essentially parallel. If a light from a point source *close to* the lens is used, however, the focus point is now at a greater distance from the lens (Figure 9-7). In order to produce the same focus point, a thicker lens is needed.

The eye has two major refracting surfaces: the cornea, which accounts for about 70 percent of the refraction, and the lens, which accounts for about 30 percent of the refraction. However, the refracting system can be thought of as one. The refracting properties of the optical structures of the eye focus an *inverted* image on the retina as a number of point sources of light (Figure 9-8).

figure 9-8

REFRACTING
SYSTEM OF THE
EYE

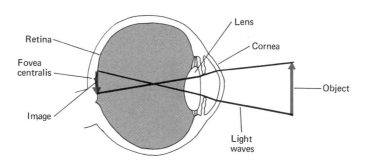

The refracting system of the eye includes the cornea and the lens. The optical properties of this system are such that an inverted image is projected onto the retina.

In the normal eye the image is focused on the retina. When the eyeball is too short or the refracting system is too weak, however, the image is "focused" behind the retina. This condition is known as *farsightedness* or *hypermetropia.* When the eyeball is elongated or the lens system is too strong, the focal point of the image is in front of the retina, a condition known as *nearsightedness* or *myopia* (Figure 9-9). Both nearsight-

figure 9-9

DIAGRAMMATIC REPRESENTATION OF THE NORMAL, NEARSIGHTED, AND FARSIGHTED CONDITIONS IN THE EYE

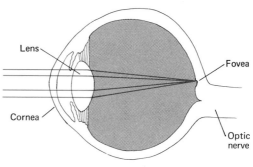

NORMAL EYE

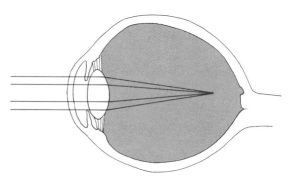

NEARSIGHTED

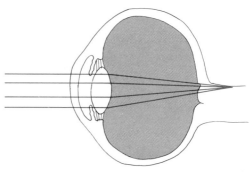

FARSIGHTED

edness and farsightedness can be corrected by appropriate lenses in front of the eye – convex lenses that cause light to converge in the case of farsightedness and concave lenses that cause light to diverge in near-sightedness (Figure 9-9).

The components of the optic system of the normal eye are not perfect. More usually the cornea, but sometimes the lens, has an imperfect curvature, leading to *astigmatism.* Astigmatism is the inability of the eye to focus lines in all directions. In most cases the astigmatism is minor and the distortions of the image are ignored by the brain. When astigmatism becomes appreciable, distortion along an axis is recognized by the brain. In cases where astigmatism occurs a special lens is used for correction. Glasses with correction for myopia, hypermetropia, and astigmatism are very common.

Accommodation   The lens is under constant tension due to the pulling of the ligaments in the zonule and therefore has a minimum curvature refracting power. When the source of the image is close to the eye, the curvature of the lens is increased by contraction of the meridional and circular fibers. This process is called *accommodation.*

As a person becomes older, the lens becomes less and less elastic and does not accommodate well for close objects. This loss of accommodation appears to be due to denaturation of lens protein. The eye is then essentially in fixed focus for a certain distance and corrective lenses are required for focusing on near objects.

CATARACTS This is a condition that causes the lens to become opaque, and is a relatively common occurrence in older people. The opacity is probably due to denaturation of the lens protein and deposition of calcium. Lenses in this condition are removed surgically to restore vision. However, a large part of the refractive power of the eye is lost when the lens is removed, and a strong corrective convex lens is needed to focus an image on the retina. If only one lens is removed, the image produced by the corrective lens is larger than the image produced by the normal eye, and depth perception is impaired. The use of contact lenses, plastic lenses that fit over the pupillary region of the cornea, can correct the difficulty, so that the image is normal and depth perception restored.

The Pupil   The pupil functions to control the amount of light that enters the eye; thus in darkness the pupil is wide, and in bright light the pupillary area decreases. The dimensions of the pupil are controlled by the muscles of the iris, the *sphincter pupillae,* whose contraction leads to constriction of the pupil. This contractile element is under reflex control, the initial receptors in the pathway being the visual cells of the retina.

Depth of Focus   Depth of focus refers to the limits (forward and backward) of distance from a point of focus that an image remains in focus. The depth of focus for the lens system depends on the size of the pupil opening. The smaller the opening, the greater the depth of focus. Figure 9-10 illustrates this situation by means of a camera. In (a) the lens aperture is small, and a great deal of the background is in focus; in (b) the aperture is wide and only the subject is in clear focus. The pupil has other functions; for the optical system of the eye is not so perfect that all light striking the sur-

figure 9-10

DEPTH OF
FOCUS

face is focused to a point. Distortions occur especially at the periphery, and the pupil, by regulating the amount of light, eliminates a great deal of the distortion by simply eliminating the peripheral areas.

Visual Acuity

Visual acuity is the ability of the eye to distinguish two close point sources of light. Clinically this acuity is measured by using a chart and testing the individual's ability to read the chart from a fixed distance, generally 20 feet. The ability to read letters on the chart with normal eyes is categorized as 20/20 vision. If, however, the individual can read only letters a normal person can read at 100 feet, this is indicated as 20/100 vision. If a test demonstrates that an individual can read letters at 20 feet that normal vision can distinguish only at 15 feet, the vision is "better than normal" and said to be 20/15 (Figure 9-11).

Depth Perception (Position of Objects)

There are several ways in which the eye provides information on the relative positions of objects. First, if the size of an object in the field of view is known, then the brain can automatically compare the other objects in the field to the known object. Second, when the head is moved from side to side, objects that are near appear to move, whereas those far away appear to remain stationary. Stereoscopic vision requires the activity of both eyes, since each eye receives a slightly different image of the same object (Figure 9-12). It is the differences between these two images that is interpreted by the brain as a three-dimensional single image and from which automatic judgments can be made on relative positions of objects. (Module 9A)

The Retina   The retina is the location of the light receptor cells and is essentially an extension of the brain. The retina can be thought of as having three layers: the receptor cells and pigment cells form the outermost part, a middle layer of bipolar cells, and an inner layer of ganglioniclike cells (Figure 9-13). The receptor cells face away from the source of light, which necessitates the collection of these nerve fibers from the outer surface to the inner surface of the retina. These unmyelinated fibers form the optic nerve, and where they penetrate the retina, there are no receptor cells, and a blind spot exists—the *optic disc*. The pigment layer absorbs extraneous light that might randomly stimulate receptor cells and create a poorer image.

The receptor cells in the retina are the *rods* and *cones*. Rods are highly sensitive (have a low threshold) to all wavelengths of visible light (light waves are a small part of a spectrum that also includes radio waves, ultraviolet waves and so forth) and are responsible for noncolor vision. They are the most numerous of the light receptor cells in the retina, accounting for about 95 percent of the 150 million cells.

Cones have a higher threshold for light than rods and are responsible for seeing images in color. There are three types of cone cells, each

figure 9-11

(a) SNELLEN CHART (REDUCED) FOR MEASURING VISUAL ACUITY (b) CHART FOR DETERMINATION OF ASTIGMATISM)

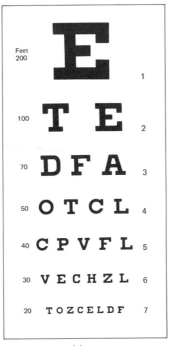

(a)

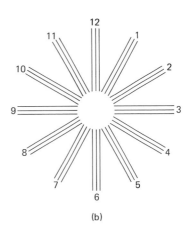

(b)

Astigmatism leads to lines in one axis appearing darker than lines in the other axes.

figure 9-12

STEREOSCOPIC
VISION

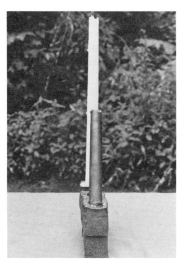  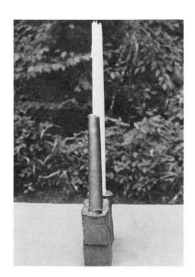

The individual eye sees an object differently and the information which reaches the brain is integrated into a three-dimensional image, as represented by the middle illustration, the image seen by both eyes. The left photo shows what the left eye alone sees, the right photo what the right eye sees.

with a maximum sensitivity to a particular wavelength (measured in nanometers), corresponding roughly to blue (435 nm), green (540 nm), and red (565 nm). Stimulation of several kinds of cones simultaneously results in mixing of the wavelengths to provide intermediate colors, for example, a red and green to produce yellow (Figure 9-14).

Both rods and cones are highly structured cells, containing stacks of disclike membranous structures that contain the photosensitive pigments involved in the visual mechanism (Figure 9-15). Both rods and cones have cilialike structures near the base of the membranous discs.

Many rods synapse with a single bipolar cell, but only one or a few cones synapse with a bipolar cell. A similar relationship exists between the bipolar cells and the ganglionic cells whose axons form the optic nerve. The importance of this arrangement is that the bipolar and ganglionic cells are able to sum up the limited light input from the rods to produce an image. The more or less one-to-one relationship of cone synapses means that more light is needed to produce an image, as there is little summation, but the image is extremely sharp. The cones are most numerous in the center of the retina; in fact, the *macula* is a region in the center of the retina containing only cones. The rods are peripheral, and one can actually see an object better in dim light by gazing slightly away from the object, so that the light falls on the peripherally located rods. The neural pathway for vision is shown in Module 9A.

Chemistry of Vision   The initial event in the visual process is a photochemical reaction in which light supplies the energy for a chemical change. The chemical present in rods is *rhodopsin*, sometimes called visual purple, which is split in a series of steps to the protein *scotopsin* and to *retinene*, a vitamin A derivative (Figure 9-16). After a series of steps, these compounds then regenerate rhodopsin.

Although the cones all contain the retinene molecule found in rods, the protein is slightly different in each of the classes. It is believed that this difference is responsible for the specificity of color vision.

clinical con-siderations   We have already covered some of the more common disorders of the eye (nearsightedness, farsightedness, and cataracts). Another condition that is found in about 1 percent of females and in about 9 percent of

Color Blindness   males is *color blindness*. Actually the name is a misnomer, as complete color blindness is extremely rare (approximately 1 in 100,000,000). The usual case is the inability to perceive one of the three basic colors and its resultant mixtures. This is demonstrated by clinical charts used to detect color blindness.

Glaucoma   Glaucoma is due to accumulation of aqueous humor within the eye, producing an increase in the intraocular pressure. The increase in pressure

figure 9-13

GENERAL
SYNAPTIC
ARRANGEMENT
IN THE RETINA

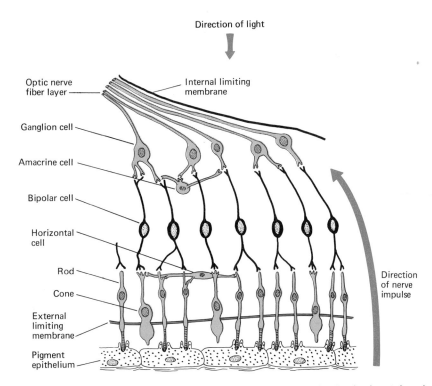

Direction of light

Optic nerve fiber layer
Internal limiting membrane
Ganglion cell
Amacrine cell
Bipolar cell
Horizontal cell
Rod
Cone
External limiting membrane
Pigment epithelium

Direction of nerve impulse

Notice that information can be transmitted horizontally via the horizontal and amacrine cells.

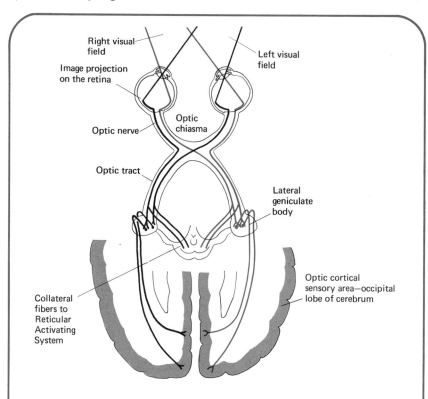

The neuronal circuitry that constitutes the visual pathway is the means by which light-induced impulses from retinal receptor cells are integrated into visual images in the brain. That process begins when light from the visual field enters the eye. What the right eye sees (the visual field) is slightly different from what the left eye sees, although there is a large degree of overlap between the two. The impulses that are generated from the photochemical event are conducted through the nerve cell layers of the retina through the *optic nerve.* The retinal image is actually split as the nerve fibers from the nasal half of one retina cross over in the *optic chiasma* to join the fibers from the temporal half of the opposite (contralateral) retina which do not cross over. Most fibers eventually synapse with cell bodies in the *lateral geniculate body,* which consists of essentially one cell type. At this point it should be noted that some integration has taken place within the retina, and further integration of the visual signal occurs in the lateral geniculate body where many optic fibers converge on a single geniculate body cell. From the geniculate body, fibers course back to the occipital lobe of the cerebral cortex, an area which is termed the *visual cortex.* Some fibers from the optic tract go also to the *pretectal nuclei,* which controls pupillary size.

The lateral geniculate body integrates signals from both eyes and is apparently responsible for depth perception. The visual cortex is responsible for the final integration of the image, a process carried out by the large number of cells which lie in layers in the cortex. From here information about the visual image is sent to other areas of the brain.

module 9B

PROCESSING OF
INFORMATION IN
THE SPECIAL
SENSE ORGANS

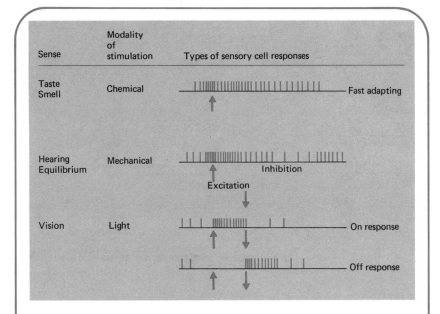

The special sense organs are designed to provide information about specific kinds of stimulus. The receptor cells in the taste buds and in the olfactory tract respond to chemicals, the receptor cells in the retina of the eye respond to light, and the receptor cells in the ear respond to mechanical stimulation. All these forms of stimuli, chemical, light and mechanical, are forms of energy, and the role of the individual sensory cell is to transduce or convert these various forms of energy into electrical energy associated with nerve impulses. A second, but also important function of the receptor cells is to amplify the input signal. Under optimal conditions the human ear has a threshold for sound energy in the order of 8×10^{-18} to 4×10^{-17} watts. To indicate how sensitive the ear receptor cells are, at the rate of 5.10×10^{-17} watts/second it would take 10 billion years to accumulate enough energy to keep a 15 watt bulb lit for one second. The energy output from receptor cells can, in some cases, be as much as a million times the energy of the stimulus.

Receptor cells often produce spontaneous impulses, and stimuli act to change the *frequency* of the spontaneous activity. One advantage of the system of spontaneous activity is the ability of sensory cells to reflect both excitatory and inhibitory activity by changes in the frequency of the firing of these cells. In silent, or nonspontaneously firing receptors, only excitation can be signaled. Many sensory neurons show *adaptation* where the frequency returns to near normal in spite of the continued presence of the stimulus. Thus sensory information is carried in a *frequency code.*

figure 9-14

CONE CELLS

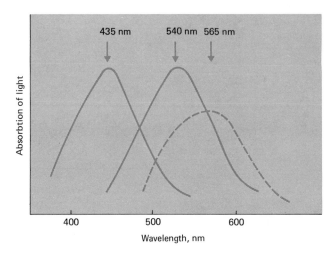

Light absorption patterns for the three types of cone cells responsible for color vision.

is due to obstruction of the flow of aqueous humor from the anterior chamber and, if unrelieved, leads to a situation in which the intraocular pressure is greater than the pressure in the retinal blood vessels. The blood vessels collapse and the retina dies from anoxia (lack of oxygen). Tests for glaucoma are now given routinely as part of the eye examination. A number of medications may relieve the pressure, but in cases in which they fail, the excision of a small portion of the iris provides a

figure 9-15

ULTRA-
STRUCTURAL
VIEW OF
PHOTORECEPTOR
CELLS

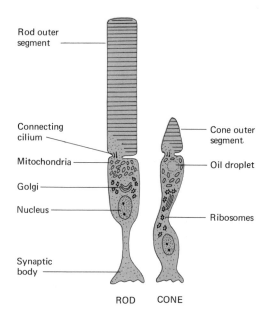

new channel for the movement of aqueous humor, thus relieving the pressure.

Conjunctivitis Inflammation of the conjunctiva is a fairly common eye disease induced by infections or allergic reactions. In the former situation, the eyes appear red and bloodshot, and in the latter, the inflamed area appears cloudy and milky.

the ear The hearing organ can be thought of as having three compartments: an external ear, a middle ear, and an inner ear.

anatomy

The External Ear The flexible, protruding portion of the external ear is the *pinna* or *auricle*, which acts as a sound collector. In man this function is almost negligible, but in animals that have large pinnae and muscles that can move the pinnae to a position that picks up sound most efficiently, the pinnae serve as amplifiers. The *external acoustic meatus* is a canal leading from the pinna to the *tympanic membrane*, the boundary of the middle ear.

The Middle Ear The middle ear, a hollowed-out space in the temporal bone, houses the ear bones (Figure 9-17). The middle ear is connected by the *Eustachian tube* to the nasopharynx, and the arrangement allows the air pressure within the middle ear to equal the external air pressure. Changes in external pressures are noticed when there is a fairly rapid change in altitude, as, for example, in an elevator, airplane, or when diving under water. Such changes make the tympanic membrane bulge and become taut, and a conscious effort such as swallowing is often used to open the Eustachian tube in order to equalize the pressure on the membrane. In

figure 9-16

EFFECT OF
LIGHT UPON
RHODOPSIN

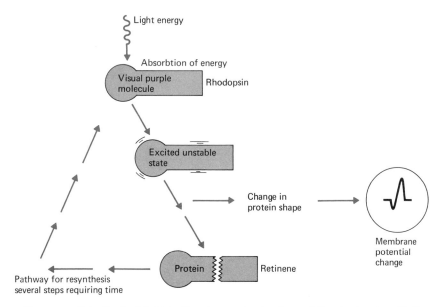

The essential effect of light is the change in structure of the rhodopsin with the resultant separation of the protein (opsin) from the pigment (retinene).

figure 9-17

THE ANATOMY
OF THE EAR

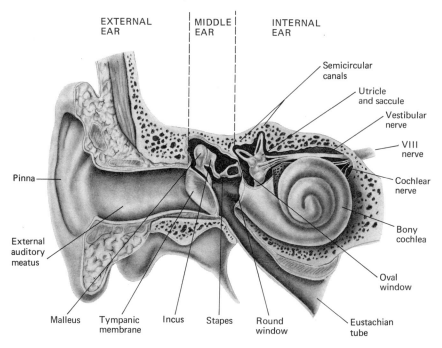

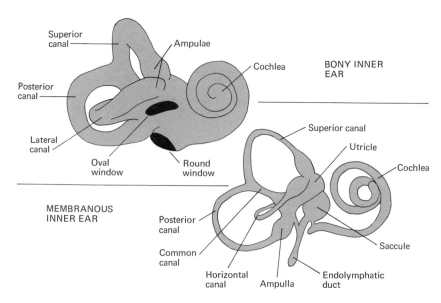

general, changes in pressure are usually gradual and are compensated for spontaneously.

Because of their shapes, the ear bones are given the names *malleus* (hammer), *incus* (anvil), and *stapes* (stirrup). The bones articulate in such a way that they form a continuous pathway from the *tympanic membrane* to the *oval window*, the beginning of the inner ear.

The Inner Ear   The inner ear consists of an *osseous* and *membranous labyrinth*. The osseous labyrinth includes the *vestibule*, the *semicircular canals*, and the *cochlea*, all lined by a membrane that secretes a fluid called *perilymph*. The base of the stapes contacts a membrane-covered opening of the vestibule, the oval window (Figure 9-17). The cochlea has coiled canals which are divided into the *scala vestibuli* (upper) and the *scala tympani* (lower) by the *basilar membrane* (Figure 9-18). The basilar membrane ends short of the apex so the fluid in the canal is continuous. The end of the scala tympani is covered by the round window.

The membranous labyrinth lies within the osseous labyrinth and contains endolymph, a secretion somewhat different from perilymph. In essence the membranous labyrinth is responsible for the formation of a tubelike structure, the *cochlear duct*, within the canals of the cochlea (Figure 9-18). The *organ of Corti* is located within the cochlear duct with the receptor hair cells resting on the basilar membrane. Above and touching the hair cells is the overhanging *tectorial membrane* which may play a role in stimulation of the receptor hair cells (Figure 9-18).

physiology of   Sound, like light, can be viewed as having the form of waves. Sound
hearing   waves are produced by anything that compresses the air molecules in one area while simultaneously producing an adjoining area that is com-

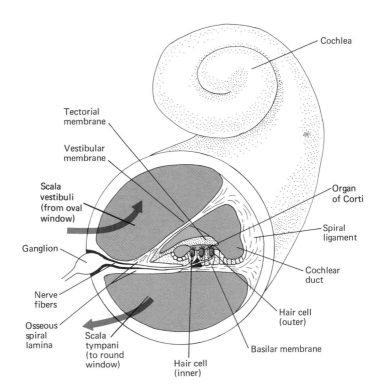

figure 9-18

DIAGRAMMATIC
REPRESENTATION
SHOWING THE
ORGAN OF
CORTI

posed of loosely packed air molecules. Energy is needed for sound-wave production, and the wave moves by air molecules colliding with other air molecules. The individual molecules do not move very far, but the sound wave may travel for miles, depending on the amount of initial energy. Sound travels much more slowly than light (about 1000 feet per second); for example, a man can calculate the approximate distance from where he stands to where lightning strikes by counting the seconds from the light flash until the sound of the thunder reaches him. Thunder is sound created by the expansion of air by the electric discharge, and lightning striking 1 mile away would produce thunder that would be heard approximately 5 seconds later.

The human ear can generally hear sound waves between the frequencies of 15 to 20,000 cycles per second (cps), although with age the higher frequencies tend to be lost, especially in men. Pitch depends on the frequency of the sound wave, and it has been said that humans can distinguish approximately 340,000 different sounds. The difference between threshold levels of sound and loudest level that can be tolerated is 1000 billion times (1,000,000,000,000 times). Using such large figures is awkward, and sound is measured by a logarithmic system; instead of 1000 billion times, which is equal to 10^{12}, each exponent level is called the *bel*. In the above example, the loudest sound level tolerated by the human ear would be 12 bels, the difference between threshold level and maximum. If the sound were 100 times the threshold level, the difference would be 10^2 or 2 bels. In actuality the term decibel (db) (deci = one-tenth) is used for sound measurement. Bel numbers must be multiplied by 10 to convert them into decibels; 2 bels would then be 20 db.

Noise pollution is a serious problem in our society, and excessive sound may lead to degeneration of hearing and in some cases to deafness. Figure 9-19 gives the sound levels of various kinds of activity. Although many states limit the long-term exposure of workers to 80 db, sound levels over this value are commonly encountered. A motorcycle has a sound output of 100 to 110 db, a power lawn mower about 100 db, an elevated train over 110 db, a discotheque at full volume approximately 120 db. (Going from 80 to 100 db is an increase of 100 times.) The sonic boom from jet aircraft creates a sound level of up to 160 db.

The sound wave transmits its energy to the receptor cells via the ear mechanism. After moving through the auditory meatus, the sound waves initiate vibrations of the tympanic membrane, which are in turn relayed through the middle ear bones to the oval window by the plunging action of the stapes. Movement of the oval window inward increases the fluid pressure in the scala vestibuli, moves the basilar membrane, and billows the round window membrane (Figure 9-20). The movement of the basilar membrane is dependent on the frequency and amplitude of the sound; higher-frequency sounds induce wave formations that start on the area of basilar membrane closer to the oval window, whereas lower-frequency sounds cause wave formations to start further along the basilar membrane.

The hair cells rest on the basilar membrane and are so-called because of the regular projections from the cells that resemble cilia. It was once thought that the movement of the hairs caused by changes in pressure in the scala vestibuli was responsible for inducing generator potentials on the cells, but there is evidence that the hairs are stiff rather than flexible and that movement of fluid produces shearing forces at the base of the hair, thereby electrically exciting these cells.

The middle ear makes transmission of sound from air to fluid an efficient process. The energy impinging on the tympanic membrane is eventually concentrated on the smaller area of the oval window with an amplification of about 20 to 1. The ear can also diminish as well as amplify sound energy. Two muscles that are responsive to sound are attached to the ear bones, and the activation of these muscles induces a rapid pulling at right angles to the direction of the bones' movement. The result is a dampening of the motion of the ear bones and a corresponding dampening of the amplification.

clinical considerations
Hearing loss can occur because of loss of ability to conduct the sound by the eardrum, the ossicles, and the oval window, or because of loss of part or all of the nerve function. Examination by use of tuning forks and more sophisticated instruments can reveal whether conduction loss or nerve loss is involved, and in the case of the latter, which frequencies are no longer heard. Properly selected hearing aids can compensate for conduction losses by acting essentially as an amplifier.

figure 9-19

DECIBEL EQUIVALENTS OF VARIOUS SOURCES OF SOUND (NOISE)

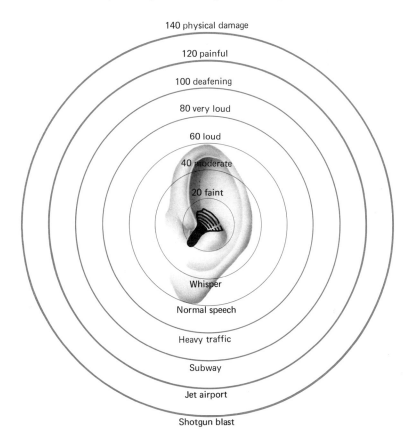

140 physical damage
120 painful
100 deafening
80 very loud
60 loud
40 moderate
20 faint

Whisper
Normal speech
Heavy traffic
Subway
Jet airport
Shotgun blast

figure 9-20

MECHANISM OF
SOUND
DISCRIMINATION

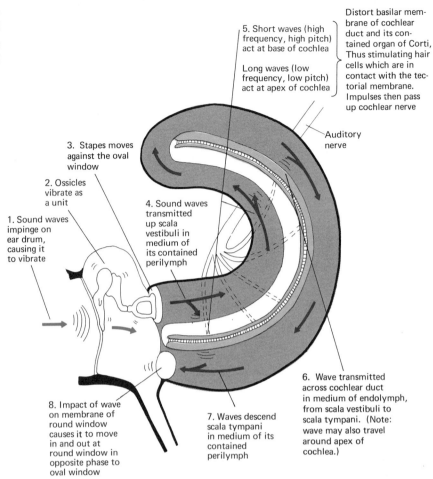

5. Short waves (high frequency, high pitch) act at base of cochlea

Long waves (low frequency, low pitch) act at apex of cochlea

Distort basilar membrane of cochlear duct and its contained organ of Corti. Thus stimulating hair cells which are in contact with the tectorial membrane. Impulses then pass up cochlear nerve

Auditory nerve

3. Stapes moves against the oval window

2. Ossicles vibrate as a unit

4. Sound waves transmitted up scala vestibuli in medium of its contained perilymph

1. Sound waves impinge on ear drum, causing it to vibrate

6. Wave transmitted across cochlear duct in medium of endolymph, from scala vestibuli to scala tympani. (Note: wave may also travel around apex of cochlea.)

8. Impact of wave on membrane of round window causes it to move in and out at round window in opposite phase to oval window

7. Waves descend scala tympani in medium of its contained perilymph

Serous Otitis Media   Serous otitis media refers to a condition in which the middle ear is filled with fluid, generally as a result of respiratory infection or allergic reaction. Unless treated, scar tissue may form and lead to loss of hearing. Drainage is the usual remedy, along with keeping the passages clear.

Chronic Otitis Media   Chronic otitis media refers to a number of infective conditions that may lead to erosion of the ear bones and permanent closing of the Eustachian tube or inflammation of the eardrum. All these cases, unless treated, lead to loss of hearing.

Meniere's Disease   Meniere's disease is characterized by *tinnitus* (hearing noises), *vertigo* (dizziness), and gradual loss of hearing. The disease is due to an overproduction of endolymph, and since the endolymph is continuous throughout the cochlea and the vestibula, both equilibrium and hearing are impaired. The attacks of vertigo are disabling, since they are usually severe and last for several hours. Treatment may cure the vertigo, but invariably it destroys the hearing.

Otosclerosis   *Otosclerosis* is a condition in which the bone of the otic capsule is resorbed and is replaced by irregularly laid down new bone. The new bone
growth covers the oval window and immobilizes the stapes. In some
cases the growing bone causes damage to the VIII nerve. This condition
has been estimated to be present in 4 percent of the population, generally in adults. Treatment involves the use of a hearing aid and in some
cases corrective surgery. In the latter, a new tympanic membrane is
formed from a graft, and a plastic "stapes" replaces the damaged one.

equilibrium   Equilibrium is a function of the *vestibular apparatus*, the posterior
labyrinth which encompasses the *utricle* and the three *semicircular
canals* (Figure 9-17). The endolymph is continuous throughout these
structures, as they are connected directly or by ducts.

The three semicircular canals lie at right angles to one another, each
having an enlarged area at the end called the *ampullae*. The ampullae
contain a septum on which are the *cristae*, composed of aggregates of
sensory hair cells imbedded in a gelatinous matrix. These hair cells are
stimulated by the movement of fluid within the canal, which results
when the head is rotated. Since there are three semicircular canals, one
of them is bound to be affected by rotation of the head in any direction.
The canals are capable of detecting the start of rotation, acceleration of
the rotation, or the stopping of rotation, but not rotation at a fixed speed.

The utricle has outpocketings *(macula)* containing hair cells with tips
imbedded in a gelatinous matrix. Granules of calcium carbonate, called
otoconia or *otoliths*, sit atop the gelatinous material. The hair cells are
at slightly different angles, and movement of the head causes the otoconia to stimulate certain hair cells, sending impulses to the brain.
Interestingly, although the utricle and saccule are similar in structure,
there is no evidence that the saccule is functional in man.

The signals from the semicircular canals are integrated by the central
nervous system, and appropriate signals are sent to muscles, which then
correct for any change in equilibrium. The semicircular canals do not
act in a static situation but are an effective sensory mechanism when
the head is being rotated in some plane.

taste   The ability to taste depends on the substance being in solution and reaching the receptor cells, the *taste cells*. The taste cells are localized in the
taste buds which are found in projections, or *papillae*, on the surface of
the tongue (Figure 9-21a). The taste buds are aggregates of taste cells
arranged in onionlike layers, with their tips projecting toward the taste
pore. The tips of the taste cells have *microvilli*, which are probably
stimulated by food. The taste cells contact the sensory nerve fibers that
carry the stimuli to the central nervous system by way of the trigeminal
and glossopharyngeal nerves.

The sense of taste appears to be limited to four basic tastes – sweet,
sour, salty, and bitter – which are localized in various areas of the tongue
(Figure 9-21b). Various kinds of sugars, glycols, amino acids, and certain salts can elicit a sweet response. Only small amounts of artificial
sweeteners are used in foods, since the receptors are more sensitive to
their chemistry than to natural sugars. Sour taste is generally associated

figure 9-21
TONGUE AND
TASTE BUDS

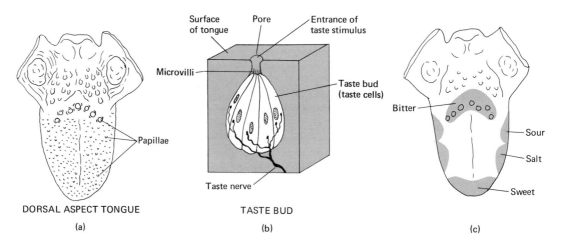

(a) and (b) Structure of the tongue and fine structure of a taste bud. (c) Areas of
specific taste reception on the tongue.

with concentration of hydrogen ions. Salt sensation depends mainly on
concentration, however, and some salts such as potassium iodide do
produce a bitter taste. Bitter taste can be elicited with a variety of compounds. Many poisonous compounds are bitter, and strong concentrations of a bitter substance can cause a rejection of the substance. A
mixture of substances producing only one of the tastes described above
can result in a mixture of sensations. In orange juice we can taste the
sweetness due to the sugar and the sourness due to the citric acid. The
taste depends on the concentration of the sensation-producing substance and the sensitivity of the receptors to that substance. One sensation can override another if its concentration is extremely high in relation to the other. This principle is used in flavoring medicines such as
cough medicine, which is taken in liquid form.

We have discussed taste in isolation, when in fact the eating and
drinking of foods also involve *tactile* (touch) and *olfactory* (smell) sensations. All of these senses lead to the sense of *flavor* that is associated
with food. An easy yet interesting experiment is to hold one's nose while
eating and to determine the taste of the food.

smell   The olfactory organs are located in the upper nasal fossae and include
the olfactory cells that end in a large vesiclelike structure from which
cilia emerge (Figure 9-22). At the basal end, they continue as unmyelinated nerve axons, which form bundles in the olfactory nerve.

How olfaction works is not completely understood. Several scientists
have postulated that the shape of a molecule determines its odor, but
there are inconsistencies that make this theory unacceptable. There is a

figure 9-22

ANATOMY OF
THE OLFACTORY
SYSTEM

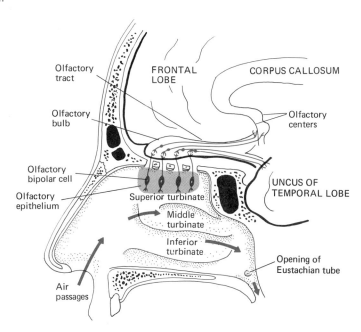

distinct difference in the olfactory organ's threshold for certain odors.
The threshold to vanillin is reached when there are 2 vanillin molecules
for each 10,000,000,000,000 molecules of air, whereas threshold for
diethyl ether is approximately 1 molecule per 1,000,000,000 molecules
of air. Thus sensitivity to vanillin is 10,000 times that of ether.

There are several interesting facets to sensitivity to particular odors.
Just as in most sensory systems, adaptation occurs. However, adaptation to one odor does not necessarily mean diminution of sensitivity to
another odor. In fact, in some cases the threshold to certain odors can be
raised. Some odors that are pleasing at low concentrations are unpleas-
ant at higher concentrations. Interestingly, many such compounds are
used in perfumes.

summary

**gross
anatomy —
the eye**

1. Eyeball: three layers
   (a) fibrous tunic: outermost
       sclera: opaque
       cornea: transparent, highly innervated
   (b) vascular tunic: middle
       ciliary body: ciliary processes, ciliary muscle, and ciliary ring
       iris: ring of circular muscle containing varying amounts of
           pigment
   (c) nervous tunic: innermost
       retina: nerve cells
       epithelial layer
2. Lens: modified elongated epithelial cells
   (a) aqueous humor: fluid in anterior and posterior chambers of
       eye; maintains intraocular pressure and has nutritive function

(b) vitreous body: gelled structure in posterior chamber
3. Ocular muscles
4. Eyelids: tarsal glands, secrete oily lubricant
5. Lacrimal glands: secrete tears

physiology of vision

1. Eye is a dioptric system, has refractive powers
    (a) refraction: bending of light due to slowing of light waves
        convex lens: bends light to converge at focal point
        concave lens: diverges light
        refractive surfaces of eye: cornea and lens; cornea accounts
            for most of refraction
    (b) farsightedness (hypermetropia): image "focused" behind
        retina
    (c) nearsightedness (myopia): image "focused" in front of retina
    (d) astigmatism: distortion of image due to distortion in cornea
    (e) accommodation: adjustment of lens curvature for close vision
    (f) depth of focus: distance from point of focus that an image re-
        mains in focus
    (g) visual acuity: ability to distinguish two close sources of light
    (h) depth perception: based on reference to objects of known size
        and relative movement of objects when head is moved
2. Retina
    (a) receptor cells: face away from source of light
    (b) rods: most numerous, highly sensitive to all wavelengths of
        light
    (c) cones: higher threshold, three types, each with different sensi-
        tivity; responsible for color vision
    (d) synaptic arrangement with bipolar and ganglionic cells allows
        rods to sum up stimuli
    (e) chemistry: photochemical reaction involving protein and vita-
        min A derivative (retinene)

clinical considerations

1. Color blindness
2. Glaucoma: accumulation of aqueous humor
3. Conjunctivitis: inflammation of conjunctiva

gross anatomy — the ear

1. External ear: pinna, external acoustic meatus (canal), tympanic
    membrane
2. Middle ear: Eustachian tube, ear bones
3. Inner ear:
    (a) osseous labyrinth: vestibule, semicircular canals, cochlea, and
        lined by membrane that secretes perilymph;
    (b) membranous labyrinth: lies within the osseous labyrinth, con-
        tains endolymph

physiology of hearing

Sound waves move tympanic membrane; moves ear bones; moves oval
window. Latter movement increases pressure on scala vestibuli, moves
basilar membrane according to frequency of sound; hair cells stimulated
and start impulse to CNS.

clinical considerations

1. Serous otitis media: middle ear filled with fluid
2. Chronic otitis media: infective conditions that may lead to erosion of ear bones and permanent closing of Eustachian tube
3. Meniere's disease: excess endolymph leads to hearing noises, vertigo, and gradual loss of hearing
4. Otosclerosis: new bone growth covers oval window and immobilizes stapes

equilibrium

1. Semicircular canals (3): at right angles to one another; ampullae contain cristae, sensory hairs which are stimulated by movement of fluid when head is rotated
2. Utricle: hair cells in outpocketings, stimulated by otoconia
3. Saccule: communicates with cochlear duct; also contains hair cells stimulated by small carbonate bodies (otoconia)

taste

Taste buds: on surface of tongue, four basic types—sweet, sour, salty, and bitter

smell

Olfactory cells: in upper nasal fossae; mechanism not known

10

blood

formed elements
erythrocytes
leukocytes
platelets

composition of plasma

**hemocytopoiesis and
hemocyte destruction**
formation
destruction
control

physiology
fluid balance
hemostasis and clotting
anticoagulants

temperature control and
respiratory functions
defense mechanisms
acid-base regulation
transport
blood types and
transfusion

clinical considerations
plasma
red blood cells
white blood cells
hemoglobin diseases
platelets
hemophilia
erythroblastosis fetalis
physiological saline

It is a difficult problem to classify blood. Is it a tissue fluid? Is it a "fluid organ"? Or is it merely a composite of many components from different organs? Because blood has so many different functions and constitutes such a large part of the body (about 5 to 7 percent), its treatment in this chapter will be as a "fluid organ," an integral part of the cardiovascular system.

As blood flows through the smallest vessels, fluid escapes through their walls, producing tissue fluid, which in turn bathes the tissue cells. Every cell is affected by the tissue fluid, and, in turn, the tissue fluid reflects the metabolic activity of the cells. This tissue fluid is the "internal environment," and the surprising constancy of the tissue fluid and the blood, in spite of the activity of the cells, constitutes homeostasis.* Many of the functions of blood discussed in this chapter clarify the homeostatic mechanism that maintains the body in a healthy state.

If a volume of blood is placed into a centrifuge tube and spun, separation of solids from fluid is eventually obtained; plasma constitutes approximately 55 percent (Figure 10-1). Each major fraction has many components and many different functions. Actually the blood is so diverse a fluid organ that beyond the introductory level we should avoid using the term "blood" and instead name the specific component when discussing function; for example, platelets are involved in clot formation, and white blood cells are part of a defense mechanism.

formed elements

The formed elements consist of *erythrocytes* or *red blood cells* (RBC), *leukocytes* or *white blood cells* (WBC), and *platelets*. The distribution and general characteristics of these formed elements are summarized in Table 10-1.

erythrocytes (red blood cells)

During development, red blood cells undergo structural changes directly related to their function as carriers of *hemoglobin*. Hemoglobin is a pigmented protein (an essential part of the molecule is iron) responsible for the transport of oxygen and carbon dioxide. The red blood cell goes through a series of maturing stages. In the final stage it loses its nucleus and becomes a container for the respiratory pigment.

With the loss of the nucleus, the red blood cell becomes a biconcave disc, about 7 μ in diameter. Biconcavity shortens the distance that gas

figure 10-1

CENTRIFUGED BLOOD

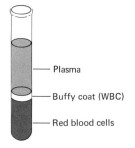

— Plasma

— Buffy coat (WBC)

— Red blood cells

The plasma constituents (55%) being the lightest form a layer on the top of the tube. The white blood cells (WBC) form the thin, middle buffy coat, while the heaviest components, the red blood cells, layer at the bottom of the tube.

* Blood also plays a role in *hemostasis*, discussed in this chapter, and not to be confused with *homeostasis*.

table 10-1
FORMED
ELEMENTS OF
THE BLOOD

CELLS	AVERAGE (CELLS/MM^3)	RANGE (PERCENT WBC^a)	CHARACTERISTICS^b	FUNCTION
Erythrocyte		–	7.5μ	Oxygen and
Male	5,200,000	–	No nucleus	carbon dioxide
Female	4,500,000	–	Biconcave disc	transport
				Buffering
Leukocytes	9000			
Neutrophil	5500	65 to 75	Neutrophilic	
(polymorpho-			staining granules	
nuclear			7 to 9μ	Phagocytosis
leukocyte)			Multilobed nucleus	
			Granular	
			Drumstick^c	
Eosinophil	300	1 to 4	Acid staining granules	Phagocytosis of
			9 to 10 μ	immune com-
			Two-lobed nucleus	plexes;
			Granular (coarse)	Stores small
				amount of
				histamine
Basophils	75	0.5 to 1	Basic staining	Stores
			granules	histamine
			7 to 9 μ	
			S nucleus	
			Granular (fine)	
Lymphocyte	3000	20 to 35	6 to 8 μ (large = 15 μ)	Antibody
			Large nucleus	synthesis
			Scant cytoplasm	
			Nongranular	
Monocyte	500	2 to 8	14 to 20 μ	Phagocytosis
			Round nucleus	
			Abundant cytoplasm	
			Nongranular	
Platelets	250,000 to 450,000	–	3 μ	Hemostasis
			No nucleus	
			Disc-shape	

^{a} WBC = white blood cells.
^{b} Size determined from fresh and not dried blood.
^{c} About 3 percent of neutrophils have a "drumstick-shaped" appendage on the nucleus that can be seen; it is the chromatin of the XX chromosome pair. The appearance of a "drumstick" is a means of identifying the "sex of a cell" (female).

molecules need to travel to and from any hemoglobin molecule. The red blood cell membrane is quite elastic, allowing the cell to change shape easily. This plasticity is an important adaptation. The smallest blood vessel (capillary) invariably has a diameter less than that of the red

figure 10-2

RED BLOOD
CELLS *IN VIVO*

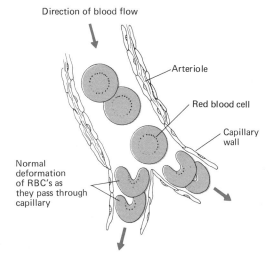

Direction of blood flow

Arteriole

Red blood cell

Capillary wall

Normal deformation of RBC's as they pass through capillary

blood cell, necessitating a shape change for the red blood cell as it squeezes through the vessel (Figure 10-2).

A slightly younger version of the mature erythrocyte, the *reticulocyte*, accounts for approximately 1 percent of the red blood cells. Reticulocytes contain ribosomes and endoplasmic reticulum (hence their name). They are involved in hemoglobin synthesis, in spite of a lack of nucleus and DNA. The cytoplasm evidently contains sufficient RNA to allow for synthesis during the limited life span of the blood cell.

leukocytes (white blood cells)

The white blood cell group is less numerous in total number of cells, but it contains a variety of cells specialized for different functions. The white blood cells are conveniently separated on the basis of their affinity for stains or on the degree of granulation as seen by light microscopy (Table 10-1). Unlike red cells the white cells are true cell types (Figure 10-3) and represent a range from active to quiescent cells. The white blood cells containing granules also contain an enzyme *peroxidase*, which leads us to assume that the granules are lysosomes and are involved in phagocytosis. One type of granular white blood cell, a *basophil*, contains the anticoagulant *heparin*, but the cell's function in the clotting mechanism is unknown. A good example of an actively secreting cell is the *plasma cell*, a subtype of the lymphocyte series, which is involved in antibody synthesis. The plasma cell, in contrast to the mature small lymphocyte, contains more organelles and cytoplasm, signifying a more active cell.

Although the types of white blood cells show sufficient differences to distinguish one from the other, in general it is difficult to correlate the specific function of the white cell types with their ultrastructural modifications. We can say that neutrophils and monocytes, for example, are involved in phagocytosis and localizing infections and that lymphocytes are adapted for antibody production.

figure 10-3

TYPES OF
WHITE BLOOD
CELLS

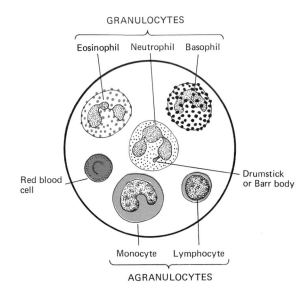

GRANULOCYTES

Eosinophil Neutrophil Basophil

Red blood cell

Drumstick or Barr body

Monocyte Lymphocyte

AGRANULOCYTES

platelets   Platelets undergo structural modification similar to that of erythrocytes as they mature into their final enucleated, disc-shaped cell. Technically platelets are not cells but cytoplasmic fragments of a giant precursor cell called the *megakaryocyte* (mega = large, karyocyte = cell). Nevertheless platelets have organelles for synthesis and in general they are metabolically quite active (Figure 10-4). Platelets are involved in blood coagulation and hemostasis (the staunching of bleeding) – mechanisms that require energy and specific enzymes. Platelets also have other roles that apparently require protein synthesis. For example, they act as carriers of specific substances such as *serotonin.* Serotonin, a powerful agent for smooth muscle contraction, is formed in the lining of the stomach and small intestine; it is picked up at the intestines and transported by the platelets. This continuous action of pickup and release requires the presence of specific enzymes.

figure 10-4

MEGAKARYOCYTE

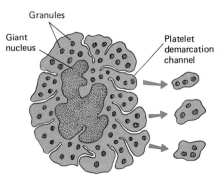

Granules

Giant nucleus

Platelet demarcation channel

Formation of platelets from their precursor cell, the megakaryocyte.

MEGAKARYOCYTE   PLATELETS

table 10-2

CONSTITUENTS
OF PLASMA

COMPONENT	EXAMPLE	APPROXIMATE CONCENTRATION	EXAMPLE OF FUNCTION
Water		90 percent	Universal solvent, transport
Proteins	Albumin	3.2 to 4.5 g/100 ml	Osmotic pressure, pH regulation
	Globulin	2.0 to 3.5 g/100 ml	Immune response
	Fibrinogen	0.2 to 0.4 g/100 ml	Clotting + hemostasis
Carbohydrates	Glucose	60 to 100 mg/100 ml	Source of energy
Lipids	Cholesterol	115 to 340 mg/100 ml	Structural units (cell membranes)
	Triglycerides	10 to 190 mg/100 ml	Cell membrane
Gases	Oxygen (Po₂)	80 to 90 mm Hg/liter	Regulation of breathing; aerobic glycosis
	Carbon dioxide (Pco₂)	35 to 45 mm Hg/liter	Regulation of breathing; pH regulation
Ions	Sodium	136 to 142 meq/liter	Osmosis
	Calcium (total)	9.0 to 10.5 mg/100 ml	Clotting
	Calcium (ionized)	4.2 to 5.2 mg/100 ml	
	Magnesium	1.8 to 3.0 mg/100 ml	Enzyme cofactor
	Potassium	4.0 to 4.8 meq/liter	Nerve transmission
	Flouride	28 mg/100 ml	Hardening of teeth and bone
	Iodine	4.0 to 8.0 μg/100 ml	Thyroid hormone
	Chloride	350 mg/100 ml	Osmosis
Metabolic products	Urea nitrogen	8 to 20 mg/100 ml	
	Uric acid	2.1 to 7.8 mg/100 ml	
	Lactic acid	5 to 20 mg/100 ml	
Other substances	Iron	50 to 150 μg/100 ml	Hemoglobin
	Vitamin A (fasting)	15 to 60 μg/100 ml	Vision
	Vitamin C	0.5 to 1.5 mg/100 ml	Maintains connective tissue
	Amino acid nitrogen	4 to 6 mg/100 ml	Metabolism

Values for gases are given for arterial whole blood per liter.

composition
of plasma

The fluid portion of blood is 90 to 92 percent water and 8 to 10 percent solutes (Table 10-2). Proteins constitute the largest portion of the solute materials, and they provide many of the functions described below. It is believed that life originated in the sea and that land animals evolved from a basic stock which migrated to fresh water. This ancestry is imprinted in the blood in that the concentration of salts in whole blood and in plasma resembles a dilute sea water.

In addition to proteins and salts, plasma contains a variety of nonelectrolytes of which sugars, lipids, and metabolic waste products such as urea are examples. The yellowish color of plasma is due to the presence of bile pigments, which may increase in certain disease states to produce a yellowish cast to the eye and skin. Plasma also acts as a vehicle for the transport of gases and secretory and excretory products.

If whole blood is allowed to clot (Figure 10-5), within a period of time the clot will withdraw from the sides of the tube; the fluid expressed is called *serum*. Serum is primarily plasma minus the protein *fibrinogen*, which constitutes the meshwork of the clot.

hemocytopoiesis and hemocyte destruction

The process of blood cell formation is called *hemocytopoiesis* or *hematopoiesis*. In the adult this activity occurs in two general areas: *bone marrow* and *lymphatic* tissue. Marrow, also called the *myeloid* center, produces red blood cells, some white cells, and platelets. Lymphocytes and monocytes, produced in very small numbers, stem primarily from lymphatic tissue (for example, spleen, tonsils, and nodes); they are termed *lymphoid elements*. The newly formed cells enter general circulation by passing through thin-walled sinusoids found in the myeloid and lymphoid tissues. Whereas most of the red blood cells produced are found circulating in the bloodstream, only a small fraction of the white blood cells circulates (Figure 10-6).

formation

During embryonic and fetal periods there is no separation of the two centers. The earliest blood cells form intravascularly by direct cell division of the lining cells of the primitive blood vessels. The first cells to form are erythrocytes, which manufacture hemoglobin to carry oxygen. Liver and spleen soon take on the primary function of hemocytopoiesis until the middle of the fetal period when the marrow and lymphoid centers start producing cells. In adults, most of the active marrow is found in the ribs, sternum, and vertebra, and to a limited extent in the pelvis, femur, and tibia.

destruction

Little is known about the location and mechanism of blood cell removal from the systemic circulation when these cells are no longer functional. The liver, spleen, and marrow are hemocyte "graveyards," but the best calculations show that less than 10 percent of the blood cells are removed by these organs. Quite obviously, either some other areas are involved in cell removal or the method for calculating cell destruction

figure 10-5

CLOT FORMATION

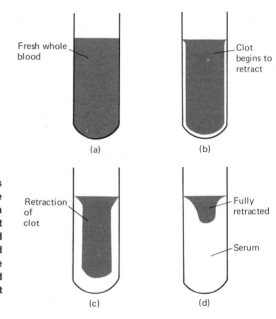

The sequence of events seen as whole blood in a tube undergoes clotting. After a brief period of time, the clot begins to withdraw and serum, a straw-colored fluid which is plasma minus the clotting proteins, is expressed (squeezed out) as the clot retracts [(c) and (d)].

Fresh whole blood

Clot begins to retract

(a)   (b)

Retraction of clot

Fully retracted

Serum

(c)   (d)

figure 10-6

HEMATOPOIESIS

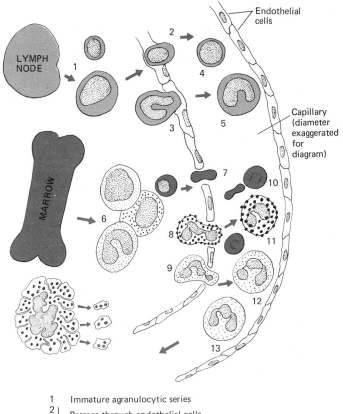

1	Immature agranulocytic series
2 3 }	Passage through endothelial cells
4	Mature lymphocyte
5	Mature monocyte
6	Immature granulocytic and erythrocytic system
7 8 9 }	Passage between endothelial cells (diapedesis)
10	Mature RBC
11	Mature basophil
12	Mature neutrophil
13	Mature eosinophil

The process of formation of blood cells by progressive differentiation. Stem cells in the marrow and lymph nodes undergo division under command of a variety of physiological signals and form specialized replacement cells, which in turn give rise to fully differentiated functional blood cells.

needs improvement. Old platelets are believed to be isolated in the lungs, where they are acted upon by the lung tissue phagocytes, sometimes called *dust cells*.

The life span for an erythrocyte is about 120 days; it is less than 11 days for the white blood cells and platelets. The degradation of cells is not necessarily complete, however, for most of the iron from the red blood cells is reutilized by the marrow to make new red cells.

control   Knowledge about the mechanism controlling blood cell production is
meager. One possible explanation is that as the cells break down, they
form a very simple feedback mechanism—the destruction of the cell
releases its organelles or some other cytoplasmic substance, which then
serves as a stimulus for hematopoiesis. A similar feedback mechanism
could be established on the basis of materials released from the living
cell; for example, as the hemocytes circulate, they secrete an inhibitor
having the ability to turn off stem cell mitosis in the marrow and lymphatic tissues. A hormonal substance secreted by the kidney is believed
to be in operation for the production and release of red blood cells; it is
called *erythropoietin* or *erythropoietic stimulating factor* (ESF). Most
of the evidence supporting the regulation of this stimulating factor is
indirect, for the chemical structure is unknown, and erythropoietin is
difficult to detect in the plasma. Some investigators believe that it is
utilized only when a critical need for red blood cells occurs and that the
normal replacement of red cells (1/120 of the daily volume) is regulated
by another scheme. A possible feedback mechanism is depicted in Figure 10-7.

figure 10-7

REGULATION OF
HEMATOPOIESIS

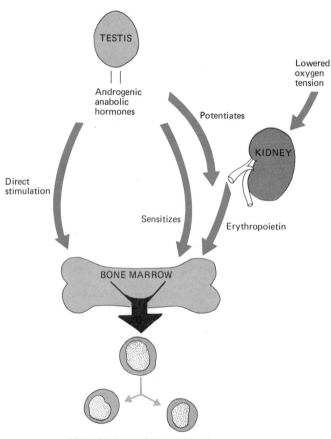

Some physiological factors involved in hematopoiesis.

Other factors are involved in the maturation of blood cells. The development of a red blood cell, for example, needs vitamin B_{12}. The lining cells of the gastrointestinal tract produce a factor that aids in the absorption of vitamin B_{12}, which is then stored in the liver. If there is a lack of gastrointestinal factor or of vitamin B_{12} in the diet, a primary anemia occurs (lack of mature red blood cells). It is for this reason that vitamin B_{12} is called the antianemic factor of the liver.

physiology

fluid balance

Since water is the most abundant molecule in the body's chemical composition, the distribution and balance of water are of great importance to maintaining homeostasis. The movement of certain ions in water, such as sodium, approximates the movement of water, and fluid balance is therefore really a combination of changes in water and electrolyte balance. It is for this reason that the detailed treatment of fluid balance will be discussed in Chapter 16 (Urinary System) and not here.

hemostasis and clotting

Blood is involved in all stages of *hemostasis* (Module 10): (a) constriction of the blood vessel, (b) formation of aggregates of platelets, (c) formation of fibrin strands, (d) the combination of cells and fibrin forming a clot, and (e) the retraction of the clot. Clotting itself involves a number of enzyme-activated events, the details of which are complex and beyond the scope of this discussion. Thirteen different factors are recognized in the formation of a clot, but only the four major factors are presented here.

FACTOR I. Fibrinogen is one of the largest proteins in plasma. Conversion of the fibrinogen to fibrin strands is the essence of the clotting mechanism. The soluble fibrinogen splits into fibrin subunits, which then polymerize into fibrin strands.

FACTOR II. Prothrombin is the precursor of the enzyme *thrombin*, which catalyzes the conversion of fibrinogen to fibrin. Prothrombin is formed in the liver. Vitamin K is important in its synthesis.

FACTOR III. Thromboplastin is a protein-fat complex found in the plasma, within the endothelium, or in the platelets. Thromboplastin in the presence of calcium and other clotting factors forms a *prothrombin activator* that is responsible for the conversion of prothrombin to thrombin.

FACTOR IV. Calcium is involved in almost every major phase of hemostasis.

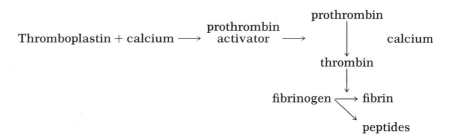

By definition, a stationary clot is called a *thrombus*. A clot or even a fragment of a clot that circulates is called an *embolus*. *Thromboembolism* is a catchall term for the condition in which both events occur.

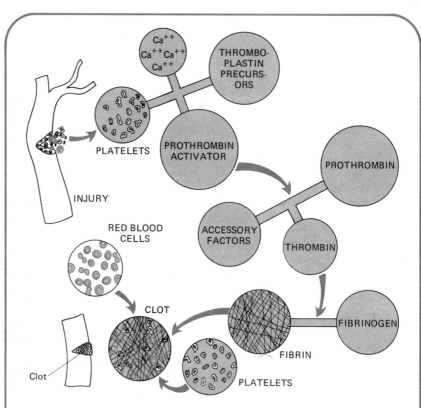

Hemostasis is the arrest of bleeding and involves the constriction of blood vessels, the aggregation of blood platelets to form a plug, and the formation of fibrin strands to reinforce the plug.

The localized constriction of blood vessels is in response to nerve stimulation produced by the injury process. Platelets aggregate at the injured site and by themselves are capable of stopping blood loss from the smaller vessels by becoming attached to the exposed collagen in the injured vessels and releasing compounds that cause other platelets to adhere. Fibrin is formed through either of two pathways, the extrinsic pathway or the intrinsic pathway, the former being the more common. The extrinsic pathway utilizes a lipoprotein from the injured cells, several plasma factors (protein), and calcium ions to produce a prothrombin activator. Thrombin is produced from prothrombin by the enzymatic action of the prothrombin activator, and in turn acts as an enzyme to convert the soluble protein fibrinogen to the insoluble fibrin. The fibrin forms long intertwining strands that trap blood cells and strengthen the clot. Platelets present in the clot cause it to retract, pulling the vessel walls closer together and making the clot tighter. Fibrin can also be formed by the intrinsic pathway, in which platelets supply the lipoprotein and in which additional plasma factors produce the prothrombin activator. The pathway shown above from prothrombin down is common to both pathways, the portion to the left constitutes the initial portion of the extrinsic pathway, while the portion shown near the top constitutes the initial part of the intrinsic pathway.

Clot Retraction

As mentioned earlier in the chapter, blood placed in a test tube will clot within a short period of time, and within an hour the clot will undergo retraction (Figure 10-5). Clot retraction is likely to occur in vessels, although it has not been truly documented. If clot retraction does occur in a blood vessel, perhaps it functions to strengthen the clot, thereby effecting a better blockade. Another possibility is that retraction would tend to bring the torn walls in closer approximation, especially in smaller vessels. Any of these events would aid in the arrest of bleeding.

Clotting and Bleeding Times

Two informative procedures utilized by the clinician are *clotting* and *bleeding times*. In a nontreated glass tube, normal blood incubated at 37°C will clot within 6 to 17 minutes. Abnormal clotting time frequently is a sign of serious disease, such as *hemophilia*. However, there is a variety of blood diseases that still have normal clotting times. Bleeding time is measured by pricking the earlobe or the fingertip and blotting the wound with absorbent paper at intervals until the bleeding stops. Normally, the blots will disappear in 6 to 9 minutes or less. Bleeding period beyond this time span is an indication of platelet deficiency or absence of a clotting factor (again, such as hemophilia).

Clotting is not always a desirable event, and the body has means for breaking down accidentally formed clots. *Fibrinolysins* or *plasminogens* are enzymes that circulate in the plasma and break down fibrin. The plasminogens are believed to be synthesized by endothelial cells.

anticoagulants

The mast cells of connective tissue secrete a carbohydrate called *heparin*. Heparin has multiple functions in that it (a) inhibits the activation of prothrombin and (2) prevents existing thrombin from catalyzing the conversion of fibrinogen to fibrin. It is doubtful if sufficient heparin circulates in the blood at any one time to act as a meaningful anticoagulant, but larger concentrations of heparin injected into the body will serve to prevent coagulation. A commonly used anticoagulant, commercially called *Dicumarol*, retards the formation of several clotting factors in the liver. For example, vitamin K is needed for the formation of prothrombin; Dicumarol competes with vitamin K in the reaction and blocks the formation of prothrombin.

For storage of blood outside the body, the most frequently employed compounds are *citrate, oxalate salts*, and *EDTA (ethylenediamine tetraacetate)*, which bind with calcium. This reaction effectively removes calcium as a factor in coagulation.

temperature control and respiratory functions*

defense mechanisms

The nucleated blood cells are all involved in defense, especially against foreign materials such as bacteria. The cells serve in three ways. First, the granulocyte neutrophil is phagocytic and will engulf harmful substances. To a lesser extent the eosinophils and basophils are also phagocytic. Material ingested into these cells is then acted upon by the cell's lysosomes (see Chapter 1). Monocytes can escape from the bloodstream into adjacent tissues and transform into macrophages or phagocytes. Second, the lymphocyte-plasma cells are capable of forming antibodies in response to antigenic stimulation. A major part of the gamma globulin

* See Chapters 15 and 17 for a discussion of these topics.

figure 10-8

BLOOD
BUFFERING

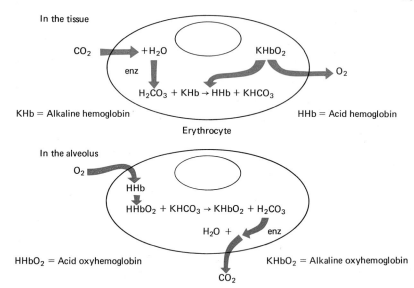

Blood buffering as one of the major factors involved in pH regulation.

fraction of the plasma is composed of antibodies manufactured by lymphocytes. Third, blood cells leave the vessels and populate other defense centers such as the *reticuloendothelial* system, a network of cells and fibers found in organs such as the spleen and liver. The ability of cells to squeeze through the endothelial wall and leave (or enter) the bloodstream is called *diapedesis;* the steps of diapedesis are outlined in Figure 10-6.

acid-base
regulation

To maintain its normal 7.4 pH, blood must be able to accommodate rapidly to the addition of the acids or bases that enter the blood in its exchange with tissue fluids (Figure 10-8). The major buffers of the blood are plasma proteins, hemoglobin in red blood cells, phosphate complexes, and the bicarbonate ion. As carbon dioxide is picked up by the blood, it forms carbonic acid with water. The acid will dissociate into hydrogen and bicarbonate ions ($CO_2 + H_2O \rightarrow H^+ + HCO_3^-$). Hydrogen ions from cell metabolic reactions enter the bloodstream immediately, combining with the free bicarbonate ion to form carbonic acid — a very weak acid. In this way, very strong acids are converted into weak acids, keeping the pH approximately at the neutral level. The bicarbonate system as a buffer is important, because the extracellular bicarbonate level is high (20 times as much bicarbonate as carbonic acid) and because most of the carbon dioxide formed by metabolism is eliminated during exhalation.

If a strong base entered into the bloodstream, it would combine with carbonic acid (not all of the acid disassociates) to form bicarbonate and water. Even though the buffering system is not an absolute one, the production of a weak acid from a strong acid, or a neutral salt from a strong base, is a very important homeostatic mechanism in maintaining proper acid-base balance. Because it is difficult to determine the concentration of plasma carbon dioxide and bicarbonate concentration, clinical laboratories measure the carbon dioxide combining power of the blood plasma (the so-called alkali reserve). Under normal circumstances, the carbon dioxide combining power is about 30 mmoles/liter, but may increase dramatically in severe alkalosis or decrease sharply in severe acidosis.

transport   Blood transports many materials to the systems; some samples of these materials are as follows:

1. *Nutritional material:* carbohydrates, fats, proteins, vitamins, and amino acids.
2. *Regulators:* hormones, vitamins, enzymes, and neurosecretory substances.
3. *Wastes:* carbon dioxide, urea, uric acid, and nitrogenous breakdown products from sources other than proteins.
4. *Gases:* carbon dioxide, oxygen, and nitrogen.
5. *Defense materials:* phagocytes, immunoglobulins, clotting factors, fibrinogen, and anticlotting substances.

blood types and transfusions   Red blood cells carry on their membranes specific proteins acting as antigens. Two important ones are designated by the capital letters A and B. The activities of antigens and their corresponding antibodies are described in greater detail in Chapter 24. Some red blood cells have A, some have B, and others have both A and B. Cells with neither A nor B are designated as O. Therefore four major possible red blood cell types can be described on the basis of their antigenic material—A, B, AB, and O. In the plasma there are "natural" antibodies corresponding to each of these proteins. These are designated as *anti-A* and *anti-B*, or by Greek letters α or β. It is not known why the body has these antibodies which agglutinate the red blood cells if they come in contact with them.

The determination of the red blood cell antigen and the plasma antibody is genetically controlled, and naturally circulating antibodies (or *agglutinins*) against an individual's own red blood cells are not common. In certain clinical conditions such as anemia or hemorrhage, the transfusion of blood to restore blood volume to levels needed for adequate perfusion of the tissues has become a standard procedure. Since not all blood is compatible, care must be exercised in selecting proper blood donors. In practice, blood typing of the donor precedes the transfusion, and if time permits the recipient's blood should be crossmatched with the donor's to prevent incompatible reactions such as agglutination or lysis which could be fatal to the recipient.

In order to ascertain compatibility of blood types (Table 10-3), the bloods of the donor and recipient are crossmatched. In this procedure the plasma and cells of both recipient and donor are separated by centrifugation and the donor's red blood cells with their antigens are incubated with the recipient's plasma containing agglutinins. If, after incubation at 37°C for 20 minutes, no hemolysis (breakdown of red blood cells) or agglutination occurs, then it is assumed that the donor and recipient are compatible (Figure 10-9).

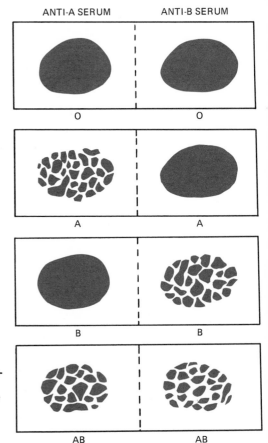

figure 10-9

BLOOD TYPING
FOR
COMPATABILITY

Blood typing prior to giving a blood transfusion is essential in determining compatability between host and donor blood. Membrane bound antigens may react with plasma antibodies to cause agglutination as shown on the right.

Other procedures for typing blood are used. To determine one's blood type, two basic sera are used – anti-A and anti-B. If the red cells are agglutinated by alpha (α), the person is classified type A. Agglutination with beta (β) serum classifies type B. Agglutination by both alpha and beta means the blood is AB; if there is no agglutination with alpha and beta, the blood is then typed O.

We can also see from Table 10-3 that type O blood could theoretically be utilized as a universal donor, since the red blood cells do not react with any agglutinins. As a rule, however, transfusions are given with a specific blood type, and only in an emergency would an O donor be used for a type A, AB, or B individual. Even though the O red blood cells would not agglutinate in the plasma of the recipient, the O blood contains antibodies against A and B and would affect the recipient's own red blood cells by producing clumping. However, since the patient has so many red blood cells in comparison to the antigens infused, the degree of agglutination would be relatively slight and thus not produce serious complications.

The genes controlling the major blood types are dominant; that is, they will exert their activity if present. The absence of red blood cell antigens

table 10-3
ABO BLOOD
TYPES

GROUP[a]		AGGLUTINOGENS ON THE RBC	AGGLUTININS IN THE PLASMA
Genotype	*Phenotype*		
AA	A	A	β
AO			(anti-B)
BB	B	B	α
BO			(anti-A)
AB	AB	AB	None
OO	O	None	α and β
			(anti-A + anti-B)

	Sera		
anti-A	anti-B[a]	Cells
+	+	AB
−	+	B
+	−	A
−	−	O

[a] Genotype = the specific gene at a specific locus on the chromosome.

Phenotype = a group or a class to which an individual can be assigned on the basis of one or more genes.

A plus sign indicates agglutination.

A minus sign indicates no agglutination.

or agglutinogens producing type O blood is a recessive characteristic.

There are many other blood types (M, N, P, Hr, and so on) that can cause rare transfusion reactions, but these factors are generally poorly antigenic, and the resulting transfusion reactions are usually of minor importance. In addition the genic frequency of these groups is relatively low.

One important subtype is the *Rh factor*, so named because it was discovered in the blood of experimental rhesus monkeys. The Rh factor is an antigen found on the red blood cell membrane. In Europe, this antigen occurs in 85 percent of the population, and the individuals are classified as Rh positive (Rh⁺). Individuals who do not have this factor are classified as Rh negative (Rh⁻ or rh). Unlike A, B, O, and AB types, the plasma never contains an Rh agglutinin. However, agglutinins can be made artificially if an Rh-negative person receives Rh-positive blood. If sufficient antibodies to the Rh factor are produced, it can bring about a destruction of the red blood cells. A disease of pregnancy that affects the fetus, *erthroblastosis fetalis*, is discussed in another section of this chapter.

Unlike A, B, O, and AB types, the Rh factor is a little more complicated in that the full genetic statement depends on three genes on three different chromosomes. These genes are designated as *CDE* or *cde*. Each parent contributes only one set of genes. Thus a chromosome may contain *D* or *d*, but not both. Although there are as many as 50 different genetic combinations, only six types are common in most populations and are presented in Table 10-4.

The knowledge of blood groups has values other than for use in transfusion. Because blood groups are genetically controlled, they can be used for identification, sometimes necessary in legal situations. Ethnologists

table 10-4
EXAMPLES OF
Rh BLOOD
GROUPS[a]

GENOTYPE	PHENOTYPE	PERCENTAGE[a]
CDE/CDE	Rh+	2
CDe/cde	Rh+	33
CDe/CDe	Rh+	17
cDe/cDE	Rh+	12
cDe/cde	Rh+	2
cde/cde	rh	15

[a] Caucasian population of European ancestry.

(scientists who deal with the origin and distribution of human races) use blood groups as a marker for determining racial origins and migration. For example, the American Indian is 88 percent type O blood, whereas the Asiatic Indian is only 30 percent type O blood. Chinese and Australian aborigines are considered to be 100 percent Rh positive.

clinical considerations

When discussing clinical aspects related to blood, the reader must keep in mind that blood alterations may directly reflect a disease of the cells themselves or a disease condition of a nonvascular tissue. For example, *leukemia* is a disease of the hemopoietic centers in which the number of white blood cells is increased. However, a person can have a higher white blood cell count (*leukocytosis*) caused by infection—for example, from an inflamed appendix. In both examples, the white blood count is elevated, but the latter elevation is a response (a defense mechanism) to an infection located in some part of the body and not to cancer of the blood. The magnitude of the increase is also a significant piece of information in diagnosis.

plasma

Three organs are primarily responsible for maintaining the contents of the plasma: the liver, kidneys, and lungs. Damage to any one of these organs would affect the composition of the blood plasma, protein synthesis, electrolyte concentrations, and acid-base balance.

red blood cells

Deficiency of red blood cells is more common than excess, but both conditions can produce serious disease. *Anemia* is a lack of red blood cells or a deficiency of the hemoglobin content per cell. Sometimes, although the number of red blood cells is normal, they are immature and do not contain enough hemoglobin (primitive red blood cells have nuclei that take up considerable room). Anemias can be caused by a variety of conditions such as diet, tumors of the hemopoietic center, and liver damage (Figure 10-10). A disease that *directly* retards the marrow's production of erythrocytes is called a *primary anemia;* a *secondary anemia* results from the direct loss of erythrocytes, such as by bleeding.

white blood cells

A deficiency of white blood cells is termed *leukopenia* (leukemia and leukocytosis represent states of increased white blood cells)—see Figure 10-11. Leukopenia frequently occurs with infectious diseases such as tuberculosis or virus pneumonia, and a white blood cell count is an aid in making a diagnosis. Prolonged and extreme leukocytosis can produce an anemia, since only a limited amount of cells can be carried by

figure 10-10

THE
ANEMIAS

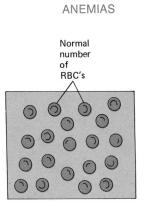

Normal
number
of
RBC's

Cause:
   stem cell
   failure;
   hematopoietic
   failure;
   i.e., radiation

Cause:
   bleeding
   or loss of
   mature cells;
   i.e., hemolysis

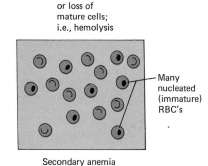

Fewer
cells

Many
nucleated
(immature)
RBC's

Normal   Primary anemia   Secondary anemia

the plasma. If the white blood cell count goes up, the red blood cell and platelet count generally goes down.

Infectious mononucleosis is a relatively common disease of young adults, the causes of which are unknown. The symptoms are usually swollen glands (lymph nodes), fever, and a general tiredness. The blood picture is characterized by an increased number of monocytes.

hemoglobin   Hemoglobin abnormalities can result from inheriting an abnormal gene
diseases   or genes. The abnormal hemoglobins are identified by a letter (C, E, S, and others). For example, hemoglobin S causes the disc-shaped red blood cell to take on a sickle shape. This change of shape may be correlated with a weak red cell membrane that results in red blood cell hemolysis and produces the disease called *sickle-cell anemia* (Figure 10-12).

platelets   Inadequate platelet production or excessive platelet destruction produces the disease *thrombocytopenia*. Bleeding and coagulation times

figure 10-11

LYMPHOCYTIC
LEUKEMIA

Normal red
blood cells

Immature
monocytes

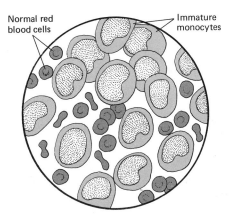

Under normal circumstances only a few mature monocytes are seen in a sample of blood. However, cancer of the hematopoietic centers causes an abnormal leukocytosis (increase in number of WBC). Large numbers of immature, relatively undifferentiated lymphocytes are seen in the blood and red cell production and function is impaired.

figure 10-12

SICKLE-CELL
ANEMIA – A
GENETIC
DISEASE

**Among some peoples of
Mediterranean or African
origin there is a high incidence of an abnormal gene
for hemoglobin. If this gene
is present, the abnormal
hemoglobin causes the normal disc-shaped red cells
to assume a sickle shape,
and these abnormal cells
are fragile, tend to break
down (hemolysis), and thus
cause serious anemia.**

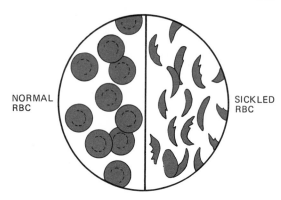

NORMAL
RBC

SICKLED
RBC

may be prolonged, and the structural integrity of the small vessels can
break down. Hemorrhagic diseases result from a deficiency of platelet
factors as well as low concentrations of plasma thromboplastin. It is
obvious that external bleeding following an injury or even the simple
removal of a tooth can be a very serious problem, but even greater dan-
gers lie in the undetected internal bleeding of muscles, membranes, or
organs. Bleeding into joints is a frequent manifestation of hemophilia,
producing inflammation and even deformities (Figure 10-13).

The abnormal bleeding from microvessels is frequently termed *purpura,* and many diseases produce it. Microbleeding is also characterized
by small blotches on the skin called *petechiae,* also a reflection of capillary fragility. One clinical test for measuring the structural soundness of
small blood vessels is to apply suction pressure and to study the petechial
formation. One interesting facet of petechial formation is that the mechanism of red blood cell escape from the capillaries is still unknown.

Hemophilia

One of the specific factors necessary for clotting is *antihemophilic globulin* (AHG). An absence or even a diminution of antihemophilic globulin
leads to poor thromboplastin activity, which, in turn, affects thrombin
production. The net result is a prolonged clotting time, and the individual
is termed a "bleeder." The disease is a sex-linked recessive trait, carried
by the female but manifested in the male.

Erythroblastosis
Fetalis

Because of the low frequency of the Rh-negative gene in a population,
if a woman is Rh negative, the odds are all in favor that her husband
will be Rh positive. The Rh-positive gene is dominant. Therefore when
pregnancy occurs, the chances are that the fetus will also be Rh positive (RhRh or Rhrh). Generally in the first pregnancy such a blood type
difference between the mother and fetus is not serious. However, if the
Rh-negative woman has had several previous pregnancies, and each
fetus was Rh-positive, she could be sensitized to Rh. The Rh antigen
escapes from the placenta in the earlier pregnancies and enters into the
maternal circulation producing an immune response, namely, anti-Rh
agglutinins. The fetus of the last pregnancy would therefore be exposed
to these agglutinins that were previously manufactured and retained by
the mother. They pass freely from the maternal to the fetal circulation
and, if the level of these antibodies were sufficiently high, it could cause

figure 10-13

HEMOPHILIA

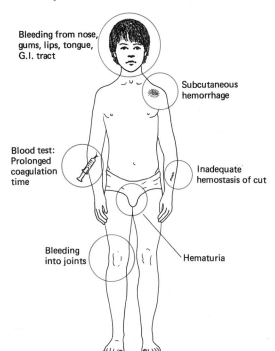

Bleeding from nose, gums, lips, tongue, G.I. tract

Subcutaneous hemorrhage

Blood test: Prolonged coagulation time

Inadequate hemostasis of cut

Bleeding into joints

Hematuria

Manifestations of hemophilia, a genetic blood deficiency disease.

agglutination and breakdown of the fetal red blood cells; death of the fetus *in utero* may occur. The seriousness of this disease has been minimized greatly in recent years by the judicious use of gamma globulins (see Chapter 22 on antibodies and antigens).

physiological saline

Fluid therapy is a common procedure for patients who have lost serious amounts of water and salts as such or indirectly through blood loss. Fluid is needed to restore pressure as well as to replace solutes. The first requirement is that the administered fluid be isotonic with the body fluids. Second, the relative amounts of sodium, calcium, potassium, and magnesium must be balanced. Unlike the cations, the anions are of lesser importance, but generally chloride is preferred. When fluids are introduced into the body by means other than by mouth, the procedure is termed *parenteral.* Sometimes parenteral administration of an isotonic glucose solution will be given along with the balanced salt solution.

summary

1. Erythrocyte: red blood cell (RBC) with a major function of gas transport.

formed elements

2. Leukocytes: white blood cell (WBC); protection by localizing infections, phagocytosis, and antibody production
    (a) granular: neutrophil, basophil, acidophil (eosinophil)
    (b) nongranular: lymphocytes, monocytes

3. Platelets: principal cell involved in coagulation, thrombosis, and hemostasis; platelets may possibly nurture the microvasculature by releasing specific secretions

plasma
1. Composition
   (a) water
   (b) proteins: principal proteins are albumin, globulin, and fibrinogen
   (c) electrolytes: salts
   (d) nonelectrolytes: sugars, lipids, urea, bile pigments
2. Serum: plasma minus fibrinogen

hemocytopoiesis and hemocyte destruction
1. Production
   (a) bone marrow (myeloid centers)
   (b) lymphoid tissue
2. Destruction
   (a) liver
   (b) spleen
   (c) marrow
   (d) lungs (remove platelets)
3. Control
   (a) erythropoietin stimulating factor: raises the hormone erythropoietin level, which stimulates production and release of RBC
   (b) feedback mechanisms theorize for WBC and platelets; based upon substance(s) released when blood cells die which stimulate the marrow and lymphoid organs to produce more WBC and platelets

physiology
1. Water balance
2. Hemostasis and clotting
   (a) clotting times: blood in a nontreated glass tube will clot at 37°C within 6 to 17 minutes
   (b) bleeding time: a small wound made by the gentle pricking of an earlobe or fingertip to produce bleeding will stop within 6 to 9 minutes (sometimes less) as the wound is blotted with absorbent paper
   (c) anticoagulants
      heparin: produced by mast cells; inhibits activation of prothrombin and conversion of fibrinogen to fibrin by existing thrombin.
      Dicumarol: commercial anticoagulant
      calcium complexing and chelating compounds: citrate, oxalate, EDTA (ethylenediamine tetraacetate) bind with calcium and are used for blood storage outside of the body
3. Temperature control
4. Respiratory function
5. Defense mechanisms
   (a) phagocytosis
   (b) antibody synthesis
   (c) reticuloendothelial system
6. Acid-base regulation (blood buffers)
   (a) plasma protein
   (b) hemoglobin
   (c) bicarbonate ion
   (d) phosphate complexes

7. Transport
   (a) nutritional materials: proteins, carbohydrates, fats, amino acids, vitamins
   (b) regulators: hormones, vitamins, enzymes
   (c) wastes: carbon dioxide, urea, uric acid
   (d) gases: carbon dioxide, oxygen, nitrogen
   (e) defense: globulins, clotting factors, anticoagulants, phagocytes
8. Blood types
   (a) major antigens: A, AB, B, O, Rh+ (positive) and Rh− (negative)
   (b) poorly antigenic types: M, N, P, Hr

clinical con-siderations

1. Leukemia: increase white blood cell numbers produced by a malignancy
2. Leukocytosis: increase white blood cells produced in response to an infection
3. Leukopenia: decrease number of circulating white blood cells
4. Primary anemia: marrow production of erythrocytes is retarded
5. Secondary anemia: low number of erythrocytes due to direct loss as in hemorrhage
6. Hemoglobin abnormalities: change in proteins produces change in shape and other manifestations as seen in sickle cell anemia
7. Thrombocytopenia: inadequate platelet production
8. Thrombocytosis: abnormal number of circulating platelets
9. Purpura: abnormal bleeding from the microvessels
10. Hemophilia: poor thrombin production due to the absence of the antihemophelic globulin; a sex-linked recessive trait carried by the female and manifested in the male
11. Erythroblastosis fetalis: disease state that affects the fetus due to incompatibility between mother (rh) and fetus (Rh); antibodies to Rh are produced by mother that enter the fetal circulation and break down the erythrocytes containing Rh factor
12. Physiological saline: a balance salt solution used to restore pressure and ions in the circulation following an abnormal loss of fluid and salts as would occur in hemorrhage

11

the heart

gross anatomy
location
pericardium
surface anatomy
chambers
blood supply
nerve supply

cellular and tissue special-izations

physiology
cardiac cycle
cardiac output
electrocardiogram
   (ecg or ekg)
heart sounds
pulse

control
neural regulation

hormonal control
chemical substances

factors influencing function
respiration
temperature
posture
anemia
exercise
age

clinical considerations
myocardial ischemia and
   infarction
fibrillation
cardiac arrhythmias
cardiac valve deficiencies
pericarditis
coronary artery disease
cardiac failure

The heart has always been viewed with awe. To primitive man it was a source of courage. In some societies a man could be assured bravery by merely eating the heart of the vanquished or of some noble beast such as the lion. To a citizen of the Middle Ages the heart was the center of the intellect and governed man's behavior. Even to this day we use the phrase, "He has a good heart," to describe a warm, generous human being. Physiologically, it would be more accurate to state that "He has a good brain" when describing some aspect of man's behavior. Although we now have a better concept of heart function, its dramatic appeal has not been lessened.

In spite of its essential importance in human function, the heart is structurally a singularly unimpressive organ, being merely a bag of muscles. Only when we study its performance does its uniqueness become evident. Daily, the heart pumps over 10,000 quarts of blood, and assuming an average rate of 70 beats per minute, the heart beats almost 100,000 times a day. It is doubtful if another human muscle could perform at this rate without tiring within minutes.

The heart functions as a pump to maintain adequate blood flow throughout the body. Actually the heart is a double pump. The right side, receiving blood from the body, pumps it to the lungs, and the left side, which receives the blood from the lungs, pumps it to all of the other organs.

The term *cardi* refers to the heart. Thus *myocardium* is heart muscle; *cardiovascular* refers to heart and blood vessels; *cardiac arrest* is when the heart suddenly stops; and *electrocardiogram* is the electrical record of events that occur during the contraction of the heart.

gross anatomy

location

The heart is a cone-shaped organ located in the *mediastinum*, the space in the thoracic cavity between the lungs. The heart's position is at an angle, so that more than half of the organ lies to the left of the midline (Figure 11-1). The top, or *base*, of the heart is at the level of the space between the second and third ribs (second intercostal space). The bottom, or *apex*, is on line with the fifth intercostal space.

pericardium

Because the heart moves freely when it beats, it needs some structure to separate it from the surrounding organs; otherwise friction might produce lesions on the respective organs. Even though the heart resides in the mediastinum, it is still enclosed in its own sacular structure, the *pericardium*. The pericardium is a fibrous connective tissue envelope consisting primarily of two layers: an inner serous layer that adheres so closely to the heart muscle that it actually becomes the outer covering of the heart, and the outer fibrous layer, which connects at the base of the heart to the large arteries and veins. Separating these two layers is a potential space, the *pericardial cavity*, containing a thin watery film that keeps the pericardial membranes lubricated. Certain heart diseases result in fluid accumulation, and the potential pericardial space then becomes a real cavity or reservoir.

surface anatomy

In Figure 11-2, an interior view of the heart is illustrated. Most of the heart's base is formed by the two receiving chambers, the *atria* (*atrium*, singular) and the great vessels (the aorta, pulmonary arteries, and the

figure 11-1

HEART IN SITU

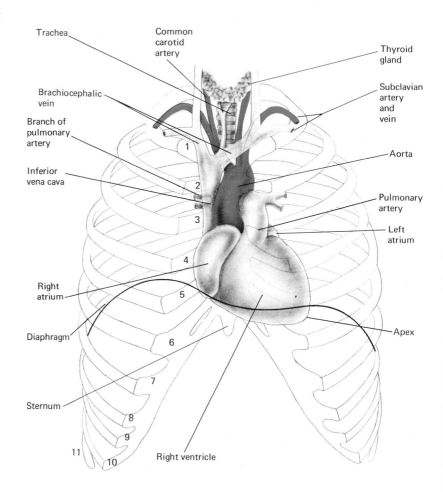

Trachea

Common carotid artery

Thyroid gland

Subclavian artery and vein

Brachiocephalic vein

Branch of pulmonary artery

Aorta

Inferior vena cava

Pulmonary artery

Left atrium

Right atrium

Diaphragm

Apex

Sternum

Right ventricle

superior vena cava). Part of the atrium forms a little external flap and is called the *auricle.* The thick-walled *ventricles* form the main body of the heart; the lower end of the apex is primarily the left ventricle.

The general demarcations of the cardiac chambers are seen on the external surface as grooves. The coronary artery branches (blood vessels of the heart) follow the grooves as they course to various parts of the heart.

chambers   The right and left atria are thin-walled muscular chambers (Figure 11-2). The right atrium receives the poorly oxygenated blood returning from all parts of the body by way of two principal veins, the superior and inferior vena cava. Also opening into the right atrium is the *coronary sinus*, which marks the entrance site of the returning blood from the heart wall per se. The smaller left atrium receives the four pulmonary veins linking the lungs to the heart.

On the floor of each atrium is a channel leading into the corresponding

figure 11-2

AN INTERIOR
VIEW OF THE
HUMAN HEART

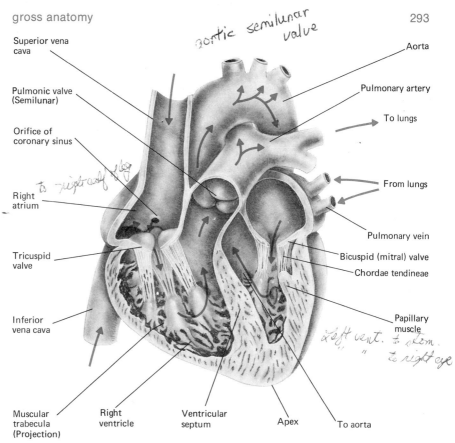

aortic semilunar valve (handwritten)

Superior vena cava

Aorta

Pulmonic valve (Semilunar)

Pulmonary artery

To lungs

Orifice of coronary sinus

Right atrium

From lungs

Tricuspid valve

Bicuspid (mitral) valve

Chordae tendineae

Pulmonary vein

Inferior vena cava

Papillary muscle

Muscular trabecula (Projection)

Right ventricle

Ventricular septum

Apex

To aorta

ventricle, the *atrioventricular* opening. On the right side, the opening is guarded by the *tricuspid* valve, and on the left side, the corresponding valve is called the *bicuspid* or *mitral* valve. These valves are so named because structurally they are composed of cusps or flaps of the heart lining that close as the chamber fills up with blood (Figure 11-3). This closure prevents blood leaking in from the atria to the ventricles as they are filling. Small muscles *(papillary)* attached by tendons *(chordae tendineae)* prevent them from inverting (Figure 11-2).

Semilunar valves guarding the junctions of the major vessels emerging from the heart permit blood flow in only one direction and control the flow in and out of the heart. Similarly constructed semilunar valves are found throughout the veins and perform the same function of keeping the blood flow in one direction.

blood supply   It seems odd that an organ receiving thousands of milliliters of blood per minute in its chambers would need a separate blood supply. This vascularity is necessary, because the heart's walls, particularly the ventricles, are so thick that most of the muscle cells are too far removed from the blood flow through the atria and the ventricles to receive sufficient nourishment.

Coronary arteries are the major source of blood flow to the heart walls. These vessels are the first to branch off the aorta; they branch at

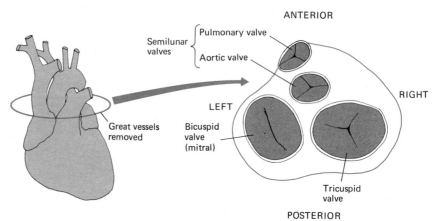

figure 11-3

SECTION OF THE HUMAN HEART SHOWING HEART VALVES

almost the very point where the aorta leaves the heart. Because of their location in relation to the aorta, the heart is assured of receiving blood under the highest pressure available as well as blood rich in oxygen and nutrients.

Each of the major branches, the *right* and *left coronary arteries,* follows a groove around the heart, giving off many branches that *anastomose* (intercommunicate) and supply the heart tissues. Blood is drained into small cardiac veins, and eventually these tributaries empty into the large venous channel, the coronary sinus (Figure 11-4).

figure 11-4

THE CORONARY CIRCULATION

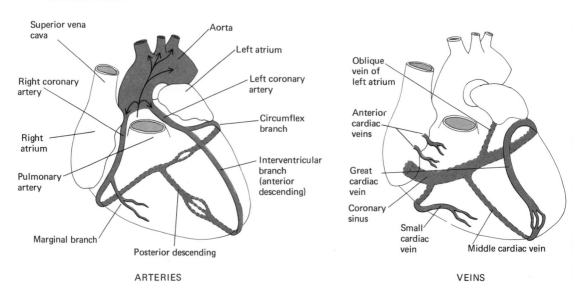

It has been reported that coronary blood flow ranges from 2½ to 10 percent of the total cardiac output, but this range is only an estimation.

nerve supply   Although cardiac muscle has an intrinsic rhythmicity, that is, it will alternately contract and relax without any outside stimulation, the heart does have a highly organized conducting system for impulse transmission. This conducting system produces a coordinated contraction of the atria and ventricles that would not be possible if the action potential merely diffused from one muscle fiber to another.

Sinoatrial Node   Located in the back wall of the right atrium is a specialized mass of cardiac muscle, the *sinoatrial node* (S-A) (Figure 11-5). If this node is excised from the heart, it will beat approximately 70 per minute. Thus, the S-A node is the point of impulse origin and also the primary controller of heart rate. For this reason, the S-A node is termed the *pacemaker*, and its rhythmic depolarization is the basis for the rhythmic contractions of the entire heart.

Atrioventricular Node   In the lower part of the right atrial wall is another node, the secondary pacemaker or *atrioventricular node (A-V node)*. Impulses reaching the A-V node are delayed for a few hundredths of a second before going to

figure 11-5

THE PACEMAKER
AND CONDUCTING
SYSTEM OF THE
HEART

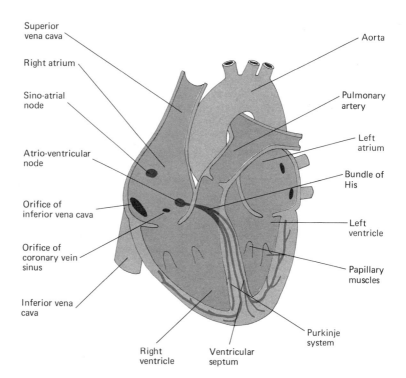

Superior vena cava
Aorta
Right atrium
Pulmonary artery
Sino-atrial node
Left atrium
Atrio-ventricular node
Bundle of His
Orifice of inferior vena cava
Left ventricle
Orifice of coronary vein sinus
Papillary muscles
Inferior vena cava
Purkinje system
Right ventricle
Ventricular septum

Specialized bundles of heart muscle tissue (the nodal tissues) behave as metabolic clocks rhythmically discharging (depolarizing and repolarizing) so that pacemaker tissues and their conducting fibers assure coordinated synchronous sequence in the contraction of the auricles and ventricles.

the ventricles. This lag permits atrial emptying before ventricular contraction commences.

Bundle of His and Purkinje Fibers

From the A-V node, the action potential passes through a group of specialized cardiac muscle fibers adapted primarily for transmission and not for contraction. These fibers are called the *bundle of His*. The bundle (actually right and left bundle branches) passes down through the interventricular septum until it reaches the heart apex, and then it gives off branches to the left and right myocardial walls. The branches subdivide, and the terminal portions are called the *Purkinje* fibers. This system provides a more rapid impulse conduction to all ventricle parts (at least five times more rapid than if the stimulus had to pass through the cardiac muscle tissue per se). Because of the rapid conduction of the action potential, all muscles in the large ventricles on both sides contract simultaneously instead of in a gradual wave, producing a much more efficient pump.

In summary, impulses start at the S-A node and slowly travel through the atrial muscle wall producing a contraction. The stimulus is picked up by the A-V node, which delays the impulse for a fraction of a second. Then the signal is sent through the bundle of His to the Purkinje fibers in all parts of the ventricle to produce a contraction (Figure 11-5).

The extrinsic nerves supplying the heart stem from the vagus nerve (parasympathetic) and from the $T1$ to $T4$ spinal nerves (sympathetic).

cellular and tissue specializations

In many respects cardiac cell structure resembles that of skeletal muscle cells but with several specific features (Figure 11-6). Cardiac fibers contain more mitochondria than the skeletal muscle cells. Since the heart never truly rests, in the sense that skeletal muscle may not be used for extended periods, cardiac muscle cells require a steady source of energy provided by the mitochondria.

figure 11-6

MICROSCOPIC AND ULTRA-STRUCTURAL VIEWS OF CARDIAC MUSCLE

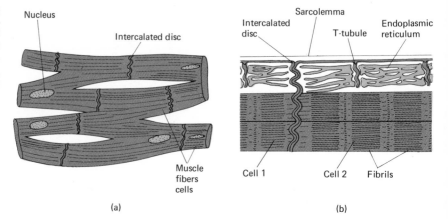

(a)   (b)

The structural organization of heart muscle as seen under the light microscope and the electron microscope show many similarities between heart muscle and skeletal muscle however, cardiac muscle shows a great deal of branching and the presence of intercalated discs (connections between muscle cells).

Where adjacent fibers meet, end to end, the zone is seen as a dark wavy line. These areas are called *intercalated discs* (Figure 11-6). The details of an intercalated disc resemble desmosome connections of epithelial cells referred to elsewhere. The intercalated discs, however, provide for a much greater interdigitation between the adjacent cells than observed in epithelial cells. Since the shortening of one muscle fiber affects the adjacent fiber, it is possible that the intercalated disc provides a more efficient connection between cells, thus producing the smooth synchronous contraction seen in the beating heart.

Traditionally, cardiac muscle is described as forming a *syncytium;* that is, the cell membrane is incomplete and bridges with adjacent cell membranes. However, electron microscopic studies have shown conclusively that cardiac cells are distinct entities. Although there is no anatomical syncytium, cardiac muscle fibers do form a great number of branches, providing a structural arrangement for rapid impulse spread through heart tissue. In addition, at the intercalated discs, the membrane resistance to conduction is low. Thus, functionally cardiac muscle behaves as a syncytium.

Heart muscle cells contract more slowly than skeletal muscle, but they do have a much longer refractory period. Probably the heart's unique feature is the muscles' innate contractility. The heart can be separated from the organism, placed in a jar with the proper nutrients, and it will continue to beat for hours without any extrinsic stimulus; even excised parts of the heart will beat independently.

The bulk of the heart wall is composed of cardiac muscle tissue and is referred to as the *myocardium.* These muscle fibers are uniquely arranged in circular and oblique fashion, so that with each contraction, the heart figuratively "wrings itself out of blood." The inner lining of the heart is the smooth *endocardium;* it is composed of squamous epithelium and a thin layer of fibrous connective tissue, and it provides an almost frictionless surface for the blood. The covering layer of the heart was discussed previously as part of the pericardium.

physiology

cardiac cycle

The design of the heart is such that the right side receives blood into its atrium from the systemic circulation by way of the two large veins, the anterior and posterior vena cavae, and the small coronary sinus (Figure 11-2). From here blood passes into the right ventricle, which, upon contraction, forces it into the pulmonary arteries going to the lungs. Blood returns from the lungs into the left atrium and then goes into the large left ventricle, from which it is pumped out to all the organs of the body with the exception of the respiratory tissue of the lung. Frequently the right side of the heart is called the *pulmonary pump,* and the left side is referred to as the *systemic pump.*

The actual contraction period of the heart is called *systole,* and the relaxation period is called *diastole.* In Figure 11-7, the cycle on the heart's left side is illustrated, showing relative pressures at each phase. The right side of the heart functions similarly except that the pressure values are considerably lower.

The cycle begins with the activation and contraction of the atrium. The atrium pressure is greater than the ventricle's, and blood passes

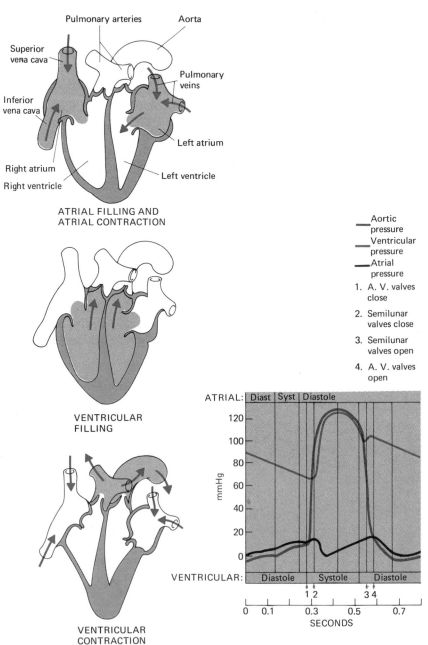

figure 11-7
THE CARDIAC
CYCLE

ATRIAL FILLING AND
ATRIAL CONTRACTION

VENTRICULAR
FILLING

VENTRICULAR
CONTRACTION

through the mitral valve to the ventricles. After the ventricles fill, they begin to contract (systole). The pressure builds up until it is greater than the atrial pressure, and the mitral valve closes. During this time no blood can be ejected out of the ventricles until the blood pressure exceeds the pressure in the aorta to open the aortic valve guarding the exit. Ventricular contraction maintains the high pressure that exceeds the aortic pressure until the systolic phase is completed; not until the ventricle empties does the pressure fall below the aortic pressure, and the aortic valves close once again. During ventricular diastole, the ventricular pressure drops to a level below the atrial pressure. The mitral valve again opens, and the ventricles slowly fill once more repeating the cycle.

A cardiac cycle on the average lasts about 0.8 second and provides a heart rate of about 70 to 75 beats per minute. The atrial systole lasts about 0.7 second, and ventricular diastole lasts about 0.4 second. Normally, a second impulse cannot spread along the same muscle tissue for approximately 0.3 second; during this time, the heart is said to be *refractory*. The speed of an impulse through any part of the heart is quite rapid. For example, the duration of conduction through the ventricles is on the average of 0.6 second, or a rate of about 3 to 4 per second in the Purkinje fiber.

cardiac output

In a resting condition, the heart ejects 5.5 liters of blood per minute through the aorta, and this blood volume is called the *cardiac output (CO)*. With each contraction (HR = heart rate) 80 ml of blood leaves the ventricle; this quantity is referred to as the *stroke volume (SV)*, each ventricle having a stroke volume of 80 ml of blood. Thus the cardiac output can be simply expressed as

Rest

$$CO = SV \times HR$$

Exercise

Variations in cardiac output during exercise are proportional to the degree of effort involved. During extreme physical exertion, the output can increase five to six times, or over 30 liters per minute. However, there is a limit to the extra work the heart can perform. This stored potential is frequently referred to as the *cardiac reserve*. Even mild exertion will produce a 25 percent increase in cardiac output. Because of their training, athletes generally have a higher stroke volume and cardiac output but a lower heart rate. The proportional decrease in a well-exercised heart's rate over a length of time is an important survival factor in that the heart is less taxed. The first man to break the 4-minute mile had an exceptionally large but normal heart. His cardiac output at rest was of such magnitude that the heart rate was less than 40 beats per minute. When this athlete's heart rate tripled, his heart was beating at 120 beats per minute, a rate considerably less than the doubling of a heart rate of a normal, healthy but untrained individual (75 × 2 = 150 beats).

Starling's Law

Starling's "law" states that a relationship exists between cardiac fiber's length prior to contraction and the force of their contraction (analogous to skeletal muscle). The application of this law would be as follows. During exercise the blood returning to the heart increases due to the massaging effect of the contracting skeletal muscles on the veins (Chapter 12) and the increase in cardiac output due to heart stimulation. Consequently, this increased blood volume increases the venous pressure in the atria and ventricles, stretching the heart muscles. The stretched or enlarged heart would then contract more forcefully to produce a greater stroke volume and cardiac output.

Recent evidence, however, shows that the human heart does not increase in size (except during strenuous exercise), nor is there any appreciable increase in venous pressure during exercise. The higher cardiac output is attributed to action of the sympathetic nervous system (Chapter 8) and possibly to adrenal hormones (Chapter 18) increasing the heart rate. However, even if increase in stroke volume were due primarily to increased heart rate following sympathetic stimulation, this effect does not necessarily mean that the Starling mechanism is never in operation. What may occur is that during normal events, nerve control operates, and the *Starling effect* is seen only in an abnormal condition; or the *Starling mechanism* is an imperceptible part of all cardiac muscle contraction even when the heart is stimulated during exertion (for example, operating on a beat-to-beat basis to assure that the outputs of the right and left ventricles are maintained equally).

electro-
cardiogram
(ECG or EKG)

When the muscle walls of the atria or ventricles are stimulated, an action potential spreads along the fibers similar to that described for skeletal muscle. During and prior to this contraction period, a minute amount of electric current also spreads to the skin. Naturally, when the cardiac muscle is at rest, no voltage will appear on the surface of the body. When the myocardium is excited, it goes through a series of well-characterized electrical changes as a function of time; the surface electric potential between two points on the skin will also change with time. Because of this phenomenon, it is possible to record and study the heart's action without exposing it or utilizing internal probes. Surface electrodes are used to measure the electric current emanating from the excitation of the heart. The procedure is called *electrocardiography,* and the record is an *electrocardiogram* (ECG). The electrocardiogram records the potentials as fluctuations on a moving paper strip, or the cardiac pattern can be viewed on an oscilloscope screen.

The physics of electrocardiography involves not only the actual current spread, but also those factors interfering with current distribution and the heart's position with relation to the electrodes placed on the skin. The most frequently employed system to record heart action is to place electrodes on the arms and legs, measuring the voltage between any two electrodes, or to use a single-lead electrode on different parts of the chest and compare the records. A characteristic normal recording is illustrated along with abnormal recordings in Figure 11-8.

The electrocardiogram is used frequently in diagnosis and for monitoring hospitalized patients with diagnosed heart diseases. By hooking the oscilloscope to a patient, the clinician can maintain a constant vigil of the patient's heart activity. The impulses also can be translated into sounds, so that the observer may either listen to or view the patient's heart action.

heart sounds

The orderly phases of the cardiac cycle produce distinctive sounds that can be heard with a stethoscope. The first sound ("lub") is produced by the closure of bicuspid and tricuspid valves, marking the beginning of ventricular systole. The second shorter sound ("dub") occurs at the end of ventricular systole and is the result of the closing of aortic and pul-

figure 11-8

NORMAL AND
ABNORMAL
ELECTROCARDIO-
GRAMS (ECG)

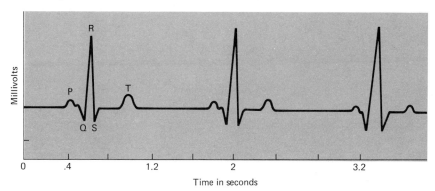

Time in seconds

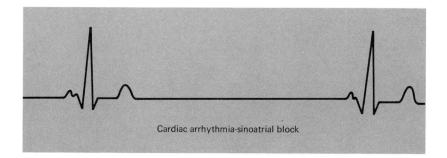

Cardiac arrhythmia-sinoatrial block

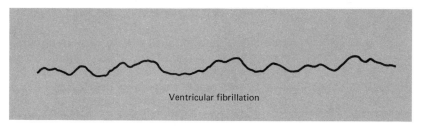

Ventricular fibrillation

In the normal ECG the P wave represents depolarization of the auricles, the QRS represents depolarization of the ventricles, and the T wave represents ventricular repolarization.

monic valves. The blood's rush into the ventricles creates a vibration occasionally heard as a third sound during diastole. The actual sound of the heart, as well as the rate, is important in studying the heart. By placing the stethoscope at various locations on the chest wall, specific parts of the heart can be heard. For example, the mitral valve action can be heard by placing a stethoscope over the intercostal space between the third and fourth ribs. Other positions for the stethoscope are diagrammed in Figure 11-9.

pulse   When blood is forced into the aorta, a pressure wave is created that travels along the aorta and its branches. This pressure expands the arteries. In areas where the artery lies close to the surface and over an

figure 11-9

ANATOMICAL
AREAS FOR
LISTENING TO
HEART SOUNDS

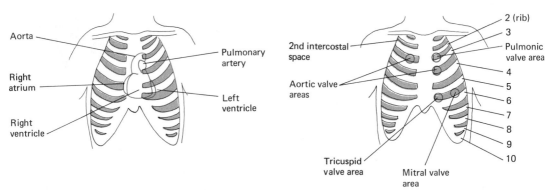

Aorta

Pulmonary
artery

Right
atrium

Left
ventricle

Right
ventricle

2nd intercostal
space

Aortic valve
areas

Tricuspid
valve area

Mitral valve
area

2 (rib)
3
Pulmonic
valve area
4
5
6
7
8
9
10

ANTERIOR SURFACE OF
HEART PROJECTED ON CHEST

CARDIAC AREAS FOR AUSCULTATION

**By placing the stethoscope at different sites on the chest specific heart sounds
can be clearly heard. Thus, if there was a mitral valve defect (lup-ssss-dup) it could
be best picked up at the intercostal space between the third and fourth ribs.**

unyielding surface (a bone), the expansion or *pulse* can be *palpated*
(felt). The radial artery at the wrist is a site commonly used for recording
pulse rate. Each pulse beat is in synchrony with cardiac systole and occurs about 0.1 second later. Pulse strength reflects the cardiac output;
during exercise the pulse is very strong, and following hemorrhage the
pulse is very weak. Pulse may be obtained in areas other than the wrist
such as the temple, mastoid process, and ankle.

control   At any moment, the demand for blood by the tissues varies, and the heart
accordingly responds by adjusting the cardiac output. Exercise, resting,
and unusual emotional states are but a few of the conditions that can
alter the metabolic requirements of the tissue and affect a change in
heart action. Although the heart does have an intrinsic contracting capability, mechanisms must be present whereby the heart can respond to
the metabolic tissue requirements. The important mechanism is neural
control and, to a lesser extent, control by circulating humoral elements,
but the overriding regulation of the heart is the body tissues' utilization
of oxygen. (Module 11)

neural   The parasympathetic stimuli travel by way of the X cranial nerve to a
regulation   terminal ganglion located in the wall of the heart (Figure 11-10). The
short postganglionic neurons then go to the pacemaker. Sympathetic
motor impulses start from the upper thoracic spinal nerves (*T1* to *T4*),
and after synapsing in the vertebral or cervical ganglia, the postganglion
fibers travel in the cervical nerves and penetrate all parts of the heart.

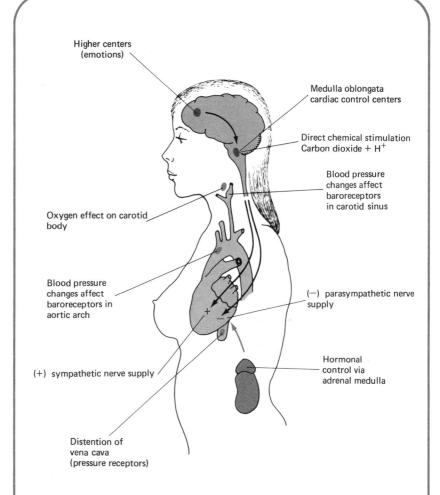

Higher centers
(emotions)

Medulla oblongata
cardiac control centers

Direct chemical stimulation
Carbon dioxide + H⁺

Blood pressure
changes affect
baroreceptors
in carotid sinus

Oxygen effect on carotid
body

Blood pressure
changes affect
baroreceptors in
aortic arch

(−) parasympathetic nerve
supply

Hormonal
control via
adrenal medulla

(+) sympathetic nerve supply

Distention of
vena cava
(pressure receptors)

The heart's automatic rhythmicity is the result of specialized pacemaker tissues which spontaneously discharge (depolarize). This depolarization spreads
via a conducting system in such a way that the heart muscles contract in a
coordinated pattern. Superimposed over the automatic rhythmicity are both
chemical and neural influences which may modify the cardiac output to meet
the demand of the environment, thus in an emergency the cardiac output
would be increased, and after the emergency or physical demand ceased,
the cardiac output would be decreased. The cardiac control centers (an accelerator center and an inhibitory center) are located in the medulla oblongata.
These cardiac control centers respond to a variety of neural and chemical
signals (shown in diagram) that alter cardiac output via the sympathetic and
parasympathetic branches of the autonomic nervous system which innervate
the heart. The cardiac control centers also respond directly to changes in
carbon dioxide concentration and pH, and the heart itself is sensitive to hormones of the adrenal medulla (epinephrine and norepinephrine).

figure 11-10
NEURAL CONTROL
OF THE HEART

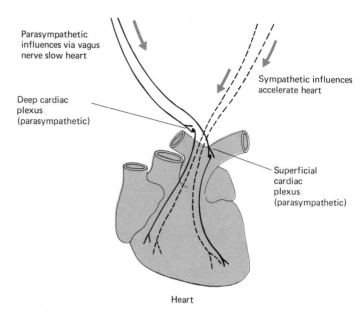

Parasympathetic
influences via vagus
nerve slow heart

Sympathetic influences
accelerate heart

Deep cardiac
plexus
(parasympathetic)

Superficial
cardiac
plexus
(parasympathetic)

Heart

Like many other visceral organs the heart is dually innervated. Parasympathetic (cholinergic) fibers in the vagus nerve slow the heart, while sympathetic fibers (andrenergic) speed the heart.

The vagus also contains the sensory neurons that transmit impulses from the heart to the central nervous system.

Cardiac Inhibition-
Stimulation

If the vagus nerve is cut on either side, the heart immediately responds by accelerating to almost double its normal rate. This indicates that the vagus nerve tends to impose a continuous *braking* effect on the heart. Most heart rate adjustment is proportional to the amount of vagal stimulation. It is as if a vehicle were under constant acceleration and the adjustments in rate of speed were dependent on how often a brake was applied. In contrast, sympathetic stimulation is used almost exclusively when the body is under stress or in an emergency in which there is an abnormal call for blood. The action of the sympathetic nervous system on the heart is to override rapidly the inhibitory effect of the vagus and to excite the cardiac tissue.

Cardiac Centers

Inhibitor-stimulator control centers governing nerve-stimulation output to the heart are located in the medulla of the brain (Module 11). Within these centers, impulses from the brain's higher parts, or sensory impulses directly from the body, come in contact with motor nerves going to the heart. For example, seeing an alarming object or witnessing a traumatic event is "recognized" in the cerebrum. Impulses resulting from observing this event are eventually transmitted to the medulla, where it stimulates the motor neurons in the *cardiac accelerator center* to increase the number of sympathetic impulses reaching the pacemaker regions of the heart, and thereby accelerate heart rate. If the cerebral stimulus is of a lesser nature, the action may simply affect a depression of vagal stimulation that will also elevate the heart rate.

General sensory information, for example, temperature changes in the skin, will bring about a corresponding change in heart action; depending on the nature of the stimulus, a specific part of the cardiac center will be stimulated. The same procedure is also associated with pain; a blow to the solar plexus not only is registered in the cerebrum as pain, but an impulse is also transmitted to the *cardioinhibitory center* of the medulla, where it is transferred to the vagus to bring about a slowing down of heart action. Sometimes heart action inhibition, because of the impact on the solar plexus, is so great that a temporary abnormal low blood pressure results producing fainting. (Other factors also can come into play as we see in the next paragraph.)

Special Receptors and Cardiac Reflex

In the aorta's walls are specialized nerve endings known as *pressoreceptors*, which are extremely sensitive to blood pressure changes (Figure 11-11). When the blood vessel walls are stretched, the pressoreceptors are stimulated. The impulse is carried to the medulla, where it excites the cardioinhibitory center to decrease the heart action. This re-

figure 11-11

CHEMO-
RECEPTORS AND
BARORECEPTORS
OF THE ARTERIAL
SYSTEM WHICH
AFFECT THE
HEART

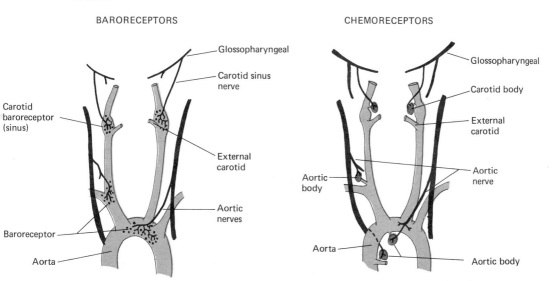

A variety of sensory signals feed directly into the cardiac control centers in the medulla oblongata to modify the sympathetic and parasympathetic influences on the heart. Several sensory receptors important in regulating cardiac output are shown above.

flex helps prevent blood pressure from becoming too high. The sensory motor circuit is called the *aortic reflex*. Nerves with similar pressoreceptors are also found in a depression or sinus in the wall at the bifurcation of the common carotid artery. Likewise, when these vessels dilate, the pressoreceptors are stimulated and initiate the *carotid sinus reflex*.

In addition, within the aorta and carotid arteries are several small bodies (about 1 mm in size), the *aortic* and *carotid bodies*, which contain *chemoreceptors*. The chemoreceptors respond to changes in the oxygen and carbon dioxide content of the blood. When oxygen concentration drops, the chemoreceptors are affected. They send an impulse to the cardioaccelerator center to increase heart action sufficiently to compensate for the diminished oxygen supply per volume of blood. Other lesser cardiac reflexes are present, but their actions play a relatively small role in the normal regulation of the heart.

hormonal control   If all the nerves to the heart were severed, the heart would continue beating. What is unusual is that a heart in this condition will beat in relation to body needs, indicating that some other type of control is present. This second type of regulation is referred to as *hormonal control*, since the hormones involved in the regulation are compounds carried by the blood.

The transplant heart serves as an excellent model for illustrating hormonal regulation. When the heart is removed, all nerves and blood vessels are of course cut. When the transplanted heart is put into the patient, however, only the blood vessels are rejoined. The heart transplant therefore is without neurogenic regulation. When the heart transplant recipient exercises, no immediate pulse change is recorded. But 1 to 2 minutes later, the pulse rate will increase. This time lag reflects the period required for hormonal mediators to accumulate and travel to the heart effecting some regulation.

Epinephrine and   The hormones epinephrine and norepinephrine are secreted by the
Norepinephrine   adrenal medulla; both affect the heart in a manner similar to the sympathetic division of the autonomic nervous system in that they produce an increase in heart beat rate and force. Epinephrine specifically shortens the time of contraction.

Thyroxine   Thyroxine is a hormone synthesized by the thyroid gland and increases the metabolism of all cells. When metabolic rates are increased, the need for nutrients and waste removal is also increased. The heart responds by increasing its cardiac output. In addition to this indirect effect on the heart, thyroxine also has a direct action on cardiac muscle, increasing its excitability, which in turn produces an increase in heart rate.

chemical   In addition to various hormonal agents, the heart is also affected by
substances   general circulating chemical substances. For example, the strength of the cardiac muscle contraction appears to be dependent on the concentration of calcium and phosphate ions inside and outside the individual muscle fibers, respectively. Whether it is the calcium level within the individual cells or the loss of potassium from the cardiac muscle cells

that affects the contraction is not entirely certain. However, that ions are
involved in autoregulation of the heart appears to be a valid assumption.

Serotonin   Serotonin is stored in the platelets. In experimental animals, it has been
demonstrated that it produces a stimulating effect on the cardiac muscles (sustained contraction and increased rate). Serotonin is similar in
chemical structure to another important secretion, *histamine*. Histamine is released from all damaged cells, but it is especially stored in
mast cells and basophils. Whether or not histamine also directly affects
heart tissue is not fully documented.

factors influencing function

As a person breathes in, the cardiac output increases; with exhalation,
the cardiac output will fall. This change in output is due to changes in
the intrapleural pressures of the lungs, which will be discussed in
Chapter 15.

respiration

temperature   Temperature will produce an increase in the rate of oxygen consumption by the tissues, leaving a slight *anoxic* (lack of oxygen) condition,
and cardiac output will be increased to relieve the anoxia. The increased
cardiac output that is observed during exercise or when an individual
has a high fever is due in part to the elevation of body temperature.

posture   Cardiac output depends on the blood's return into the heart. When a person is upright, the blood in the lower extremities must overcome the pull
of gravity. This gravitational factor causes the blood flow to slow down,
producing "pooling" of blood in the legs. The net result is a slight decrease in cardiac output. In an erect position the heart rate may show 5
to 10 beats more per minute than in a reclining position.

anemia   Any condition resulting in hemoglobin decrease, either by cell loss or a
failure to synthesize sufficient hemoglobin, produces a relative anoxic
condition in the tissues. The cardiac output will therefore increase as a
homeostatic response to the insufficient oxygen transport system. In this
way, a proper oxygen amount is provided to the tissues. When there is a
serious loss of red blood cells resulting from hemorrhage, the effect on
cardiac output is compounded by fluid and other blood cell loss. These
deficiencies will affect viscosity and blood pressure, which in turn will
alter the cardiac output.

exercise   During exercise, muscle metabolism increases with a concomitant decrease in oxygen. This deficiency brings about vasodilation of the muscle
vessels, allowing the blood to pass through the tissues with little resistance and return rapidly to the heart. The net result of the added flow to
the heart is increased cardiac output. In addition, physical exertion
brings the sympathetic portion of the autonomic nervous system into
play, which stimulates heart rate.

age   At birth the heart beat is between 125 and 150 beats per minute, and the
count gradually decreases with age until the normal adult resting rate
of 70 beats per minute is reached. The changes in heart rate related to

age are due to various complex factors that cannot be included in this discussion.

clinical considerations

Each heart has its own capacity for performing labor. Whenever the occasion arises for increased activity, the heart can call upon its cardiac reserve to meet the demands. The same way that some individuals are weaker than others, some normal hearts have less strength and less cardiac reserve. Hearts that are abnormal by birth and disease must call upon their cardiac reserve so frequently that the excessive taxation on the muscles limits the life span of the heart.

myocardial ischemia and infarction

When the coronary blood supply to the heart is reduced, a relative anoxia develops, which affects the repolarization of the heart muscle cells and reduces heart action. If the blood supply to part of the myocardium is completely cut off—for example, blockage of a branch of the coronary artery—the muscle cells in the area will die. The lack of blood supply to a restricted area is called *ischemia*, and if this lack leads to cell death, it is called an *infarction*. This condition is one of a number of causes that can produce a "heart attack." In both cases, the remaining heart muscle must compensate for the contractile tissue loss. After an infarct, the dead tissues are phagocytized, and tough scar tissue forms in the damaged region. Frequently, the remaining healthy tissue will enlarge and permit full return to all normal activities.

fibrillation

Heart contraction is an efficient, orderly, and coordinated activity. If for any reason the muscle fibers contract in a random fashion, fibrillation occurs. Ventricular fibrillation is usually fatal, because the blood is not ejected from the heart, and thus the coronary and cerebral circulation that are both critical for life will fail. Examples of conditions that produce ventricular fibrillation are lack of oxygen or a physical stimulus of long duration, for example, the passage of an electric current through the body (electrocution).

cardiac arrhythmias

Variation of the rate, rhythm, or synchrony of the heart are called *arrhythmias*. *Bradycardia* refers to a slowing down of the heart beat, and the opposite condition is called *tachycardia*. When an impulse to the heart is interrupted, a variety of arrhythmias can occur. For example, if the Purkinje bundle is completely blocked, the ventricles no longer receive an impulse from the S-A node. *Heart block*, as the condition is called, is readily detected by an abnormally slow pulse and a characteristic change in the electrocardiogram, indicating that the ventricles are beating independently of the pacemaker, at their own intrinsic rhythm rather than in conjunction with the atrial contraction.

cardiac valve deficiencies

If the valves guarding the entrances and exits to the heart fail, the chambers do not fill properly, the fibers do not contract maximally, and the tissues suffer from an insufficient blood supply. Sometimes the abnormality is due to valves becoming stiff, and they fail to open properly; or conversely, they do not close all the way allowing fluid leakage. Whatever the cause, the heart must compensate by increasing its rate and degree of contractions of each beat.

pericarditis   The term *pericarditis* refers to pericardium inflammation and an increase of fluid in the pericardial sac. The excess fluid acts as a resistance
to cardiac action and does not permit the heart to perform normally.

coronary artery   One cause of chest pains usually associated with a heart attack is a de-
disease   creased blood flow to the heart muscle. If, for any reason, branches of
the coronary arteries become blocked or the smooth muscles of the coronary arteries go into spasmodic contraction, there is a temporary coronary insufficiency (lack of oxygenated blood supplied to the heart muscle). This condition brings about an extreme pain, generally in the left
side of the chest and also to the left arm and shoulder. This condition
is termed *angina pectoris*. Angina is a fairly common disease due to the
hardening of the arteries or accumulations of lipid deposits in the internal wall of the arteries. Both interfere with proper blood flow to the
heart muscle.

cardiac failure   The term *cardiac failure* can be defined as an inability of the pumping capacity of the heart to meet the body's metabolic needs. One type
of cardiac failure results from a lack of blood flowing to the heart muscle
(myocardial infarction). The heart muscle deprived of nutrients and
oxygen immediately shows a diminished cardiac output, and the condition in turn affects other organs. The kidney produces less urine, which
results in fluid retention by the kidney and therefore retention of extracellular (tissue) fluid. Initially, the retention of fluid by the kidney and
other tissues will increase the volume of blood in the vessels and venous
return to the heart. The venous resistance decreases because of the
stretching of the veins by the extra blood volume. The extra flow of blood
to the heart is a compensatory mechanism to help the heart make up
for the lessened cardiac output. If the disease is severe, however, this
compensating mechanism of increased venous return will enlarge and
stress the heart and produce a variety of secondary manifestations (excess tissue fluid in the lungs also called pulmonary edema) that will
cause further traumatization.

summary   The heart is a "bag" of involuntary muscle which contracts continually
and rhythmically without rest almost 100,000 times per day, pumping
key   the blood throughout the body.

1. Approximately the size of a man's fist; lies in the mediastinum
gross   2. Pericardium: a double serous membrane sac that surrounds the
anatomy   heart
3. Chambers: four chambers; the right atrium opens into the right
ventricle, and the left atrium opens into the left ventricle
4. Valves: guarding the channels between each atrium and ventricle,
bicuspid on the left and tricuspid on the right; pulmonic and aortic
valves prevent backflow of blood into the pulmonary artery and aorta,
respectively
5. Coronary artery: nourishes the cardiac muscle
6. Nerve innervation: heart rate is stimulated by the sympathetic division of the autonomic nervous system and inhibited by the parasympathetic division

7. Conduction of nerve impulse: sinoatrial node is the pacemaker of the heart; nerve impulses travel from the pacemaker to the sinoventricular node, and then the action potential is distributed via branches of specialized muscle fibers collectively called the bundle of His

cellular-tissue specialization

1. Numerous mitochondria increase the respiration activity of the cell
2. Intercalated discs provide for greater cell contact than would be found in most cell junctions
3. Fibers branch extensively, which facilitates diffusion of the action potential

physiology

1. Cardiac cycle
   (a) The circuit of blood within the heart is the right atrium – right ventricle – pulmonary artery – lungs . . . returning from the lungs – pulmonary vein – left atrium – right ventricle – aorta
   (b) Contraction phase is called systole; relaxation phase is called diastole
   (c) Cycle lasts about 0.8 second, rate of 70 to 75 beats per minute
2. Cardiac output: with each contraction, the heart puts out approximately 80 ml blood
3. Exercise: physical exertion will increase cardiac output as much as five to six times
4. The electrocardiogram (EKG or ECG) is a measurement of electric current recorded on the surface of the body, reflecting electrical charge produced by the contracting heart muscles
5. Heart sounds: "lub," the first sound produced by the closure of the bicuspid and tricuspid valves, marks the beginning of ventricular systole; "dub" occurs at the end of ventricular systole, produced by the closing of the aortic and pulmonic valves
6. Pulse: pressure wave created when the blood is forced into the aorta and expands this vessel and its branches; pulse is in synchrony with cardiac systole

control

1. Emotional and metabolic state affects heart rate
2. Most regulation of the heart is via the X cranial nerve, the vagus
3. The cardiac center (acceleration and inhibition) is located in the medulla
4. Special receptors in the aortic and carotid bodies respond to changes of blood pressure and to changes in oxygen and carbon dioxide content of the blood
5. Heart is also under the influence of hormones, particularly epinephrine, norepinephrine, thyroxine
6. Chemicals other than hormones also affect heart rate, such as serotonin and histamine

factors influencing function

1. Respiration: cardiac output will increase with inhalation and decrease with exhalation
2. Temperature: cardiac output is affected proportionally to temperature increase
3. Posture: gravitation becomes an important factor in returning blood

to the heart; hence an upright position produces a slight decrease in cardiac output and an increase in heart rate compared to that of the reclining position

4. Age: the heart rate gradually decreases with age from birth until the individual reaches adulthood; from this point on, changes in heart beat related to age are due to many factors

clinical con-siderations

1. Infarction: a lack of blood supply to a restricted area of the heart is called ischemia, and if the condition produces cell death, it is called an infarction

2. Fibrillation: the contraction of ventricle muscle fibers in a random fashion

3. Arrhythmias: irregular or loss of rhythm; bradycardia refers to slowing down of the heart rate, and the opposite is called tachycardia; heart block is when the bundle of His is blocked, the ventricles no longer receive an impulse from the pacemaker, and the heart begins to function at its own intrinsic rhythm rather than under control

4. Pericarditis: inflammation of the pericardium and an increase of fluid in the pericardial sac

5. Coronary: blockage of a branch of the coronary artery that leads to insufficient perfusion of the heart causing chest pains and death of heart cells; called a heart attack or angina pectoris

6. Cardiac failure: inability of the pumping capacity of the heart to meet the body's metabolic needs, producing a variety of secondary manifestations such as edema

12

blood vessels, lymphatics, and circulation

anatomy
arteries
capillaries
veins
special systemic
  circulatory circuits

cellular specializations
endothelial cell

physiology
transcapillary exchange
hemodynamics

control
neurogenic regulation
hormonal control

factors influencing function

clinical considerations
aneurysm
arteriosclerosis and
  atherosclerosis
varicose veins
phlebitis
hypertension
ischemia
shock
edema

lymphatic system
lymph vessels
lymph fluid
lymphoid tissue
functions of lymph

From a physiological point of view the task of blood vessels is to supply organs with nutrients, oxygen, and information (hormones) and to remove products of cellular metabolism. This function does not necessarily imply that blood vessels play a passive role in blood distribution and exchange of its constituents. Blood flow is regulated by the contraction and relaxation of the vessel walls.

In the broadest classification, blood vessels can be subdivided into three main categories: the *arterial system*, the *microvascular system (capillary bed)*,* and the *venous system* (Figure 12-1). The primary concern of the arteries is to conduct blood to the microvascular system where the actual exchange between blood and tissue cells occurs. The microvasculature is composed primarily of capillaries, but precapillary arterioles and postcapillary venules, which are also permeable, could also be included. The arterial circulation might be divided into the *pulmonary* (going to the lungs) and the *systemic* (going to the re-

figure 12-1

THE ARTERIAL
AND VENOUS
SYSTEMS
SHOWING THE
MAJOR BLOOD
VESSELS

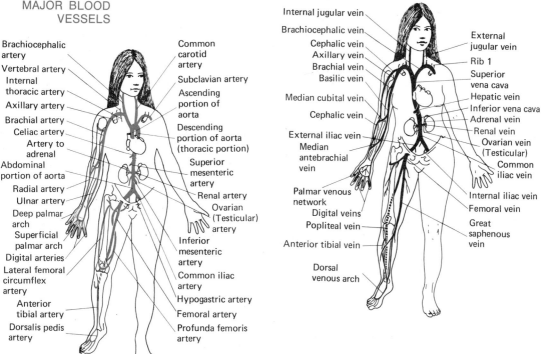

* Scientists interested in microvascular research would include in their field all microscopic blood vessels, the blood flowing through them, and the connective tissue elements adjacent to the vessels.

mainder of the body) circuits. The venous circulation collects blood from the microvasculature and returns it to the heart for a new cycle. Some organs, such as the brain, have unique circulation; these areas can be treated as special cases.

We can start our discussion of systemic circulation at the *aorta*, the major supply vessel emerging from the left side of the heart. It ascends behind the *manubrium* (breast bone), arches, descends along the dorsal wall of the thorax, and at the level of the twelfth thoracic vertebra enters the abdominal cavity. Along its route it gives off many branches, which subdivide further or go directly to an organ. Within the organs the arteries subdivide several more times to form an enormous bed of small capillaries. In this specialized area the exchange of nutrients, wastes, and gases between the blood and the interstitial fluid occurs. The capillaries then drain into veins located adjacent to the arteries. These veins ultimately unite to form three major vessels: the *superior vena cava* draining the upper torso, the *inferior vena cava* draining the lower body, and the *hepatic portal vein,** which transports blood from the gastrointestinal region to the liver (Figure 12-1).

The pulmonary circulation is a relatively simple circuit consisting of right and left pulmonary arteries carrying blood to a microvascular bed of the lung tissue and two major pulmonary veins draining the blood from the lungs into the left side of the heart (Figure 12-1).

In this chapter the properties of blood vessels are discussed with emphasis on how these properties relate to the essential function of exchanging materials among the environment, the blood, and the tissues. Since endothelial cells are the key link in this exchange, the discussion will be augmented with a detailed description of endothelial ultrastructure and how this relates to permeability.

anatomy   With the exception of vessels of the microvascular area, the structure and orientation of the layers making up any blood vessel are quite similar (Figure 12-2). The three layers, from the inside out, are called the *intima, media,* and the *adventitia.* The intima is lined with special epithelial cells called *endothelium.* The next two layers, the media and adventitia, are composed of a granular ground substance containing a variety of connective tissue fibers, elastic, collagen, reticular, connective tissue cells, and smooth muscle cells.

Three types of fibers are found in the media: (a) the intercommunicating and delicate reticular fibers, which probably act as vessel scaffolding or support, although in the smallest vessels they probably act as a sieve to bar the passage of certain macromolecules and cells; (b) coarse collagen fibers, which give the vessels their maximum capabilities to withstand the stress of pressure; (c) elastic fibers, which provide blood vessels with their reversible extensibility and thus help to maintain

---

* A portal vein is a unique vessel. It begins at a capillary bed, but unlike a regular vein (which either joins another vessel or enters the heart directly), it ends in a capillary bed of another organ. By definition, therefore, a portal vein collects blood from a capillary bed and delivers the blood to another capillary bed. This adaptation, as seen in the hepatic portal vein, provides the vehicle for storage of sugar as glycogen by the liver cells; the sugar-ladened blood from the intestine goes through the capillaries of the liver before entering the heart.

figure 12-2

ORGANIZATION
OF AN ARTERY
AND VEIN SHOWN
IN CROSS
SECTION

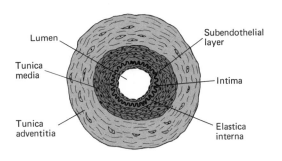

SMALL ARTERY

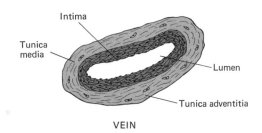

VEIN

blood pressure. The major components of the media are fibroblasts and smooth muscle cells. In the adventitia, fibrous connective tissue is predominant. The thickness of all layers vary; in general veins have larger adventitial layers than arteries.

arteries   For descriptive purposes, the arteries are primarily divided into *elastic* and *muscular arteries*, and *arterioles.*

Elastic Arteries   The great vessels leaving the heart (the aorta and the pulmonary artery, as shown in Figure 12-1, and their immediate branches) are *elastic arteries*. The elastic arteries measure more than 1 cm in diameter and are further characterized by walls composed of large numbers of elastic fibers. This elastic tissue is generally compressed into 50 or so bands in the middle region of the wall.

   The function of the elastic tissue is to allow the vessel, particularly the aorta, to expand when the heart contracts and to assist in maintaining blood pressure. By distending their walls, the elastic arteries provide a temporary blood reservoir to be utilized between heart beats. When the heart rests, the blood flow in the vessels would stop if the elastic fibers did not recoil to produce a continuous, albeit pulsatile, flow. One of the many manifestations of aging is a lessening of elasticity in the vessel walls, "hardening of the arteries." The elastic arteries lose their ability to accommodate the outflow of the heart.

Muscular Arteries   The middle-sized arteries (0.4 to 1.0 cm) are structurally identified by a middle layer composed primarily of smooth muscle fibers. The vascular needs of body organs or areas are an ever-changing phenomenon, and

· figure 12-3

THE MICRO-
VASCULATURE
SHOWING
PRECAPILLARY
SPHINCTERS

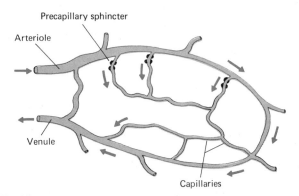

From B. W. Zweifach, Josiah Macy, Jr. Foundation, 1950.

the mechanism for redistributing blood is partially the result of muscle tissue contraction within the vessel walls.

Arterioles   Whereas muscular arteries are *distributors*, the arterioles (0.5 mm to 20 μ) are *regulators* in that they control the flow of blood into the capillary bed (the smooth muscle of the vessel is under the control of the autonomic nervous system). The minimal degree of arteriolar contraction is referred to as *vascular tone*, and the partial constriction of the vessels accounts for the major degree of resistance to blood flow. The maintenance of tone is primarily by stimuli coming from sympathetic innervation. The phenomenon of tone is mentioned at this point to highlight the fact that the greatest blood pressure drop occurs in the arteriolar regions, where the resistance is greatest.

As the arterioles decrease in diameter, connective tissue layers are lost. Just prior to forming a capillary bed, the arterioles are seen as simple endothelial tubes with a few adjacent, isolated smooth muscle fibers. The latter are the *precapillary sphincters* (Figure 12-3) and, when present, represent the last arterial muscle control of blood flow into the capillary bed. When the precapillary sphincter muscles contract, the diameter decreases, impeding or stopping the flow of blood through the constriction.

Notwithstanding the groupings of arteries by size, significant differences exist even within each group. The chemical composition of the wall of the arm's medium-sized *brachial* artery is not the same as the chemistry of the anatomically equivalent *femoral* artery in the leg. For example, the cholesterol and calcium contents are dramatically higher in the femoral artery (leg) than in the brachial artery (arm) as an individual reaches middle age.

capillaries   The capillaries (4 to 12 μ) are the exchange sites for materials among cells, interstitial fluid, and blood (Figure 12-4). In the final analysis, irrespective of tissue, the microvascular system is the bridge between individual cell activity and the total functioning organism.

Morphologically, capillaries are more than "naked" endothelial tubes. In Figure 12-4 are diagrammed the other elements (basement membrane, pericytes, and connective tissue elements) that are part of the capillary unit.

figure 12-4

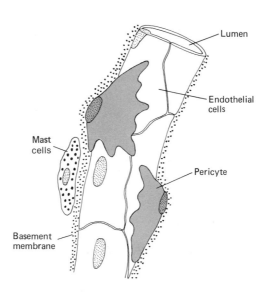

A variety of specially adapted small vessels also exists. The capillary bed can be bypassed by direct connections, called *arteriovenous shunts*, between the arteries and veins. The latter vessels are larger than capillaries (about 35 μ). In certain endocrine organs and in hemopoietic tissue such as the marrow, spleen, and liver, amorphous vessels of varying diameters (5 to 30 μ) called *sinusoids* replace the ordinary capillary. These vessels have regular endothelium and *phagocytic* cells for their lining; as blood sluggishly flows through these channels, it is possible for the phagocytic cells to "filter" the fluid by using their ability to engulf unwanted foreign material.

veins   The collecting vessels (20 μ to 1 cm) returning blood to the heart are more difficult to categorize than arteries, because the transition from the smallest venules to largest veins is more gradual. In general, when compared to arteries, the veins are thinner walled, contain fewer elastic and muscle fibers, and have a larger caliber than the companion artery. These anatomical features provide some insight into their functions.

Because blood pressure in the venous system is low and sometimes almost negligible (0 to 12 mm Hg), there is a need for supportive action. For example, fewer fibers in the vessel walls permit a greater distention, thereby producing sluggish flow in the lower extremities and pooling of blood. To contend with gravity, the nonrigid veins are "massaged" by skeletal muscle contraction during muscular activity. This action pushes the blood in the direction of the heart (Figure 12-5). In addition demi-cupped valves within the canal (almost always in pairs) prevent backflow (Figure 12-5).

special systemic   Unlike most body organs the skin has little autoregulatory control of its
circulatory   circulation, the changes of skin circulation being more related to the
circuits   physiological needs of the entire body. An excellent example of this is seen in the skin's *thermoregulatory* function (Chapter 17).

Skin   It should be pointed out that the skin is an excellent "window" of the

figure 12-5

VENOUS VALVES
AND THE FLOW
OF VENOUS
BLOOD

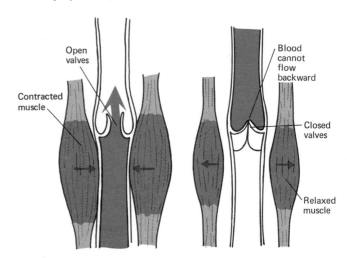

Muscular contractions squeeze or milk the blood from the veins toward the heart.
The valves in the veins shown above provide an anatomical basis for the one way
flow.

body. The dramatic changes in a patient's skin (lack of color derived
from the blood, coldness, and clamminess) occurring during shock are
an excellent indication of circulatory deficiency.

Spleen   The spleen services the circulatory system in a number of ways. Hemopoiesis, red blood cell destruction, and removal of platelets are some
important duties. Another major splenic function directly related to
blood flow is the release of blood during circulatory stress. Blood can be
stored in the spleen's venous sinuses. In man the storage role of the
spleen is considerably smaller than in other mammals and probably
plays a less important role. Nevertheless, during strenuous exercise the
muscle fibers of the spleen's capsule contract and squeeze out several
hundred milliliters of blood; the number of cells per milliliter of splenic
blood is high, and their release increases the hematocrit (the number of
red blood cells in the blood), which in turn provides for increased oxygenation of tissue.

Cerebral   The rate of flow and quantity of blood in the brain is remarkably con-
Circulation   stant. This situation is to be expected, since fluctuations in the composition of the brain tissue fluid would lead to abnormal function of the
neurons. The cerebrum is provided with a dual arterial supply. At the
base of the brain is the *circle of Willis,* an anastomosis of vessels formed
from the *basilar* artery and the two *internal carotids.* From the circle of
Willis branches emerge and go to various parts of the cerebrum. Because
of this collateral circulation, the brain has a theoretical mechanism for
continuous vascularization. If one of the major tributaries to the circle
is blocked, the other vessels could maintain adequate blood flow. This
fail-safe mechanism is probably functional only in the young.

figure 12-6

PORES IN
CAPILLARY
MEMBRANES

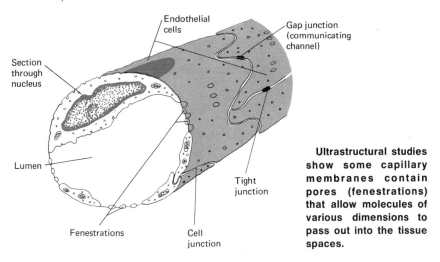

Ultrastructural studies show some capillary membranes contain pores (fenestrations) that allow molecules of various dimensions to pass out into the tissue spaces.

Liver Circulation   The liver can release blood accumulated in the very permeable hepatic sinuses and in this respect resembles the splenic circulation. Hepatic circulation is unique in that the blood draining the stomach and intestine by way of the *hepatic portal vein* (about 1 liter per minute) flows through the liver first before entering general circulation. In addition the liver receives about 350 ml of blood per minute from the *hepatic artery*, making it truly one of the most vascular organs in the body.

Other specialized areas of vascular flow, coronary circulation, the hypothalamic-hypophyseal portal system, and the placental-fetal circulation are discussed elsewhere in the text.

cellular   For years, physiologists have theorized on the existence of "pores" that
specializations   allow materials to leak through membranes, and this theory was an accepted explanation for permeability. Electron microscopy shows

endothelial cell   discontinuities *(fenestrations)* of certain cell membranes, and a variety of pores or breaks in some capillary membrane does exist which permit molecules of varying dimensions to pass through (Figure 12-6). How-

Capillary   ever, the electron microscope also discloses the presence of numerous
Permeability   inpocketings of the endothelial membrane and large numbers of vesicles in the cytoplasm. What distinguishes these vesicles (often referred to as *plasmalemma* vesicles) is that they are bound by a similar unit membrane as the cell plasma membrane, and that they are frequently observed in a row or as a "chain" traversing the cytoplasm. Although a continuous link of vesicles opening on both sides of the capillary (blood and tissue sides) has not been observed, a workable theory is that the vesicles provide the mechanism that transports substance across the blood vessel wall (Figure 12-7). This type of transcapillary exchange could be likened to pinocytosis discussed earlier. For example, if ferritin (iron particles that are observable with the electron microscope) are injected into the bloodstream, within 2 to 3 minutes these particles will be observed in pockets of the endothelial membrane and within membrane-bound vesicles of the cytoplasm (Figure 12-8). It must be stated that the

figure 12-7

TRANSCAPILLARY
EXCHANGE VIA
VESICLES

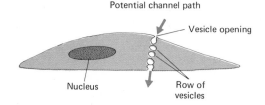

phenomenon of solute transport across the membrane and cytoplasm of endothelium is still an unanswered question.

Some recent experimental data provide another interpretation of how the endothelial cells can participate actively in capillary permeability. The endothelial cells shown in Figure 12-9 are considered to be in a contracted state; this action could possibly pull the adjoining cell surfaces apart, forming a temporary channel which would allow larger molecules to pass through. The observation that endothelial cells contain contractile proteins makes this theory more plausible. A summary of factors influencing distribution and flow of blood in the microvascular system is presented in Figure 12-10.

Capillary Barriers   The cell substructure of the capillary endothelium can impede the passage of molecules, for example, plasma proteins, from the blood to the tissues and at the same time facilitate the passage of both smaller and larger molecules through the cell membrane. (How this type of transit is accomplished is, in itself, a major area for investigation.)

In Figures 12-3, 12-9, and 12-10, the adaptations for preventing loss

figure 12-8

FERRITIN
PASSAGE
ACROSS
CAPILLARY
MEMBRANE

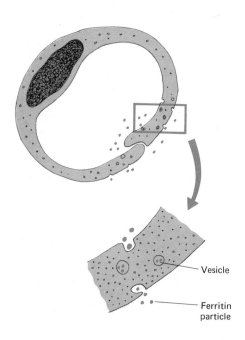

figure 12-9
TRANSCAPILLARY
MOVEMENT

Endothelial
cell

ENDOTHELIAL PROCESSES
CONTRACT

CREATION OF TEMPORARY
CHANNEL

Transcapillary movement of materials by formation of temporary channels created by contraction of endothelial cells.

of material are quite evident. The junctions between cells are closely apposed and may even form interlocking connections. The surfaces of the cells seldom are more than 100 Å apart. What space exists is generally filled with a homogeneous matrix or is interrupted by tight junction desmosomes, discussed in an earlier chapter. Usually a mucopolyssaccharide matrix with minute fibrillar structure (basement lamina) of 40 to 50 Å in thickness may act as an additional barrier.

In some organs the selective permeability aspects of the endothelial tubes are further enhanced. Evidence supports the concept that the capillaries of the brain constitute the *blood-brain barrier* and that small antigens or even ions that normally would pass through a skin capillary are prevented from leaking into the nervous tissue. The blood-brain barrier is another adaptation to maintain a constancy of environment for the brain.

The blood-brain barrier develops with age, for brain capillaries are

figure 12-10

SUMMARY
DIAGRAM SHOW-
ING FACTORS
INFLUENCING
BLOOD FLOW IN
THE MICRO-
VASCULATURE

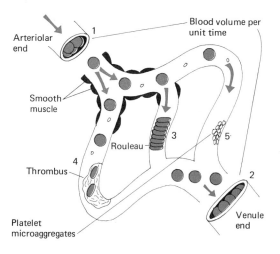

Blood volume per
unit time

Arteriolar
end

Smooth
muscle

Rouleau

Thrombus

Platelet
microaggregates

Venule
end

Factors 1 and 2 indicate the volume of blood (per unit time) reaching and leaving the area via major vessels (arteries and veins): Factor 3, Rouleau formation: Factor 4 represents thrombosis (intravascular clots) and Factor 5, microaggregates of platelets.

more permeable in early life. The anatomic features that presumably produce the barrier are as follows.

1. Brain capillaries as seen by microscopy do not have gaps between them.

2. A continuous basement membrane surrounds the capillaries.

3. External to the basement membrane is another membrane (incomplete) formed by the *astrocytes* (supporting tissue of the nervous system). The incomplete nature of this outer membrane *might contribute* to the differential permeability of similarly sized compounds seen in brain circulation; for example, basic compounds penetrate more rapidly than acidic ones.

One important clinical implication of the blood-brain barrier is that disease frequently breaks down the barrier. The clinician can use the abnormal permeability that results to locate the pathologic area. Certain substances *(thorium-228)* are not penetrated by x-rays and are visible in an x-ray film. These substances are generally colloidal, and their large particles do not leak out of a capillary. In the region of the unhealthy tissue, inflammation breaks down the blood-brain barrier. If thorium is

figure 12-11

RADIOGRAPHIC
LOCALIZATION OF
BLOOD VESSELS
(ANGIOGRAM)

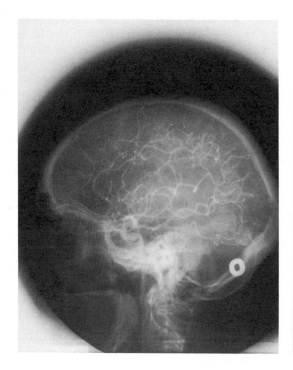
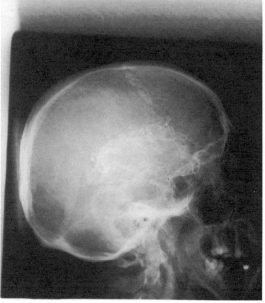

injected into the blood, it will escape and specifically mark the area of inflammation (Figure 12-11).

In summary, the capillary has many structural devices for producing a barrier or a passageway. The fine structure of the endothelium varies in different tissues. Capillaries in the kidney are primarily porous (for filtration), whereas capillaries in muscle tissue are not. The transit of most molecules results from differences in their concentrations between the capillary lumen and the tissue fluid (diffusion). Differences in blood pressure along the capillary (pressure gradients) also contribute to transit of molecules, but to a lesser extent than diffusion. In the last analysis the ultrastructural capillary specializations are so varied that the probability of finding a unifying theory to explain the selective permeability of a capillary is quite slight.

physiology

transcapillary exchange

The study of exchange across a cell membrane is a major frontier of science, although some features of exchange appear quite understandable. During the blood's course through a capillary, its water content is exchanged with the water of the tissues at least 30 times. This extraordinarily rapid exchange is understandable because of the presence of numerous "pores" (90 Å) in the capillary membrane, which are 30 times larger than a single water molecule (3 Å). The transit of other molecules is not so easy to explain. For example, does the oxygen pressure gradient drop gradually in a linear fashion along the length of the capillary or is the oxygen delivered primarily at one end?

Capillary Blood Pressure

Blood pressure within the capillary varies, but a reasonable estimate would be equivalent to 25 mm Hg pressure at the arterial end of a capillary and only 9 mm Hg at its venous end. Escape of fluid is therefore favored at the arterial end and reabsorption at the venous end. Figure 12-12 illustrates the factors important in water exchange. The overall force driving fluid from the capillary at the arterial side is equivalent to 36.5 mm (Table 12-1). This value includes blood pressure (BP), tissue negative pressure (TNP),* and tissue osmotic pressure (TOP). Plasma osmotic pressure, due primarily to the high concentration of proteins, causes fluid to flow from the tissues into the capillary. At the venous end, blood pressure drops to 9.0 mm Hg and all other values remain approximately the same.

The net result is that cells are continuously bathed in fresh, nutrient-rich fluid. With reabsorption, cellular excretions and secretions enter the blood and are eventually removed from the blood or utilized in other areas of the body. The imbalance or difference of forces at the arterial and venous ends of the capillary results in excess tissue fluid formation; more fluid is forced out at the arterial end than is taken in at the venous end (a guarantee that sufficient tissue fluid will be available). The fluid balance is maintained by lymphatic capillaries (see lymphatics) which remove that fluid from the tissues not handled by the capillaries them-

---

* The evidence supporting the notion that there is a tissue negative pressure is experimental and still controversial. However, its presence does not affect the concept of factors involved in capillary exchange.

figure 12-12

FACTORS
IMPORTANT IN
CAPILLARY
EXCHANGE OF
FLUIDS

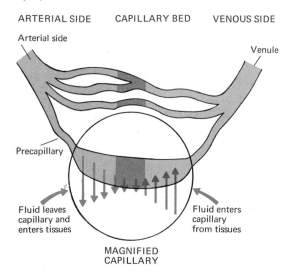

ARTERIAL SIDE   CAPILLARY BED   VENOUS SIDE

Arterial side

Venule

Precapillary

Fluid leaves
capillary and
enters tissues

Fluid enters
capillary
from tissues

MAGNIFIED
CAPILLARY

selves. Sometimes the dynamic equilibrium is upset and tissue fluid drainage does not keep pace with formation; this produces an accumulation of excess fluid in the tissue spaces, a condition called *edema* (see clinical considerations).

In addition to water, numerous water-soluble materials (salts and sugars) pass through the capillary membrane. These substances are made up of larger molecules and have a permeability coefficient less than water. For example, sucrose, which has a molecular weight almost 20 times that of water, is only 40 percent as permeable as water.

Not all molecules diffuse across the capillary membrane via pores. We have seen that large lipid-soluble materials are capable of diffusing directly through membranes by dissolving lipid components in the cell membrane. General anesthetics are lipid soluble and act rapidly because of their high coefficient of lipid permeability; that is, they are capable of rapid penetration through the lipid portion of the endothelial membrane.

In summary, a combination of diffusion, pores, a modified pinocytosis, and lipid solubility accounts for most of the transport across an endothelial cell.

hemodynamics   One cannot overemphasize the primary function of the circulatory system, namely, to deliver a continuous blood supply adequate to meet the varying needs of the body. Since the blood is transported in a closed circuit of branching nonrigid vessels, certain principles of *hydrodynamics* (or in this instance *hemodynamics*) must be explained.

In addition to the physical factors related just to moving the fluid, circulatory physiology is somewhat complicated by the fact that the potential total volume of the microvasculature is greater than the total volume of blood. This means that blood is continuously displaced from one region to another. What determines blood volume? What factors

table 12-1
CAPILLARY
FILTRATION[a]

OUT	IN
BP = 25.0 mm	POP = 28 mm
TNP = 7.0 mm	
TOP = 4.5 mm	
36.5 mm	Net: 36.5 mm − 28 mm = 8.5 mm (out)
OUT	IN
BP = 9.0 mm	POP = 28 mm
TNP = 7.0 mm	
TOP = 4.5 mm	
20.5 mm	Net: 20.5 mm − 28 mm = 7.5 mm (in)

[a] Adapted from a presentation by A. C. Guyton in *Textbook of Medical Physiology*, 3d ed. Philadelphia, Pa.: Saunders, 1966. Tissue negative pressure is the force of solid or semisolid elements that press against the blood vessel.

BP   = blood pressure
TNP = tissue negative pressure
TOP = tissue osmotic pressure
POP = plasma osmotic pressure

affect blood pressure and the rate of flow, and how they are controlled? How does the body endlessly adjust to the local needs of the body? These questions are discussed in the following sections.

Blood Volume   The blood volume of an individual depends on many variables such as age, size, sex, environment, or even activity. When a known amount of a nontoxic dye, such as T-1824 (the dye is bound to plasma albumin and restricted to the vascular space), is injected into the blood and the degree of dilution is measured after a given period of time, the blood volume determination is about 5000 ml for a person of average size. Another way in which this quantitation can be stated is that the blood volume ranges between 7.5 to 10.0 percent of total body weight. Whatever measurement is used, be aware that these are averages, convenient for memory; they cannot be used rigidly in a clinical situation. If the blood volume of a patient is of critical importance and if time and equipment are available, the patient's blood volume must be determined, rather than relying on a statistic.

The blood and tissue fluids maintain a dynamic steady state as far as volume and composition are concerned, but the interchange between these two fluids is great. Any disturbance of the equilibrium between these fluid compartments will alter the blood volume. Excluding disease (for example, hemorrhage or loss of fluids by vomiting), the blood volume is dependent on (a) intake of fluids, (b) storage of water by the tissues, (c) elimination of water by kidney, skin, and so on, and (d) formation of plasma, the noncellular portion of the blood.

Blood Pressure   With each contraction of the heart, blood is pumped into the aorta and pulmonary arteries and eventually into their branches. The force exerted on the walls of the vessels represents the *blood pressure*. (If the aorta were cut, a column of blood 6 to 8 feet high would spurt out.) This pressure expands the blood vessels, but since the heart contractions are intermittent, the alternation of pressures creates a *pulse* (described in Chapter 12).

Arterial pressure is fundamentally dependent on blood flow rate (also referred to as *cardiac output*) and peripheral resistance; the volume of blood returning to the heart influences cardiac output. Maintenance of an adequate *pressure head* to supply the various tissues is essential. For example, the blood pressure in the arteries of the brain of a standing individual is 30 to 40 mm Hg less than the pressure within the aorta at heart level. This difference means that a force equivalent to 30 to 40 mm Hg is utilized to drive blood "upstream" to the brain. If, following hemorrhage, there is a marked drop in arterial pressure, the cerebral blood supply particularly will be affected by the decreased pressure and the brain tissue will be inadequately supplied with blood. The brain cells, quite sensitive to oxygen depletion, will soon stop functioning. If the blood supply is interrupted for several minutes, consciousness is lost, and irreversible brain damage can occur. This example, in part, explains why fainting is a protective device; a fainting person is put into a prone position with the heart and head at the same level, thereby reducing the pressure needed to bring blood to the brain.

Cardiac Output   In the last chapter the cardiac cycle was discussed. The force of contraction, stoke volume, and the rate of the heart will affect the pressure in the vessels. During systole, the force of the blood on the vessel walls is at its highest. When measured in one group of young adults, it averages 110 mm Hg (all measurements are above atmospheric pressure; therefore 110 mm Hg really represents 760 mm Hg + 110 mm Hg = 870 mm Hg). During diastole, the blood pressure falls considerably, to about 70 mm Hg. Both of these measurements are important, and for this reason blood pressure is stated as systole-diastole – 110/70 in this example. The reader should note that these values are only for *arterial blood in the brachial artery;* pressures vary in the different vessels.

Blood Flow   We can picture the arterial system as a hollow tree with a *trunk* (aorta), *branches* (arteries), twigs (arterioles), and *leaf veins* (capillaries). The combined cross-sectional diameters of two branches exceed the diameter of the original vessel, and the total surface area of an arteriolar region is 100 times greater than any major artery. Since blood flow refers to the amount of fluid that will pass a given point in a given time, it is obvious that when blood moves from a vessel into its branches, the rate of flow decreases. To state it in another manner, a fluid flows through a vessel of a narrow diameter with greater difficulty than it does through a larger vessel. Blood pressure is directly affected by changes of flow $(P = F \times R)$;* therefore as blood flows through the arterial tree, both pressure and rate decrease.

If we inject a tracer substance into an arm vein, the tracer material can appear in the heart within 2 to 14 seconds. On the average, circulation time of the blood unit through the body is about 25 seconds; in the aorta the velocity reaches about 20 cm per second or 0.45 miles per hour.

---

* P = pressure; F = flow; R = resistance.

Resistance and
Viscosity

One important property of vessels related to flow is friction. No matter how smooth the lining of a blood vessel appears, it provides some *resistance* to flow. Friction increases as the diameter of a vessel decreases.

Viscosity refers to those features of a fluid that create a force opposed to the direction of flow. Resistance to flow, for example, factors that slow down circulation, will increase viscosity, which in turn will further slow the blood. Diseases that directly or indirectly cause the freely moving isolated blood cells to form aggregates (clumps) impede blood flow by increasing the blood viscosity. These events enhance additional cell aggregation, which in turn further increases viscosity and decreases blood flow.

Other factors that affect viscosity are hematocrit, vessel diameter, temperature, and shear rate. Blood flows in layers, and the velocity difference between the layers of blood produces a shearing force.

Measurement of
Arterial Blood
Pressure

The routine method for measuring human blood pressure is indirect rather than by the direct method, which requires *cannulation* (insertion of a tube) of the blood vessel. The indirect method, convenient as it is, is less accurate, but it does provide valuable clinical information. The ausculatory procedure (to examine by listening for sounds) gives both systolic and diastolic pressure and utilizes a *sphygmomanometer* recording (Figure 12-13). This instrument is a rubber bag enclosed by a cloth cuff connected to a calibrated scale (mercury manometer), an inflating bulb, and a deflating valve. The technique is to place the cuff around the arm above the level of the elbow, placing the stethoscope bell in the angle of the forearm and upper arm above the brachial artery. Because of the unyielding qualities of the cuff, when air is pumped into the bag, the pressure is directed inward, collapsing the brachial artery. At this point no sound is heard. As air is slowly released, the point at which blood pressure exceeds cuff pressure is the systolic value (the blood pressure needed to force open the lumen of the collapsed artery); the first sound is heard. The sound is produced by the spurting blood and the vessel's motion. With further air pressure reduction, the sounds become fainter due to less turbulent blood flow. The phase when the sounds disappear is considered the best index of diastolic pressure. In the normal adult male, the brachial artery systolic blood pressure range is between 140 and 110 mm Hg, and the diastolic pressure range is between 95 and 60 mm Hg.

The pressure difference between systolic and diastolic pressures is the arterial *pulse pressure*. A normal pulse pressure is around 40 mm Hg. Pulse pressure is affected by the distensibility of the vessels and by cardiac output. A high reading might therefore indicate blood vessel loss of elasticity and a low value might indicate a shock state.

Measurement of
Venous Pressure

Direct measurement of venous pressure in the right atrium can be made by threading a catheter into the heart. In clinical situations in which there is abnormally elevated venous pressure, indirect methods are used to provide general rather than specific information. For example, abnormal venous pressure is indicated if the jugular vein remains distended when the patient is in a prone position. Likewise, the veins in the hand can be used as a manometer. By dropping the arm below heart

figure 12-13

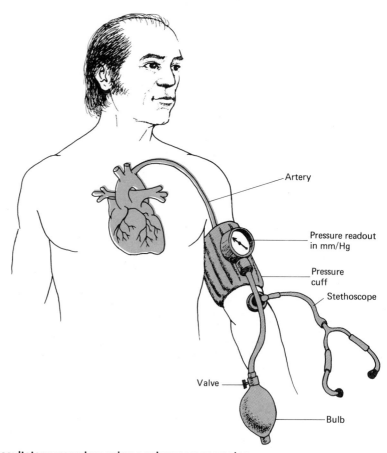

Artery

Pressure readout
in mm/Hg

Pressure
cuff

Stethoscope

Valve

Bulb

Auscultatory procedure using a sphygmomanometer.

level, the veins in the hand become distended and stand out. When the hands are raised above heart level, the veins slowly collapse. The number of centimeters above the heart that produces a visible collapse of the veins can be taken as an estimate of the venous pressure measurement. This method is useless for detecting low venous pressure.

control   As the reader will recall from the discussion on blood (Chapter 10), the total blood volume of the body is much less than the total capacity of the vessels would be if the latter were all dilated at a given moment. Theoretically, the greater portion of the 5 liters of blood can be pooled in the *splanchnic* area (stomach, intestines, liver, and so on) if all these organs' capillary beds are open. Having a total vascular bed that far exceeds the blood volume is another example of the supply and demand economy that can be observed time and time again in nature. It is obvious that distributing blood unequally requires some type of control.

neurogenic   Earlier in this chapter the point was made that the main control of blood
regulation   flow was by arteries with a layer of smooth muscle. Since the arterioles

figure 12-14
NEURAL CONTROL
OF VASOMOTOR
ACTIVITY VIA THE
AUTONOMIC
NERVOUS SYSTEM

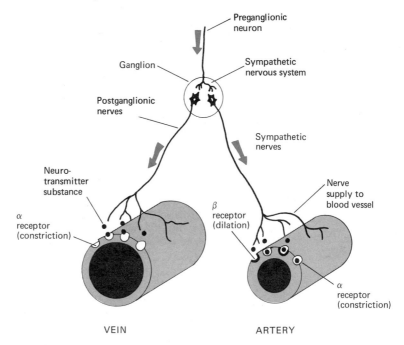

VEIN   ARTERY

are the principal group of such arteries, the arteriolar region is the primary site of regulation. Vascular tone is maintained principally by the continuous transmission of sympathetic vasoconstrictor impulses. Vasodilation stimuli of parasympathetic origin are intermittent and in general serve only local tissue needs. The major blood flow control is related to the needs of large body areas rather than to local demands. The need to cool the body requires blood redistribution from major areas such as the gut region to the skin. This shift is brought about by sympathetic vasoconstriction. In contrast the increase of facial color following an embarrassing incident is an example of a local vasodilation reflex; this change is not solely under neurogenic control (Figure 12-14).

hormonal control   Complementing the neurogenic control of blood vessel diameter are hormones that produce marked blood flow alterations. This effect is especially true of hormones from the adrenal medulla, epinephrine and norepinephrine, which act directly on the blood vessels producing (usually) constriction.

factors
influencing
function

As the conditions of a local tissue area change, the area's vascular flow changes to meet the needs of the cells. This type of blood flow alteration occurs frequently without nervous system mediation and is called *metabolic autoregulation*. This adaptive mechanism permits localized hemostatic adjustments without involving major areas of the body.

The exact mechanism of autoregulation is unknown, but most evidence indicates that oxygen concentration plays an essential role. The reader will recall that the point of origin of a microvascular bed is usually marked by a precapillary sphincter. Let us suppose that a given local

figure 12-15

METABOLIC
AUTOREGULATION
OF MICRO-
VASCULAR FLOW

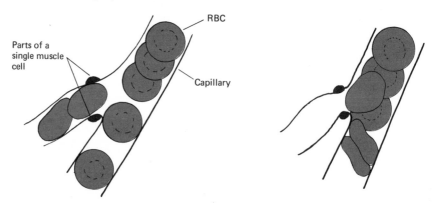

High metabolic activity in the vicinity of the precapillary sphincter above triggers contraction of sphincter, thus decreasing available oxygen, which in turn lowers metabolic activity and sphincter relaxes again.

area increases its metabolism, utilizing a good deal of the available oxygen. The precapillary sphincters would then relax, for they (like all muscle tissue) require oxygen to sustain a contracted state. The sphincter relaxation allows the capillary to fill with blood and the local area and the sphincter muscle to become saturated with oxygen. The precapillary sphincter muscle could once again contract (with a force exceeding the blood pressure in the vessel), effecting a closure. Oxygen concentration of the blood therefore could effect a cyclic opening and closing of the sphincter, which would regulate the microcirculation of the local region (Figure 12-15).

Blood pressure is also regulated indirectly by various other factors. Some activate and inhibit the vasomotor center in the brain; others can affect the blood vessel directly.

In the walls of the aortic arch and in the *carotid arteries* are the special nerve endings *(pressoreceptors)* that respond to changes in the tension of the walls. Stimuli from the pressoreceptors *inhibit* vasoconstriction and *decrease* blood pressure. If following hemorrhage the arterial pressure drops, the arterial walls recoil slightly and the receptors are no longer excited; the vasomotor center is no longer inhibited and emits impulses bringing about vasoconstriction and an increase in blood pressure (Figure 12-16).

The pituitary produces an antidiuretic hormone that plays a major role in the regulation of urine formation; thus, indirectly, the antidiuretic hormone is important in the short-time regulation of blood volume (see Chapter 16).

The kidney also serves as a center for indirect vasomotor control. An adrenal cortex hormone *(aldosterone)* is believed to minimize urine formation by increasing the absorption of sodium and other ions (Chapter 18). The consequences are that less water and salts are lost by urinary excretion, the blood volume increases, and there is blood pressure elevation. The kidney is believed to produce a hormone *(renin)* that combines with a plasma protein to produce the vasoactive substance *angiotensin.* There is some evidence that angiotensin may be the con-

figure 12-16

THE VASOMOTOR
CENTER AND
FACTORS WHICH
AFFECT VASO-
MOTOR ACTIVITY

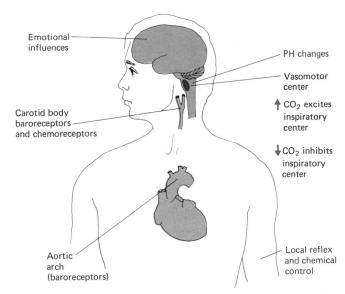

Emotional influences

PH changes

Vasomotor center

↑ CO_2 excites inspiratory center

↓ CO_2 inhibits inspiratory center

Carotid body baroreceptors and chemoreceptors

Aortic arch (baroreceptors)

Local reflex and chemical control

trolling agent for aldosterone production, and that angiotensin may work directly on the blood vessel wall, affecting vasoconstriction. These reactions, however, are still theoretical. Interestingly, blood flow through the kidney is not affected by alterations of blood oxygen levels (Figure 12-17).

Some investigators theorize that vasoactive substances are produced with increased metabolism. For example, carbon dioxide is a strong stimulant to the sympathetic centers in the medulla, producing vasoconstriction. Following muscle activity, there is an increase in carbon dioxide concentration and a decrease in oxygen. The higher level of carbon dioxide signals the vasomotor centers to increase blood pressure, which hyperperfuses (increases flow) the tissue with fluid; the cells thus exposed to additional oxygen and nutrition return to their preactive physiological state. Changes in hydrogen ion concentration or lactic acid due to increased metabolism affect blood vessels in different ways (Figure 12-16).

Since blood flow is in part dependent on the volume of blood, another nondirect mechanism for maintaining blood flow is the fluid shift in a capillary bed. If, for any one of a number of reasons, the volume of blood is diminished, a pressure drop in the microvascular bed occurs. The net result is that more tissue fluid enters the capillary (see Table 12-1) until the normal pressure is restored. Conversely, if the pressure volume in a capillary bed is above normal, the force to drive out fluid exceeds the passage into the capillary until the pressure is decreased to the normal range.

clinical
considerations

aneurysm

The walls of the vessels, like any tubular structure, may be weakened due to a developmental defect or some traumatic event. When the weakened portion becomes dilated, it is called an *aneurysm.* The aneurysm can rupture, producing a fatal hemorrhage, or it may extend into

figure 12-17

KIDNEY AND
VASOMOTOR
CONTROL

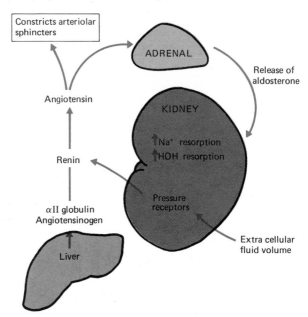

the adjacent tissue, traumatizing the nerves and producing paralysis.
For unexplainable reasons the ascending portion of the *aorta* is the most
frequent site of wall weakness; the cerebral vessels are also prone to
aneurysms.

arteriosclerosis   Arteriosclerosis, commonly called "hardening of the arteries," is due
and   primarily to the aging of elastic tissue found within the wall (much as a
atherosclerosis   rubber band loses its stretch ability with time and use) and the replacement of the elastic fibers with other connective tissue fibers. Deposits of
large amounts of calcium and cholesterol also produce hardening of the
arteries. The failure of vessels to stretch produces high blood pressure
with all of its potential negative manifestations. One specific variation
of arteriosclerosis is *atherosclerosis*. The disease includes all aspects of
degeneration and inflammation of the vessel wall, but it is usually associated with fatty deposits in the intima. As the lipid accumulates, connective tissue fibers become involved to form *plaques* along the inner
lining. The plaques produce secondary complications, for example,
thromboses, hemorrhage, and ulcerations (Figure 12-18).

varicose veins   A common disease of veins is *varicocoel*, characterized by a dilation of
veins (particularly in the legs where venous return must overcome
gravity). Because of failure of the valves to prevent backflow, blood
accumulates in the vessels, and the expansion exerts a pressure on the
adjacent tissues. This condition is unsightly and painful and may give
rise to phlebitis (see below). Dilated veins in the rectal walls are called
hemorrhoids, but their pathology is also due to other factors.

phlebitis   Phlebitis refers to an inflammation of the endothelium of a vein. The real
danger in phlebitis is that the walls become "sticky" and trigger the

figure 12-18

ATHERO-
SCLEROSIS—THE
DEPOSITION OF A
CHOLESTEROL
PLAQUE

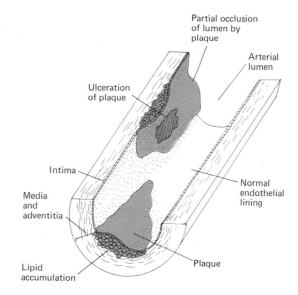

formation of a thrombus, or clot, within a blood vessel. Sometimes such a thrombus may break loose and be carried via the blood vessels and subsequently occlude or block a number of smaller vessels. Such free-moving clots are called *thromboemboli* (singular *embolus*).

hypertension A diastolic pressure above 90 mm Hg indicates *hypertension* or high blood pressure. There are too many events (anxiety) that can elevate systolic pressure to make this value a meaningful index of pathology. The major danger of hypertension is that cerebral vessels that have weakened by disease or age may rupture under the strain of constant exposure to pressures beyond the limits of the wall, thereby producing a fatal hemorrhage.

ischemia Areas deprived of blood for lengths of time may become necrotic (death of tissue) and gangrenous (tissue decay due to interference with local tissue nutrition). Vessels may be blocked by a thrombus or constricted by some external pressure such as a tumor. Bed sores are a plague that exemplify the effect of constant pressure on local cutaneous blood vessels. The pressure on a blood vessel lying over an unyielding bony prominence causes partial constriction of the blood vessel and produces a local absence of blood or ischemia.

shock Shock results when there is a marked difference between the available circulatory blood (blood volume) and the total capacity of the vascular system (Module 12A). The common denominator in all circulatory failure is probably *hypovolemia*, a low-volume state usually associated with a low-flow state. This state of inadequate perfusion produces microcirculation impairment (stagnation of flow, plasma loss, and aggregation

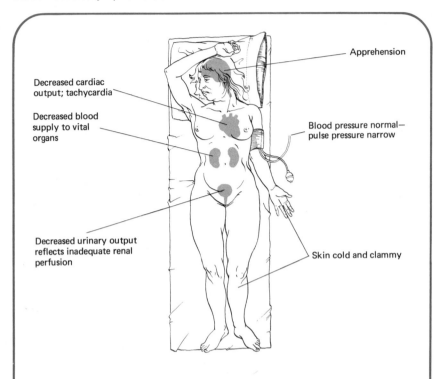

Apprehension

Decreased cardiac
output; tachycardia

Decreased blood
supply to vital
organs

Blood pressure normal—
pulse pressure narrow

Decreased urinary output
reflects inadequate renal
perfusion

Skin cold and clammy

Shock or circulatory failure is the result of decreased cardiac output and is
characterized by an acute and persistent deficiency of blood supply to the
tissues. Diminished perfusion of blood to the vital organs such as the brain,
liver, kidneys, and heart is particularly damaging. Some types of shock are
associated with blood loss (or plasma loss) such as from severe traumatic
injury or severe burns; in other cases there is no loss of blood but a failure
to distribute blood efficiently to the vital organs (as in myocardial damage
or in massive infection or septicemia). Any condition that severely affects
the pumping action of the heart can cause *cardiac shock.* In addition, factors
that decrease venous blood return may also produce shock. If shock is severe,
a vicious feedback loop is established in that the circulatory organs are affected by the lack of blood, which in turn further decreases cardiac output.
This condition is termed *progressive shock* and results from such progressive
changes as a weakened heart, thrombosis and increased capillary permeability. If the deterioration from shock is not halted, eventually the individual will
go into *irreversible shock,* a state which leads to death regardless of the
therapy. Shock is readily diagnosed, and is shown graphically in the diagram.
For example, inadequate urine production or lack of urine production is one
good indicator of inadequate circulation to vital organs. In summary, shock
represents an inability of the circulatory system to maintain an effective
balance between cardiac output, blood volume, and vasomotor control. This
being the case, some forms of shock may be treated effectively by body fluid
(and blood) replacement and with vasomotor drugs.

of red blood cells), which leads to tissue cell destruction (the cells are starving). When this happens in the brain or heart, death may occur.

edema An excess of tissue fluid in the extracellular spaces or edema usually results from one or more of the following conditions: (a) increase of blood pressure (increased venous resistance), (b) a drop in blood osmotic pressure (through the loss of plasma proteins), (c) abnormal permeability in the microvasculature (produced by poison), (d) blockage of lymph drainage (tumor or trauma). Edema is a characteristic of many diseases, especially those of the kidney. The accumulation of fluid 10 percent above normal is clinically significant.

lymphatic system Authors vary in their treatment of the lymphatic system in that some textbooks include lymph vessels and lymphoid tissues as a part of the circulatory system; in other books it is a separate unit (Figure 12-19). Embryologically, structurally, and functionally it appears that the lymphatic system should be considered as part of the general circulation. The system consists of aggregations of *lymphoid* tissue (predominantly lymphocytes) and vessels varying in diameter from capillaries to macroscopic tubes (*lymphatics* or *lymph* vessels) which eventually drain into the venous circulation. With rare exception every tissue is drained by lymphatics. In some regions such as the skin, the number of lymph capillaries is so extensive that the penetration of the narrowest gauge hypodermic needle will penetrate or cut the vessels. The "system" plays an important role in fluid balance, returning proteins to the general circulation, fat absorption, hemopoiesis, and in defense.

lymph vessels Basically, the lymphatic vessels are similar to veins in that they are endothelial-lined tubes with thin walls and valves. Unlike the blood circulatory system, the lymphatic circulation is not closed. It begins with capillaries starting off as blind tubes permeating the intercellular spaces of tissues, and these merge to form larger vessels. Eventually, all of the lymph flows into two major lymphatic trunks: the *right lymphatic duct,* which drains only the upper right quadrant of the body, and the *thoracic duct,* which drains lymph from the remainder of the body. Each major trunk ends where it joins a subclavian vein on its respective side. By these channels materials are returned to the blood circulation.

lymph fluid Lymph is a pale, straw-colored clear fluid that resembles blood serum. If a sample of lymph is taken from an individual who has not eaten for several hours, the fluid analyzed will contain 95 percent water and 5 percent solids in the form of proteins (albumin, globulin, fibrinogen), glucose, calcium, sodium, chloride, and urea.

The principal circulating cellular element in the lymph is the lymphocyte, and the number of lymphocytes is about equal to the lymphocyte number circulating in the blood.

lymphoid tissue Aggregations of lymphoid tissue (Figure 12-19) called *lymph nodes* are strategically located. They are especially large and plentiful (30 to 40

Nodes nodes) in the cervical, axillary, and groin regions, and because of their

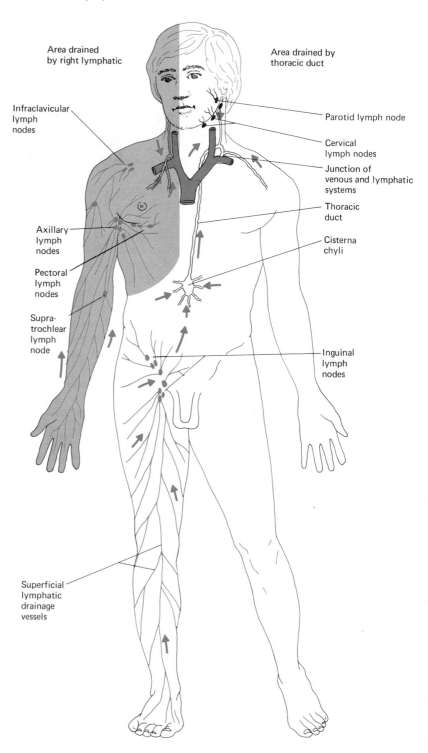

figure 12-19

THE LYMPHATIC
SYSTEM IN SITU

Area drained
by right lymphatic

Area drained by
thoracic duct

Infraclavicular
lymph
nodes

Parotid lymph node

Cervical
lymph nodes

Junction of
venous and lymphatic
systems

Thoracic
duct

Axillary
lymph
nodes

Cisterna
chyli

Pectoral
lymph
nodes

Supra-
trochlear
lymph
node

Inguinal
lymph
nodes

Superficial
lymphatic
drainage
vessels

figure 12-20

THE SPLEEN IN
SITU AND DETAIL

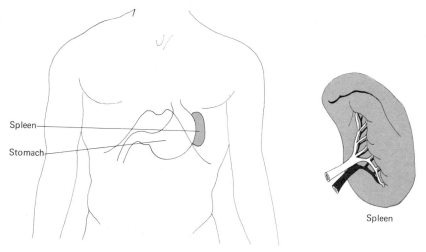

Spleen

Stomach

Spleen

function in defense, these regions are especially significant because they
"guard" the potential portals of the torso against the spread of infection, for example, from the arm into the trunk. Almost without exception, tissue fluid picked up by the lymph capillaries percolates through
at least one lymph node before entering the systematic blood circulation
by way of the right and left subclavian veins. Within the nodes, particu-
late matter is filtered and removed (phagocytized) from the lymph fluid;
centers for the synthesis of antibodies against foreign materials are present; and new lymphocytes are given off. The antibody function is of special significance in health and modern medicine, and is treated in more
detail in Chapter 23 under Defense Mechanisms.

Organs   In addition to lymph nodes, lymphoid tissue comprises the bulk of the
special organs. These large lymphoid organs are the *spleen* (the largest),
thymus gland, *tonsils*, and *appendix.* The spleen is a very soft, highly
vascular organ that lies against the diaphragm near the left kidney (Figure 12-20), and it is easily molded by the adjacent structures that touch
it (stomach, kidney, and so on). Its lymphoid activity is related to the
formation of new lymphocytes, filtration, and antibody production
(Chapter 22); it is also a center for the destruction of old blood cells and
a reservoir for red blood cells.

The thymus gland is located in the mediastinum (Figure 12-21) and
until quite recently was a puzzle to scientists and clinicians. It is now
believed to be the "master lymphoid organ" that programs other lymphoid tissue to recognize and separate *self* from *foreign* substances so
that antibody production is specifically directed against harmful agents
(Chapter 22). The thymus grows during the prepuberty years, but with
sexual maturity and aging undergoes slow involution (decreases in
mass) until it almost completely disappears. Tonsils are discussed in
Chapter 13; their lymphatic functions are quite similar to those described for lymph nodes.

figure 12-21
THE THYMUS
GLAND

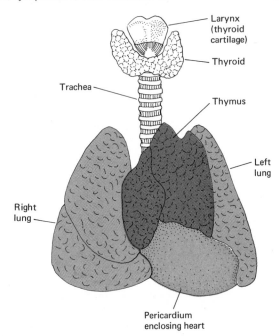

The function of the appendix is still questionable. Its potential role as the "thymus of the posterior end" has been postulated, but its specific functions are still unknown. Small islets of lymphoid tissue called *Peyer's patches* are found in the walls of the intestine; they are described in Chapter 13.

functions of lymph

Fluid Balance, Protein Return, Absorption of Fat

FLUID BALANCE Lymph is formed primarily from the fluid that diffuses from the capillaries and bathes the cells (*tissue fluid*). Since the venous end of the capillary bed cannot reabsorb all the tissue fluid that escapes, the nonabsorbed fluid (as well as abnormally excessive amounts) is returned to the blood by lymph capillaries (Figure 12-12). This function of assisting the capillaries in returning fluid to the general circulation is of great clinical importance. Although the bulk of tissue fluid is reabsorbed by the capillaries, any blockage of the lymphatic vessels eventually leads to a buildup of trapped tissue fluid (*edema*) (Figure 12-22). One theoretical explanation of how tissue fluid is taken up by the lymph vessels is shown in Figure 12-23.

PROTEIN RETURN A small percentage of protein also escapes from the high-pressure arterial end of a capillary, but capillaries cannot reabsorb proteins. Therefore one major function of the lymphatic vessels is to return the escaped proteins to the general blood circulation. The mechanism for this high degree of special permeability by the lymph vessels is unknown.

FAT ABSORPTION If an individual drinks a cup of cream or ingests a rather fatty meal, within a few hours the translucent lymph would appear quite milky. This opaqueness is due to the absorption of fats at the

figure 12-22
EDEMA

EARLY STAGE

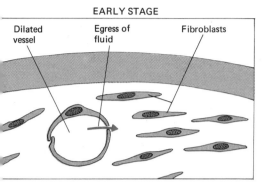

Dilated vessel   Egress of fluid   Fibroblasts

LATER STAGE

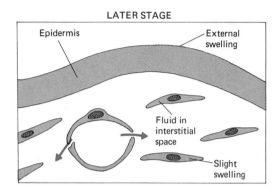

Epidermis   External swelling

Fluid in interstitial space

Slight swelling

intestinal lining by special lymph capillaries called *lacteals*. At least one-third of all of the digested fats are absorbed by the lacteals and transported by the lymphatic system to the blood.

LYMPH FLOW The circulation of lymph is dependent on external forces since there is no pump (heart) found in the system. The means by which lymph is moved is quite similar to that described for venous return. Breathing movements (inspiration elevates intraabdominal pressure, which in turn creates a pressure on the thoracic duct) and the massaging action of skeletal muscles on the lymphatic vessels provides sufficient increases of pressure to move the lymph slowly but steadily to the points at which it enters the subclavian veins.

summary

anatomy

1. Arteries: the vessels that carry blood from the heart to the body can be broadly organized into two groups: the pulmonary circulation carrying blood to the lungs and the systemic circulation which carries blood to the remaining organs

2. Veins: the vessels that return blood directly or indirectly to the heart can be distinguished from arteries generally by their thinner walls and by the presence of internal valves, which prevent backflow of blood

3. Microvasculature: bridging the arteries and veins is the area of smallest blood vessels and consists of
   (a) capillary bed
   (b) precapillary arterioles
   (c) postcapillary venules

4. Microanatomy of blood vessels other than capillaries and the smaller arterioles; a blood vessel is composed of three layers:
   (a) intima: endothelium
   (b) media: smooth muscle and connective tissue
   (c) adventitia: fibrous connective tissue

5. Arteriovenous shunts: frequently blood goes directly from an artery to vein without traversing the capillary bed

6. Special systemic circulatory circuits:

figure 12-23

UPTAKE OF
TISSUE FLUIDS BY
LYMPH VESSELS

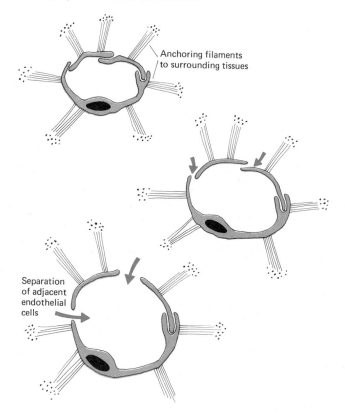

Anchoring filaments
to surrounding tissues

Separation
of adjacent
endothelial
cells

From article by L. V. Leak, *Microvascular research,* 2:384, Academic Press, New York, 1970.

**cellular spe-
cializations**

(a) skin
(b) spleen
(c) cerebral circulation
(d) liver circulation: hepatic portal vein

1. Capillary permeability
   (a) pores or fenestrations
   (b) vesicles
   (c) intercapillary channels
2. Capillary barriers
   (a) certain capillaries do not have gaps between them
   (b) a continuous basement membrane may surround the capillaries
   (c) a blood-brain barrier has been theorized, the nature of which is
       not known; limits permeability of the capillary in the brain

physiology

1. Transcapillary exchange
2. Capillary blood pressure: reasonable estimate would be equivalent
   to 25 mm Hg pressure at the arterial end of the capillary and only 9 mm
   Hg at the venous end

3. Blood volume: blood volume depends upon age, size, sex, and other variables. Reasonable estimate is about 5000 ml for an average size person, which would constitute between 7.5 to 10 percent of total body weight

4. Blood pressure: with each contraction of the heart, the blood pressure is equal to a column 6 to 8 feet high if the aorta were cut; a normal blood pressure would be approximately 120 mm Hg for systolic pressure and 80 mm Hg for diastolic pressure (values are for arterial blood in the brachial artery)

5. Other factors that effect hemodynamics (physical features related to blood flow) are

    (a) resistance

    (b) viscosity

        hematocrit

        vessel diameter

        temperature

        shear rate

6. Sphygmomanometer: measures blood pressure by listening to systolic and diastolic sounds

7. Measurement of venous pressure: direct measurement can be made by threading a catheter into the right atrium

control

1. Neurogenic regulation

    (a) vascular tone is maintained principally by the continuous transmission of sympathetic vasoconstrictor impulses

    (b) vasodilation stimuli or parasympathetic origin is intermittent and in general serve only local tissue needs

2. Hormonal control

    (a) epinephrine

    (b) norepinephrine

factors influencing function

1. Autoregulation: exact mechanism unknown, but is believed that the oxygen concentration of the tissue plays a central role

2. Pressoreceptors: in the walls of the aortic and in the carotid arteries are special nerve endings that respond to changes in tension of walls; information is transmitted to the vasomotor center in the medulla

3. Antidiuretic hormone: important in the short-time regulation of blood volume

4. Angiotensin: kidney believed to produce a hormone (renin) that combines with a plasma protein to produce this vasoactive substance, which works directly on the blood vessel wall and produces vasoconstriction

5. Metabolic changes

    (a) hydrogen ion concentration

    (b) lactic acid levels

    (c) carbon dioxide concentration

clinical considerations

1. Aneurysm: a weakened portion of a wall which can become dilated and even rupture and produce a hemorrhage

2. Arteriosclerosis: due primarily to aging of the elastic tissue found

within the wall and the replacement of these fibers with less elastic collagen fibers

3. Atherosclerosis: variation of arteriosclerosis in which there is degeneration and inflammation of the vessel wall and fatty deposits in the intima

4. Varicose veins: valves in veins fail, and blood accumulates and expands vessel; pressure on adjacent tissue becomes painful; hemorrhoids is example of varicose veins in the rectum

5. Phlebitis: inflammation of the endothelium of a vein causing the wall to become sticky; may even trigger thrombus formation

6. Hypertension: a diastolic pressure above 90 mm Hg is indicative of high blood pressure

7. Ischemia: local areas deprived of blood for lengths of time become necrotic and even gangrenous

8. Shock: occurs when a marked difference exists between the available circulatory blood (blood volume) and the total capacity of the vascular system; hypovolemic state (low-flow) occurs; this state of inadequate perfusion affects the microvasculature and the tissues of the body

9. Edema: an excess of tissue fluid in the extracellular space

lymphatic system

1. Lymph vessels: structurally similar to veins

2. Lymph fluid: lymph is a pale, straw-colored clear fluid that resembles blood serum

3. Lymphoid tissue
   (a) lymph nodes: aggregations of lymphoid tissue strategically located in the body
   (b) spleen
   (c) thymus gland
   (d) tonsils
   (e) Peyer's patches
   (f) appendix

4. Functions of lymph
   (a) fluid balance
   (b) protein return
   (c) absorption of fat
   (d) filtering of lymph

the digestive system and nutrition

13

gross anatomy
mouth
tongue
salivary glands
pharynx
esophagus
stomach
small intestine
large intestine
rectum
accessory organs
blood supply
nerve supply

**microanatomy and
cellular specialization**
mucosa
muscularis
submucosa
serosa

physiology
movement
secretions and action of
   digestive enzymes
absorption

control
saliva

gastric secretion
histamine and hydrochloric
   acid secretion
pancreatic juice secretion
bile secretion
intestinal juice secretion

factors influencing function

nutrition
water requirements
mineral requirements
proteins
carbohydrates
lipids
vitamins

clinical considerations
obstruction
gastroenteritis
gastrointestinal ulcers
gall bladder
vomiting
appendicitis
diarrhea
constipation
hepatitis
starvation
obesity

Man is an *omnivorous* (feeding on plants and animals) animal, and his diet is determined to a large extent by his culture rather than by his biology. The food man eats, with rare exception, cannot be utilized directly, and it must be digested or broken down into smaller components that can be absorbed. This process is the principal function of the digestive system. Much of digestion is essentially hydrolysis and enzymatic activity. Hydrolysis is the basic mechanism for carbohydrate, protein, and fat digestion—the three major components of man's diet—but the enzymes that catalyze hydrolysis differ for each food substance. Only the few minerals and vitamins essential for good health need not go through the preliminary steps of digestion.

Digestion and the subsequent absorption and elimination of non-absorbed food stuffs fall to a series of organs that form a long, rather complicated tubular system, the *gastrointestinal* tract (also called the *alimentary* tract, the *GI* tract, or simply the *gut*). Three accessory organs—the *pancreas, liver*, and *salivary glands*—assist in digestion. Most of the organs are situated in the peritoneal cavity, a part of the *celom* (general body cavity) lined with a peritoneal membrane. Module 13A illustrates the general arrangement of the digestive tract and related organs.

Each organ is specifically adapted for different stages of digestion. The *stomach* assists in the mechanical breakdown of food and initiates the beginning of enzymatic digestion; in the *small intestine* most of the digestion and absorption of the resulting smaller constituents occur; the *large intestine* has no digestive powers but serves in water uptake and preparing the nondigested material for elimination.

It is an interesting observation that most organic materials must first be broken down and then reassembled into similar units again to be utilized by the body. For example, the amino acids that result from protein digestion are the same amino acids that are converted to new proteins by the body. Yet no species of animal, including man, can directly utilize the proteins he ingests. This observation is even true in animals that practice cannibalism.

gross anatomy

mouth

The boundaries of the mouth are the cheeks laterally, the hard and soft palates superiorly, the tongue and lower jaws inferiorly, the lips frontally, and posteriorly there is no boundary since the mouth opens into the pharynx. In the mouth are the *gingiva* (gum), teeth, and tongue.

Tongue

The tongue is made up primarily of skeletal muscle. Most of the visible part of the tongue is the anterior, which moves freely; the larger root is hidden (Figure 13-1). The anterior part is loosely attached to the floor of the mouth by a *lingula frenulum;* occasionally this membrane is very short and the movement of the tongue is restricted.

In addition to its role in chewing and swallowing, the tongue is important to man because it assists in speech and contains receptors for taste (Figure 13-2). The rough surface of the tongue is due to several types of *papillae* (elevations) that are heavily supplied with taste buds (Figure 13-2).

salivary glands

Three pairs of salivary glands pour their secretion into the mouth, and the fluid aids in swallowing and chewing as well as initiating a small

figure 13-1
ANATOMY OF
MOUTH REGION
SHOWING
SALIVARY
GLANDS

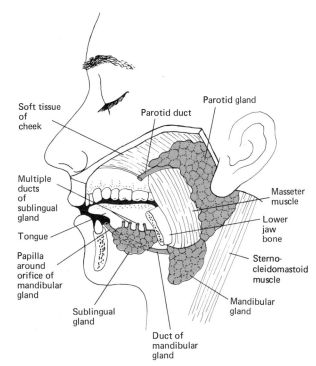

amount of carbohydrate hydrolysis. The *parotid* gland (Figure 13-1) is
the largest of the three and lies below the ear. Its duct (*Stensen's*)
crosses the masseter muscle and opens into the mouth adjacent to the
second molar in the upper jaw. The *sublingual gland* (Figure 13-1), as
the name implies, is located below the tongue and may have one or more
ducts that open into the membrane on the floor of the mouth. The *submandibular gland* is underneath the lower jaw; its duct empties into the
floor of the mouth generally quite near the ducts of the sublingual gland.

figure 13-2
THE TONGUE,
TASTE BUDS,
AND TONSILS

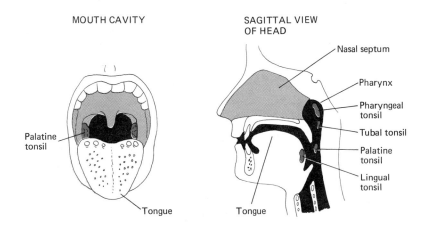

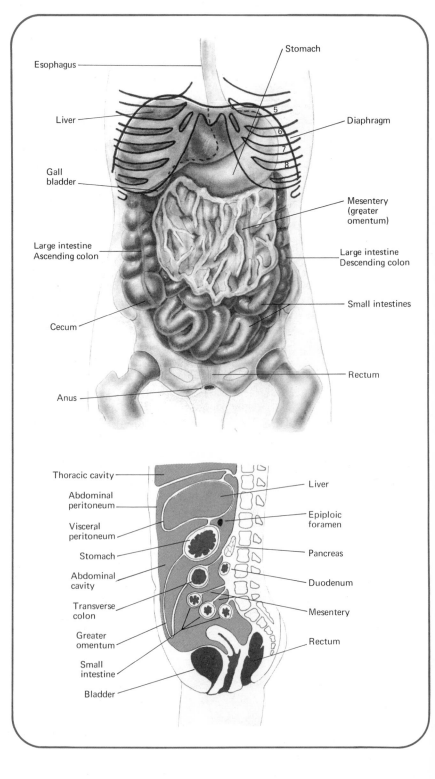

Esophagus

Stomach

Liver

Diaphragm

5
6
7
8

Gall
bladder

Mesentery
(greater
omentum)

Large intestine
Ascending colon

Large intestine
Descending colon

Small intestines

Cecum

Rectum

Anus

Thoracic cavity

Liver

Abdominal
peritoneum

Epiploic
foramen

Visceral
peritoneum

Pancreas

Stomach

Abdominal
cavity

Duodenum

Transverse
colon

Mesentery

Greater
omentum

Rectum

Small
intestine

Bladder

The digestive system consists of a lengthy tube (mouth, pharynx, esophagus, stomach, small and large intestines, rectum and anus) and a number of associated glands (salivary, pancreas, liver, and gall bladder). Collectively these structures function in the digestion and absorption of food, and the elimination of the residue. In sequence the following functions are carried out: in the mouth the particle size of the food is reduced by the chewing action of the teeth and the addition of saliva aids in swallowing the food. The pharynx and esophagus convey the food to the stomach where it is churned and mixed with hydrochloric acid and enzymes to initiate digestion. The completion of digestion takes place in the small intestine where most of the absorption of the digested particles into the blood takes place; liquids are also absorbed through the intestinal wall. In the large intestine the major reabsorption of water and electrolytes occurs, and the residue is prepared for elimination. The excretion of the waste is the principal function of the rectum and the anus. The churning and propulsion of food are handled by the muscle layer of the digestive tract; the inner lining of the stomach and intestine contain cells which produce the enzymes involved in digestion. It is an interesting note that the digestive system is first to develop within the embryo.

pharynx   The pharynx is a nonrigid tubular organ, and its importance is highlighted by the fact that it contains seven openings: two from the middle ear, two from the nose, one each from the mouth, larynx, and esophagus, respectively. The pharynx serves two systems—digestive and respiratory; the chamber is subdivided into the *oral pharynx*, which is associated with the mouth, the *nasopharynx*, which is associated with the nose, and the *laryngeal pharynx,* which communicates with the esophagus and larynx (voice box).

Within the pharynx are three pairs of tonsils that form an incomplete ring of lymphoid tissue around the pharynx and "protect" it and the internal organs against infection. The tonsils produce antibodies against foreign proteins, and they also filter lymph. The *lingual tonsils* are located in the root of the tongue; the *palatine tonsils* are embedded in the mucosa of the lateral wall of the pharynx; and the *pharyngeal tonsils* are found on the posterior wall near the point where the oral pharynx communicates with the pharynx (Figure 13-2).

esophagus   The *esophagus* is a straight muscular tube about 10 inches in length that runs from the pharynx to the stomach (Figure 13-3) and lies behind the windpipe in a collapsed condition except when food is passing through. The opening of the esophagus into the stomach has no regulatory valve, and only the constriction of the esophagus itself regulates the transport of food.

stomach   The stomach is a large saccular organ which can extend its walls to accommodate over 2 liters of material. It is J shaped, and a good portion of the organ is tucked up under the dome of the diaphragm, reaching almost to the tip of the sternum. The various parts of the stomach are shown in Figure 13-3.

figure 13-3

DIGESTIVE TRACT

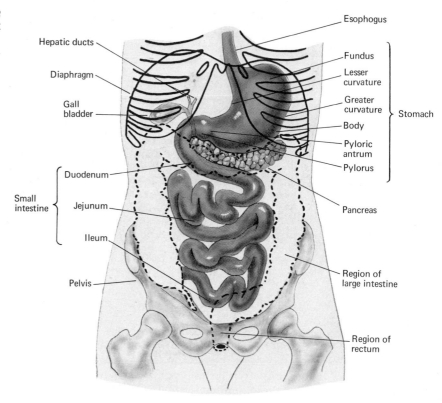

Detailed anatomy of digestive tract showing the subdivisions of the various organs.

The opening between the esophagus and the stomach is controlled by muscles at the gastro-esophageal junction. The distal opening of the stomach leading to the small intestine is narrowed by the *pyloric sphincter*, which may or may not be open dependent upon the state of digestion in the stomach. The sphincter is so narrow that only fluids are squirted into the intestine.

small intestine   The small intestine is a long tube (in the average adult it is 22 feet) divided into three parts called the *duodenum, jejunum*, and *ileum* (Figure 13-3). Because of its great length, the intestine is coiled within the restricted peritoneal cavity and is only loosely supported by the mesenteries. The duodenum is the shortest section (10 inches), but it has the largest diameter (2 inches). The jejunum is about 8 feet in length and tapers to the ileum (12 feet in length), which has a final diameter of about 1 inch. The duodenum receives the ducts from the liver and from the pancreas. The ileum is distinguished by patches within the wall, *Peyer's patches*, which are aggregations of lymphoid tissue.

figure 13-4
THE APPENDIX
AND ILEOCECAL
VALVE

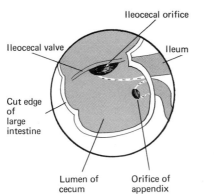
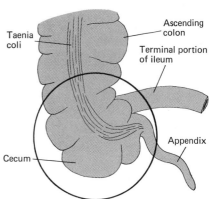

large intestine

The communication between the small and large intestine is guarded by the ileocecal valve (Figure 13-4), which prevents the contents of the large intestine from backflowing into the ileum. Beyond the sphincter the large intestine or *colon* widens (2½ inches), and the first segment is called the *caecum*. The section contains a fingerlike projection, the *vermiform appendix*, whose walls are permeated with lymphoid tissue. At one time the appendix was considered to be a vestigal organ and of no value to man; it was considered a nuisance structure because it frequently became inflamed and necessitated surgical removal. The present opinion is that it may do the equivalent work of the tonsils as an organ of defense against infection, but at the other end of the digestive system.

The colon extends superiorly from the caecum to the lower right edge of the rib cage, and this segment is known as the *ascending colon*. The colon then makes approximately a 90-degree turn (the *right colic flexure* or *right hepatic flexure*) and crosses to the left abdominal wall to about the level of the ninth or tenth rib. This portion is called the *transverse colon*. At the spleen it makes another right-angle turn and moves posteriorly to become the *descending colon*. At the pelvis the colon becomes S shaped *(sigmoid colon)* and terminates at the rectum at the level of the midsacral region (Figure 13-5). The total length is about 5 or 6 feet.

rectum

The rectum is a muscular tube about 6 inches long that continues downward from the sigmoid colon and ends in an opening called the *anus*. The anus has an internal and external sphincter, the internal ring enclosed by involuntary muscle and the external by voluntary muscle; the latter is involved in the regulation of defecation (Figure 13-5).

accessory organs

Several organs are tied to the GI tract structurally and functionally. The salivary glands (discussed previously), the pancreas, and the liver are derivatives of the embryonic gut, and even in postnatal life they maintain their connections with the gut wall by ducts. The three organs synthesize materials that are needed in digestion and for this reason are termed "accessory digestive organs."

figure 13-5

THE LARGE
INTESTINE AND
RECTUM

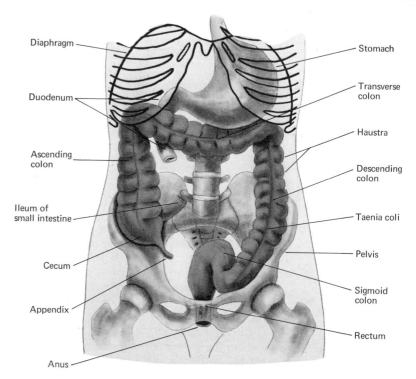

Diaphragm

Stomach

Transverse colon

Duodenum

Haustra

Ascending colon

Descending colon

Ileum of small intestine

Taenia coli

Pelvis

Cecum

Sigmoid colon

Appendix

Rectum

Anus

Pancreas   The pancreas is an exocrine (secretions leave by ducts) and endocrine (secretions leave by way of the blood) organ. The endocrine portion, which consists of islets of cells scattered throughout the exocrine tissue, produces the hormone insulin, and the exocrine portion produces digestive enzymes. The pancreas is about 5 to 7 inches in length and about 1 to 2 inches in width. It lies in a loop formed by the duodenum and is connected to the duodenum by two ducts (the major duct is called *Wirsung's duct*). The point where the enzymes are discharged into the duodenum is called *ampulla of Vater*, and the *sphincter of Oddi* controls the flow of enzymes from the duct into the gut (Figure 13-6).

Liver   The liver is the largest single organ in the body, and because of its multifunctions, it will be discussed again in several sections of the book. The major functions are summarized in Module 13B.

The liver secretes bile that aids in the digestion of fats. Although bile is continuously secreted, it is utilized only when fat is in the intestine. At other periods bile is stored and concentrated in the gall bladder. The sphincter of Oddi closes and the bile backtracks up the *common bile duct* to the *cystic duct* and then to the *gall bladder* (Figure 13-6). When fat enters the duodenum, the gall bladder contracts, the sphincter relaxes, and bile is secreted.

blood supply   The digestive system has an excellent blood and lymphatic circulation. The esophagus receives several small branches from the aorta and the

figure 13-6

THE GALL
BLADDER,
PANCREAS, AND
ASSOCIATED
DUCT SYSTEM

CUTAWAY VIEW OF INTESTINE TO SHOW
ENTRANCE OF DUCTS INTO INTESTINE

GROSS VIEW OF BILIARY
AND PANCREATIC DUCTS

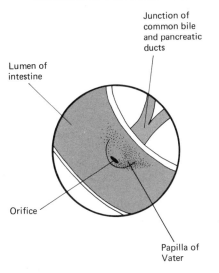

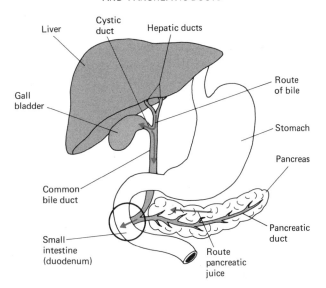

thyroid and bronchial arteries. The stomach and midgut are supplied by
numerous branches of the celiac and superiormesenteric arteries. Blood
is drained from the gastrointestinal system by corresponding veins that
join to form the large hepatic portal vein (see Chapter 12). The blood is
carried to the liver by the hepatic portal vein, where it passes through
the liver tissue. The liver is drained by way of the hepatic vein, which
flows into the posterior vena cava, which in turn empties into the heart.
The lymphatic drainage of the GI tract is illustrated in Figure 13-7, and
its extensive branching partially explains why cancer in the digestive
system (cancer cells can travel through the lymphatics) frequently presents such a complicated clinical picture.

nerve supply   The digestive tract is richly supplied with nerve fibers from a variety of
nerve plexuses lying adjacent to the organs they innervate. Both sensory
and motor stimuli are carried by these nerves.

Parasympathetic   The glossopharyngeal nerve (IX) supplies the pharynx and the upper
esophagus; the vagus (X) exerts control from the lower esophagus to the
lower bowel or colon; and the pelvic nerve controls the lower bowel,
rectum, and anus. The parasympathetic impulses stimulate gut motion
and enhance the digestive process.

module 13B

SOME MAJOR
FUNCTIONS OF
THE LIVER

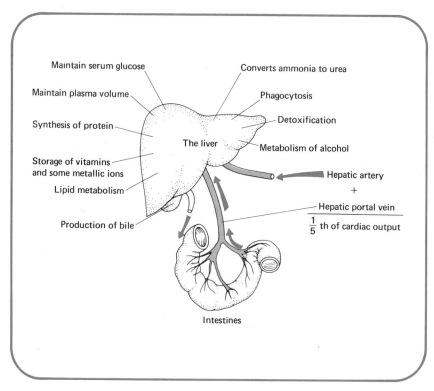

Sympathetic   Radiating especially from the solar plexus (celiac and superior mesenteric ganglia) are many fibers that terminate in the walls of the viscera.
The sympathetic stimuli inhibit gut motion and work antagonistically to
the parasympathetic nervous system.

microanatomy   Structural adaptations that are closely related to digestive functions are
and cellular   seen at both the tissue and cellular levels. The wall of the gut is not
specializations   homogenous in that many types of cells are present and arranged in
specific layers. Working inward to outward, the wall gut is composed of
(a) the *mucosa*, an epithelial connective tissue lining, (b) the *submucosa*, a loose type of connective tissue, (c) the *muscularis*, (d) a layer
of smooth muscle, and (e) a *serosa* of connective tissue. Most of the
specializations are found in the mucosa and muscularis; the two connective tissue layers, the submucosa and serosa, do not change much
throughout the digestive tract.

mucosa   The epithelial lining differs in each digestive organ, and to a high degree
the differences or specializations reflect the state of the food in that
given area. For example, when the gut contents are a solid (ingested food
or feces), the linings of the organs are stratified (mouth, esophagus,
rectum-anus), whereas a single layer of the columnar epithelium is

figure 13-7

BLOOD SUPPLY
TO THE
DIGESTIVE TRACT

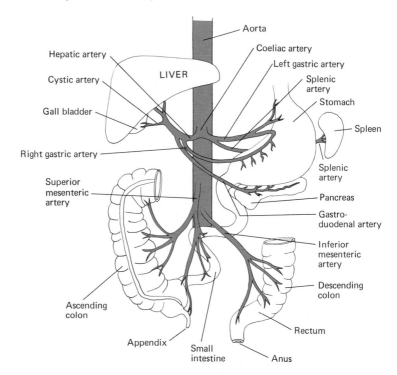

generally found in the parts in which the food is in a liquid state. In general the mucosa is a rather thick wet layer (1.5 mm) that is thrown into folds: *longitudinal folds* in the esophagus, *ridges* or *rugae* in the stomach (Figure 13-8), *villi* in the intestine, and *columns* in the anal area. The rugae are transitory and provide extra storage space. They disappear when the stomach is distended. The villus is a unique adaption for absorption, and the microscopic projections increase the surface area of the intestine several hundred times (Figure 13-9). Each villus contains a blood capillary and a lymph capillary (also called a *lacteal*). The latter is especially adapted to absorb fats.

At the cellular level the digestive system lining contains several interesting types of cells. *Goblet cells* are one-cell glands that secrete mucus, and they are distributed throughout the mucosa except in the esophagus; these cells are especially numerous in the colon. The stomach contains *parietal* and *chief* cells, which produce hydrochloric acid (HCl) and enzymes, respectively. The cells that form *Brunner's glands* in the duodenum are worth mentioning, because their secretion is highly alkaline and neutralizes the acidity of the food as it enters the duodenum. For reasons still unknown, the stomach lining cells are not attacked by the gastric fluid acidity. This adaptation is restricted to the stomach, for the duodenal lining cells do not have this built-in protective mechanism and rely on Brunner's glands to counteract or buffer the

figure 13-8

CHANGES IN THE
STOMACH
FOLLOWING
INGESTION OF
FOOD

CONTRACTED STOMACH   DISTENDED STOMACH

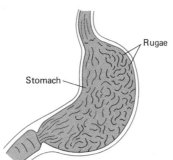

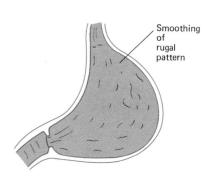

The rugae are ridges or folds in the gastric mucosa which stand out clearly in the empty stomach. As the stomach is distended following a meal, the rugae smooth out.

gastric hydrochloric acid. If hyperacidity is extended over a long period, even Brunner's gland cannot cope with the excess acid, and areas of the duodenal lining begin to erode *(ulcer)*.

muscularis   The predominant constituent of the muscularis is smooth involuntary muscle, which is organized in a circular and longitudinal pattern. These layers contract and produce a slow rhythmic wave of movement that propels the digesting food within the tubular gastrointestinal tract. This

figure 13-9

THE INTESTINAL
MUCOSA AND
DETAILED
STRUCTURE OF A
VILLUS

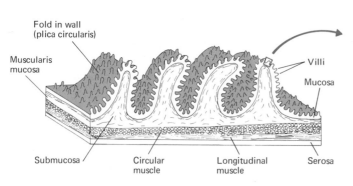

INTESTINAL WALL

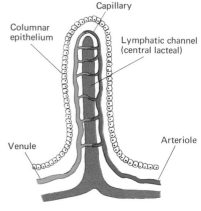

DIAGRAMATIC ➔ ENLARGEMENT
OF VILLUS

figure 13-10

PERISTALTIC
ACTIVITY

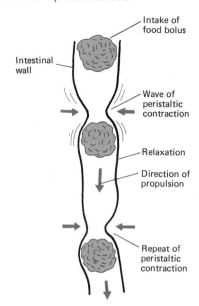

Intake of
food bolus

Intestinal
wall

Wave of
peristaltic
contraction

Relaxation

Direction of
propulsion

Repeat of
peristaltic
contraction

motion is called *peristalsis* (Figure 13-10) and accounts for almost 100 percent of transport since gravity is a negligible factor (a man can stand on his head and drink a glass of water "defying the laws of gravity").

The muscularis of the esophagus is thick, and unique in that the upper 2 to 3 inches contain voluntary and not involuntary muscle. This adaptation is a protective device that permits some voluntary regurgitation (to cast up swallowed food). At the lower end of the esophagus the contracted muscularis acts as a crude valve and until it relaxes, food does not pass readily into the stomach.

The gastric muscularis is arranged in three distinct bands: the *circular, longitudinal,* and *tangential.* The contraction of the three bands simultaneously results in a compression of the stomach from three directions and a literal churning of food with the gastric juices.

The muscularis of the small intestine is similar in structural orientation to the esophageal muscularis. In the colon the muscularis is modified in that the longitudinal fibers are not arranged uniformly around the wall but aggregate into narrow bands called *taeniae coli* (Figure 13-11). This arrangement gives the colon a saccular appearance and is capable of a unique motion called *mass peristalsis.* The solidifying waste in the colon is propelled at intervals between extended periods of no contraction and no movement. The muscularis of the rectum has the pattern of the esophagus and small intestine, and only in the anal canal is it modified to form the sphincters.

submucosa   The submucosa supports the mucosa lying next to the muscularis and consists of a loose type of connective tissue. In those areas in which the mucosa is thrown into folds, for example, villi, the submucosa forms the core.

figure 13-11

TAENIAE COLI
AND HAUSTRA OF
THE COLON

PORTION OF COLON

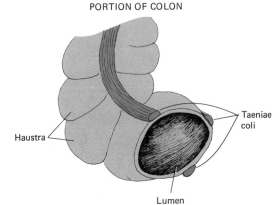

The large intestine contains no villi and the outer wall contains large sacculations, the haustra. Three longitudinal bands of muscles, the taeniae coli, are visible on the surface.

Haustra

Taeniae coli

Lumen

serosa   The serosa, the outermost layer, is also a loose type of connective tissue, and except in the esophagus and duodenum, it fuses with the serous lining of the abdominal cavity to form the mesenteries that support the gastrointestinal organs.

physiology   The GI tract is so sensitive to both chemical and neurogenic stimuli that motility of its organs is difficult to study directly. A principal means of studying tubular motion is to give the patient a radiopaque material and observe its passage by X-ray or fluoroscopy (Figure 13-12). Another means of measuring the propulsion of food is to have the patient eat a specific food that will be used as a tracer and withdraw samples from various parts of the gut at different time intervals and look for the tracer.

movement

Mastication   The value of chewing food as an aid to digestion is debatable. One aspect of chewing is certain—that for a majority of individuals, the mechanical process provides a pleasure response and simultaneously initiates a flow of digestive juices—"good digestion awaits digestive enzymes."

Swallowing   Swallowing (Figure 13-13) is automatic and it occurs in several stages. The first step is when the tongue pushes against the roof of the mouth and forces the food backward (and frontward in infants who have not yet learned to purse their lips to block that exit). The *soft palate* is elevated by the movement of the tongue blocking off the nasopharynx. As the food enters the pharynx, the larynx is elevated and its opening (*glottis*) is pushed against the *epiglottis*, sealing off the opening into the respiratory tube. The tip of the glottis also guides food down the esophagus. The food enters the esophagus and is squeezed down into the stomach by peristalsis.

Stomach   Peristalsis in the stomach is a rhythmic undulating contraction pre-
Movement   ceded by a brief moment of relaxation. A large peristaltic wave occurs every 25 seconds.

Intestinal   The peristaltic motion of the small intestine is coupled with *segmented*
Movement   movement, and the food is not only propelled forward but it is thoroughly

figure 13-12

RADIOGRAPH
OF THE
DIGESTIVE
SYSTEM

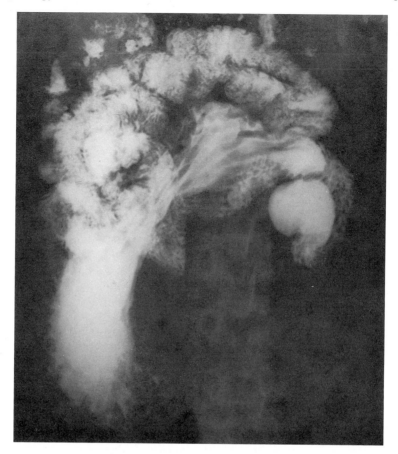

The digestive system may be studied by x-ray examination by ingesting a radio-paque material (often barium salt). The radiopaque material conforms to the shape of the bowels and absorbs x-rays better than the tissue; thus it is possible to visualize the whole digestive tract to localize a tumor or bowel obstruction.

mixed with the enzymes; the activity is sometimes likened to the action of a cocktail shaker.

Colon Movement   In the large intestine food is moved *en masse* or by *mass peristalsis.* Since a sizable fraction of food can be nondigestible (for example, diets rich in plant products), the extended time within the colon provides ample opportunity for the bacteria to act upon the metabolic residue and break it down into particles suitable for elimination. During the periods of rest, large quantities of water are absorbed, returning the contents to a semisolid or solid state.

Defecation   The emptying of the rectum is a voluntary act in response to stimuli primarily from the stretching of the rectal walls by the accumulating feces. However, in individuals with a loss of nerve connection between the brain and lower parts of the spinal cord (parapalegics), reflex defeca-

figure 13-13

THE THREE
STAGES OF THE
SWALLOWING
REFLEX

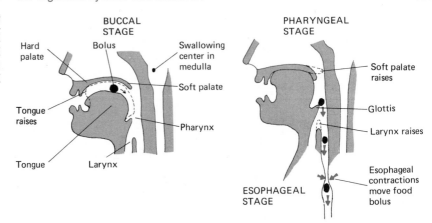

tion will occur, a nonvoluntary act indicating that the control is purely at the spinal cord level. Evidently the stretching of the rectal walls will eventually evoke a corresponding motor response from the spinal cord, contracting the rectal wall and forcing the sphincter to relax.

Feces contain a little undigested material, a small amount of water, excesses of digestible materials, hemoglobin pigments, and a tremendous number of sloughed epithelial cells and living or dead bacteria. The malodorous characteristic of feces is derived from *hydrogen sulfide, scatole,* and *indole,* all products of amino acid catabolism by bacteria. The appearance of feces (also called *stool*) can be a useful diagnostic aid. For example, many parasites responsible for gastrointestinal disturbances show up in feces. If bile is absent from the intestine, the stool usually appears grayish brown. A black, tarry-colored stool may indicate bleeding high in the gastrointestinal tract, while bright red blood in the stool suggests hemorrhoidal bleeding.

secretions and action of digestive enzymes

The salivary glands produce water, salts, mucin, and one digestive enzyme, *salivary amylase.* About 1.5 liters of saliva are secreted daily. The amylase acts upon complex carbohydrates and splits them into disaccharides.

Saliva

Gastric Juices

HYDROCHLORIC ACID The parietal cells of the stomach produce a very high concentration of hydrogen ions by an unknown mechanism. In addition, these unique cells must extract chloride ions from plasma, which is then coupled to the hydrogen ion from the cells to produce the acid.

PEPSIN Pepsin acts on the peptide linkage of native proteins (Chapter 2), breaking the large protein molecules into the smaller *proteoses* and *peptones* and sometimes even into amino acids. Pepsin is stored within the chief cells as *pepsinogen.* Pepsin is a unique protein in that it can work in a medium as acidic as pH 2. The conversion of the inactive pepsinogen to the active pepsin is initiated by hydrochloric acid, and then the system becomes *autocatalytic* (self-activating) in that pepsin converts more pepsinogen to pepsin.

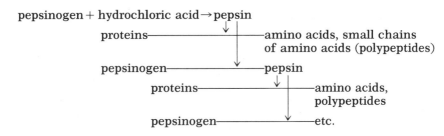

pepsinogen + hydrochloric acid → pepsin

RENNIN A protein found in milk, *casein*, is clotted by rennin, and only then is it digestible. Obviously rennin is a very necessary enzyme during infancy when milk constitutes such an important percentage of the diet, and becomes less important as the individual matures.

LIPASE A minimum amount of lipid digestion occurs in the stomach. The limited fat breakdown in the acidic stomach is because lipase, like most enzymes, degrades at a low pH. Pepsin and rennin, as mentioned previously, are unique enzymes in that they function optimally in an acid medium.

MUCIN Mucin is also a component of the gastric juices and serves to lubricate the food and possibly to protect the living cells against the hydrochloric acid made within the stomach cavity. Mucin, however, has no known active digestive function.

Pancreatic Juice   The pancreas secretes copious amounts of enzymes that enter the duodenum, and unlike the gastric enzymes, they operate at an alkaline pH, around 8.0 to 8.2. The pancreas helps to make the intestine alkaline by contributing sodium bicarbonate to the pancreatic juice.

TRYPSIN This enzyme, like pepsin, is secreted in an inactive precursor form, *trypsinogen*. Trypsinogen, in the presence of another enzyme *enterokinase* (comes from the intestinal mucosa), is converted to trypsin.

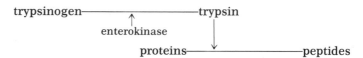

A proteolytic enzyme similar to trypsin is *chymotrypsin*, which is converted from its inactive precursor, *chymotrypsinogen*. Trypsin catalyzes this reaction.

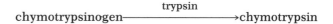

Another enzyme that can be isolated in the pancreatic juice is *carboxypeptidase*. This enzyme is quite specific in that it acts on a specific part of the peptide.

LIPASE The degree of hydrolysis by pancreatic lipase is still questionable.

AMYLASE In the intestine complex carbohydrates are broken down into di- and monosaccharides by pancreatic *amylase*.

NUCLEASE These enzymes are specific for nucleoproteins, which are degraded to nucleosides and bases.

Intestinal Juice   The digestive enzymes secreted by the intestines as part of the intestinal juice are best characterized by their ability to "finish the job." For example, there are *dipeptidases* that split *dipeptides* into two amino acids; *aminopeptidases* which catalyze the separation of terminal groups of amino acids; *carbohydrases*—for example, *maltase, lactase,* and *sucrase*—which act upon *maltose, lactose,* and *sucrose,* respectively, to produce simple sugars or monosaccharides (see Table 13-1). All of these substances are end products, and no further breakdown is necessary for absorption. The intestine also secretes an *intestinal lipase* as well as *enterokinase* (mentioned previously).

table 13-1

DIGESTIVE
ENZYMES[a]

LOCATION OR ORGAN	SECRETION	ENZYME	SUBSTRATE	PRODUCT[b]
Mouth	Saliva	Amylase	Polysaccharide	Maltose
Stomach	Gastric juice	Pepsin	Nearly all proteins	Peptides and amino acids
	Hydrochloric acid[a]	Renin	Caseinogen (milk)	Casein (protein)
		Lipase	Long-chain fats Triglycerides	Di- and mono-glycerides, *fatty acids*
Intestine	Pancreatic juice	Trypsin	Proteins	Peptides and *amino acids*
		Chymotrypsin	Proteins	Peptides and *amino acids*
		Peptidases	Peptides	*Amino acids*
		Nucleases	Nucleoproteins (nucleotides and proteins)	Nucleosides, bases
		Amylase	Polysaccharides	Maltose
		Lipase	Triglycerides	Di- and mono-glycerides, glycerol, *fatty acids*
Intestine	Intestinal juice	Peptidase	Peptides	*Amino acids*
		Sucrase	Sucrose	*Glucose and fructose*
		Maltase	Maltose	*Glucose*
		Lactase	Lactose	*Glucose and galactose*
		Lipase	Triglycerides Fat chains	Di- and mono-glycerides, *fatty acids*
		Nucleases	Nucleotides	Nucleosides, and so on

[a] Hydrochloric acid is not an enzyme, but plays a major role in digestion.
[b] Products italicized are absorbed in this state. Other products may or may not, for example, proteins, polypeptides, and so on.

Liver Bile   The liver produces bile, a compound composed of water (98 percent), mucin, cholesterol, pigments, and minute amounts of other substances. Bile that is not utilized immediately is stored in the gall bladder, where the bile salts may be increased as much as tenfold. Bile emulsifies lipids to form small particles, providing a large surface area for lipase activity. If bile is not present in the duodenum, large amounts of fats remain undigested and are eliminated in the feces. The pigments that give bile its characteristic yellow-green color come from the degradation of hemoglobin. The major pigment is *bilirubin* (yellow), and its oxidized product is *biliverdine* (green).

absorption   Absorption (Table 13-2) of digested foods is the function of the small intestine. Structurally, it is admirably suited for this function—long in length, the presence of villi that increase many thousandfold the area for absorption, and with a high degree of vascularity. In the stomach, a minor amount of absorptive activity can take place, specifically for certain foods (alcohol) and certain proteins (the latter absorption is prevalent in individuals who have food allergies and apparently absorb whole proteins in the blood).

table 13-2

ABSORPTION OF FOOD

MATERIAL ABSORBED	AREA OF ABSORPTION	END-PRODUCT UTILIZATION
Water	Entire gastrointestinal tract, especially in the small and large intestine	Blood and lymph capillaries into systemic circulation[a]
Inorganic salts	Small and large intestine	Same as for water
Vitamins	Stomach and small intestine	Same as for water
Amino acids	Small intestine	Blood capillaries → portal vein → liver → synthesized into enzymes and other proteins, systemic circulation (synthesized into proteins)
Sugars	Small intestine	Blood capillaries → portal vein → liver → utilized as energy by liver cells, systemic circulation (energy), excess stored in liver as glycogen
Glycerides, glycerols, fatty acids	Small intestine	Lacteals → thoracic duct → jugular vein → systemic circulation → fat depots
		Blood capillaries → portal vein → liver → storage or synthesized into new products → systemic circulation

[a] Systemic circulation means to be delivered to cells throughout the body as needed.

Carbohydrates   Some 14 different sugars have been reported to be absorbed by the intestine, but glucose is the primary sugar absorbed.

Proteins   The amino acid products of protein digestion are absorbed by the intestinal cells, and the amino acids then pass into the capillary in each villus. Some small amounts of amino acids remain in the villi cells to form proteins needed by each intestinal epithelial cell, but the bulk of the amino acids enter the blood.

Lipids   Digested fatty acids have two pathways in which they can enter general circulation. Some digested fats immediately recombine to form a triglyceride that can be absorbed by the mucosal cells and pass into the lacteals. The absorbed fats will be transported by the lymph vessels and eventually will enter the systemic circulation at the jugular veins where the major lymph vessels end. Other breakdown products of digestive fats are water soluble and are absorbed directly into the capillary of each villus.

Water and Minerals   Water passes through the mucosal epithelium by passive diffusion, but movement of ions such as Cl^-, Na^+, K^+, and H^+ frequently requires an active transfer system. In general, monovalent ions, for example, Cl^-, OH^-, Na^+, and K^+, are absorbed more readily than polyvalent ions, for example, Ca^{2+}, Mg^{2+}. Water and electrolytes are absorbed primarily in the small intestine and, to a lesser extent, by the colon.

control   Movement in the digestive tract is primarily under neurogenic control, whereas secretion is regulated primarily by hormones and other humoral (body fluid) agents (Table 13-3). Of course, this division of control is not 100 percent in that humoral agents can also affect motion. The wall of

table 13-3

HUMORAL
REGULATION OF
DIGESTIVE JUICES

ORGAN MUCOSA	HORMONE	STIMULUS TO HORMONE SECRETION	TARGET CELLS AND EFFECT
Stomach	Gastrin	Secretogogues (polypeptides)	Stimulates chief and parietal cells to secrete gastric juices
Intestine	Secretin	Hydrochloric acid	Stimulates intestinal mucosa to secrete intestinal juice; pancreas to form intestinal juice; liver to form bile
Intestine	Enterogasterone[a]	Duodenal contents	Inhibits secretory activity of the gastric mucosa
Intestine	Pancreozymin	Hydrochloric acid, secretogogues, gastrin	Stimulates secretion of pancreatic juice
Intestine	Cholecystokinin	Fat in the duodenum	Brings about contraction of the gall bladder

[a] This is not a single hormone, but a term representing possible hormones and a wide variety of metabolic products, for example, peptides and hydrogen ions.

the gastrointestinal tract contains a nerve network that is composed of two layers: the inner layer is called the *Meissner or submucosal plexus* and the outer, *myenteric or Auerbach's plexus*, is located between the layers of muscle in the wall. Because both plexuses are in the gut wall, they are sometimes referred to as the *intramural plexus.*

The many neurogenic reflexes that regulate gut activity originate in these layers, such as localized movement. The coordination of peristalsis is also due to the action of these nerve networks; in general, the intramural plexuses will stimulate the rate and extent of the contractions.

Each digestive organ receives parasympathetic and sympathetic innervation from the autonomic portion of the central nervous system. The parasympathetic stimulates gastrointestinal activity principally by stimuli carried by the vagus nerve. The sympathetic system tends to counteract the vagal regulation and inhibits gastrointestinal activity. Sympathetic innervation is not restricted to inhibition, for the contraction of two sphincters (the ileocecal and the internal anal sphincter) is stimulated by the sympathetic nerves.

saliva   The secretion of saliva is a reflex reaction to sensory stimuli. The smell or sight of food, as well as the presence of food in the mouth that stimulates mechanical and chemical receptors in the mucosa, will elicit a salivary response.

gastric secretion   The secretion of gastric juices is divided into three phases: *cephalic, gastric,* and *intestinal.* Psychological factors play a major role in the "cephalic *(head)* phase." The smell, sight, or taste of food, even agreeable thoughts about food, will elicit a copious flow of gastric juices (Figure 13-14).

During the gastric phase, *secretagogues* (certain foods or their breakdown products) will stimulate secretory activity in the gastric mucosa. One theory is that the *secretagogues,* and perhaps the stretching of the gastric wall as food enters, stimulate the pylorus part of the stomach to

figure 13-14

THE CEPHALIC
PHASE OF
GASTRIC
SECRETION

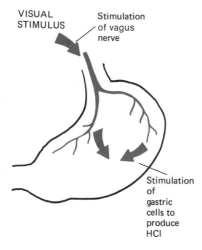

VISUAL
STIMULUS

Stimulation
of vagus
nerve

Stimulation
of
gastric
cells to
produce
HCl

Psychological or emotional factors acting through the brain's association areas, limbic system, and central autonomic control evoke gastric responses even before the ingestion of food. Such reflex responses can become conditioned to visual or other sensory stimuli associated with anticipation of feeding.

figure 13-15

THE
SECRETAGOGUE
MECHANISM—
THE GASTRIC
PHASE

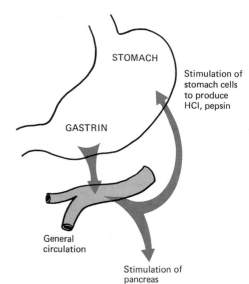

STOMACH

Stimulation of
stomach cells
to produce
HCl, pepsin

GASTRIN

General
circulation

Stimulation of
pancreas

The arrival of food in the stomach triggers the cells of the gastric mucosa to produce and release the hormone gastrin. Gastrin in turn stimulates both the stomach and the pancreas to increase secretary activities associated with the digestive process.

produce a hormone, *gastrin*, which in turn stimulates the production of hydrochloric acid and pepsin (Figure 13-15).

If all of the nerves going to the stomach are cut experimentally and food is put into the duodenum manually, stomach juices are secreted. It appears that an *intestinal gastrin* is produced by the duodenum that is similar in function to the gastrin produced by the stomach. Thus the "intestinal phase" of gastric secretion would be that period when food first leaves the stomach and enters the small intestine, stimulating the production of the intestinal gastrin.

histamine and hydrochloric acid secretion

The secretion of hydrochloric acid by the gastric mucosa can be inhibited by agents that block or degrade histamine. Histamine is a powerful stimulator of hydrochloric acid secretion, so it is possible that the histamine released by nerves acts as a coregulator of hydrochloric acid production.

pancreatic juice secretion

Neurogenic control over the flow of secretions from the pancreas can be demonstrated by stimulating the vagus which will increase secretion and by cutting the vagus which will inhibit secretion. In the latter situation, however, sufficient secretion will continue so that the digestive function is not seriously impaired, and this fact indicates humoral regulation. Such control was discovered at the turn of the century; the agent was named *secretin*. The discovery is of lasting importance, because it was the first hormone to be discovered.

The presence of proteins, fats, and a little acid in the small intestine stimulates the release of secretin, which then passes into the bloodstream. When the secretin reaches the pancreas, it stimulates the production of digestive enzymes. Another hormone from the intestine, *pancreozymin*, is also believed to be a stimulator of pancreatic enzymes.

bile secretion   Although the liver secretes bile continuously (0.5 to 1.0 liter per day), an injection of secretin will increase the production of bile (the hormone has no effect on the gall bladder). Bile production is also increased when blood flow through the liver is enhanced. The bile is stored and concentrated in the gall bladder until it is needed.

The release of the stored bile is under control of another hormone secreted by the duodenum when fats from the stomach enter the duodenum. This hormone *cholecystokinin* stimulates the gall bladder to contract. Increased pressure within the gall bladder triggers a neural reflex, which relaxes the sphincter muscle in the bile duct, allowing the bile to enter the intestine.

intestinal juice   Less is known about the regulation of intestinal enzymes than regulation
secretion   of those for the pancreas. A hormone, *enterocrinin*, produced from an extract of intestinal mucosa is known to increase intestinal enzyme secretion without affecting pancreatic juice or bile secretion. Mechanical stimulation will also stimulate activity, for even a denervated segment of the intestine will produce enzymes if the walls are manipulated or subjected to pressure.

factors influ-   Pavlov's classic experiment on the conditioned reflex (Chapter 8) beau-
encing function   tifully illustrated the potential interrelationship of digestive functions to stimuli quite remote from digestion. For example, hunger pains (gut motility and secretory activity) are frequently initiated by a time factor rather than need. Man is a creature of habit and usually feels the need for lunch around high noon almost without regard of his food intake at breakfast.

The state of the digestive system is frequently a barometer of the individual's emotional state at a given time – indigestion, cramps, vomiting, or ulcers may be produced by a persistent state of anxiety or fear. One frequently cited experiment indicating emotional effects on the digestive apparatus is called the *"executive monkeys."* The animals in the experiment were trained to press a lever at given intervals, which prevented them from receiving a shock. Within a relatively short period of time, the monkeys in this type of stressful environment developed ulcers. The proof that the *need to pull the lever* and *not the occasional shocks* created the stress producing an ulcer was demonstrated in anther experiment.

nutrition   The early history of nutrition is intimately tied with the history of chemistry. It was not until the nineteenth century that scientists began to analyze food chemically and to associate its composition with body maintenance and good health. Prior to this time, little if any thought was given to proper diet. We could almost accept as fact that the farmer knew how to maintain his livestock in a healthier condition than his family. Food intake was conditioned by practical factors such as supply and local customs. Even as late as the beginning of the twentieth century, good nutrition simply meant ample proteins, carbohydrates, fats, minerals, and water. It was not until the 1920s that vitamins were added to the essential list for growth.

Today we are still concerned about nutrition in spite of our knowledge in this area. For reasons that extend beyond the scope of this book, malnutrition and even starvation are becoming more prevalent, notwithstanding the increase in the world's technological skills. What is even more paradoxical, the incidence of malnutrition is increasing among the affluent due primarily to *fad diets* related to weight control or to maintenance of "eternal youth" and vigor. Recently, the practice of keeping weight gain to an absolute minimum during pregnancy has been challenged by individuals concerned with nutrition.

However, what has sharpened the focus on nutrition most in recent years is the discovery that dietary deficiencies in early life may not be reversible, especially in the brain and in other parts of the nervous system. We have also learned that a severe calcium deficiency during the formative years will lead to rickets. If the condition is not corrected, malformed bones will develop that will persist into adulthood. Even though the individual may be disfigured and even slightly handicapped in his movement, his potential as a functioning and valuable member of society is not impaired. However, if the child suffers from protein deficiency through the first four years of life, development of the brain may be impaired irreversibly (the brain does not develop new cells during life). In addition to lower intelligence and impaired motivation, these children may have poorer motor coordination and thus acquire fewer skills than would normally be expected.

Survival depends on an organism replenishing the materials lost during metabolism, and since even the most efficient body loses most of its energy as heat, the prime function of nutrition is to restore this loss. Six components are essential to a good diet: *proteins, fats, carbohydrates, minerals, vitamins,* and *water.* Intake varies from individual to individual as well as from cultural group to cultural group, but proteins from beef are of no greater value than similar proteins from fish, oysters, or soybeans; glucose derived from beets, sugarcane, or honey is recognized by the body merely as glucose. Some foods, however, are more complete than others; for example, not all proteins contain all of the essential amino acids. What is important is that an ample supply of each constituent be present and that the total caloric content per day be at least equal to the amount expended. We should not ignore, however, the admonition of Carl von Voit, a pioneer investigator in metabolism and nutrition, who proposed over a century ago as one of the criteria for good nutrition, "A diet must be tasty!"

In this section only the nutritional requirements of a balanced diet are discussed. Dietary standards are not absolute, and most of the values expressed in the text or in the tables are given as a normal range.

water requirements   Although the exact percentage in a tissue is difficult to quantitate because water exists in so many forms, a range between 50 and 95 percent would cover most normal conditions. Water is obtained by drinking, as a component of food, to a slight degree from the air breathed, and as a metabolic by-product. Water loss occurs from expiring air, sweating, urination, and defecation. Water intake is directly related to water output, which, in turn, is dependent on metabolic activity. During a normal work day, with normal temperatures, the body will lose about 2.5 liters of water.

mineral requirements

The principal *cations* of the body are *potassium, magnesium, calcium,* and *sodium;* the principal *anions* are *chloride, bicarbonate, phosphate, sulfate,* and *plasma proteins.* Iron is an essential ingredient in hemoglobin and constitutes the principal mineral in erythrocytes. The role of these minerals (*macronutrients*) is discussed elsewhere in the text. Over 20 additional minerals (*micronutrients*) have been isolated from various tissues, but only five are documented to be essential for normal growth: *cobalt, copper, manganese, zinc,* and *iodine.* The first four elements usually bind with hormones and act as activators. The normal values for cobalt, copper, manganese, and zinc are unknown, and the estimates given in the literature are so broad that they are almost valueless.

Iodine is an exception in that the dietary needs are known, and someday they may be shown to be essential. In recent years a great deal of attention has been focused on the role of fluoride because of its effectiveness in retarding tooth decay. It is also of value in skeletal development. In all probability it is essential in trace amounts; no one has ever demonstrated or reported a fluorine-deficient condition in man or experimental animal.

In summary, mineral metabolism is a vital process that is characterized primarily by the exceptionally small quantities needed for good health. The fact that so little is present in a normal diet indicates that cells are capable of absorbing most of the trace elements available and then concentrating them.

proteins

Not all proteins will support growth because some do not contain, or contain too little of, a necessary amino acid; a diet containing only these types of proteins is almost worthless. *Essential amino acids* refer to amino acids that cannot be synthesized by the body in adequate amounts and must be a part of the diet.

Since most of the amino acids are reconstituted into proteins again, we might ask what value there is in continuously breaking down proteins into amino acids and then resynthesizing them into proteins once again. One possible explanation is that the continuous catabolism of proteins provides an enormous source of raw materials for the synthesis of proteins. At any moment of life, thousands of homeostatic adjustments are made that require enzymes (proteins). Once the response is made, the enzymes may not be needed. By breaking them down immediately, a supply of amino acids is provided for another needed enzyme. To stockpile an equivalent amount of building units for just enzyme synthesis alone would be uneconomical.

An excessively high protein diet (beyond 224 g per day) is worthless as malnutrition therapy or for "extra muscle" so avidly sought after by health faddists. The body can only handle a restricted amount of protein in a limited span of time, and "extras" are simply eliminated as waste. Direct administration of amino acids, either parentally or intravenously, is also of little value to counteract malnutrition, since the extra amino acids are rapidly broken down and spilled out in the urine.

The minimal amount of protein recommended by various health organizations for a normal adult male is about 5 g a day. The average middle-class individual in the United States ingests about 200 g per day. A safe estimate of protein intake is that it should account for at least 15 percent of the total calorie intake. The protein requirement for special cases, for example, pregnant women or nursing mothers, is considerably above the minimum.

carbohydrates

Carbohydrates account for 50 to 60 percent of the diet in the United States. In some parts of the world where proteins are scarce or difficult to obtain, carbohydrates account for an even higher percentage of the diet. In contrast to proteins, the carbohydrate dietary requirements have a wide latitude because sugars can be obtained from proteins. In addition, the body can utilize its stored fats as an alternate source of energy. The carbohydrates needed per day can therefore merely be approximated depending primarily upon the general utilization of sugar and the percentage of fat and protein in the diet.

One estimate for the United States teen-age population puts the carbohydrate consumption at almost 2 pounds per day, with the principal sources being sugars (candy, fruit, and to a lesser degree vegetables). Societies utilizing carbohydrates as their principal source of food (polished rice in the Far East) are quite prone to developing vitamin B deficiency. The very nature of the diet limits the intake of the vitamin, which functions as coenzyme in carbohydrate metabolism. The more rice a man eats, the more vitamin B he needs, and because vitamin B is not completely supplied by the rice, a cycle leading to malnutrition occurs.

lipids

Until recently it was assumed that lipids or fats were not essential for normal nutrition and that the fats needed for building membranes and for certain secretions were readily manufactured by the body from products obtained from carbohydrate and protein metabolism. It is more likely that the body is incapable of synthesizing all of its needed lipids and that a totally fat-free diet could be deleterious to health.

Fats contain more calories per unit weight than any other food. Logically, they should be used as a major calorie source to bolster a diet. However, most individuals rebel against a fat diet taken orally, and a satisfactory emulsion that could be given intravenously has not been developed.

Because cardiovascular diseases account for the greatest number of adult nonaccidental deaths and the deposits of *cholesterol* and phospholipids within the blood vessels appear to accumulate proportionally with age, many investigators have attempted to demonstrate a reciprocal relationship between fats and diseases. This thinking has led to a concerted effort on the part of physicians and nutritionists to restrict those fats (saturated) from the diet that stimulate the synthesis of cholesterol. To date, the evidence supporting the value of a fat-free diet is not conclusive, and we should be cautious about living on a "total fat-free diet" or even a "saturated-fat-free diet" until we know more about the dietary requirements for fats. A diet limited in fats is usually recommended by clinicians. For the more affluent members of our society, fats may account for as much as 40 percent of the calories, notwithstanding the fact that Americans in the United States consume more proteins than most other people. Most of this fat is "hidden" in that it is incorporated in better cuts of meat, in fried foods, and in the symbolic dishes of the United States, the hot dog and hamburger. One of the paradoxes of the affluent society is that they are eating less than their grandparents but gaining more.

vitamins   Vitamins are organic compounds, form part of active sites of certain enzymes, or are constituents of substances such as the eye pigments. They play an essential (some play a vital role) in health and growth, and because, without exception, they cannot be synthesized by the organism, their absence produces specific vitamin-deficient diseases. A limiting characteristic of vitamins is that only minimal amounts are stored, and some vitamins cannot be stored at all. For good health an individual must therefore have certain vitamins daily, since he cannot call upon any appreciable reserve. The dietary requirements vary with the age, sex, and the state of the individual (pregnancy imposes an additional need for vitamins).* One word of caution about vitamin intake is that excesses may be quite damaging particularly for vitamins A, C, D, and E.

Vitamin A (5000 IU)   Liver and vegetables are excellent sources of vitamin A. In plants it is found in precursor form, *carotene*, which is converted to vitamin A in the intestinal wall. The function of vitamin A in the body is to form one of the visual pigments, and its absence leads to "night blindness." It also plays a role in maintaining a healthy state of skin and membranes.

Vitamin B Complex   The vitamin B complex refers to a number of vitamins that are chemically and functionally closely related. They are water soluble, widely distributed in foods, and usually function as coenzymes in intermediary metabolism.

THIAMINE (B_1) (1.2 mg)   Thiamine is especially prevalent in grains, beans, and pork. Only small quantities can be stored, which means it must be part of the daily diet. Vitamin B_1 functions in the breakdown of carbohydrates and proteins; the requirements of the vitamin vary with the caloric intake of these two foods as well as with the general metabolism. The nervous system and the heart require large amounts of glucose for normal functioning, so that a deficiency of thiamine brings about nerve degeneration and weakening of heart muscles.

RIBOFLAVIN (B_2) (1.8 mg) Riboflavin is widely found in both plant and animal tissues (particularly in liver). Vitamin B_2 is a coenzyme for H_2 transfer in the oxidative system (Chapter 2), and yet riboflavin defi-

---

* The recommended allowance, provided parenthetically following the name of each vitamin, is only an estimate that should insure that the minimal requirements are met. Vitamins A and D are given in international units (IU), and all other vitamin dosages are expressed in milligrams (mg) or micrograms (μg).

ciencies produce only mild side effects. Sores or cracking at the corners of the mouth or headaches are a few of the manifestations.

NIACIN (16 mg) Niacin is a widely distributed vitamin found in liver, fish, wheat, and beans; Niacin (also called *nicotinic acid*), like ribo-flavin, is a coenzyme that functions in cellular respiration. The disease state of niacin deficiency is called *pellagra*, and it is quite common in developing areas of the world where proteins are minimal in the diet. Inflammation of membranes, skin irritation, muscle weakness, and in severe cases hallucinations and delirium may occur from a lack of the vitamin.

PANTOTHENIC ACID Pantothenic acid is a part of coenzyme A, which plays a variety of metabolic roles (Chapter 14). Evidently, this vitamin is so widespread in foods that no deficiency has ever been reported.

INOSITOL A dietary requirement for inositol has never been established. Similar to pantothenic acid, it is so prevalent that even a minimal diet contains sufficient inositol. It is believed to be involved in lipid metabolism.

BIOTIN (250 μg) Trace amounts of biotin are found in meat, eggs, milk, and vegetables. Deficiencies are rare, but when they occur, gastrointestinal disturbances result. It functions as part of the coenzyme responsible for combining CO_2 with organic compounds.

CHOLINE Choline functions in fat metabolism and as a precursor in the synthesis of acetylcholine. Deficiencies of this vitamin in humans probably does not exist, and the daily requirements are not known.

PYRIDOXINE (B_6) Pyridoxine, an important coenzyme for protein synthesis, is found principally in meat, milk, and vegetables. Vitamin B_6 deficiency in humans is quite rare. When it does exist, severe gastrointestinal disturbances (nausea, diarrhea) occur. Pyridoxine is sometimes given to pregnant women experiencing severe "morning sickness" (nausea and vomiting); the success of this treatment is questionable.

FOLIC ACID (0.15 mg) Folic acid or folacin is involved in the formation of DNA and in the development of erythrocytes. Anemia is, therefore, a serious clinical feature of this vitamin deficiency. The vitamin is found principally in leafy green vegetables.

CYANOCOBALAMIN (B_{12}) (5 μg) Vitamin B_{12} is found in liver, meat, eggs, and milk; it is also manufactured by the gastrointestinal tract. The vitamin has a stimulating effect on erythrocyte formation (the antianemic factor), and it is believed to be a coenzyme needed in the metabolism of amino acids. A B_{12} deficiency (by diet or malfunction of the liver) will produce *pernicious anemia* (because until B_{12} was discovered as the antianemic factor, this type of anemia did not respond to the usual treatment for anemia of that era).

Ascorbic Acid
(Vitamin C)
(70 to 100 mg)

Ascorbic acid or vitamin C is found in large quantities in leafy green vegetables and citrus fruits. Vitamin C deficiency (*scurvy*) is generally not common in static societies. In most societies, a diet evolves in such a way that it will include one or more sources of vitamin C, but in atypical living situations, for example, aboard ship or with a moving army, scurvy is a potential threat since the major supply of ascorbic acid, fruits and vegetables, are generally not available. Prior to this century, sailors suffered from vitamin C deficiency until it was accidentally discovered that consuming limes prevented scurvy. For years, British sailors received a lime ration, although no one understood why it was good therapy, and the tag, *"limey,"* jokingly given to the British sailor of yesterday persists today.

Although this vitamin has been studied extensively, its nutritive metabolic role is still unknown. Ascorbic acid is known to affect the connective tissue elements, and since this tissue is ubiquitous (widely distributed), vitamin C deficiency produces widespread effects. Blood vessels break down, and bleeding is common; bones become brittle; teeth fall out; wound healing is impaired. Vitamin C is not stored by the tissues, so that the recommended dosage must be ingested daily. The belief that excess amounts of vitamin C will prevent the common cold, or accelerate a cure, is still without full documentation. Although the theory has a logical basis, and some recent work provides some support for the theory, the evidence is still far from definitive.

Calciferol
(Vitamin D)
(400 IU)

Calciferol labors under several names including *activated ergosterol, 7-dehydrocholesterol,* or simply *vitamin D.* Vitamin D is not commonly found in foods except for liver and milk, but fortunately the skin in the presence of sunlight can synthesize the vitamin. So many foods are fortified with vitamin D that its lack is becoming a less common problem. The vitamin increases the rate of calcium binding by the intestinal lining cells.

Tocopherol
(Vitamin E)
(10 to 30 mg)

The role of the tocopherols (vitamin E) in human nutrition is equivocal, so it is questionable if a true case of vitamin E deficiency can occur. It is sometimes called the antisterility vitamin, because in nonprimate mammals, a deficiency will affect the testis and in females may produce an abortion. There is some evidence that the vitamin may be involved in lipid metabolism, and in experimental rodents, a deficiency appears to hasten the syndrome of old age. The latter effect is based upon some evidence that vitamin E is an antioxidant.

Vitamin K

Ample amounts of vitamin K are manufactured by the bacteria of the colon, so that the dietary requirement is zero. Vitamin K is needed for the formation of prothrombin by the liver, but the exact role is not known. It also has been implicated in the formation of blood factors, such as Factor VII. During prolong treatment of a bacterial infection with antibiotics, very often the helpful bacteria that synthesize vitamin K are also wiped out by the drugs, and as a result the patient may develop bleeding problems.

clinical
considerations

obstruction

The digestive system is structurally a tubular system, and conditions that block the lumen, for example, abnormal growth (tumors), muscle spasms, or kinking of its walls, are of major clinical importance. The increased activity of peristalsis proximal to the obstruction is frequently very painful. Obstructing the passage of food, especially in infants, will quickly lead to a nutritional problem, and in serious diseases, the blockage will produce vomiting, bleeding, and even rupturing of the wall.

gastroenteritis

Inflammation of the lining of the digestive tract called *gastroenteritis* can be produced by overindulgence (food or alcohol), by psychic tension,

figure 13-16

HISTOLOGY OF A
GASTRIC ULCER

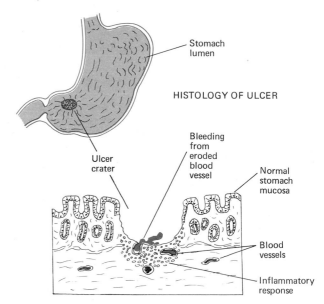

HISTOLOGY OF ULCER

Stomach
lumen

Bleeding
from
eroded
blood
vessel

Ulcer
crater

Normal
stomach
mucosa

Blood
vessels

Inflammatory
response

and by parasitic and bacterial infections. One common manifestation of gastroenteritis is that a small amount of gastric fluid is forced into the esophagus producing a burning sensation, erroneously called *heartburn* (because the pain is felt in the chest in the region of the heart). Pernicious anemia may result from prolonged gastroenteritis, because the mucosa fails to maintain its normal secretory activity, which includes the production of the antianemic factor (Chapter 10). The antianemic factor combines with vitamin B_{12} and stimulates the bone marrow to produce red blood cells.

gastrointestinal
ulcers

An *ulcer* is a break in the mucosa, and if the destruction of the tissue is not checked, the ulcer may even *perforate* (make a hole) in the wall producing hemorrhage. The ulcer may also allow the contents to seep into the peritoneal cavity (Figure 13-16). This condition is critical because the digestive contents are loaded with bacteria that are extremely harmful when they are not contained within the digestive tract.

The most frequent site to ulcerate is the pyloric region of the duodenum followed by the area comprising the lesser curvature of the stomach in which the acid content of the food is quite high. Ulcers are the result of any factor or combination of factors capable of increasing the gastric acid secretion or interfering with the buffering action of the duodenal alkaline secretion. There are occasions when the pH and Brunner's glands are functioning normally, and ulcers will form because the food is propelled too quickly for the duodenal secretion to neutralize the acidity. Whatever the cause, an ulcer is a painful condition, and the continuous bleeding that frequently occurs will produce a secondary anemia.

gall bladder   Many diseases of the gall bladder result from a blockage of the ducts by the precipitation of bile salts that eventually aggregate to form small stones. The obstruction of the bile duct is very painful because of the peristalsis and the inflammation that results from an interference with the blood supply. The *gall stones* dam the duct, and the bile backs up into the liver. The excess bile pigments then accumulate in all parts of the body, producing a yellowish cast to the skin and eyes. The condition is called *jaundice*. Excessive amounts of bile will also overextend the storage capacity of the gall bladder, producing an inflammation that is quite painful and debilitating.

vomiting   Vomiting *(emesis)* is a cataclysmic reflex reaction that is regulated by a vomiting center in the medulla. A combination of actions (swallowing, a forcible contraction of the diaphragm and of the abdominal muscles) squeezes the stomach and propels some of its contents into the esophagus. Vomiting's importance as a defense mechanism is equaled only by the discomfort of the occurrences. Vomiting produced by gastroenteritis or viral infections is a protective device to allow the stomach to rid itself of materials that are irritating. The vomiting center may receive signals from (a) the semicircular canals *(motion sickness)*, (b) the cerebellum *(motor coordination)*, (c) extra amounts of metabolites circulating in the blood as occurs in pregnancy, or (d) the pain center in the brain.

One result of clinical importance is that excessive vomiting causes a loss of fluid and electrolytes. If the loss is solely from the stomach, hydrochloric acid is removed and blood alkalinity results; if the vomiting produces a loss of duodenal alkaline secretion, acidosis will occur. Acidosis can produce coma and may even degrade some enzymes.

Occasionally, it is necessary to induce vomiting by artificial means. A tried and true method is by irritating the pharynx with the index finger. *Emetics* (substances capable of producing vomiting) are used to bring up toxic substances, and the more commonly used materials are *salt water, tartar,* or *dry mustard.* When a caustic agent is swallowed accidentally, to induce vomiting would be doubly harmful. A rule of thumb is not to regurgitate any substance that was harmful to the tissues on the way down, for it may be equally harmful on the way back.

appendicitis   Inflammation of the appendix is produced by food becoming trapped in the appendix cavity because of an obstruction. This condition produces a breakdown in the lining and provides an excellent environment for invading bacteria to accumulate. The bacterial infection will further irritate the lining to produce greater infection and inflammation. The inflammation will in turn produce increased peristalsis and nausea, cramps and sharp pains. One inherent danger in *appendicitis* is that the increased peristalsis may rupture the appendix, spilling the bacterial contents within the body cavity to produce a general infection called *peritonitis* or a peritoneal abscess.

diarrhea   *Diarrhea* is the result of rapid transport of fecal material through the colon and rectum. The mucosa produces excessive secretions in response to stimuli (toxins, infections, and so on), which in turn will put extra pressure on the colon walls to produce a rapid and massive peristaltic wave. As in vomiting, uncontrolled diarrhea results in a loss of fluid and electrolytes and concomitant side effects of change in pH and dehydration. Diarrhea of this nature is a major cause of death in infancy.

constipation   Constipation results from a failure to evacuate the bowels after a 2 to 3 day period. This condition is not serious and is usually caused by poor health habits rather than a pathological situation. Because of the food stasis, excessive amounts of water are absorbed producing a hard dry feces which, of course, complicates the condition. Constipation over a long period of time, however, should be regarded as a danger sign of a possible obstruction in the colon or rectum, which may be produced by a growth or spasm in the wall.

Routine constipation is remedied by *cathartics*, a general term for agents that in some manner retain or add water to the undigested bowel contents. The extra volume of water stretches the intestinal walls to stimulate a more forceful contraction. Some cathartics are irritants and cause the mucosa to secrete fluid (castor oil contains a small amount of a deadly poison extracted from the castor bean); gelatins are used because they retain water; oils coat the gut wall and inhibit water absorption.

hepatitis   Hepatitis or inflammation of the liver can be brought about by a number of diverse causes such as virus infection, drugs, poisons, or parasites. The common denominator, regardless of the initial cause of the inflammation, is a decrease in the number of functioning liver cells. One of the most definitive symptoms is a deep jaundice, a yellowing of the skin due to the elevated blood bilirubin levels. Since the liver produces clotting proteins, another symptom of hepatitis is a tendency to bleeding and bruising. More distressing is the accumulation of toxins that are normally broken down by the liver. As the toxin level of the body increases, the central nervous system may be affected. For many forms of hepatitis there is no specific therapy, and prevention is of special importance. The usual treatment consists of bed rest, diet, control of protein and salt intake, and an absolute avoidance of alcohol. If, however, the hepatitis is produced by an infection, treatment would also include specific care such as the use of antibiotics.

starvation   It is truly incredible that in the greatest age of technology in recorded history, when a garden-sized plot of land can provide a yield greater than an acre of land produced a few decades ago, starvation and malnutrition should increase at an alarming rate. Unless this trend is checked by some means, it has been estimated that *at least half of the world population will be suffering from starvation by the year* 2000. Accurate predictions about the future are at best very difficult to make, but even if the estimations stated in this section are exaggerated, the starvation trend is still an alarming one and requires immediate attention. At present better than 30 percent of all the children in the developing areas of the world will suffer some permanent damage due to starvation; this figure also is increasing at an alarming rate.

Starvation is not to be equated with *hunger* or *appetite;* even the latter two words are not synonyms. Hunger is felt as a sharp contraction in the gut region and is probably due to variations in the blood sugar level. Appetite has its base within the hypothalamus. Essentially, starvation is *self-immolation;* the body burns itself out in its attempt to provide energy to maintain beating of the heart, to synthesize new enzymes, to breathe, and so on.

During starvation the fat depots are the first to be utilized for energy. If the caloric diet is not increased, eventually muscle proteins will be used as raw materials (Figure 13-17). Just before death, even some of the tissues of the vital organs will be utilized.

figure 13-17

THE EFFECTS
OF STARVATION

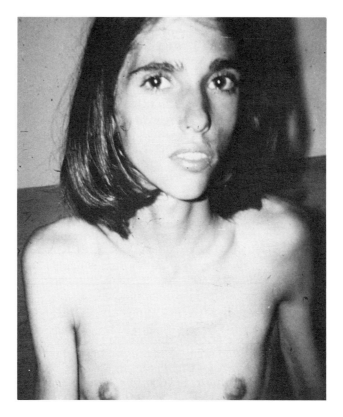

In the absence of sufficient caloric intake the body's energy needs are met by breaking down fat and protein, thereby producing severe wasting of the body. In the next decade as many as 15 million may die of starvation. The patient shown is starving not because food is unavailable but due to a diseased state known as anorexia nervosa (the lack of desire and even inability to eat). (Photo courtesy of Dr. Boris Senior, Tufts University Medical School.)

An abnormal behavioral pattern parallels the metabolic changes in starvation in that a general lassitude or stupor or even hallucinations can occur. Although we read about individuals, especially during religious fasts, achieving cosmic states, starvation is a bitter, long, and painful death. In those instances when death does not occur, starvation affects the individual's physical and mental development and pathetically leaves unerasable scars.

Unlike so many diseases of mankind for which no cure is known, we know what must be done to prevent starvation—simply provide food to those who are hungry. New means for producing and retrieving proteins and carbohydrates are needed, since the estimate that each day there are an additional 150,000 mouths to feed reflects a growing population rate that is increasing faster than technology can close the gap.

obesity   Another paradox of our culture is that along with malnutrition and starvation, overweight is a primary nutritional (and probably clinical) problem in the United States. At least 50 percent of the population is believed to be overweight to some degree, and 10 percent of this group is classified as *obese*. Since the majority of overweight individuals have one or more diseases (gout, diabetes mellitus, hypertension, or heart disease), obesity could very well be the principal "epidemic" in our country.

An individual is classified as obese when his weight is 15 percent over the ideal weight (Table 13-4). The ideal weight is really a *weight range*, for some people have excessively large skeletons, and they are not truly overweight. A simple semiquantitative test for obesity is to measure the excess subcutaneous fatty tissue by pinching a fold of skin with calipers. Obesity is one of the few diseases that truly responds to preventive medicine; however, because our knowledge of the factors producing obesity is inadequate, the treatment is generally short-lived. Only about 2 percent of the individuals who lose weight will maintain the loss beyond the first year.

The various syndromes described for obesity may be classified into two categories: (a) *metabolic obesity* is a weight gain that occurs due to some alteration of the metabolism, either by expending less energy due to a sedentary existence or as seen when an endocrine tumor affects fat and carbohydrate metabolism; (b) *regulatory obesity* results from a psychogenic disturbance. Which type is more prevalent or more damaging is difficult to determine (Figure 13-18).

The factors that affect intake of food and metabolic rate are very complicated. For example, at least six centers in the hypothalamus alone have been implicated in appetite and eating. It is obvious that control problems will arise in a system that has so many levels of regulation. That is why it is still wisest for dieters to utilize a simple diet that merely limits caloric intake while maintaining nutritional balance. If the diet can include a strategem related to the likes and dislikes of the individual's food tastes, then a permanent weight loss is a good possibility. For example, there is nothing spiritually or morally wrong with eating a concentrated starch as a potato. However, a boiled potato has only 100 calories, whereas the same size potato cooked as French fries has almost

table 13-4

HEIGHT-WEIGHT
TABLE FOR MEN
AND WOMEN[a]

HEIGHT IN INCHES	WEIGHT IN POUNDS					
	UNDERWEIGHT	SLENDER	NORMAL	STOCKY	OVERWEIGHT	OBESE
Young Men						
63	111	121	131	141	151	170
64	114	124	134	144	155	175
65	117	128	138	148	159	179
66	120	131	141	152	163	184
67	123	134	145	156	167	188
68	126	138	149	160	171	193
69	130	141	152	164	175	198
70	133	145	156	168	180	203
71	136	148	160	172	184	209
72	140	152	165	177	189	214
73	143	156	169	181	194	219
74	147	160	173	186	199	225
75	151	164	178	191	204	231
76	155	168	182	196	209	237
77	159	173	187	201	215	243
78	163	177	192	206	220	249
Young Women						
58	88	95	103	111	119	134
59	90	98	106	114	122	138
60	93	101	109	117	125	142
61	95	104	112	120	129	146
62	98	106	115	124	132	150
63	101	109	118	127	136	154
64	103	112	122	131	140	158
65	106	116	125	134	144	162
66	109	119	128	138	148	167
67	112	122	132	142	152	172
68	115	126	136	146	156	176
69	119	129	140	150	160	181
70	122	133	143	154	165	186
71	125	136	147	158	170	192
72	129	140	152	163	174	197
73	132	144	156	167	179	202
74	136	148	160	172	184	208

[a] Weight for height classifications based on measurements of young college men and women (measurements made without shoes or clothing).
Underweight = 15 percent or more below average weight.
Slender = 7.5 to 15 percent below average weight.
Normal = Average weight for college men, 21 to 29 years of age and for college women, 17 to 29 years of age.
Stocky = 7.5 to 15 percent above average weight.
Overweight = 15 to 30 percent above average weight.
Obese = More than 30 percent above average weight.

From D. W. Sargent: "Weight-Height Relationship of Young Men and Women," *Am. J. Clin. Nutr.*, 13:318, 1963.

figure 13-18

OBESITY

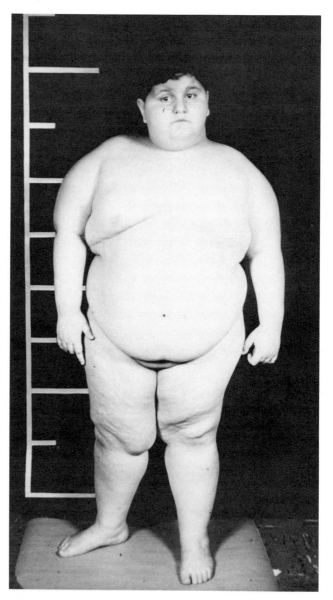

In this patient the obesity was the result of a tumor which affected the appetite centers in the hypothalamus. Other more common causes of obesity are either metabolic or psychogenic in origin. (Photo courtesy of Dr. Boris Senior, Tufts University Medical School.)

300 calories. Another impressive statistic is that the last spoonful of dessert (about 25 calories) if left on the plate each meal will add up to almost 10 pounds of weight *not* added at the end of one year (1 pound of fat = 3400 calories).

A note of caution about dieting is that the "street wisdom" about the success of one diet over another has little scientific value; the success invariably results because the nature of the diet subjectively appeals to the dieter. In addition, specialized or fad diets are of very little value to the dieter in that they are generally so different to the normal pattern of eating that the person must return to eventually, that they have only a short-run effect. Bananas may be fun three times a day while 10 to 15 pounds are being lost, but even a monkey has a more varied diet. Finally, when the weight to be lost amounts to more than 10 percent of the present weight, it is wise to have the counsel and watchfulness of a physician who is knowledgeable about metabolism. During extreme dieting, the free fatty acid levels in the blood may rise to four times normal; no one knows how the body handles this excess of free fatty acids. Patients on a complete fast diet (only water) for over 30 days have been known to develop gout, anemia, and a drop in blood pressure.

summary

**gross
anatomy**

1. Mouth: divided into two parts, one, the space between cheeks and lips—gums and teeth, and two, the large oral cavity
2. Tongue: muscular organ utilized for chewing, swallowing, speech; location of taste buds
3. Pharynx
   (a) respiratory and digestive pathway
   (b) divided into oral pharynx, nasal pharynx, and laryngeal pharynx
   (c) tonsils: palatine, lingual, and pharyngeal
4. Esophagus: communicating tube between pharynx and stomach
5. Stomach
   (a) storage organ
   (b) divided into fundus, body, and pylorus
   (c) openings into and out of the stomach regulated by two valves, the cardiac and pyloric, respectively
6. Small intestine
   (a) divided into duodenum, jejunum, ileum
   (b) ileocecal valve: between small and large intestine
7. Large intestine
   (a) divided into cecum, ascending colon, transverse colon, descending colon, rectum, and anal canal
   (b) sacculations: (haustra) which give the large intestine a distinct appearance
   (c) veriform appendix: a fingerlike outpocketing of the cecum
8. Accessory organs
   (a) salivary glands: parotid, submaxillary, submandibular
   (b) liver: largest organ of the body; tucked under the diaphragm; two major and two minor lobes; under the right lobe is the pear-shaped gall bladder
   (c) pancreas: a 6-inch gland which lies in a loop of the duodenum
9. Blood supply: major source from numerous branches of the celiac and superior mesenteric arteries; blood drained from the digestive system by corresponding veins, which join to form the large hepatic portal vein that enters into the liver
10. Nerve supply: parasympathetic (IX and X cranial nerves) provide

stimulus which enhances digestive functions; sympathetic innervation, radiating from the solar plexus, inhibits digestive activities

microanatomy and cellular specialization

The wall of the gastrointestinal tract is composed of four distinct layers
1. Mucosa
   (a) epithelial lining
   (b) modified into longitudinal folds in the esophagus, rugae in the stomach, villi in the intestines, and columns in the anal region
   (c) villus: unique adaptation for absorption; each villus contains a blood capillary and lymph capillary (lacteal)
   (d) secretory cells: goblet cells secrete mucous; parietal and chief cells produce hydrochloric acid and enzymes, respectively and Brunner's glands (intestines) whose alkaline secretion helps to neutralize the acid contents of the stomach when they pass into the intestine
2. Muscularis: the second layer, predominantly composed of smooth muscle
   (a) muscle is arranged in circular, longitudinal, and tangential layers
   (b) taeniae coli: aggregate bands of smooth muscle in the colon are not arranged uniformly, but in aggregates or bands; this arrangement gives the colon a saccular appearance (haustra)
3. Submucosa: supports the mucosa; lies next to the muscularis, and it is composed of a loose type of connective tissue
4. Serosa: outermost layer is also a loose connective tissue; except in the esophagus and duodenum, serosa fuses with the lining of the abdominal cavity to form mesenteries which support the gastrointestinal organs

physiology

1. Movement: a characteristic feature of the gastrointestinal tract is motility—movement as seen in
   (a) mastication
   (b) swallowing
   (c) peristalsis: segmented movement (intestine) and mass movement (colon)
   (d) defecation
2. Saliva: contains one digestive enzyme, salivary amylase, which acts upon carbohydrates and splits them into disaccharides
3. Gastric juice
   (a) hydrochloric acid
   (b) pepsin: acts on proteins
   (c) rennin: acts upon milk and casein (obviously rennin is a very important enzyme during infancy when milk constitutes the largest percentage of the diet)
   (d) lipase: acts on lipids
   (e) mucin: lubricates the food and possibly protects the cells of the stomach against the hydrochloric acid that it secretes; mucin, however, has no digestive function
4. Pancreatic juice: the pancreas secretes copious amounts of en-

zymes that enter the duodenum and, unlike gastric enzymes, operates at an alkaline pH around 8.0 to 8.2

    (a) trypsin: breaks down proteins

    (b) carboxypeptidase: breaks down proteins

    (c) lipase: acts on lipids

    (d) amylase: acts on complex carbohydrates

    (e) nucleases: enzymes specific for nucleoproteins

  5. Intestinal juice: enzymes secreted by the intestine and are best characterized by their ability to "finish the job"

    (a) dipeptidases: splits dipeptides into two amino acids

    (b) aminopeptidases: separates terminal groups of amino acids

    (c) carbohydrases: such as maltase, lactase, and sucrase which act upon maltose, lactose, sucrose to produce simple sugars or monosaccharides

    (d) intestinal lipase: acts upon lipids

  6. Liver bile

    (a) composed of water mucin, cholesterol, pigments, and trace amounts of other substances

    (b) stored and concentrated in the gall bladder

    (c) emulsifies lipids to form small particles, providing a large surface area for lipase enzymatic activity

    (d) the yellow-green color of bile comes from pigments which, in turn, come from degradation of hemoglobin

    (e) major pigment is bilirubin (yellow) and its oxidized product, biliverdin (green)

  7. Absorption: the small intestine is the principal organ for absorption for digested foods as well as water and minerals; minor amounts of absorption can take place in other areas of the gastrointestinal tract

  8. Control of secretions

    (a) saliva: reflex reaction to sensory stimuli, such as the smell or sight of food as well as the presence of food in the mouth

    (b) gastric secretion: certain foods as well as thoughts of foods can stimulate secretory activity in the gastric mucosa; secretagogus released from foods is theorized to stimulate the pylorus portion of the stomach to produce a hormone gastrin, which in turn stimulates the production of hydrochloric acid and pepsin; hydrochloric acid is also believed to be under the control of histamine

    (c) pancreatic juice: both neurogenic and hormonal regulation; secretin is the hormone released from the mucosa in the presence of food in the intestine and stimulates the production of digestive enzymes

    (d) bile secretion: liver secretes bile continuously, but a hormone secreted by the duodenum, cholecystokinin, precipitates the release of stored bile

    (e) intestinal juice secretion: both mechanical as well as neurogenic stimuli are believed to increase intestinal enzyme secretion; enterocrinin can be produced from an extract of the intestinal mucosa, and it is known to increase intestinal enzyme activity

factors influencing function Probably the most important group of factors that influence the digestive system is the emotional state of the individual. Indigestion, cramps, vomiting, or ulcers can be produced by a persistent state of anxiety.

nutrition

1. Good health depends upon a proper balance of carbohydrates, proteins, lipids, minerals, water, and adequate amounts of vitamins
2. Vitamins
   (a) vitamin A: needed to maintain a healthy state of skin and membranes
   (b) vitamin B: a complex of vitamins that chemically and functionally are used as coenzymes in the intermediary metabolism
   (c) ascorbic acid or vitamin C: needed to prevent scurvy, a disease which affects bones, gums, and wound healing; exact nutritive metabolic role of the vitamin is still unknown
   (d) calciferol or vitamin D: increases the rate of calcium binding by the intestinal lining cells
   (e) tocopherol or vitamin E: value in human nutrition is equivocal, and it is questionable if a true case of vitamin E deficiency can occur; some evidence that the vitamin may be involved in lipid metabolism
   (f) vitamin K: ample amounts are manufactured by the bacteria of the colon so that the dietary requirement is usually zero; vitamin needed for the formation of prothrombin by the liver

clinical considerations

1. Obstruction: anything that obstructs the passage of food can be painful and decrease nutrition; the latter situation is a special problem in infants
2. Gastroenteritis: inflammation of the lining of the digestive tract
3. Gastrointestinal ulcers: a break in the mucosa which may perforate and produce a hemorrhage; ulcers are very painful; most frequent site is the pyloric region of the duodenum and in the lesser curvature of the stomach
4. Gall bladder diseases: result from blockage of the duct or precipitation of bile salts that eventually aggregate to form small gall stones; if the stones block the bile duct and bile backs up into the liver, a yellowish cast is produced to the skin and eyes, the condition called jaundice
5. Vomiting: a cataclysmic reflex reaction, which forcibly squeezes the stomach and propels some of its contents into the esophagus and the mouth; excessive vomiting will cause loss of electrolytes; emetics are substances capable of producing vomiting
6. Appendicitis: inflammation of the appendix is produced by food being trapped in the cavity that eventually leads to inflammation and breakdown of the lining; produces nausea, cramps, and sharp pain; danger that the appendix may rupture, spilling the bacterial contents within the body
7. Diarrhea: rapid transport of fecal material through the colon and the rectum; as in vomiting, uncontrolled diarrhea results in a loss of fluid and electrolytes; diarrhea in infants is a very serious condition
8. Constipation: not a serious condition and usually caused by poor health habits rather than a pathological situation; cathartics is a general

term for agents that in various ways help to alleviate constipated condition

9. Hepatitis: inflammation of the liver; brought about by a number of diverse causes such as virus infection, drugs, poisons, or parasites

10. Starvation: essentially a self-immolation in that the body burns itself out in an attempt to provide energy to maintain heartbeat, synthesis of new enzymes, breathing, and so on. During starvation, the fat depots are the first to be utilized for energy, and if the caloric diet is not increased, muscle protein will then be used as raw materials; just before death, even some of the tissues of vital organs are broken down for energy

11. Obesity: an individual is classified as obese or extremely overweight when his weight is 15 percent over the ideal norm

14

metabolism and energy exchange

metabolic pathways
carbohydrate metabolism
lipid metabolism
protein metabolism
interaction between
  carbohydrates, lipids,
  and proteins
nucleic acid metabolism

**overall regulation
of metabolism**

clinical considerations
galactosemia

phenylketonuria
alkaptonuria

energy exchange
direct calorimetry
indirect calorimetry

metabolic rate
basal metabolic rate
factors influencing
  metabolic rate
respiratory quotient
exercise

Food in the digestive system is subjected to various treatments including dilution, changes in pH, and enzymatic breakdown, and the usable products of these treatments move across the cellular membranes to enter the body's metabolic machinery. That machinery is designed to provide the energy needed for the work of the cells, as in the contraction of muscle cells or the synthesis (anabolic) activity of the liver cells when they make blood proteins. In the case of the former, the energy shows up in the form of movement and heat, and in the latter, much of the energy is put into the chemical bonds of the newly synthesized proteins with only a relatively small amount of heat produced.

metabolic pathways

The metabolic activities of the cells of the body must provide for the energy needs as well as for all the synthetic activities that are part of the organism. These requirements demand an intricate, coordinated system. This chapter outlines the pathways by which cells deal with the various classes of molecules, how these pathways interact, how they are regulated, and how metabolism is related to the energy needs of the body as a whole.

carbohydrate metabolism

The main source of energy for the cells is derived from carbohydrates. A metabolic pathway for the breakdown of glucose and the capture of energy in the form of ATP was described in Chapter 2 and is outlined in Figure 14-1. We now need to look at the other metabolic pathways open to glucose.

The monosaccharides, glucose, fructose, and galactose, are the main products of carbohydrate digestion, with glucose being by far the largest in quantity. These monosaccharides move through the lining cells of the digestive system, active transport playing some role in this movement, and eventually they enter the liver via the bloodstream. Glucose is *phosphorylated* (has a phosphate group attached to it) when it enters the liver cell, a process that is catalyzed by the enzymes *hexokinase* and *glucokinase.* The former acts on all six-carbon sugars, and the latter only acts on glucose. *Kinase enzymes*, as a class of enzymes, aid in the attachment of phosphate groups to molecules; ATP is usually the donor.

Both fructose and galactose can be converted to glucose by a series of enzymatically mediated reactions (Figure 14-2). Fructose 6-phosphate to glucose 6-phosphate is a one-step process, whereas galactose conversion requires the utilization of *uridine triphosphate,* a high-energy compound with a structure similar to ATP. By reversing the reactions, glucose can also supply fructose and galactose when needed.

Glycogenesis

Glycogenesis is the process of glycogen synthesis. Glycogen is a long polymer of glucose and is often found as insoluble particles in the cell, the advantage of such an arrangement being that large amounts of glucose can be stored in this manner without influencing the osmotic pressure. Glycogen is found mainly in the liver and muscle. Although the concentration of glycogen is higher in the liver (up to 8 percent), muscle with only about 1 percent glycogen has a larger mass than liver and is therefore also important in glycogen storage. Glycogen is synthesized from glucose by the utilization of high-energy compounds (Figure 14-3). Glucose 6-phosphate, which can be formed from glucose and ATP, is

figure 14-1

SUMMARY OF
REACTIONS IN THE
BREAKDOWN OF
GLUCOSE
(GLYCOLYSIS
AND THE KREBS
CYCLE)

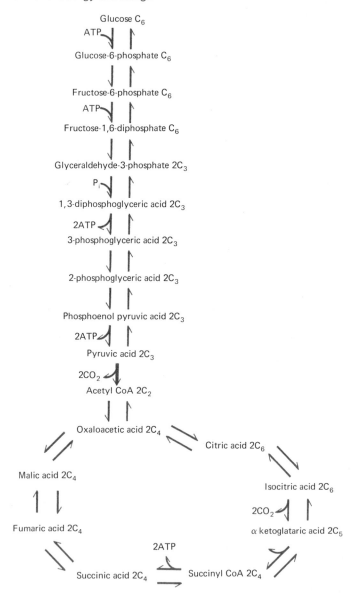

converted to glucose 1-phosphate by enzymatic action. Glucose 1-phosphate reacts with uridine triphosphate (UTP) to form uridine diphosphate glucose (UDPG). Uridine diphosphoglucose reacts with glycogen, so that the glucose is added on to the glycogen to make the large molecule that is the storage form, and UDP is released. Uridine diphosphate can be reconverted to UTP by reaction with ATP.

$$UDP + ATP \rightleftharpoons UTP + ADP$$

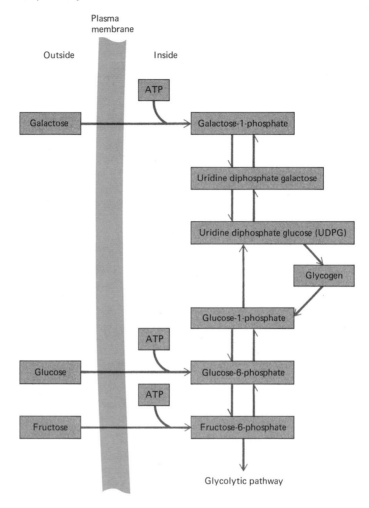

figure 14-2

PATHWAYS FOR
CONVERSION OF
MONOSAC-
CHARIDES IN THE
LIVER

Glycogenolysis   *Glycogenolysis* is the process of the breakdown of glycogen to glucose molecules. Although it would appear that a simple reversal of the synthetic pathway would be used in the breakdown of glycogen to glucose, another pathway is utilized (Figure 14-3). A *phosphorylase* enzyme splits a glucose off glycogen while adding a phosphate group to the glucose to make it a *glucose 1-phosphate.* This pattern of alternate pathways in breakdown and synthesis is found in many of the metabolic pathways that will be discussed in this chapter.

PHOSPHORYLASE AND CYCLIC ADENOSINE MONOPHOSPHATE Phosphorylase is found in both the inactive and active states in the cell. Its activation requires the presence of a special form of adenosine monophosphate, *cyclic adenosine monophosphate* (cyclic AMP), which is formed from ATP by enzymes in the membranes of cells (Figure 14-4). Glucagon, a hormone released from the pancreas (Chapter 18), stimulates

figure 14-3

PATHWAYS FOR
GLYCOGEN
SYNTHESIS AND
BREAKDOWN

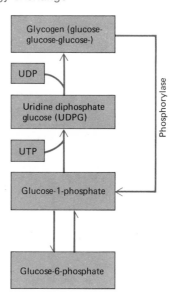

the production of cyclic AMP in liver cells, which in turn increases the amount of active phosphorylase and increases glycogenolysis. Epinephrine acts in the same way. Cyclic AMP production is stimulated by a number of different hormones and agents in different tissues, and this change has led to cyclic AMP being called the *second messenger;* the *first messenger* would be the hormone or other chemical agent that stimulates cyclic AMP production.

Glycolysis and the Kreb's Cycle Both glycolysis and the Krebs cycle were described in some detail in Chapter 2, and the reactions are summarized in Figure 14-1. Glucose is broken down to two 3-carbon fragments during glycolysis by anaerobic reactions. The pyruvic acid that results can be shunted to form lactic acid if no oxygen is available, but this process can only proceed for a very short time before the cell's metabolic machinery shuts off. Under normal circumstances, pyruvic acid is aerobically broken down to carbon dioxide and water in the Krebs cycle with the production of energy-rich $NADH_2$. The energy of the electrons from $NADH_2$ is captured in ATP by a series of reactions that take place in the mitochondria.

The Krebs cycle plays a central role not only in the metabolism of carbohydrates, but also in the metabolism of fats and proteins. Small intermediates associated with metabolism of the three classes of compounds, at some time or other, are found in the Krebs cycle. Indeed, the carbon atoms of carbohydrates, lipids, and proteins are interconvertible via the action of the Krebs cycle. All the reactions in the Krebs cycle are reversible except for the formation of glucose from lipids. The cycle is a mechanism for synthesis as well as degradation.

Pentose Monophosphate Shunt The glycolytic pathway is the major pathway for the metabolism of glucose. Another pathway for handling glucose is the *pentose monophosphate shunt,* which may account for up to 30 percent of the glucose

figure 14-4

THE ROLE OF
CYCLIC AMP IN
HORMONE-
STIMULATED
GLYCOGENOLYSIS

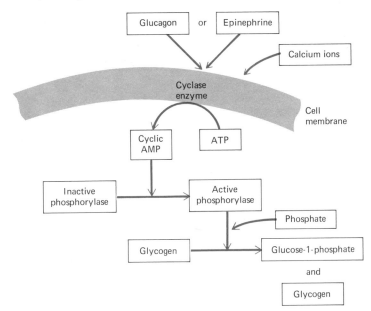

figure 14-4

THE ROLE OF CYCLIC AMP IN HORMONE-STIMULATED GLYCOGENOLYSIS

metabolism in the liver. Pentose sugars are 5-carbon sugars, such as the ribose of RNA. Metabolism in this pathway is aerobic and provides for the synthesis of ribose and the reduced form of NADP, which accepts hydrogens in the same way as NAD. The reduced form of NADP is used in the synthesis of fats and amino acids.

Gluconeogenesis   *Gluconeogenesis* is the process by which glucose is formed from non-carbohydrate sources. Gluconeogenesis is influenced by the lack of carbohydrates in the diet and also by the action of specific hormones from the pancreas and adrenal cortex. The effect of these hormones is to increase protein breakdown making amino acids that can be converted to glucose.

Regulation   When glucose enters the blood from the digestive system, it is transported to various cells where it is phosphorylated to *glucose 6-phosphate*. For most cells this phosphorylation is a device for "capturing" glucose, as glucose 6-phosphate does not pass out of the cell but rather enters the metabolic pathways leading to breakdown or synthesis of glycogen. An exception is found in liver cells, where glucose can be dephosphorylated by a *phosphatase* enzyme and then reenter the blood (Figure 14-5). When the concentration of glucose in the blood is higher than normal, glucose is converted by the liver cells to glycogen, whereas glycogenolysis takes place when glucose levels in the blood begin to decrease below normal. Intestinal cells that act to absorb glucose from the digested food also have phosphatase enzymes, since the glucose must move out of the intestinal cell into the circulation. Unlike liver cells (Figure 14-5), they do not synthesize large amounts of glycogen.

Insulin, a hormone synthesized by the pancreas, helps to regulate glu-

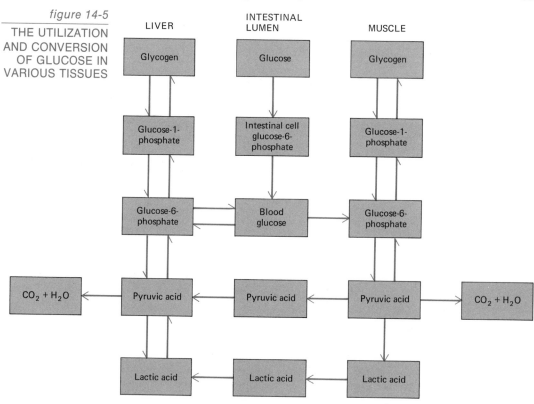

cose concentration in the blood. When insulin secretion is low, the blood glucose can go as high as 300 mg percent, and the excess glucose shows up in the urine. Insulin regulates glucose levels by affecting either glycogenolysis or glycogenesis as well as the rate at which nonliver cells can take up and utilize glucose. Chapter 18 contains a more detailed discussion of insulin and its function.

lipid metabolism   Lipids, especially the neutral fats, play a large role in supplying energy for the body's needs. Neutral fats are composed of glycerol and three fatty acids, and the digestive enzymes split the neutral fats into these components. The digested components cross the membranes of the intestinal lining cells, where the fatty acid is combined with glycerol from another source to form small droplets of *lipoprotein*, called *chylomicrons*, which enter the lymphatic system. The neutral fats in the chylomicrons are broken down to glycerol and fatty acids by an enzyme *lipoprotein lipase*, which is found primarily in the blood and in adipose tissues. The metabolic products are then used as a source of energy or resynthesized to neutral fat. The major areas of fat metabolism and storage are the adipose tissue and the liver.

The energy available from fat on a weight basis is over twice that available from other sources of food, and the amount of fat that can be

figure 14-6

BETA OXIDATION
OF FATTY ACIDS

Beta · oxidation of fatty acids

Beta carbon

$$R \cdot CH_2 \cdot CH_2 \cdot CH_2 \cdot CH_2 \cdot C \cdot OH + CoA \xrightarrow{\text{ATP} \quad \text{AMP} + P - P} R \cdot CH_2 \cdot CH_2 \cdot CH_2 \cdot CH_2 \cdot C \cdot CoA$$

Fatty acid

Coenzyme A

$$R \cdot CH_2 \cdot CH_2 \cdot CH_2 \cdot CH_2 \cdot C \cdot CoA \xrightarrow[\text{H}_2\text{O}]{\text{NAD, FAD}} R \cdot CH_2 \cdot CH_2 \cdot C \cdot CH_2 \cdot C \cdot CoA + FADH_2 + NADH_2$$

$$R \cdot CH_2 \cdot CH_2 \cdot C \cdot CH_2 \cdot C \cdot CoA \xrightarrow{+ CoA} R \cdot CH_2 \cdot CH_2 \cdot C \cdot CoA + CH_3 \cdot C \cdot CoA$$

Acetyl CoA

Fatty acid less
two carbons

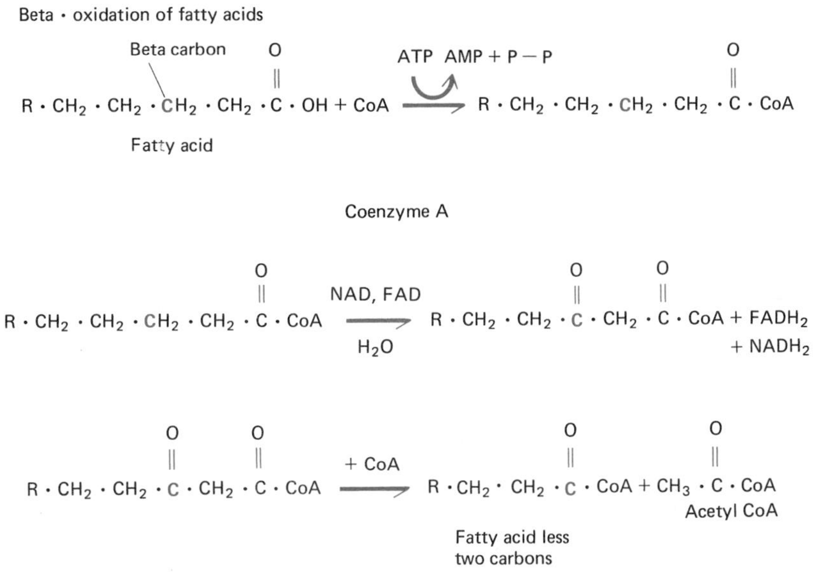

stored vastly exceeds that of glycogen; the importance of fat as an energy store is quite evident.

Catabolism of
Lipids

CATABOLISM OF NEUTRAL FATS Once neutral fats are split into their component glycerol and fatty acids, the fatty acids, which are generally chains of 14 to 20 carbons, are degraded by an oxidation mechanism to 2-carbon fragments. The 2-carbon fragments can condense with 4-carbon compounds, enter the Krebs cycle to be further oxidized, or enter synthetic reactions.

The process of oxidizing the 2-carbon fragments is termed *beta-oxidation* (β-oxidation), since the beta carbon is oxidized (the first carbon after the carboxyl group is termed alpha, the second beta, the third gamma, and so on). The reactions are shown in Figure 14-6. The essential features of these reactions are (a) the binding of coenzyme A to the carboxyl group of the fatty acid at the expense of ATP; (b) the oxidation of the beta-carbon, that is, removal of hydrogens by NAD and FAD; (c) the splitting off of a 2-carbon fragment (acetyl CoA) and the simultaneous combining of another coenzyme A to the newly exposed group. We can see why the major portion of fatty acids are even numbered with respect to carbons, for continuation of the beta oxidation leads to complete breakdown of the fatty acids that have an even number of carbons.

Fatty acid oxidation takes place in the mitochondria, and the acetyl CoA can enter the Krebs cycle to produce ATP. Without going into details of the steps involved, the breakdown of a 16-carbon fatty acid (for example, palmitic) can produce 130 ATP, with an efficiency of about 48 percent.

$$C_{16}H_{32}O_2 + 23\ O_2 \longrightarrow 16CO_2 + 16H_2O + 130ATP$$

figure 14-7

KETOGENESIS

Formation of ketone bodies

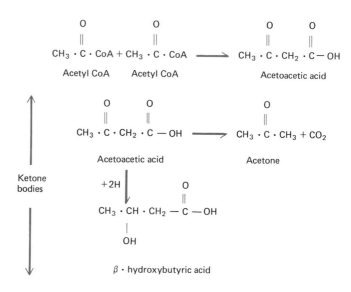

Ketone
bodies

β · hydroxybutyric acid

This efficiency is higher than that of the complete oxidation of carbo-hydrate. The oxidation of fatty acids can yield more energy than the oxidation of carbohydrates, because fatty acids begin in a more reduced state than carbohydrates. This difference is revealed in part by examination of the formulas that show that fatty acids do indeed have less oxygen than carbohydrates.

KETOGENESIS Normally a small amount of acetyl CoA does not get metabolized in the Krebs cycle, and two acetyl CoA molecules combine to form acetoacetate (Figure 14-7). Some of the acetoacetic acid is reduced to β-hydroxybutyric acid and a minor portion converted into acetone. All three of these compounds are termed *ketone bodies*, which as ketones are distinguished by the double-bonded oxygen $\left(\begin{array}{c} O \\ \| \\ -C- \end{array}\right)$ attached to one of the internal carbons. Ketogenesis then is the formation of ketone bodies. Generally, acetoacetic acid and β-hydroxybutyric acid are converted back to acetyl CoA and catabolized. However, under conditions where fat metabolism is highly increased, significant amounts of ketone bodies can be found in the blood and in the urine leading to a state termed *ketosis.* Lack of available carbohydrates is the cause of ketosis, whether brought on by starvation, diabetes (lack of insulin), or a diet that includes only fat. The buildup in the concentration of ketone bodies can lead to *acidosis*, the inability of the buffering systems in the extracellular fluids to neutralize the acid ketone bodies. The result is a lowered pH of the extracellular fluids and loss of ions, which, if allowed to continue, can be fatal. It is of interest to note that ketosis leads to the formation of enough acetone (a ketone substance) so that this volatile substance can

figure 14-8

STEPS IN THE
SYNTHESIS OF
CHOLESTEROL
FROM ACETYL CoA

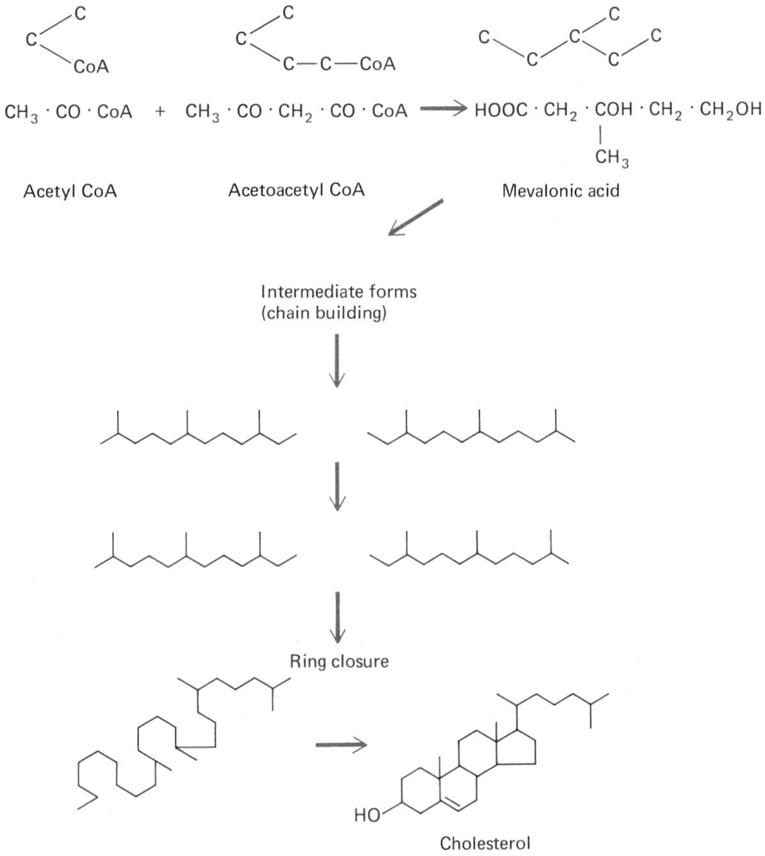

$CH_3 \cdot CO \cdot CoA$ + $CH_3 \cdot CO \cdot CH_2 \cdot CO \cdot CoA$ $\longrightarrow$ $HOOC \cdot CH_2 \cdot COH \cdot CH_2 \cdot CH_2OH$

Acetyl CoA   Acetoacetyl CoA   Mevalonic acid

Intermediate forms
(chain building)

Ring closure

Cholesterol

be detected on the breath. Because excess ketone bodies are formed by untreated diabetics, "sweet smelling breath" is a sign of a diabetic condition; the general odor is not unlike the fluid used for dry-cleaning clothes.

Fatty Acid
Synthesis
Although acetyl CoA is the raw material for fatty acid synthesis, acetyl CoA is converted to *malonyl CoA*, which is then condensed to form longer chains. Synthesis of fatty acids occurs mainly in the cytoplasm, and elongation of fatty acid chains is catalyzed by enzymes found in mitochondria. The fatty acids combine with glycerol to produce the triglyceride, or neutral fat, the major portion of such synthesis taking place in the adipose tissue and the liver.

Sterol Metabolism
Sterol molecules, such as cholesterol, play a significant role as precursors of hormones, bile salts, and membranes. Synthesis of sterol molecules occurs by the joining of acetyl CoA molecules into chains and then by forming the chains into the rings of cholesterol. The latter can be modified to form the steroid hormones as well as the bile salts (Figure 14-8). Cholesterol synthesis takes place mainly in the liver, but the

figure 14-9
INTERACTIONS
BETWEEN LIPIDS
AND
CARBOHYDRATES

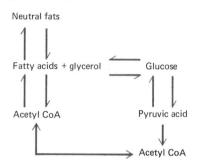

adrenal cortex, gonads, and skin are also important organs of synthesis. The ring structure of cholesterol is not capable of being broken enzymatically in the body, and sterol molecules are often excreted intact (many of the sex hormones).

Phospholipid
Synthesis

Phospholipids are found in high concentration in cellular membranes. The various phospholipids are synthesized from diglycerides (glycerol containing two fatty acid chains) and small molecules to which a phosphate has been added.

Interactions
between Lipids
and Carbohydrates

Acetyl CoA from glucose breakdown can be used for fatty acid synthesis, and acetyl CoA from fatty acid breakdown can be oxidized in the Krebs cycle (Figure 14-9). Triglyceride synthesis requires the presence of glycerol, so that when glucose synthesis is inhibited, triglyceride synthesis is also inhibited. There is no evidence that fats can be converted to carbohydrates. The relationship between protein and lipid metabolism will be discussed in the section on metabolic interactions.

Regulation

Regulation of lipid metabolism is both by diet and by hormones. Lipid catabolism is increased when carbohydrate is not available, and since glycerol synthesized from glucose metabolism is needed for lipid synthesis, anabolism is inhibited when glucose is not being utilized. Several hormones play a role in regulation of lipid metabolism. Insulin enhances lipid synthesis by increasing glucose transport across the cell membrane, thereby allowing for added glucose breakdown via the hexose monophate shunt. This mechanism in turn provides rising levels of reduced NADP that is required for lipid synthesis. The sympathetic nervous system appears to play a major role in the control of fat breakdown in adipose tissue. Norepinephrine released from sympathetic nerve endings present in adipose tissue promotes the splitting of triglycerides in fat cells, which leads to an increase in circulating triglycerides. Epinephrine and norepinephrine released from the adrenal gland are also responsible for increased fat mobilization. These agents have been shown to increase cyclic AMP in fat cells.

protein
metabolism

Each cell contains machinery for making specific proteins—the DNA codes for the synthesis of the RNA types that direct the sequence in which amino acids are joined together to make a specific protein. Al-

figure 14-10

AMINO ACID
METABOLISM

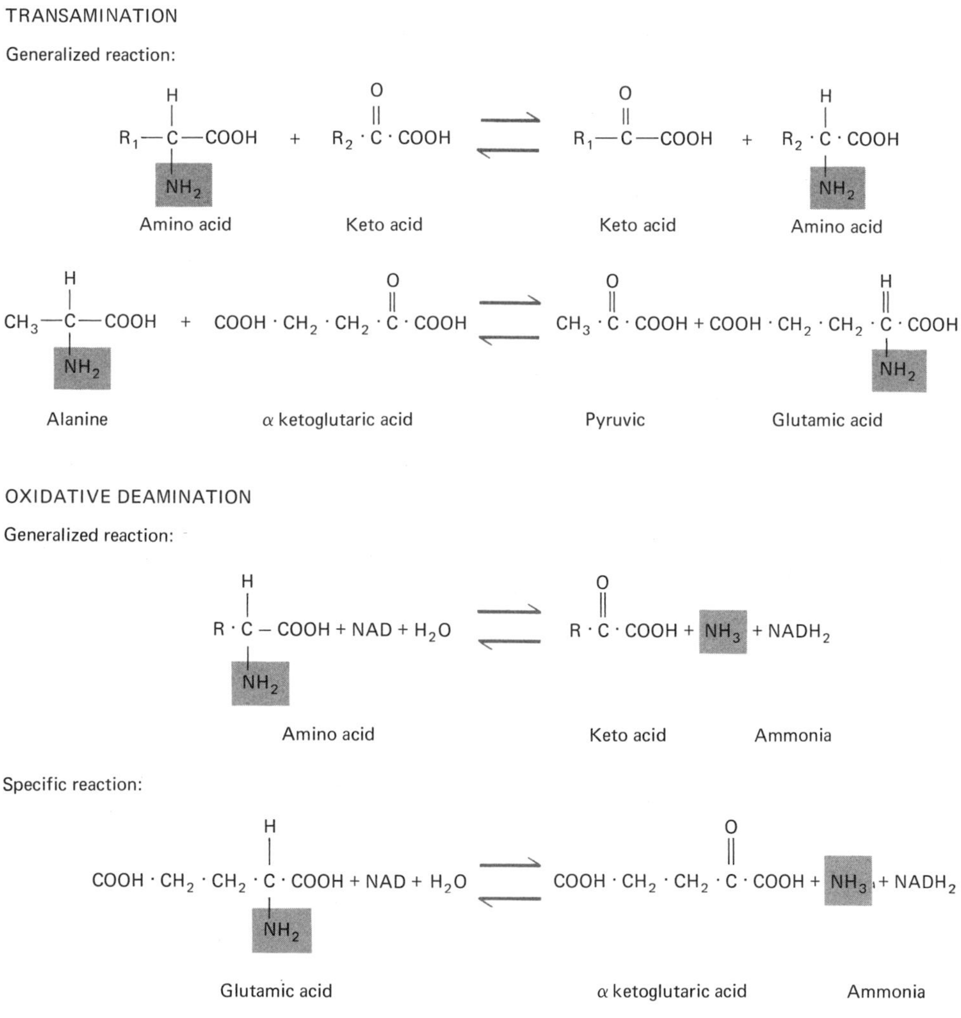

TRANSAMINATION

Generalized reaction:

$$R_1-\overset{\overset{\displaystyle H}{|}}{\underset{\underset{\displaystyle NH_2}{|}}{C}}-COOH \quad + \quad R_2\cdot\overset{\overset{\displaystyle O}{\|}}{C}\cdot COOH \quad \rightleftharpoons \quad R_1-\overset{\overset{\displaystyle O}{\|}}{C}-COOH \quad + \quad R_2\cdot\overset{\overset{\displaystyle H}{|}}{\underset{\underset{\displaystyle NH_2}{|}}{C}}\cdot COOH$$

Amino acid	Keto acid	Keto acid	Amino acid

$$CH_3-\overset{\overset{\displaystyle H}{|}}{\underset{\underset{\displaystyle NH_2}{|}}{C}}-COOH \quad + \quad COOH\cdot CH_2\cdot CH_2\cdot\overset{\overset{\displaystyle O}{\|}}{C}\cdot COOH \quad \rightleftharpoons \quad CH_3\cdot\overset{\overset{\displaystyle O}{\|}}{C}\cdot COOH + COOH\cdot CH_2\cdot CH_2\cdot\overset{\overset{\displaystyle H}{|}}{\underset{\underset{\displaystyle NH_2}{|}}{C}}\cdot COOH$$

Alanine	α ketoglutaric acid	Pyruvic	Glutamic acid

OXIDATIVE DEAMINATION

Generalized reaction:

$$R\cdot\overset{\overset{\displaystyle H}{|}}{\underset{\underset{\displaystyle NH_2}{|}}{C}}-COOH + NAD + H_2O \quad \rightleftharpoons \quad R\cdot\overset{\overset{\displaystyle O}{\|}}{C}\cdot COOH + NH_3 + NADH_2$$

Amino acid	Keto acid	Ammonia

Specific reaction:

$$COOH\cdot CH_2\cdot CH_2\cdot\overset{\overset{\displaystyle H}{|}}{\underset{\underset{\displaystyle NH_2}{|}}{C}}\cdot COOH + NAD + H_2O \quad \rightleftharpoons \quad COOH\cdot CH_2\cdot CH_2\cdot\overset{\overset{\displaystyle O}{\|}}{C}\cdot COOH + NH_3 + NADH_2$$

Glutamic acid	α ketoglutaric acid	Ammonia

though this multistep synthesis requires a large expenditure of energy, it is necessary to produce the specificity of the proteins. Cellular activity, cellular specializations, and indeed even cellular existence depend on enzyme (protein) specificity.

Metabolism of Amino Acids   Amino acid metabolism is generally involved with transfer or removal of the amino group ($-NH_2$), and two such reactions will serve to illustrate the way in which the majority of the amino acids is metabolized. TRANSAMINATION *Transamination* is the process of transferring an amino group from an amino acid to a keto acid (Figure 14-10). The example used in Figure 14-10 also illustrates one of the relationships existing between carbohydrate metabolism and protein metabolism, as α-ketoglutaric acid is an intermediate in the Krebs cycle. Alpha-ketoglutaric acid can be formed from glutamic acid, thus providing a pathway for amino acid utilization for energy. The reaction is also reversible so that glutamic acid can be synthesized from α-ketoglutaric acid.

OXIDATIVE DEAMINATION *Oxidative deamination* is the process by which the amino group is removed from an amino acid in the form of an ammonia, and a keto acid results (Figure 14-10). It is an oxidation-reduction reaction, in which the amino acid is oxidized and NAD is reduced. Again, these reactions are reversible and demonstrate a link between carbohydrate and protein metabolism.

Urea Formation

Deamination reactions produce ammonia, which if allowed to accumulate would be toxic. Ammonia is converted to urea by combining ammonia with carbon dioxide at the expense of ATP. This process is a multistep reaction, and only the summary reactions are shown below.

$$CO_2 + 2NH_3 \xrightarrow{\text{ATP}\quad\text{ADP}} NH_2\overset{\overset{\displaystyle O}{\|}}{-}C-NH_2 + H_2O$$

Urea is then collected from the circulatory system by the kidney and excreted.

Pathways for Amino Acids

Amino acids, from which the amino group has been removed, can be converted to glucose or fat by way of Krebs-cycle intermediates, pyruvic acid, or acetyl CoA (Figure 14-11). Those that give rise to glucose are called *glycogenic* and encompass 18 of the 20 common amino acids. Five of the 20 give rise to ketone bodies (acetone, acetoacetic acid) and are termed *ketogenic.* Four of the amino acids are both glycogenic and ketogenic. Certain amino acids can enter specialized pathways, as those involved in the production of nucleic acids.

Regulation

Hormones strongly influence the catabolism and anabolism of proteins. Pituitary growth hormone and insulin generally increase protein synthesis, as does the male sex hormone, although the latter's effect is mainly on muscle protein. The corticoids (adrenal) or ACTH (pitui-

---

figure 14-11

CONVERSION OF AMINO ACIDS TO GLUCOSE OR FAT

Deaminated amino acids may be converted to glucose or fat by way of Krebs cycle intermediates, pyruvic acid, or acetyl CoA.

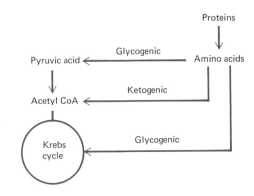

tary) that regulates glucocorticoids generally inhibits protein synthesis, essentially increasing glycogenesis. Thyroxine (thyroid) acts generally to increase protein synthesis (see Chapter 18, "Endocrine System").

interaction between carbo-hydrates, lipids, and proteins

Analysis of the energy-producing reactions demonstrates the efficiency of the intermediary metabolism, which integrates the metabolism of carbohydrates, lipids, and proteins (Module 14). The initial reactions are all hydrolytic cleavages, producing hexose (glucose) from carbo-hydrates, glycerol and fatty acids from lipids, and amino acids from protein catabolism. Glucose degradation proceeds through the glycolytic pathway to pyruvic acid and then to acetyl CoA, which enters the Krebs cycle to be oxidized to carbon dioxide and water. Glycerol can enter the energy pathway by being converted to pyruvic acid, whereas the fatty acids enter as acetyl CoA after beta oxidation. Amino acids are converted to pyruvic acid, acetyl CoA, or intermediates in the Krebs cycle. The cata-bolic reactions lead to a funneling of many kinds of compounds to a limited number of reactions associated with the Krebs cycle.

Module 14 shows the potential synthetic pathways that interrelate the carbohydrates, lipids, and proteins. These reactions are summarized as follows:

1. Carbohydrates can be converted to fats and proteins.
2. Proteins can be converted to fats and carbohydrates.
3. Fats can be converted to proteins.
4. Fats *cannot* be converted to carbohydrates.

nucleic acid metabolism

Nucleic acids include the nitrogen bases (purines and pyrimidines). These are synthesized from several compounds, including the amino acids glycine, aspartic and glutamic acids; ribose and phosphate groups complete the structure (see Chapter 2). Metabolic breakdown of the nitrogen bases leads to the production of uric acid which is excreted.

overall regulation of metabolism

Metabolism can be regulated by what is put into the metabolic mill, by hormones, and by a variety of other factors. For example, an examina-tion of the metabolic schemes presented indicates that specific mole-cules have central positions between certain metabolic pathways. An example of this is glucose 6-phosphate, which can be acted on by en-zymes to increase blood glucose, be synthesized to glycogen, be degraded to intermediates that will give rise to energy, and enter the synthetic pathways to form a lipid or a protein. Obviously, it would be inefficient if all these reactions were to occur simultaneously, especially since some of the reaction products may not be needed by the cells. The concentra-tion of the substrate of an enzyme and its products plays a large role in regulation, for if glucose in the blood were low and glucose 6-phosphate in the liver were high, the reaction would be driven to increase the con-centration of blood glucose (excluding any consideration of hormone effects).

Another way of regulating reactions is to regulate the enzyme by (a) utilizing a product of the metabolic pathway in which the enzyme is involved to inhibit the activity of the enzyme, or (b) activating or re-

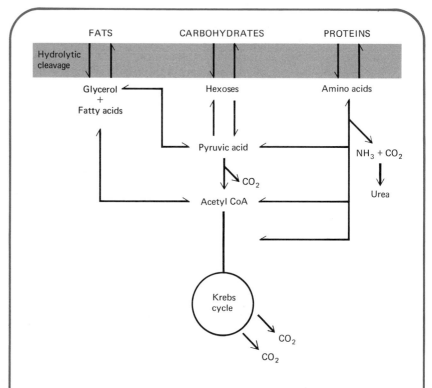

Metabolism is the sum of all the chemical reactions that occur in the body. The biosynthesis of complex molecules from simple molecules is termed *anabolism,* and generally requires chemical energy. That energy is made available by *catabolism,* the breakdown of complex molecules to simple molecules. These two processes are difficult to separate, for catabolic and anabolic reactions often occur simultaneously. Foodstuffs are the source of chemical energy that is used to run the machinery of the body. The metabolism of food produces chemical energy that can be utilized for mechanical work, transport work, or biosynthetic work.

The initial step in utilization of the main categories of foodstuffs is that of hydrolysis. The addition of water molecules to fats results in fatty acids and glycerol, to carbohydrates, hexoses, and to proteins, amino acids. Through the various reactions described in this chapter and in Chapter 2, the compounds resulting from hydrolytic cleavage are further degraded to acetyl CoA, or in the case of some amino acids, to intermediates of the Krebs cycle. Energy is captured during the degradation, and especially large amounts are made available from the products of the Krebs cycle. The scheme also allows conversion of one category to the other, except in one case, that of the conversion of fatty acids to carbohydrates.

The simplicity of the system in the central handling of the small number of compounds that result from the degradation of a large number of varied compounds is an example of the efficient patterns that have evolved in living organisms.

figure 14-12

FEEDBACK
INHIBITION

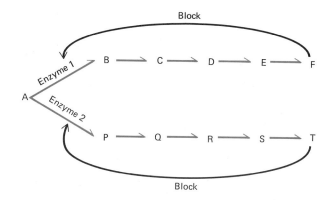

Feedback inhibition at a key point in a pathway acts as a control for choice of pathway.

pressing the gene that controls the synthesis of the enzyme. Metabolic pathways involve a number of reactions, and it has been shown that the product of a step in the pathway can inhibit an enzyme in one of the early key reactions. Figure 14-12 illustrates a reaction in which a single substrate serves several pathways. In this illustration, substrate A serves both pathways with F and T as the final products. If F inhibits enzyme E, then when sufficient quantities of F are made from A, F will shut down the pathway. In this way, A is used up only when F is needed, and the pathway of A to T is still open. It is possible for these pathways to be modulated by the amounts of F and T that are present in the cell. This type of inhibition is called *feedback inhibition.*

Metabolic activity can be controlled by the presence or absence (or concentration) of the enzyme involved. This kind of control exists in bacteria and some other lower forms, and within recent years several such controls have been found in mammalian systems. The regulation occurs either at the DNA to RNA levels (transcription) or the RNA protein level (translation).

Last, small molecules play a role in regulation of metabolism. The production of ATP is dependent on sufficient concentrations of ADP and inorganic phosphates as well as on the concentration of $NADH_2$. In a cell that is not particularly active and has high concentrations of ATP and glucose, glucose will be synthesized to glycogen by expenditure of energy from ATP.

clinical considerations

galactosemia

In the genetic disease galactosemia, the enzyme that acts to convert galactose to glucose is not present, and galactose concentration becomes abnormally high. In some way, yet unknown, high concentrations of galactose cause cellular injury that leads to severe mental retardation. If the disease is discovered early enough, galactose, a component of lactose or milk sugar, can be eliminated from the diet. At later stages in life, individuals suffering from galactosemia can develop alternate ways for converting galactose to glucose and can utilize a normal diet.

figure 14-13

PHENYL-
KETONURIA

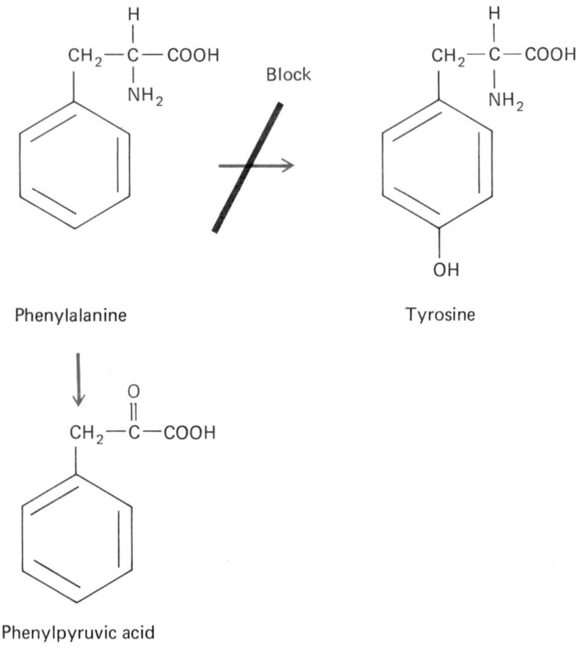

Phenylalanine

Block

Tyrosine

Phenylpyruvic acid

Phenylketonuria results when phenylalanine is not broken down to tyrosine. Phenylpyruvic acid accumulates and appears in urine as a dark pigment.

phenylketonuria

Phenylketonuria is a disease in which the enzyme that converts the amino acid phenylalanine to tyrosine is not present. This inborn error leads to accumulation of high concentrations of phenylpyruvic acid, which spills over into the urine (Figure 14-13) and can be detected. The mental retardation of those affected by this genetic defect in metabolism is generally severe. As with diseases of this type, control is possible if the disease is found early enough. Phenylalanine is an essential amino acid (it is not synthesized in adequate amounts and must be included in a diet), and unlike the treatment of galactosemia, the amino acid cannot be completely eliminated from the diet; however, limiting intake of phenylalanine does prevent mental retardation.

alkaptonuria

Alkaptonuria is a disease in which an enzyme involved in the metabolism of the amino acid tyrosine is missing, and an intermediate product, *homogentisic acid*, is excreted in the urine. Homogentisic acid is oxidized to a dark compound, so that the urine of those affected turns black on standing. Afflicted individuals appear healthy, except that with age they are likely to get osteoarthritis.

energy
exchange

The human body is a dynamic system in which molecules are being exchanged continually with the outer environment. Although from outward appearances the body might appear to be in a state of *static equilibrium*, the use of radioisotopes as tracers shows quite clearly that there is a continuous turnover of molecules, and the body is in a state of *dynamic equilibrium* in which chemical reactions are constantly taking place, and a balance is achieved. Indeed, static equilibrium is achieved only at death.

In considering what happens with respect to the energy balance of the body, a comparision can be made between the physical and biological world. Lavoisier, the French chemist, demonstrated in the late 1700s that oxidation of food by organisms was essentially the same as the combustion of organic material by fire. Both actions require oxygen and give off CO_2 and H_2O. Later studies showed that the exchange of energy involved in biological oxidations was subject to the same quantitative laws as those for physical systems.

One of the prime laws of energy is the *law of conservation of energy*, which states that energy is neither created nor destroyed even though it is undergoing change from one form to another. This law is also called the first *law of thermodynamics*.

States of energy are as follows:

1. *Chemical energy:* the energy that is associated with chemical bonds. Glucose degradation to carbon dioxide and water yields approximately 690,000 calories, which result from the breaking of the bonds in one mol of glucose.

2. *Kinetic energy:* the energy associated with a moving mass. The larger the mass and the larger the velocity of movement, the larger the kinetic energy.

3. *Potential energy:* the energy associated with relative position. An object on a desk has potential energy, since it required energy to place it on the desk. When the object falls to the floor, the energy is released as sound and heat.

4. *Heat energy:* energy in the form of heat. Within the body, chemical energy is transformed to kinetic energy and heat energy in such processes as muscle contraction. According to the law of conservation of energy, the amount of energy that is used for the contraction of the muscle and the amount of heat that is liberated during the process are equal to the amount of chemical energy that was made available by the breaking of bonds of ATP.

The balance of input and output of energy with respect to metabolic processes is an important concept. It can be measured for the body as a whole if we know how much energy is taken in as food, how much oxygen is utilized to oxidize the food, and how much heat is produced during the metabolic reactions. Body weight is an indication of the balance between energy intake (food) and energy expenditure. When these are equal, body weight remains constant.

Although the energy content of food taken in can be measured fairly accurately, the food may be processed in different ways; for example, not all the usable food may be absorbed. Therefore, measurements of heat production or oxygen consumption are used to determine the energy exchange that goes on in the body.

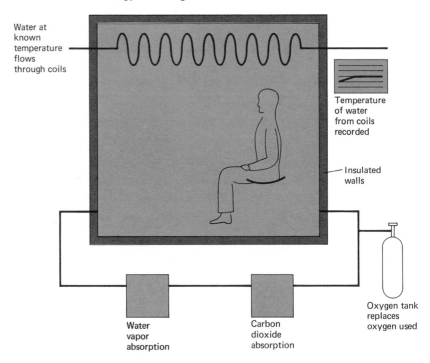

figure 14-14

DIRECT
CALORIMETRY

Water at
known
temperature
flows
through coils

Temperature
of water
from coils
recorded

Insulated
walls

Water
vapor
absorption

Carbon
dioxide
absorption

Oxygen tank
replaces
oxygen used

direct calorimetry   Calorimetry is the process of measuring either evolved or absorbed heat.
In the case of man, it is the evolved heat the reflects metabolic reactions.
In the discussion of metabolic pathways, it was shown that even when
the energy of foodstuffs is converted to ATP, about 50 to 60 percent of
the energy is converted to heat. The evolution of heat, therefore, reflects
the energy that is taken into the organism.

Calorimetric measurement is accomplished by placing an individual
in a closed container that is insulated to maintain constant temperature.
Heat radiated from the body is transferred to water contained in coils,
and the difference between the temperature of the water going into the
chamber and that coming out of the chamber is a measure of the heat
evolved (Figure 14-14).

indirect   Obviously making direct measurements of the heat evolved by metabo-
calorimetry   lism requires elaborate and expensive equipment. Calorimetry can also
be done by the indirect method of measuring oxygen consumption. This
technique is possible because the amount of oxygen consumed is related to the amount and kind of food molecules oxidized. When 1 liter
of oxygen is metabolized with glucose, 5.01 Calories are released; with
starches, 5.06 Calories are released; with fat, 4.70 Calories are released;
and with proteins, 4.60 Calories are released. For an average diet, the
mean value of 4.825 Calories/liter of oxygen is conveniently employed;
this figure assumes a balanced diet of proteins, carbohydrates, and fats.

In measuring energy liberated by indirect calorimetry, the subject
breathes oxygen from a reservoir, and the expired air is sent back to the

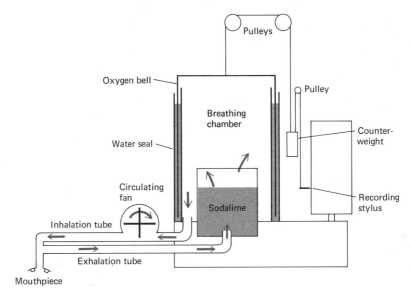

figure 14-15
BASIC DESIGN FOR
A SPIROMETER

system after passing through a container of soda lime to remove the carbon dioxide. In this way, only the oxygen that is actually consumed is removed from the reservoir (Figure 14-15).

metabolic rate The metabolic rate is the amount of energy expenditure, in Calories, over a given period of time. This rate is generally expressed in Calories per minute, Calories per hour, or Calories per day (Table 14-1). To calculate the metabolic rate in any activity, the amount of oxygen consumed per hour is multiplied by 4.825, the average number of Calories released by metabolizing 1 liter of oxygen.

oxygen consumed   15.5 liters/hr
average Calories/
    liter oxygen   4.825
metabolic rate $= 15.5 \times 4.825 = 74.8$ Calories/hr

basal metabolic rate When a quantitative comparison of metabolic rates of various individuals is wanted—young and old, male and female, active and inactive—there is a need of a standard for comparison purposes. The basal metabolic rate (BMR) is the minimal metabolic activity needed to maintain all the body's normal functions working, and the rate is expressed as Calories per square meter of body surface per hour. The procedure for determining basal metabolic rate is only a close approximation of what is minimal activity, and to achieve even this approximation, the test is made with the individual awake and resting and having had no food for at least 12 hours. The subject *hopefully* had a good night's rest, and medications are curtailed for at least 24 hours prior to the measurement to minimize stress. Measurements are taken at a temperature between 62° and 87°F to eliminate any metabolic changes due to the environmental temperature. The oxygen consumption of the reclining

table 14-1

ACTIVITY	CALORIES PER HOUR
Sleeping	65
Standing	105
Typewriting rapidly	140
Walking slowly	200
Swimming	500
Running	570

CALORIES EX-
PENDED DURING
VARIOUS TYPES
OF ACTIVITIES

Data are for a 70-kg man. Taken from A. Guyton, *Textbook of Medical Physiology*, 3rd ed. Philadelphia, Pa.: Saunders, 1966.

individual is measured over a period of time and extrapolated to 1 hour.

The basal metabolic rate is standardized so that comparisons can be made among individuals of different weights and shapes. A number of studies indicate that for individuals of the same age and sex, the metabolic rate is proportional to the surface area. Charts are available to determine the surface area in square meters of individuals of different heights and weights (Figure 14-16). Recent studies show that the relationship between metabolic rate and surface area is not quite as clear as previously thought, and that there may be a closer relationship between weight and metabolic rate. However, the 15-percent variation from the standard for a particular group provides enough leeway so that the surface area formula is still in use. A sample calculation of basal metabolic rate is shown below.

Let us assume an individual of 173 cm height weighing 70 kg (2.24 lb per kilo):

$$\text{surface area from chart} = 1.81 \text{ m}^2$$
$$\text{metabolic rate} = 74.8 \text{ Calories/hr}$$

$$\text{basal metabolic rate} = \frac{74.8 \text{ Calories/hr}}{1.81 \text{ m}^2}$$

$$= 41.3 \text{ Calories/m}^2\text{/hr}$$

factors
influencing
metabolic rate

Age and Sex

Normal basal metabolic rates differ at different ages and for different sexes (Figure 14-17). Males have measurably higher metabolic rates after approximately age three, although the young have higher basal metabolic rates than the aged.

Hormones

The basal metabolic rate can be profoundly influenced by secretion or lack of secretion from the thyroid gland. In fact, basal metabolic rate studies aid greatly in diagnosis of diseases of the thyroid. In the case of hypothyroidism (too little hormone secreted), the basal metabolic rate can fall to about 50 percent of normal, whereas hyperthyroidism (excess secretion) can account for increases in the basal metabolic rate of up to 80 percent.

The thyroid is characterized by its selective uptake of iodine, which is needed for the production of thyroxine, the thyroid hormone. An analysis of iodine uptake should reflect the activity of the thyroid in much the same way as does the basal metabolic rate. Since thyroxine is usually

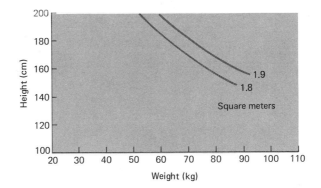

figure 14-16

GRAPH FOR
DETERMINATION
OF SURFACE
AREA

Graph for determination of surface area. Only two convergence curves are shown for simplicity.

bound to proteins in the blood plasma and since iodine is an integral part of the thyroxine molecule, an analysis of the amount of *protein-bound iodine* (PBI) in plasma or serum is an indicator of thyroid activity. This is done by precipitating the plasma protein and measuring the iodine that remains bound to it. Average values are 4.0 to 8.0 μg/100 ml, whereas hypothyroid persons have less than 2.0 μg and hyperthyroid from 8.2 to 40 μg. The protein-bound iodine technique is more accurate than basal metabolic rate measurements.

Growth hormone, insulin, adrenocortical hormones, and testosterone cause significant rises in the basal metabolic rate. Stimulation of the sympathetic nervous system, with release of epinephrine and norepinephrine, also produces a rise.

Climate and
Altitude

Climate influences the basal metabolic rate, since thyroid secretion is adapted to conform to temperature of the environment on a long-term basis. People living in the tropics have a lower basal metabolic rate than inhabitants of temperate and arctic zones. Altitude does not seem to affect it.

Specific Dynamic
Food Action

The requirement that intake of food be eliminated for at least 12 hours before a basal metabolic rate test is significant, for even a rested individual can sometimes show a high rate after eating. Each type of food produces a characteristic rise in heat production, collectively termed the *specific dynamic action of food.* Fats and carbohydrates cause about a 4-percent rise and proteins about a 30-percent rise, the increase occurring sometime after the food is ingested. The pronounced effect of proteins on metabolic rate is considered to be due to the metabolizing of energy stores that are required for degradation of the proteins.

respiratory
quotient

The respiratory quotient (RQ) is the ratio of the volume of carbon dioxide (CO_2) expired to the volume of oxygen (O_2) consumed.

$$RQ = \frac{\text{volume } CO_2 \text{ expired}}{\text{volume } O_2 \text{ consumed}}$$

figure 14-17

BASIC METABOLIC
RATES FOR THE
TWO SEXES

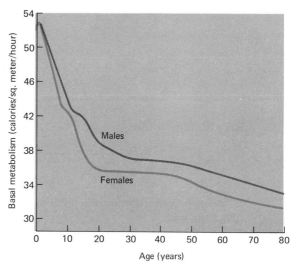

From A. Guyton, *Textbook of Medical Physiology*, Philadelphia, Pa.: Saunders, 1971.

Theoretically, the respiratory quotient depends on the source of food. For carbohydrates, the respiratory quotient can be calculated, since we know how much carbon dioxide is produced from metabolizing glucose with oxygen.

$$C_6H_{12}O_6 + 6O_2 = 6CO_2 + 6H_2O$$
$$RQ = \frac{6 \text{ volume } CO_2}{6 \text{ volume } O_2}$$
$$RQ = 1.00$$

Similar calculations can be made for fats and proteins, with resulting respiratory quotient values of 0.703 and 0.802, respectively.

Although the respiratory quotient is an aid in studies of metabolism, respiratory quotients are affected by many things; therefore data from such studies must be interpreted carefully. Subjects fed a complete carbohydrate diet do not generally produce a respiratory quotient of 1.00, since the cells not only oxidize the carbohydrate to carbon dioxide and water, but may also channel the carbohydrate to enter fat or protein metabolic pathways. The same problem exists when either fats or proteins are used in dietary sources.

exercise   The effect of exercise (work) is treated separately, since it is important to our understanding of how metabolism is affected by the everyday activities we perform. In experiments to measure the effects of specific exercises (riding a bicycle fixed in place or running on a treadmill), the subject remains in one area, and the connection between the subject and the equipment for measuring oxygen consumption need only be a flexible hose for the exchange of air or oxygen. When it becomes necessary to measure the oxygen consumption of a moving individual, such as a runner in a track meet or a worker in a factory, the equipment must

be made mobile and constructed so that it does not add to the work of
the subject.

Work   Work is defined as the product of the force required to move an object
and the distance it is moved.

$$\text{work} = \text{force} \times \text{distance}$$

If a weight of 100 kg is lifted 5 m from the floor, 500 kg of work has been
accomplished. This type of analysis is not helpful when isometric contraction (muscle contraction without shortening) occurs; however, there
are ways of calculating even this kind of work. In order to do work, energy must be expended, and that energy can be measured as oxygen consumed. In practice, indirect calorimetry is preferred, utilizing a spirometer, or a rubberized bag (Douglas bag) which collects expired air. In
the latter, the volume of inspired air can be calculated from the volume
of expired air, and the amount of oxygen and carbon dioxide in the expired air can be measured by appropriate instruments. The indirect
method using a Douglas bag to collect expired air is more portable, and
greater accuracy is achieved by careful measurements of the gas content of the expired air.

Work is classified as moderate when it involves increases of energy
expenditures up to three times basal levels; hard when it involves increases of four to eight times basal levels; and maximal where the subject cannot reach conditions in which energy expenditure is equal to
energy available, or *steady-state* conditions. Work or exercise can increase the metabolism of a single muscle up to 200 times and for the
entire body up to 20 times over a period of several minutes.

Oxygen Debt   The amount of oxygen consumed becomes proportional to the amount of
work when submaximal work is being done. However, this relationship
does not occur immediately, there being a slight lag before oxygen consumption catches up with energy consumption. After work ceases, oxygen consumption continues above resting levels for a period of time
(Figure 14-18). This recovery phase involves the *oxygen debt*, which

figure 14-18

OXYGEN
CONSUMPTION
AND WORK AS A
FUNCTION OF
TIME

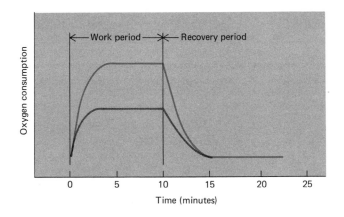

can be quite large in situations in which work is done at very high levels, as in the 100-yard dash. In such cases, almost *all* the energy is supplied by anaerobic processes with the resultant formation of lactic acid.

One of the major aspects of the oxygen debt is the lactic acid that accumulates in the muscles and in the blood, and which must be converted to carbon dioxide and water or glycogen by oxidative processes. At the present time, there is a controversy concerning how much of the oxygen debt is represented by lactic acid conversion, but there is no doubt that it represents a major portion. In any case, the body can only accumulate a limited amount of lactic acid, since the pH of the blood can be driven from pH 7.4 to 7.0 by the lactic acid. This has the effect of producing profound changes in rates of certain reactions, imbalance of salt concentrations across cell membranes, and changes in viscosity of the blood as well as other manifestations of acidosis. Even in the case in which work is done at submaximal levels and only small amounts of lactic acid are accumulated, a recovery period is noticeable in the sustained increase in heart and ventilation rates that are required to pay the oxygen debt.

Physical training has an effect on an individual's performance with respect to the oxygen debt. Training (a) increases the individual's ability to do submaximal work without going into severe oxygen debt, and (b) it increases the amount of oxygen debt that an individual can accumulate and still function. How this is accomplished is not completely known. However, it obviously concerns the ability of the circulatory system to accumulate oxygen more quickly, to carry oxygen more efficiently to the muscles, and to exchange oxygen within the muscle at a faster rate. Heart rate, cardiac output, ventilation volume, and oxygen uptake are lower for a trained individual than an untrained individual doing the same exercise.

In any physical contest such as a track meet, a warm-up has been shown to enhance the individual's performance. Warming up increases the internal temperature and allows for a general increase in metabolic activity. Specifically, oxygen exchange rates increase, rates of muscular contraction increase, and resistance in the vascular bed decreases. There is evidence that some of these same results can be obtained by raising the internal temperature by hot showers or baths.

summary

metabolic pathways

1. Carbohydrate metabolism: glucose, fructose, and galactose main products of initial carbohydrate digestion. Glucose is phosphorylated in liver by hexokinase. Fructose and galactose can be converted to glucose
   (a) glycogenesis: process of glycogen synthesis
   (b) glycogenolysis: process of glycogen breakdown to glucose. Phosphorylase, activated by cyclic AMP, splits glucose from glycogen
   (c) glucose broken down to pyruvic acid by glycolysis; anaerobic. Pyruvic acid catabolized to water and carbon dioxide; aerobic
   (d) Krebs cycle serves role in metabolism of lipids and proteins as well as carbohydrates
   (e) pentose monophosphate shunt: aerobic alternate pathway for glucose metabolism. Produces 5-carbon sugars and reduced NADP.

(f) gluconeogenesis: process by which glucose is formed from non-carbohydrate sources

(g) phosphorylation of glucose serves to capture glucose in cell. Liver has enzymes that can dephosphorylate glucose to make it available to other cells

2. Lipid metabolism: lipids have more energy on a weight basis than proteins or carbohydrates. Neutral lipids split to cross digestive cell membrane, reform, combine with protein to form lipoprotein.

(a) catabolism of lipids: fatty acids broken down into 2-carbon fragments by β-oxidation; acetyl CoA that results enters Krebs cycle. ketogenesis: formation of ketone bodies; buildup leads to ketosis, acidosis

(b) fatty acid synthesis: acetyl CoA to malonyl CoA, condensed into long chains. Combines with glycerol to produce triglyceride

(c) sterol metabolism: acetyl CoA to chains and then cyclizing of the chains

(d) phospholipid synthesis: from diglycerides

3. Protein metabolism: amino acid metabolism; generally associated with transfer or removal of amino group, either by transamination or oxidative deamination. Many amino acids can be converted to glucose

4. Interaction: hydrolysis first reaction in catabolism. Carbohydrates can be converted to fats and proteins. Proteins can be converted to fats and carbohydrates, and fats can be converted to proteins, but not to carbohydrates

5. Nucleic acid metabolism: degraded to uric acid and excreted

overall regulation of metabolism

1. Regulation by way of

(a) specific molecules which have a central role in several overlapping pathways

(b) activation or repression of gene that controls enzyme synthesis

(c) inhibition of enzyme by product

(d) small molecules such as ATP

clinical considerations

1. Galactosemia: genetic disease in which the enzyme that converts galactose to glucose is not present. Leads to mental retardation

2. Phenylketonuria: genetic disease in which the enzyme that converts phenylalanine to tyrosine is not present. Leads to mental retardation

3. Alkaptonuria: genetic disease in which enzyme involved in metabolism of tyrosine is missing

energy exchange

Dynamic equilibrium: continuous turnover of many molecules in body, balance achieved

1. Types of energy: chemical, kinetic, potential, heat

2. Direct calorimetry: measurement of heat radiated from body

3. Indirect calorimetry: relating amount of oxygen consumed to known energy values of foodstuffs

4. Basal metabolic rate (BMR): minimal resting metabolic activity

5. BMR influenced by age, sex, hormone secretion, climate, altitude, and kind of food consumed

6. Respiratory quotient (RQ): ratio of volume of carbon dioxide expired to volume of oxygen consumed; related to type of food consumed

7. Exercise: accurate measurements of energy consumed during exercise made by measuring volume and gas content of expired air

    (a) amount of oxygen consumed becomes proportional to amount of work when submaximal work is done; however, oxygen debt occurs due to lag; must be made up after work ceases. Oxygen debt can be high when doing maximum work; lactic acid accumulates during oxygen debt

    (b) training increases ability to do submaximal work without going into severe oxygen debt, and amount of oxygen debt that can be accumulated

respiratory system

gross anatomy
nasal cavities
pharynx
larynx
trachea and bronchi
lungs
pleura
blood supply
nerve supply

**microanatomy and
cellular specialization**
bronchioles
alveolus

physiology
breathing
exchange of gases

control
neural

**factors influencing
respiration**
carbon dioxide and
    hydrogen ion
    concentration
oxygen concentration
exercise and ventilation
effects of high altitudes
    and diving

clinical considerations
anoxia
hypoxia
asthma
Cheynes-Stokes breathing
emphysema
lung cancer
pneumonia
pneumothorax
tuberculosis

Living forms have evolved a variety of ways to convey gases from the environment to the interior of the cell. Unicellular organisms are separated from the environment by only a membrane (and in some forms by a cell wall), and diffusion supplies sufficient oxygen for the organism's needs. Over longer distances, diffusion is not sufficient, and larger multicellular organisms have evolved various systems to carry oxygen to the cells. Insects have a panorama of tubes that open to the exterior at one end and to the metabolizing tissues at the other. Oxygen, as air, moves through this ductwork. Many amphibians obtain oxygen through their highly vascular skin, and the lungs remain as secondary respiratory structures. Even in man, about 2.5 percent of the oxygen is obtained by way of the skin.

The human *respiratory* or *pulmonary* system in its simplest form is a beautifully balanced dual circulation of gases (oxygen and carbon dioxide) and blood separated by a semipermeable membrane. The circulation of gases is maintained by a gas pump (thorax, muscles, pleura, lungs) and two fluid pumps, the right and left sides of the heart. In the lung, oxygen is picked up by the blood cells, and carbon dioxide diffuses from the blood to be exhaled.

During the exchange of gases, several processes are in simultaneous operation. The movement of air from the atmosphere to the lungs is called *ventilation.* It is achieved by *breathing,* a method of creating differences in pressure in the chest activity. These pressure changes are a direct consequence of a coordinated contraction of muscles, especially the intercostals and those of the diaphragm and abdomen. *External respiration* refers to the gaseous exchange of carbon dioxide, oxygen, and some nitrogen that occurs between the lung cells and the lung capillary blood. *Internal respiration* is a similar exchange that occurs at the tissue level throughout the body, for example, the exchange between the liver cells and capillary blood. When the term *respiration* is used alone, it generally refers to the overall metabolic activity that occurs within cells (certain poisons inhibit respiration; they do not affect breathing or the external or internal exchanges of gases, but specifically the functioning of an important metabolic pathway such as glycolysis).

The respiratory system plays a minor role in temperature regulation and water balance, based on the amount of water vapor lost during exhalation. In normal environments, this water loss is small, but during heavy work in very cold dry environments, water loss from the respiratory system can be excessive. A third function of the system is its participation in the overall regulation of blood pH (along with the kidney, liver, and the gastrointestinal tract).

gross anatomy   The passageway for air from the exterior to the lung includes the following structures in sequence: *nasal and oral cavities, pharynx, larynx, trachea, bronchi* (singular, *bronchus*), and *pleurae* (singular, *pleura*); most of the organs are found in the thorax (Module 15A). Each lung is surrounded by a gossamer thin membrane, the pleura, forming a pleural cavity, and each pleural compartment is separated by the mediastinum.

nasal cavities   The nasal cavities shown in Module 15A are part of the nose and are separated from the mouth by the palate. Their lateral walls form by a

figure 15-1

THE GROSS
ANATOMY OF THE
LARYNX

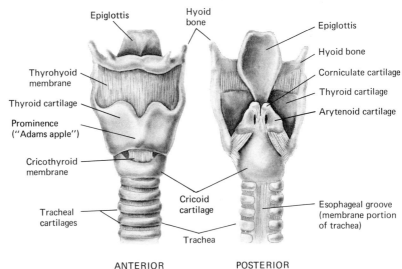

ANTERIOR   POSTERIOR

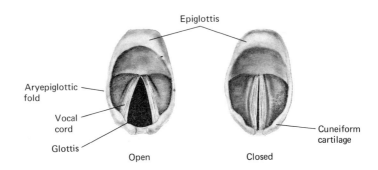

fusion of many bones (nasal, sphenoid, and so on); the medial wall that
separates the two cavities (*nasal septum*) is composed of the perpendicular plate of the ethmoid bone, the vomer, and cartilage (see Figure 4-9).
The openings of the nasal cavity to the exterior are called *nares*, and
where these cavities exit into the pharynx is called *choanae*.

pharynx   (This section was discussed in detail in Chapter 13, Digestive System
and Nutrition.)

larynx   The larynx (Figure 15-1) is an organ composed primarily of cartilagenous
plates and small muscles, and it connects the respiratory part of the
pharynx to the trachea. The larynx is about 2 inches in length, and it
generally is larger in males than females. The major laryngeal cartilage,
thyroid cartilage (Adam's apple), is also heavier in the male due to the
growth-stimulating influence of the male hormones. The opening into
the cavity of the larynx, the *glottis*, is formed by lateral folds of an
elastic membrane. The medial folds that meet in the midline to close the

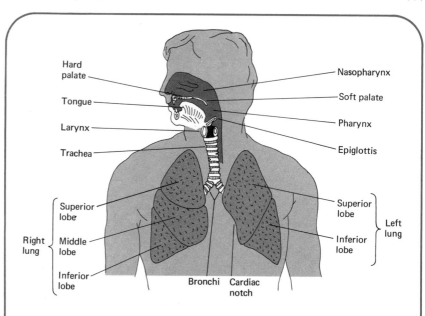

The primary purpose of the respiratory system is movement and interchange of gases between the organism and the environment: first, to supply sufficient oxygen to the blood to meet the metabolic needs of the tissues and second to remove carbon dioxide produced by the metabolizing tissues. This exchange of gases occurs in two steps: (a) at the level of the lung the oxygen is transported from the air sacs (alveoli) to the blood in the adjacent capillaries; (b) at the tissue level the oxygen is released from the blood to the tissues. The reverse exchange occurs for carbon dioxide in that the gas is picked up by the blood at the tissue level and is released from the blood into the lung air sacs. Each day the adult lung removes at least 300 liters of carbon dioxide and if an individual is exercising, this rate of removal can be increased to as much as 10 times the resting state. The removal of carbon dioxide (which forms carbonic acid) is an important factor in maintaining a normal acid-base balance.

The respiratory organs, the nose, nasal pharynx, larynx, trachea, and bronchi, serve principally to form a passageway for the unimpeded flow of air into and out of the lungs. The nose also functions to warm, moisten, and cleanse the air, and the larynx is the principal organ for sound. The lungs have been considered to be a rather passive structure in ventilation and respiration, but now the lung is considered to be a major homeostatic organ known to possess an intrinsic metabolic activity, which puts it perhaps on par with the kidney. Also significant in respiratory function are the various structures which form the thoracic cavity. These structures, such as the lung covering and the lining of the cavity (pleura), the ribs, the diaphragm, and the intercostal muscles, all work in concert to change the volume of the chest, which in turn produces the pressure differences to produce ventilation.

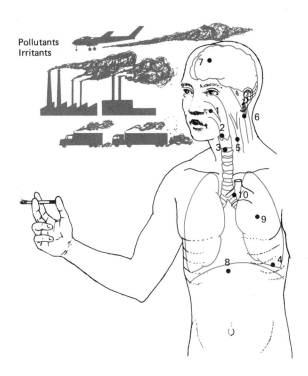

Pollutants
Irritants

The control of breathing and factors which influence breathing. Under normal circumstances the activity of the respiratory centers in the medulla oblongata and pons are affected by both chemical and neural inputs. One of the most important factors regulating respiration is the blood carbon dioxide level in the medulla. Thus an increase in CO_2 concentration (and $H+$ ion concentration) will directly stimulate the respiratory center and will increase both depth and rate of breathing, while a drop in CO_2 concentration has the opposite effect. In addition there are chemoreceptors in the carotid body and aortic arch which are sensitive to changes in oxygen concentration (and also CO_2 levels). These sensory receptors send signals to the respiratory centers and adjust their sensitivity to meet physiological demands. Other receptors in the nose, throat, bronchi and lungs respond to irritants and modify respiratory movements to clear the irritant from the air passages (coughing, sneezing). The respiratory centers although fundamentally regulated by automatic feedback controls may be influenced by higher brain centers. Voluntary alterations in breathing accompany talking and singing and emotions produce a broad spectrum of respiratory changes such as sighing, laughing, crying, yawning, gasping with fear and hyperventilating (panting) during anxiety.

1. Chemoreceptors, nasal mucosa; 2. chemoreceptors, pharynx; 3. chemoreceptors, respiratory pathway; 4. stretch receptors, ribs; 5. carotid sinus; 6. respiratory center, hind brain; 7. respiratory centers, cerebrum; 8. pressoreceptors diaphragm; 9. stretch receptors, lungs; 10. aortic body.

glottis are called the *vocal cords*, and they are responsible for sound. Vocalization is a function of the respiratory system. Since man is the only acknowledged speech-making animal, and speech is the dominant means of communication, vocalization is a significant survival function of the respiratory system.

trachea and
bronchi

The trachea is a cylindrical tube which begins at the larynx and descends parallel with the esophagus within the mediastinum to about the level of the *T*5 or *T*6. At this point, it divides into the *right* and *left bronchi*, going to the right and left lungs, respectively (Module 15A). The trachea is about 5 inches in length and 1 inch in diameter. It is kept rigid by 16 to 20 crescent-shaped rings of cartilage. Enclosing the rings and occupying the spaces between are elastic fibers, which provide the organ with elasticity so that it stretches and recoils with each inspiration and expiration. External to this elastic membrane are scattered bundles of smooth muscle.

Each bronchus enters the lungs along with large blood vessels and nerves. Like the trachea, the bronchi are elastic and move with changes in breathing. Because the angle of the right bronchus (almost a straight line with the trachea) is less than the left, foreign objects that accidentally get caught in the trachea inevitably end up in the right lung. The bronchi continue to branch, getting progressively smaller, and as they do so, the cartilage crescents become more minute and finally disappear. The smallest tubes, the *bronchioles* (about 0.25 mm in diameter), branch once more to form the *alveolar ducts* (0.2 mm). All bronchioles are surrounded by branching and anastomosing bundles of smooth muscle.

lungs

Each lung lies relatively free within its pleural cavity with the major attachment only to the trachea. The lungs are spongy and elastic, and in the newborn and young, they have a creamy pink appearance. With the passage of time, however, the accumulation of particles inhaled from the environment changes the coloration to a bluish gray; lungs exposed to prolonged urban atmospheric pollution appear deep blue or black.

The right lung divides into upper, middle, and lower lobes, and the left lung divides into an upper and lower lobe (Figure 15-2). The *apex* extends about 1 inch beyond the clavicle, and the *base* is shaped to conform with the dome surface of the diaphragm. Once breathing starts, air is trapped within the lung tissue, giving the organ a translucent appearance when photographed. This translucency provides an ideal situation for X-ray because it makes the lung visible to the observer (Figure 15-3). The exceptions are those areas covered by other organs, for example, the aorta, stomach, and liver.

pleura

The pleura is a shiny, wet, serous double membrane; a *parietal* pleura lines the thoracic wall, and a *visceral* pleura covers the lungs (Figure 15-2). The visceral pleura adheres closely to the lungs with the same clinging tendency that is found in the various plastic wraps used in modern kitchens. The pleura not only covers the organ, but dips into all

figure 15-2

ANTERIOR AND
LATERAL VIEWS
OF THE LUNGS
AND THEIR
RELATIONSHIP TO
THE RIB CAGE

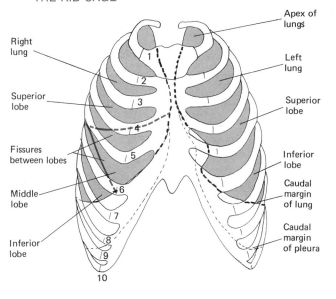

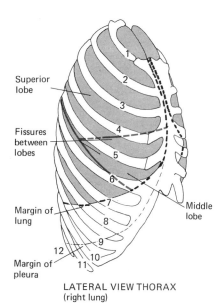

LATERAL VIEW THORAX
(right lung)

of the major and minor crevices. Between the visceral and parietal pleurae is an *intrapleural space.* It is merely a potential space since the cavity contains a microscopic film of fluid. Under abnormal conditions, however, when the fluid layer increases or air seeps in, the pleurae separate, and the intrapleural cavity lives up to its name.

blood supply   The principal blood vessels of the respiratory system are the pulmonary arteries and veins. The arteries branch from a single pulmonary artery, which emerges from the right ventricle and then divides into right and left pulmonary branches. These branches, as they enter into the lung, subdivide and continue to branch as they penetrate the lung tissue. Each lobe of the lung is drained by a large vein, which, on leaving the lung, enters directly into the left atrium. Because the veins from the right upper and middle lobes fuse into a single structure, there are only four pulmonary veins (five lobes) that return the oxygenated blood to the heart. The other structures of the respiratory system, with the exception of the nasal cavity, receive their vascular supply principally from the thyroid and laryngeal arteries, small branches of the aorta. The blood from these organs drains into a pulmonary vein or in some instances into the azygos vein. Because of the distant position of the nasal cavity to the tubular respiratory system, its vascular supply is related to branches supplying the face, such as the maxillary artery.

figure 15-3

NORMAL AND
PATHOLOGICAL
RADIOGRAPHS OF
THE CHEST

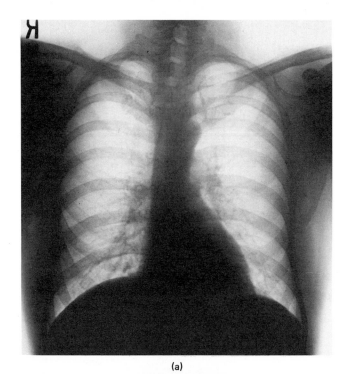

(a)

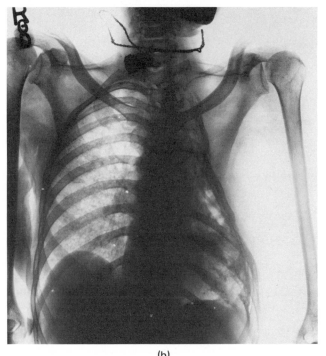

(b)

(a) *Normal:* lung appears as translucent (light) areas between ribs. (b) *Pathological:* ribs 1-10 have been crushed. Left side of chest no longer clear. Note heart outline bulging to the left. (Photos courtesy of Dr. Jerome Shapiro, Boston University School of Medicine.)

The lymphatic vessels are quite inconspicuous in the adult lung except when disease, such as tumor, produces an edema and causes the vessels to dilate. The lymph vessels course along with the arteries and veins, which follow the tubular branching airways; there are no lymphatics at the alveoli.

nerve supply

The innervation of the respiratory system is quite extensive. Sensory stimuli such as touch, pain, and temperature are carried by the V (trigeminal) and IX (glossopharyngeal) cranial nerves. The larynx and trachea are supplied with sensory and motor fibers from the vagus nerve or one of its branches, the laryngeal, and from spinal nerves. The lung proper is innervated by the vagus and thoracic spinal nerves. The phrenic nerve, with components from C2, C3, C4, innervates the diaphragm, and the intercostal nerves supply the intercostal muscles in the thoracic region.

microanatomy and cellular specialization

Microanatomically, the respiratory system might be imagined as a large symmetrical tubular tree. The *trachea* (trunk) divides into two *major bronchi* (branches), which in turn divide into four large *secondary bronchi* (smaller branches), which again divide into successively smaller *branchioles*, and so on, for about 20 or so generations of branching. The smallest branches, the alveolar ducts, which are about 0.2 mm in diameter, terminate in a cluster of thin-walled irregularly shaped sacs, the *alveoli.* These alveolar air spaces are lined with a continuous monolayer of epithelium (Figure 15-5).

bronchioles

Three cells, apart from supporting tissue, form the functional tissue of the respiration system: *ciliated epithelium, mucous-secreting goblet cells,* and *endothelial cells.* Starting in the respiratory portion of the lung and ending at the respiratory bronchioles, a *pseudostratified ciliated epithelium* with many goblet cells lines the airways. The cilia on the cells beat as frequently as 1200 times per minute and move materials away from the lung proper to the exterior. Mucous-secreting cells also protect the respiratory system by forming a sticky secretion that traps foreign materials. The trapped debris can be moved by the ciliated cells at a fairly rapid rate (about 0.5 inch per minute).

alveolus

The actual exchange of gases takes place in the 300 million alveoli, which provide the lungs with a surface area of about 75 m². Viewed by electron microscopy, the alveolar wall is seen to support a conspicuous network of capillaries surrounded by elastic fibers. The capillary membrane and the alveolar membrane fuse into a functional unit that is so thin (0.5 μ) that it appears as two structures sharing a common membrane (Figure 15-5). This adaptation, of course, permits a rapid exchange of gases between the blood and the air within the alveoli (Figure 15-6). The membrane basically consists of the plasma membrane of the alveoli cells, a basement membrane of varying thickness, and the capillary endothelial plasma membrane. In spite of the thinness of the unit, mitochondria, enzymes, and other functional units can be seen in the cytoplasm of the two cells. Even these substances vary with changes in the physiology of the lung (Figure 15-6).

figure 15-4

THE RESPIRATORY
TREE: TRACHEA,
BRONCHI,
BRONCHIOLES,
AND ALVEOLI

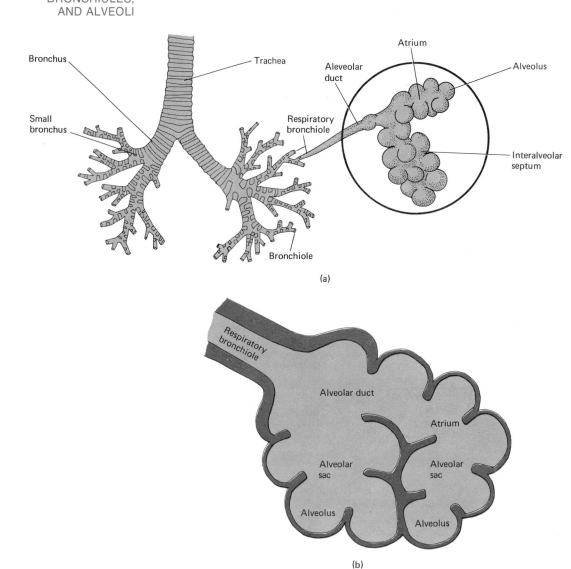

(a)

(b)

physiology   The lungs are normally rather elastic and, unless kept under negative
                pressure, would contract to only a fraction of their size. Indeed, if air
                entered the pleural space, the lung would collapse (see Pneumothorax
breathing   under Clinical Considerations). But if the pleurae remain intact the nega-
                tive intrathoracic pressure keeps the lungs fully expanded. Thus as the
                rib cage enlarges and the diaphragm is depressed during inspiration, the

figure 15-5

THE ULTRA-
STRUCTURE OF
AN ALVEOLUS AND
ITS ASSOCIATED
CAPILLARY

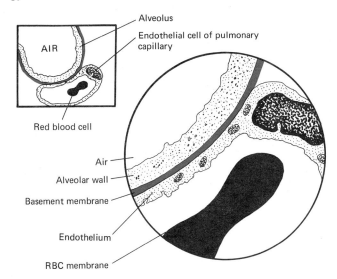

figure 15-5

THE ULTRA-
STRUCTURE OF
AN ALVEOLUS AND
ITS ASSOCIATED
CAPILLARY

negative pressure becomes greater. Because the pressure in the lungs is higher, the elastic lungs enlarge. Now the same amount of air occupies a greater space in the lungs, thereby decreasing the pressure there below that of the atmosphere, and air flows into the lungs. Thus, *inspiration* of air involves muscle movements, which decrease intrathoracic pressure, enlargement of the lungs, and movement of air from an area of high pressure (the outside) to an area of low pressure (inside the lungs). During a normal inspiration, there is a pressure difference of about −5 mm Hg. During normal *expiration* of air, the process is reversed. Movement of the diaphragm and intrathoracic muscles decrease the size of the chest cavity; intrathoracic pressure increases; and the elastic lungs recoil forcing air to move out of the lungs. It is possible to increase the intrathoracic pressure and force air from the lungs vigorously (coughing, blowing up a balloon), and during such forced expiration, the contrac-

figure 15-6

SCHEMATIC
SHOWING
BARRIERS TO GAS
EXCHANGE IN THE
ALVEOLUS

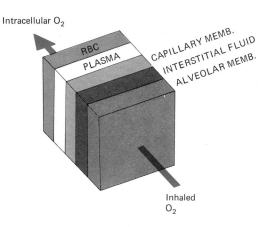

tion of the intercostal muscles and diaphragm may elevate the intra-thoracic pressure to +60 mm Hg.

The expansion of the lungs in relationship to the expansion of the chest is due to a special relationship of the pleurae that line the thorax and cover the lung. Between the two pleurae is a thin layer of fluid, which causes the two membranes to adhere to each other. An excellent analogy would be to take two plates of glass with a thin film of water between them and try to separate them. The two plates could be slipped one off the other, which shows that there is little resistance to tangen-tial and rotary movement. However, it is almost impossible to separate the two plates by pulling them apart. Likewise, the two pleurae adhere in such a way to permit great freedom of motion of the lungs within the thorax. Contributing to the contraction of the air spaces is the surface tension of their contained secretions. Recently, it was shown that alveolar cells secrete a *lipoprotein* that lowers the surface tension, per-haps as much as 10 times at the interface between the fluids "lining" the alveoli and the air. This substance is called *surfactant*, and without it the amount of pressure required to inflate the lungs would almost be impossible to maintain by thorax muscle contraction. A disease of the newborn (hyaline membrane) is believed to be due to insufficient sur-factant secretion. The condition generally leads to death of the infant because of a lack of oxygen due to insufficient gas exchange.

The total capacity of air volume of the lungs of a normal individual is about 6 liters. However, there is always gas in the lungs, although the amount may vary considerably from moment to moment. Thus at the end of a forced expiration, the lungs still contain about 1 liter of gas, the so-called *residual volume.* At the end of a normal expiration, the lungs contain about 2 liters of gas, and this volume is referred to as the *func-tional residual capacity.* During ventilation, the average adult inhales (and exhales) about 500 ml of gas, the *tidal volume* (Table 15-1). Some 350 ml of this tidal volume exchanges with the gas in the functional

table 15-1

LUNG VOLUMES
AND CAPACITIES[a]

Tidal volume	The volume of gas that enters and leaves with inspiration and expiration	500 ml
Inspiration reserve volume	The maximum amount of gas that can be inspired beyond the resting tidal volume	2500 to 3000 ml
Expiration reserve volume	The maximal amount of gas that can be exhaled at the end of a normal expiration	1000 ml
Residual volume	The volume of gas remaining in the lungs after maximal exhalation	1200 ml
Total lung capacity	The amount of gas contained within the lung at the end of maximal inspiration	6000 ml
Vital capacity	The maximal volume of gas that can be expelled from the lungs forcefully following maximal inspiration	4800 ml

[a] Modified from Comroe et al

figure 15-7

RECORDING FROM
A SPIROMETER
SHOWING
RESPIRATORY
CAPACITIES AND
VOLUMES

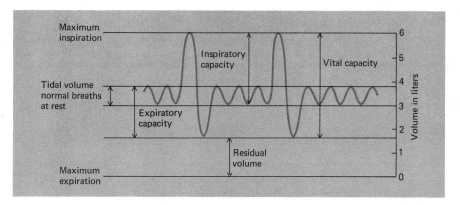

residual compartment to provide enough oxygen to make up for that absorbed in the alveolar capillaries. Conversely, each exhalation removes an equal volume of carbon dioxide from the reservoir. The reason only 350 ml of air reaches the reservoir on each normal inspiration is that 150 ml of air remains in the vast tubular system leading to the alveoli. This trapped volume of air is referred to as the *anatomic dead space* (see Figure 15-7).

The lung is ventilated at a rate of approximately 11 to 14 times per minute, and the depth of breathing as well as the rate will only vary when the body's need for oxygen or for the removal of carbon dioxide increases. Normal breathing is termed *eupnea;* breathing that is laborious and difficult is called *dyspnea;* and an increase in rate of breathing is called *hyperpnea. Apnea* refers to cessation of breathing.

exchange of gases

External Respiration

There are five factors determining the exchange of gases between the alveoli and the circulating blood: (a) the diffusion of gas according to its partial pressure, (b) the permeability of the membrane, (c) the surface of membrane available for exchange, (d) the rate of blood flow through the pulmonary circulation, and (e) the chemical reactions of the blood.

According to the gas laws, each gas in a mixture of gases exerts a partial pressure (part of the total pressure exerted by that gas) proportional to its concentration. The partial pressure exerted by a gas can be calculated if the percentage (of the total) of that gas is known and the total pressure of the mixture is known. Thus, if oxygen content of air at sea level is 21 percent and the total atmospheric pressure of air (a mixture) is measured at 760 mm of mercury, then 21 percent $\times$ 760 = 160 mm Hg is the partial pressure exerted by oxygen (such partial pressures are expressed as $P_{O_2} = 160$ mm Hg).

According to the laws of diffusion, substances (in this case, gases) diffuse from areas of high concentration to areas of low concentration (even if a semipermeable membrane is placed between the two concentractions). Because the P_{O_2} in the alveoli is greater than P_{O_2} in the blood, oxygen will move from the alveoli to the blood. As tissues use up oxygen, the P_{O_2} in the tissues falls, and oxygen will move to the tissues. The

figure 15-8

SCHEMATIC OF
EXCHANGE OF
RESPIRATORY
GASES IN THE
BODY

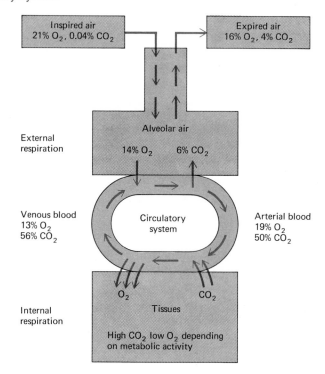

exact reverse is true for the movement of carbon dioxide. Carbon dioxide is produced as a metabolic by-product by cells. Thus, the P_{CO_2} in the cells is greater than the P_{CO_2} in the blood, and carbon dioxide moves from cells to body fluids and then from blood to the alveoli to be expired. Thus, two gradients of gas diffusion exist, one for oxygen and one for carbon dioxide. These are shown graphically in Figure 15-8.

Membranes act as a physical barrier and offer resistance to the movement of materials through them. As can be seen in Figure 15-6, gas movement is resisted by a number of barriers (alveolar membrane, capillary endothelium, interstitial fluid, and membrane of the red blood cell).

The greater the surface available for diffusion, the greater the quantity of gas diffusing across the membrane per unit time. During heavy exercise, more alveoli are activated, thereby increasing the available surface. Total diffusion capacity may increase by a factor of three, due not only to more alveoli being used, but also to the increased number of capillaries carrying blood as a consequence of pulmonary vasodilation. For example, during exercise blood moving rapidly through the alveolar capillaries does not pick up as much oxygen as slow-moving blood (since there is less time for exchange of gases), but the total volume circulating through these capillaries is great enough actually to increase the amount of gas transferred per unit of time.

Last, the transport of gases depends on several chemical reactions in the red blood cells and plasma. The plasma, even when saturated with

figure 15-9

THE
OXYHEMOGLOBIN
DISSOCIATION
CURVE

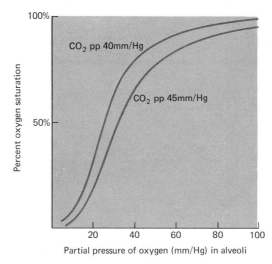

As the partial pressure of oxygen increases, the percent of oxygen saturation increases. In metabolically active tissue, local carbon dioxide concentrations affect the oxygen binding properties of hemoglobin and oxygen is released.

oxygen, could not transport enough oxygen to sustain the body. However, the red blood cells are filled with an iron-containing protein molecule, *hemoglobin*, which has a very high affinity for oxygen. This protein rapidly combines with the oxygen in the plasma and forms *oxyhemoglobin*. Without hemoglobin, the oxygen-carrying capacity of 100 ml of blood, at a P_{O_2} of 100 mm Hg, would be only approximately 0.5 ml. With hemoglobin, at the same P_{O_2}, the oxygen-carrying capacity is increased approximately 40 times (20 ml oxygen per 100 ml blood). The carrier ability of hemoglobin is due to its specific configuration and beyond the need for discussion here. Although the chemical reaction is simply written as

$$O_2 + Hb \Longleftrightarrow HbO_2$$

the mechanism is a little more complicated.

Internal Respiration   The P_{O_2} of the cells, as well as the tissue fluid bathing the cells, is lower than the circulating arterial blood. Therefore, the P_{O_2} gradient will favor the diffusion of oxygen from the blood to the tissues (Figure 15-9).

The hemoglobin molecule is uniquely adapted for the absorption and release of oxygen. Although oxygen binding and release by hemoglobin depend on the amount of available oxygen, it is not a linear or one-to-one relationship. Most of the oxygen leaving hemoglobin does so in one major spurt. In Figure 15-9, an *oxygen-hemoglobin dissociation curve* is depicted. The curve that represents release (or binding) is S shaped. We can readily see that the unusual shape of the curves reflects some very distinct advantages for the individual. With a drop of P_{O_2} from 100 to 60 mm Hg, only 10 percent of the oxygen is given up, whereas between 60 to 20 mm Hg P_{O_2}, over 50 percent of the oxygen dissociates from the hemoglobin.

So far in the discussion, only oxygen transport has been mentioned, but equally important is the transport of carbon dioxide. Being a gas, carbon

figure 15-10

CARBON DIOXIDE
TRANSPORT

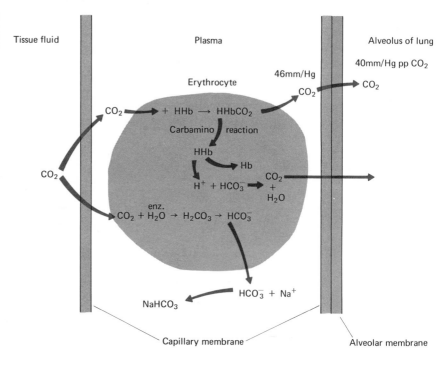

dioxide transport and removal are likewise dependent on the various P_{CO_2} tensions. Most of the carbon dioxide is transported in the plasma in the form of the bicarbonate ion (HCO^-_3), with one-third of the carbon dioxide associated with hemoglobin forming *carbaminohemoglobin* (or *carboxyhemoglobin*); a very small amount is transported simply as dissolved carbon dioxide in tissue fluids. The transport of carbon dioxide is summarized in Figure 15-10.

control

neural

Inspiration and expiration are controlled by the respiratory centers in the medulla oblongata and pons. These centers integrate a variety of sensory inputs and send signals to the muscles used in breathing. The neural signals for inspiration are generated at the *inspiratory center* in the medulla; they travel down to the fiber tracts of the spinal cord emerging through spinal nerves C2 to C4. Branches of these cervical nerves unite to form the *phrenic nerve* (on each side), which innervates the diaphragm. The motor impulses going to the intercostal muscles come from fibers that leave the spinal cord at the level of C4 to C8. Although the expiratory abdominal musculature plays a small role in normal exhalation, these muscles appear to have their own center within the medulla, and the impulses will be elaborated and transferred to these muscles in a manner similar to that described for inspiration.

factors
influencing
respiration

The principal and specific stimulus influencing respiration is chemical, and factors such as pain, emotion, sleeping, or exercise play a secondary role (Module 15B).

carbon dioxide
and hydrogen ion
concentration

Both P_{O_2} and P_{CO_2} exert their effect directly on the respiratory center, but the very fine control of ventilation is related to P_{CO_2}. Carbon dioxide dissolves readily in blood and is rapidly converted to carbonic acid by the catalytic action of the enzyme *carbonic anhydrase*. The acid then dissociates to form a bicarbonate ion (HCO_3^-) and the hydrogen ion (H^+).

$$CO_2 + H_2O \rightleftharpoons H_2CO_3 \rightleftharpoons H^+ + HCO^-$$

It is the hydrogen ion concentration that appears to be primarily influential in respiratory control. We can demonstrate that in the presence of ample oxygen, an increase of plasma P_{CO_2} of 5 mm Hg will double the respiration rate. Conversely, if a subject forcibly exhales rapidly for several breaths (hyperventilation), thus driving out the carbon dioxide from the alveoli and lowering the plasma P_{CO_2}, the inspiration center is inhibited. The experimental data indicate that the hydrogen ion concentration of the fluid bathing the brain has a direct effect on the respiratory centers.

oxygen
concentration

The respiratory centers are modulated by specialized *chemoreceptors* that are sensitive to changes in P_{O_2} concentration. Localized aggregations of these chemoreceptors are in the aortic arch and in the carotid arteries. They are called the *aortic* and *carotid bodies*, and when the arterial oxygen level falls below normal, the chemoreceptors are stimulated, relaying their signals to the brain to increase the rate and depth of respiration. While oxygen is a factor in regulation of respiration, it is probably only important during extraordinary physical conditions, such as heavy exercise.

Carbon monoxide (CO) poisoning is an excellent illustration demonstrating the role of oxygen on respiration. Carbon monoxide has a greater affinity for hemoglobin than oxygen. When both gases are present in the system, carbon monoxide will saturate hemoglobin, leaving few sites for oxygen attachment. The amount and the transport of oxygen will be reduced, and the tissues will suffer because of the insufficient oxygen nourishment by the blood. What is interesting is that the *plasma level* of P_{O_2} will be normal, since carbon monoxide does not compete with oxygen for plasma saturation. Since the plasma P_{O_2} is normal, the chemoreceptors in the aortic and carotid bodies are *not* stimulated. There is no compensatory increase in respiration to correct the low oxygen levels. An individual breathing carbon monoxide and oxygen will not vary his breathing rate, and eventually will go into a coma and die, breathing normally all the time because the plasma P_{O_2} is insufficient to meet the respiration requirements of the metabolizing tissues.

exercise and
ventilation

During extreme exertion, factors other than P_{O_2}, P_{CO_2}, and H^+ are involved in controlling the rate of respiration. Neither P_{O_2}, P_{CO_2}, nor H^+ appears to change during exercise in that the body somehow increases the ventilation process and takes in oxygen and excretes carbon dioxide as rapidly as it is formed. Evidently, inputs from other sources are in operation; probably in this mild stressful condition, hormonal control, such as epinephrine, might contribute to increase ventilation. During exercise, there is an increase in temperature, and this factor alone would undoubtedly have a direct effect on neuron metabolism in the respiratory centers.

How pain and emotion bring an accompanying change in the respiratory rate is still not known, but the response certainly implicates the higher centers of the brain. We are all familiar with the reaction to plunging into a cold body of water, and the shocking experience of being frightened is no less a stimulus on respiration.

effects of high altitudes and diving

As man moves from sea level to higher altitudes, both the atmospheric pressure and P_{O_2} decrease. But man is remarkably adaptable and can function well if given sufficient time to acclimate to decreased oxygen concentration. Andean Indians have established permanent settlements at an altitude of 18,000 feet by undergoing a number of physiological adaptations, but unacclimated people experience moderate discomfort and decrement in performance at 8000 to 10,000 feet and suffer serious difficulties (loss of consciousness) at 20,000 to 25,000 feet. Flying an unpressurized aircraft with the supplemental oxygen is possible up to 40,000 feet, but beyond this altitude, the alveolar water vapor and carbon dioxide tension equal atmospheric pressure, and gas exchange fails. Hence pressurized cabins are essential for these high-altitude aircraft. Some of the relationships to altitude, atmospheric pressure, and oxygen content of the air are shown in Figure 15-11.

Decompression Sickness

If a man makes a sudden ascent from sea level to 35,000 feet, the change (decrease) in pressure permits nitrogen bubbles to form in the blood vessels, tissues, and joints causing choking sensations, joint pains, and muscle cramps. These are the symptoms of *decompression sickness* or the *bends*. This phenomenon is even more accentuated for divers making rapid ascents from underwater to the surface. Underwater pressure increases very rapidly with increasing depths, thereby forcing more nitrogen into solution in the blood. Unless ascent is gradual to allow nitrogen to diffuse from the blood slowly, nitrogen bubbles will form causing severe bends. Breathing pure oxygen during decompression helps to get the nitrogen out of the blood.

Hyperbaric Effects

Breathing air or pure oxygen at high pressures also can be harmful. Breathing air compressed at four or more atmospheres, man experiences mood shifts, mental impairment, and loss of motor control due to *nitrogen poisoning*. This reaction can be overcome by breathing a mixture of pure oxygen and helium. Even pure oxygen can be harmful at high atmospheric pressures (*hyperbaric*), and prolonged exposure to oxygen above 6 atm causes bronchial inflammation, pulmonary congestion, edema, and convulsions.

clinical considerations

anoxia/hypoxia

The term *anoxia* refers to an absence of oxygen, but the term is somewhat inappropriate, because a condition in which there is *no* oxygen present in the lungs, blood, or tissue rarely occurs. The term *hypoxia* refers to a diminished amount of oxygen that is delivered to the tissues and in most instances better describes the situation. The anoxic or

figure 15-11

THE EARTH'S
ATMOSPHERE

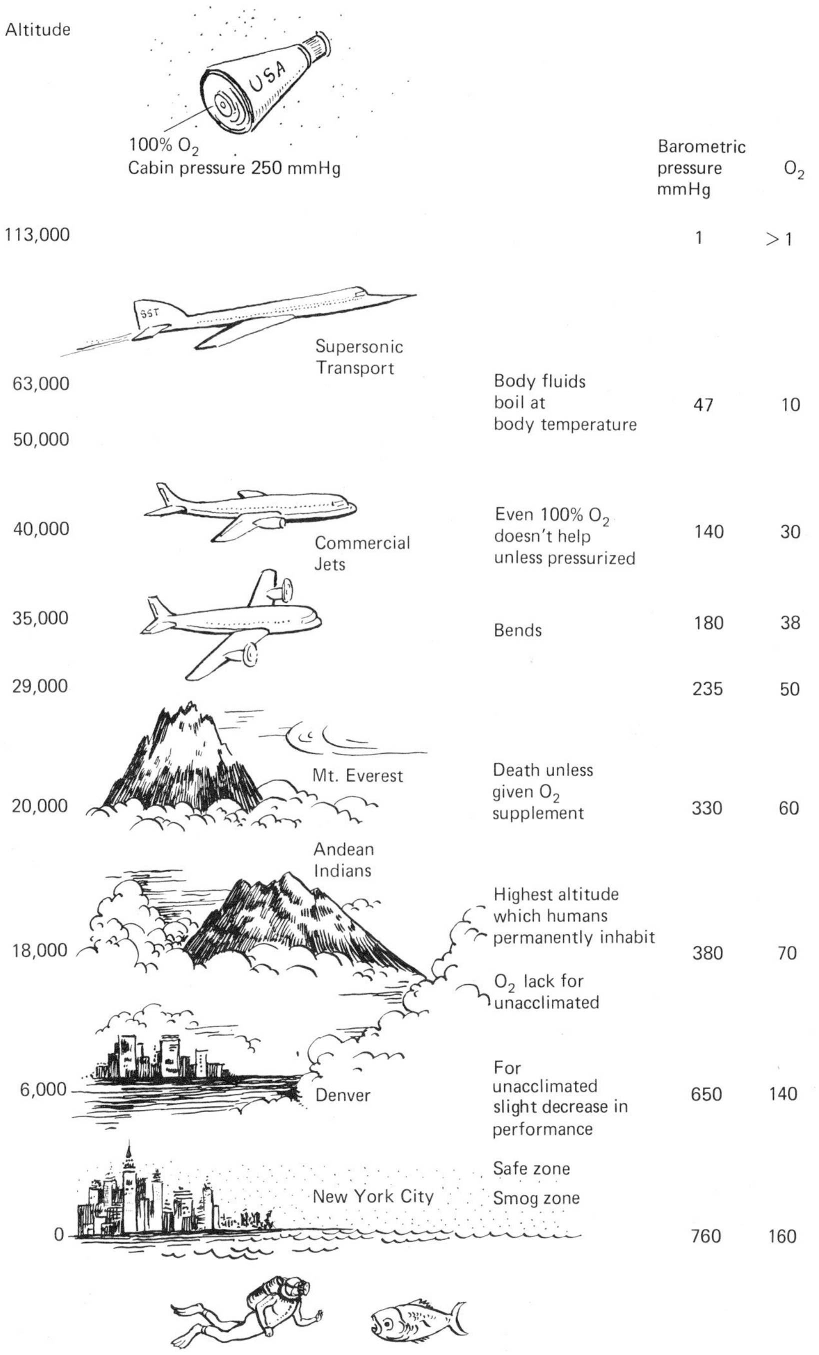

Altitude		Barometric pressure mmHg	O_2
	100% O_2 Cabin pressure 250 mmHg		
113,000		1	>1
	Supersonic Transport		
63,000	Body fluids boil at body temperature	47	10
50,000			
40,000	Even 100% O_2 doesn't help unless pressurized Commercial Jets	140	30
35,000	Bends	180	38
29,000		235	50
20,000	Mt. Everest Death unless given O_2 supplement	330	60
	Andean Indians		
18,000	Highest altitude which humans permanently inhabit	380	70
	O_2 lack for unacclimated		
6,000	Denver For unacclimated slight decrease in performance	650	140
	New York City Safe zone Smog zone		
0		760	160

The breath of life which makes up the earth's atmosphere varies with altitude. As one goes up from sea level the air becomes rarefied, oxygen content decreases as does barometric pressure. Man can acclimate up to about 18,000 feet, but beyond that height supplemental oxygen is needed.

hypoxic situation may be caused by a lack of atmospheric oxygen, anemia, poisons (carbon monoxide, alcohol, narcotics, or cyanide). Two manifestations that may occur with hypoxia or anoxia are a bluish coloration of the skin because hemoglobin is insufficiently oxygenated (oxygen gives blood its red color) and a clubbing of the fingers. The clubbing symptom is not explainable, but still remains an excellent sign of pulmonary or heart disease.

Cheyne-Stokes breathing
Any damage to the brain stem (for example, an excess of a narcotic agent, anesthetic, or an increase in intracranial pressure) may dull the sensitivity of the respiratory centers, and thus greater stimulus will be required to activate both expiration and inspiration. This being the case, there is a periodic waxing and waning of not only the rate and amplitude of breathing as overventilation (*hyperpnea*), but a compensatory slowing or cessation of breathing (*apnea*). This periodic increase and decrease in depth of breathing is called Cheyne-Stokes breathing and is often indicative of a clinical crisis.

asthma
Asthma may be characterized by episodes of wheezing, sneezing, coughing, and shortness of breath. Radiologic examination frequently shows an enlargement of the lung due to the difficulty of exhaling and difficulty of inhaling. The abnormal expiratory condition may be caused by an obstruction or by allergens. The reaction to the allergens results in edema of tissues lining air pathways (the bronchi), and this causes narrowing of the air passages (*bronchial asthma*).

emphysema
Emphysema occurs from conditions that produce long-term distension of the alveoli. The excessive expansion brings about a breakdown of the alveolar tissue by overstretching or by exerting excessive pressure on the nonexpanded alveoli. The net effect is that the available surface for exchange of gases is decreased, and respiration is diminished, thus, in emphysema individual suffers as if there were a lack of oxygen in the atmosphere. *Bronchitis* (inflammation of the bronchi), asthma, and smoking appear to be the prime producers of emphysema.

lung cancer
In the United States in 1930, there were only 2500 deaths from cancer of the lung; in 1964 over 43,000 people died of this disease. From the time of World War I (1914), the number of smokers increased very rapidly, and the obvious interrelationship of these facts cannot be ignored. According to the Surgeon General's report (1964), smoking is hazardous to the respiratory system primarily by increasing the incidence of cancer to the lips, mouth, trachea, bronchi, and lungs. Smoking will also produce nontumor diseases of the respiratory system such as emphysema. According to the American Cancer Society, lung cancer in nonsmokers numbers about 34 per million population, and for cigarette smokers, the number is increased to 786 per million. If an individual is a heavy smoker (two packs per day), the incidence of lung cancer will increase to almost 1500 per million.

An interesting phenomenon related to smoking and lung cancer is that if an individual stops smoking, there is repair and regeneration of the precancerous stages. However, once a primary cancer lesion is estab-

figure 15-12

PNEUMOTHORAX

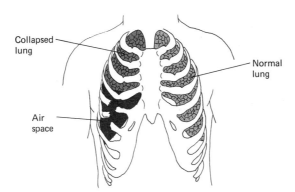

Collapsed lung

Normal lung

Air space

Any puncture of the chest wall that permits air at atmospheric pressure to enter the intrapulmonary space, which is normally under negative pressure, will cause the lung to collapse. Negative pressure is necessary to keep the lung expanded. Each lung is in a separate cavity so even if one lung collapses the normal lung can sustain life.

lished in the membrane, it is difficult to cure the disease. The death rate is frighteningly high—over 80 percent. The tragedy, of course, is that this disease is a clear example of a type that can be markedly decreased, merely by eliminating smoking.

pneumonia
Any condition that results in the alveoli filling with fluid (or pus or blood) is a pneumonia. The most common cause of pneumonia is bacterial or viral infection, but an inflammatory response (pneumonitis) can occur as a secondary manifestation of other diseases. Pneumonia is particularly prevalent among the aged and the infirm, because their chronic inactivity results in insufficient ventilation and a slow accumulation of water that would ordinarily be exhaled with normal respiration.

pneumothorax
If an opening is made through the intercostal muscles into the pleura (either from a traumatic event or a surgical procedure), the pressures between the outside and within the thorax equalize, and the lung then collapses. Obviously, without the expanded state, the alveoli are not capable of exchanging gases, and respiratory failure results. Frequently a lung is collapsed voluntarily to give it a rest; as long as the other lung is enclosed within its own cavity, breathing is possible (Figure 15-12).

tuberculosis
Tuberculosis is frequently abbreviated as TB, and in spite of the *age of antibiotics*, it is prevalent throughout most of the world. The incidence of tuberculosis in the United States was markedly reduced in the past decades, but because a segment of the population is still below minimal economic and health levels, its frequency appears to be on the upswing again. Tuberculosis is caused by a specific bacterium (*Bacillus*) that produces an inflammation and increase of fibrous tissue in the lung. The secondary manifestations are a spreading of the inflammation with a concomitant reduction of the functional lung tissue. The net effect is *depleted ventilation* and the tuberculosis patient is forced to lead a life of restricted activity.

summary

gross anatomy

1. Nasal cavity
   (a) separated from the mouth by the palate
   (b) medial wall: also called nasal septum composed of part of the ethmoid, vomer, and cartilage

      (c) lateral wall: segments of many bones such as nasal and sphenoid

      (d) nares: openings to the exterior

      (e) choanae: openings into the pharynx

2. Pharynx: combined respiratory and digestive pathway

3. Larynx

      (a) composed primarily of cartilage plates and muscle

      (b) connects the respiratory pharynx to the trachea

      (c) Adam's apple: large thyroid cartilage given this popular name because its growth is under the influence of male hormone

      (d) glottis: opening into the laryngeal cavity formed by lateral folds, the vocal cords

4. Trachea

      (a) cylindrical tube, 5 inches in length that runs from the larynx to the lungs

      (b) lies within the mediastinum

5. Bronchi, bronchioles, and alveoli

      (a) trachea splits into two bronchi, and each division continues to branch, becoming smaller and smaller until terminal bronchioles are formed (about 0.25 mm in diameter)

      (b) alveoli: each terminal bronchiole branches once more to form the alveolar duct, whose terminal portion expands into the alveolus

6. Lungs

      (a) right lung divided into three lobes, left lung into two lobes

      (b) apex of lung extends about 1 inch above clavicle, and base conforms to the dome-shaped diaphragm

      (c) lies relatively free within the thorax with the major attachment only to the trachea

7. Pleura

      (a) visceral pleura: the inner layer that adheres closely to the lungs

      (b) parietal pleura: lines the thoracic wall

      (c) intrapleural space: a potential space that is normally filled with a microscopic film of fluid

8. Blood supply

      (a) pulmonary artery: delivers blood to the lung low in oxygen

      (b) pulmonary veins: returns highly oxygenated blood to the left heart for distribution throughout the body

9. Nerve supply

      (a) sensory stimuli carried by V cranial nerve

      (b) motor stimuli principally via the X cranial nerve or one of its branches

micro-circulatory and cellular specialization

Three cells, apart from supporting tissues, form the functional tissue of the respiratory system.

1. Mucous secreting cells: forms a thick sticky secretion that traps foreign particles

2. Ciliated epithelium: beat as frequently as 1200 times per minute, moving trapped materials toward the exterior at a rate of about 0.5 inch per minute

3. Endothelium: capillary cells are in exceptionally close approximation to the alveolar cells to facilitate the exchange of gases; the endothelial-alveolar unit is about 0.5 μ thick and appears as if the two cells share a common membrane

physiology
1. Breathing
    (a) inspiration: result of a decrease in intrathoracic pressure, and air moves into the lungs by the force of atmospheric pressure
    (b) expiration: diaphragm relaxes; and rib cage decreases in size, and stretched elastic tissue of the lung recoils forcing air out
2. Capacity
    (a) total capacity: 6 liters
    (b) residual volume: amount of gas remaining in lungs after forced expiration; about 1 liter
    (c) function residual capacity: at the end of normal expiration, the lungs contain about 2 liters of gas
    (d) tidal volume: amount of gas an adult inhales and exhales; about 500 ml, and of this amount only 350 ml exchanges with the functional residual compartment
    (e) anatomic dead space: 150 ml of gas remains trapped in the vast tubular system of the lungs
3. Ventilation
    (a) lung is ventilated at approximately 11 to 14 times per minute
    (b) eupnea: normal breathing
    (c) dyspnea: laborious breathing
    (d) hyperpnea: increased rate of breathing
    (e) apnea: cessation of breathing
4. Exchange of gases—external respiration; five factors determine exchange of gases:
    (a) partial pressure of the gas
    (b) permeability of the membrane
    (c) surface area of the membrane
    (d) rate of blood flow
    (e) chemical reactions of the blood
5. Internal respiration: exchange of gases at the tissue level depends upon oxygen gradient and the available hemoglobin

control
1. Respiratory centers in the medulla
2. Phrenic nerve innervates the diaphragm

factors influencing function
1. Changes in carbon dioxide concentration
2. pH
3. Changes in oxygen concentration which affect specialized chemoreceptors located in the aortic arch and carotid arteries
4. Exercise
5. Altitude and diving

clinical considerations
1. Anoxia: absence of oxygen
2. Hypoxia: diminished amount of oxygen delivered to the tissues

3. Asthma: characterized by episodes of wheezing, coughing, sneezing, shortness of breath, and difficulty in breathing

4. Cheyne-Stokes breathing: periodic waxing and waning of rate and amplitude of breathing

5. Emphysema: results from long-term distention of the alveoli which breaks down the alveolar tissue; smoking appears to be a major factor in causing emphysema

6. Lung cancer: the primary cause of cancer to the lungs (and other areas of the respiratory system) is smoking; heavy smokers (two packages per day) increase the incidence of lung cancer by at least fortyfold

7. Pneumonia: any condition that produces an increase of fluid (or pus, blood) in the alveoli; most common cause is from bacteria or viruses

8. Pneumothorax: opening into the interpleural space; pressures outside and inside thorax equalize, and the lung collapses

9. Tuberculosis: produced by a specific bacterium that causes inflammation, which decreases the functional lung capacity

urinary system

16

gross anatomy
kidney
ureters
bladder
urethra
blood supply
nerve supply

cellular and tissue specialization
renal corpuscle
tubular nephron
excretory ducts
bladder

physiology
glomerulus filtration rate
tubular activity
urine

bladder physiology and micturition
regulation of plasma composition

control
neural
hormonal

factors influencing function
tubular resorption
glomerular filtration rate

clinical considerations
renal hypertension
glomerulonephritis
tubular nephritis
renal calculi
diuretics
artificial kidney

During metabolism, many by-products form that are useless or harmful to the body. The kidney is best adapted for the removal of many of these substances, especially those derived from protein metabolism, just as the lungs are best suited for the removal of carbon dioxide. The large quantities of nitrogen, sulfur, and phosphorus that are frequently part of the protein molecules are eliminated as *urea, sulfates,* and *phosphates.* Although the kidney is able to concentrate the waste products, a fairly large amount of water is needed as a vehicle for the elimination of the degradation products. Because water is essential for life, and the balance between the fluid compartments must be maintained at a relatively constant state, the amount of water eliminated as part of the urine is under very fine control. Finally, the kidney has an endocrine function, and the secretions are involved in the regulation of erythropoiesis and blood pressure.

The other organs of the urinary system—the *ureters, bladder,* and *urethra*—are associated with the elimination of urine from the body.

gross anatomy

kidney

Two kidneys of approximately equal size are located on the posterior wall, one on either side of the midline just above the waist. They are bean-shaped (botanists say beans are kidney-shaped), about $10 \times 5 \times 3.0$ cm, weigh about 125 g, and have a deep reddish-brown hue, which is a reflection of the degree of vascularity. Usually, the left kidney is slightly higher than the right, and both lie at the level of vertebra $T3$ (Figure 16-1). The kidneys are *retroperitoneal* (lying behind the peritoneum), and the membrane adheres so closely to the contours of the organ that

figure 16-1

. THE GROSS
ANATOMY OF THE
URINARY SYSTEM
IN SITU

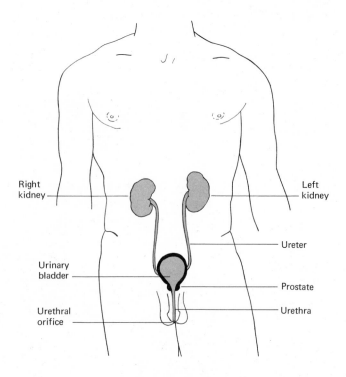

Right kidney

Left kidney

Ureter

Urinary bladder

Prostate

Urethral orifice

Urethra

when the peritoneal cavity is opened, the kidney appears to be lying within the cavity and not behind the membrane. Each kidney is loosely attached (ligaments are absent), and the investment of a large quantity of fat, the *perirenal fat* (*renal* refers to kidney), keeps the kidney from moving around. The kidneys do move slightly with each respiration, because they are in contact with the diaphragm. On the upper pole of each kidney is an adrenal (or suprarenal) gland that is not part of the urinary system. The concave part of the kidney is the *hilus*, and to this area the blood vessels, nerves, and ureter join the kidney.

ureters   The urine that is formed by each kidney is funneled into a single large ureter (Figures 16-1 and 16-2). Each ureter is a channel of about 30 cm (12 inches) that runs from the kidney to the bladder. The ureters also lie retroperitoneally. They enter the bladder from the kidneys along each posterolateral wall.

bladder   The bladder is a hollow muscular storage chamber that lies in the true pelvis, anterior to the rectum, and in the female, anterior to the uterus (Figure 16-3). Most of the bladder is retroperitoneal, and the overlying peritoneum plus three ligaments keep the bladder in place. The size, position, and relationship of the bladder to other organs vary with the amount of urine stored, as well as with the age and sex of the individual.

urethra   The duct from the base of the bladder to the exterior is the *urethra*, which is only 3.5 cm in the female, but in the adult male has a length of 20 cm because it traverses the penis (Figure 16-3). The male urethra is divided into three parts: the *prostatic urethra*, the first segment, extends from the base of the bladder through the prostate gland; the *membranous urethra* is a very small segment (1 cm) extending from the prostate gland to the floor of the pelvis, which it penetrates; the *cavernous*

figure 16-2

SAGITTAL VIEW
OF THE KIDNEY
SHOWING MAJOR
ANATOMICAL
COMPONENTS

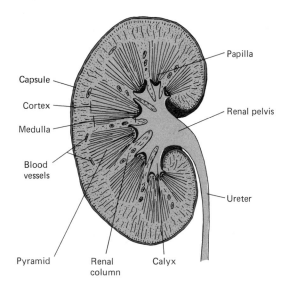

Papilla

Capsule

Cortex

Renal pelvis

Medulla

Blood
vessels

Ureter

Pyramid   Renal   Calyx
               column

figure 16-3

ANTERIOR VIEW
OF THE URINARY
BLADDER AND
RELATED
STRUCTURES

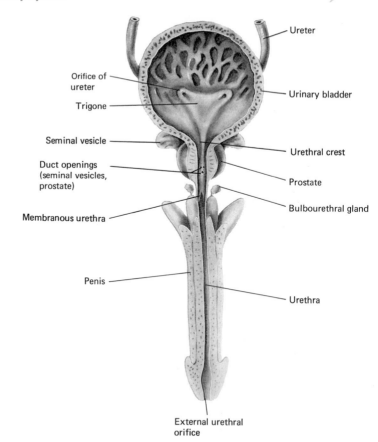

Ureter

Orifice of
ureter

Trigone

Seminal vesicle

Duct openings
(seminal vesicles,
prostate)

Membranous urethra

Penis

Urinary bladder

Urethral crest

Prostate

Bulbourethral gland

Urethra

External urethral
orifice

urethra is the portion that runs through the central part of the penis to the exterior.

blood supply   The paired short renal arteries are branches of the abdominal aorta. When the arteries reach the hilum of the kidney, they subdivide into several branches which penetrate the kidney tissue. The renal arteries are unusually wide and easily handle the large quantity of blood (1800 liters per day) that filters through the two kidneys. The remaining urinary organs are nourished by branches of the internal iliac arteries. The venous system is composed of vessels that usually run parallel to the arteries. The lymphatic vessels follow the vascular pattern; they eventually drain into the thoracic duct.

nerve supply   The kidney has an extensive vasomotor nerve supply with direct branches coming from the splanchnic nerve and branches stemming from a nerve plexus that accompanies the renal artery. Sensory fibers leave the kidney via the splanchnic nerve.

The bladder is likewise supplied with many sensory and motor nerves. The autonomic innervation comes from the upper part of the spinal cord and from the pelvic nerves.

The ureter and urethra also have a nerve supply, but the distribution and function of these nerves are uncertain. Although urine enters the bladder in spurts, it is doubtful if smooth muscle contraction of the ureters is responsible for the flow. In all probability most of the nerve fibers of the urethra and ureters are of a sensory nature (pain).

cellular and
tissue special-
ization

The homeostatic function of the kidney involves the filtering of the blood, the return to the circulation of valuable materials that are filtered out simultaneously with waste products, the concentration of these elements that will be eliminated, and the secretion of special products. As might be expected, these mechanisms require specialized structures and a close relationship between kidney cells and the circulatory system. The functional and structural unit of the kidney is not a renal cell per se (such as a liver cell for the liver), but a composite structure of renal cells and a capillary, collectively called the *nephron*. In Figure 16-4 is a schematic presentation of the nephron and its vascular supply. The nephron is composed of a capillary tuft *(glomerulus)*, a double-membrane capsule (Bowman's) that is connected to a tubular unit. The latter is divided into a *proximal convoluted tubule* (PCT), a *loop of Henle* (that may be absent), and a *distal convoluted tubule* (DCT). There are approximately 1 million nephrons per kidney; since these are not all functioning at the same time, there is a considerable reserve capacity. Nephrons may enlarge to increase capacity; for example, removal of one kidney increases the remaining kidney mass by about 50 percent within two months.

renal corpuscle

The filtering portion of the nephron is called the *renal corpuscle*, and it is composed of the glomerulus and Bowman's capsule. Although much is known about the structure of the renal corpuscle, the filtration process is still imperfectly understood.

The glomerulus is a specially adapted capillary unit that appears along the arteriole circulation. An *afferent vessel* feeds the glomerulus, and an *efferent branch* drains the unit; the latter continues to become a typical capillary bed surrounding the remaining portion of the nephron (Figure 16-5). The afferent branch is larger than the efferent branch, and the inequality of diameters creates a higher blood pressure within the glomerulus than would be achieved if the entrance and exit vessels were of equal size. The endothelium of the glomerulus is discontinuous and has a general appearance of a sieve. The diameter of the pores is about 750 Å or less, and they may account for the rapid removal of water and large molecules from the blood.

Bowman's capsule is a double-membrane structure with the inner membrane adhering to the capillary wall. This inner membrane is also believed to have gaps similar to the capillary walls because of the discontinuity of the epithelial cells. Thus the transit of materials from the blood into the nephrons could be by way of pores of the endothelium and the slits of the capsule epithelium (Figure 16-6). For the most part, channels of this nature are believed to be quite passive and only account for the passage of molecules smaller than the openings; they cannot account for the *selective permeability* that is evident in the physiology of the kidney. Another structure, which is shown by the electron micro-

figure 16-4

DETAILED
DIAGRAM OF THE
NEPHRON
SHOWING THE
VASCULAR
SUPPLY

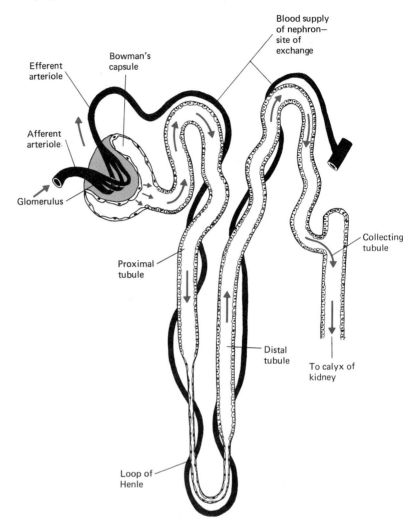

Efferent
arteriole

Bowman's
capsule

Blood supply
of nephron—
site of
exchange

Afferent
arteriole

Glomerulus

Proximal
tubule

Distal
tubule

Collecting
tubule

To calyx of
kidney

Loop of
Henle

Note that the blood from the glomerular capillary network exits via an arteriole rather than by a venule. This efferent arteriole then breaks up to form a capillary bed supplying the rental tubules. The efferent arteriole which loops around the nephron eventually enters a venule.

scope, is a basement membrane, the composition of which is not fully known. The basement membrane may be the barrier that provides the filtering apparatus with its selective permeability.

tubular nephron   Modifications of the cells that constitute the noncorpuscle part of the nephron are evident, but for the most part unusual cellular structures are not apparent. The structural modifications that do exist rarely provide a clue to the different functions of the nephron. However, cellular structural adaptations are present (for example, epithelial cells of the proximal convoluted tubule have a brush border), and it is known that all of the cells do not function in the same manner. One group of cells in

figure 16-5

DETAILED
SCHEMATIC OF
BOWMAN'S
CAPSULE AND
THE
GLOMERULUS

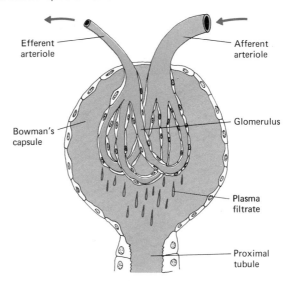

Efferent
arteriole

Afferent
arteriole

Glomerulus

Bowman's
capsule

Plasma
filtrate

Proximal
tubule

the proximal convoluted tubule will react to a vital stain, whereas an adjacent group of cells will not take up the dye. Another example of cell specificity is that glucose is absorbed in the proximal convoluted tubule, but not by the cells of the loop of Henle or in the distal tubule.

excretory ducts   The kidney is divided into a cortex and medulla (Figure 16-2). These two zones are evident even by gross observation in that the outer cortex has a darker appearance than the inner medulla. The renal cortex contains at least 1 million nephrons, and the number may be as high as 3 million. The medulla is composed primarily of ducts that unite as tributaries to form larger and larger passages in a pyramidal fashion, with the apex of the pyramid ending in a small chamber called the *calyx* (Figure 16-2). Each kidney has two or three calyces, which convey the urine into the ureter.

The passageways for urine, including the bladder, are lined with a unique *transitional epithelium*. The transitional cells are piled one on top of another in a rather random fashion, and they are capable of slipping over one another when the epithelium is stretched. The organs are able to accommodate the flow or storage of urine because of the added surface area. Urine is quite acid, and for reasons unknown, the epithelium lining is not affected by its low pH.

bladder   The microanatomy of the bladder wall is composed of three layers: an inner mucous membrane with transitional epithelial lining, a smooth muscle layer, and an outer fibroelastic layer. The smooth muscular coat is the thickest layer and accounts for the rapid elimination of the bladder's contents during urination (Figure 16-3).

physiology   Every minute, about 20 percent of the total cardiac output flows through the kidneys, which is an equivalent of 1800 liters per day. Within the renal tissue, the blood is filtered in the glomerulus, and the filtrate is the

figure 16-6

RELATIONSHIP
BETWEEN
CAPILLARY AND
CAPSULE
EPITHELIUM

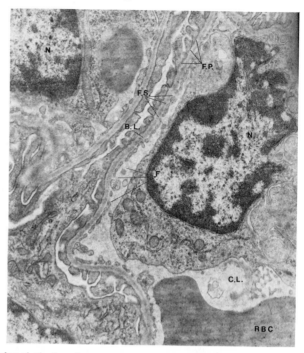

The capsular eipthelium has many processes which give rise to small "foot pads" (F.P.), which are separated from one another by filtration slits (F.S.). The slits extend to the basement lamina and have a thin membrane across their opening. The thin endothelium is also interrupted by pores or fenestrations (F.). Materials that pass from the blood to the urinary space within the capsule must pass through the fenestrations, and somehow cross the barrier created by the basement lamina.

first state in the formation of urine. If we placed a micropipette within the capsule and a sample of the glomerular filtrate was withdrawn, and in a like manner we removed a sample of the filtrate from the distal end of the proximal convoluted tubule just before it joins a collecting duct, we would discover that the filtered material undergoes some remarkable changes as it travels through the tubules of the nephron. Products are partially or totally reabsorbed, concentrated, and even new substances may appear. The nephron, therefore, is not only a filtering apparatus, it is also a vital regulating structure, especially in water and sodium balance (the principal electrolyte of the extracellular fluid). The formation of urine requires several steps, which can be labeled *filtration, tubular reabsorption,* and *tubular secretion* (Module 16). Urine is very similar in composition to plasma minus proteins, and a breakdown of its constituents is given in Table 16-1.

glomerulus
filtration rate

Within Bowman's capsule the blood flows through the glomerular capillaries under relatively high pressure, approximately 70 mm Hg. This pressure is considerably higher than that found in practically all other capillaries of the body due to the larger diameter of the afferent arteriole of the glomerulus compared with that of the efferent arteriole (Figure 16-7).

The three forces acting in the production of glomerular filtrate are (a) glomerular capillary pressure, (b) capsular hydrostatic pressure, and (c)

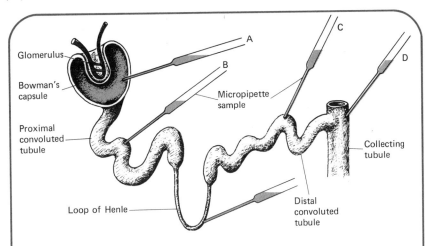

One of the great basic truths of physiology is that structure and function are inseparable. This statement is best demonstrated for the nephron or functional unit of the kidney. Thus in 1842 William Bowman, while describing the microscopic anatomy of the nephron, was able to guess its function when he said "It would indeed be difficult to conceive a disposition of parts more calculated to favour the escaping water from the blood than that of the Malpighian body. A large artery breaks up in a very direct manner into an assemblage of vessels of far greater aggregate capacity than itself and from which there is but one narrow exit." Indeed this unique anatomical relationship did favor the escape of water, for between the large diameter afferent arteriole and the small diameter efferent arteriole is a capillary bed. Such an arrangement produces a very high capillary pressure—twice that of the other capillaries, hence favoring filtration. The fact that the vessels are surrounded by capsular epithelium (aptly named Bowman's capsule) implies a specificity to the filtration process; thus larger entities such as protein and blood cells are not filtered. Later work was to show that the filtrate was almost identical in composition to the blood plasma except for the plasma proteins (A).

It remained for the extraordinarily precise and delicate work of Richards and Walker to show the function of the tubular portions of the nephron. By means of a micromanipulator they were able to insert fine capillary tubes into various portions of the renal tubule, extract the contents, and analyze them chemically. Their findings showed that at the proximal end of nephron the filtrate was identical with the plasma except for protein and that in the proximal tubule 85 percent of the water and other filtered materials were resorbed and restored to the blood (B). Most of the remainder were absorbed in the loop of Henle and the distal tubule (C and D). Subsequent investigation showed that in the proximal tubule and loop of Henle, absorption is a passive phenomenon. In the kidney exchange alterations occur in osmotic pressure due to the movement of ions, and the net result is resorption of more water. The final concentration of urine occurs in the distal tubule (and collecting tubule to a lesser extent) where water is actively transported against a concentration gradient under the influence of the antidiuretic hormone (ADH).

table 16-1

EXAMPLES
OF URINE
CONSTITUENTS

	PERCENTAGE	EXCRETED DAILY
Water	90	500 to 1600 ml
Solids	10	30 to 75 mg
Albumin		Negative
Calcium (average diet)		100 to 250 mg
Estrogens (♀)		4 to 60 μg
(♂)		4 to 25 μg
Glucose (quantitative test)		130 mg
Protein (qualitative test)		Negative
Sodium		125 to 260 meq
Urea nitrogen		6 to 17 g
Uric acid		250 to 750 mg
Blood and epithelial cells		About 4,000,000

the colloidal osmotic pressure of the blood plasma. The glomerular capillary pressure of 75 mm Hg is acting to move water, salts, and small molecules out of the glomerulus via the capillary pores into the capsule. Opposing this force are the capsular hydrostatic pressure of 20 mm Hg and the colloidal osmotic pressure of 30 mm Hg. The former is due to the fluid present in the capsule and the latter to the osmotic pressure produced by the presence of the plasma protein which does not normally pass through the glomerular pores. The result of these opposing forces is a net outward filtration pressure of 25 mm Hg.

$$75 \text{ mm Hg} - (20 \text{ mm Hg} + 30 \text{ mm Hg}) = 25 \text{ mm Hg}$$

glomerular	capsular	colloidal	glomerular
hydrostatic	hydrostatic	osmotic	filtration
pressure	pressure	pressure	pressure

Any abnormal condition such as hemorrhage or kidney disease which upsets the system and allows proteins to be filtered from the blood into the capsule would change the net outward pressure. Similarly, a fall or rise in the blood pressure would affect kidney function. Since the sympathetic system controls the size of the afferent and efferent arterioles, it is possible that under stress where sympathetic stimulation is high, complete shutdown of the kidney function can take place.

The two kidneys form a total filtrate of about 180 liters per day, of which the primary component is water and the more important solutes are glucose, sodium, and urea. If the entire filtrate of 180 liters were eliminated as urine, man would have very little time to perform other human functions. Obviously most of the filtrate is reabsorbed, since the average healthy individual, living in a nonextreme environment, will void less than 2 liters of urine per day.

tubular activity   The cells that compose the tubules are capable of actively transporting materials into the interstitial fluid, where the materials can then enter

Tubular   the capillaries that are closely associated with the tubules. It is basi-
Reabsorption   cally this process that is responsible for the reabsorption of almost all

figure 16-7

FACTORS IN-
VOLVED IN
GLOMERULAR
FILTRATION

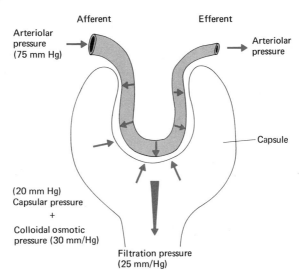

of the glucose, sodium, and water from the glomerular filtrate. An examination of the urine indicates that under normal conditions no glucose is present in the urine. Yet the concentration of glucose in the filtrate is equal to that of the blood. Thus all the glucose is normally recovered by tubular reabsorption, with active transport the main driving force in this process. It is well to realize that the active transport process can be overloaded, as when extremely large amounts of glucose appear in the blood, in which case glucose does appear in the urine. The threshold for glucose is about 150 mg percent.

Sodium is actively transported out of the filtrate across the tubular cells, so that it can then enter the peritubular capillaries. The act of actively transporting the positively charged sodium ion results in the passive movement of the negatively charged chloride ion, since the tendency is for electrical neutrality across the membrane to be maintained. The movement of these ions across the tubular cell membrane produces a concentration difference, which is expressed as an osmotic gradient. Because the concentration of salt is higher in the tubular cells, water moves from the lumen into the cells. Thus the active transport of sodium leads to the reabsorption of chloride ions and water.

Tubular
Secretion

Tubular secretion refers to the movement of materials out of the blood of the peritubular capillaries across the tubular cells and into the lumen of the tubule. Among the important substances that are secreted are potassium, calcium, and hydrogen ions.

Proximal
Convoluted
Tubule

Within the area of the proximal convoluted tubule, the bulk of the fluids and dissolved solutes are removed. By removal we mean that the materials pass from the nephron lumen into the cuboidal cells that make up the proximal tubule, and then into the adjacent capillaries that wrap around the various tubules. At least 75 to 80 percent of the filtered solute and water will be removed in the proximal tubule.

Loop of Henle
About 5 percent of the fluid passes out of the loop of Henle into the blood. The plasma membrane of the loop cells is actively involved in sodium transport, pumping it out of the fluid.

Distal Convoluted Tubule
The action of the distal convoluted tubule in removing fluids depends on whether the regulating hormones (see section on control) are present. These hormones change the permeability of the cells of the distal tubule to water. At the distal tubule, only about 15 percent of the filtrate remains, which means that the regulating hormone works solely on this volume of filtrate. Once the material leaves the distal tubule, it enters into a collecting duct in which additional water reabsorption may take place (even the collecting ducts are affected by the hormone).

urine
Urine and blood are analyzed clinically more frequently than any other body tissue or fluid. As was the case with blood, the composition of urine is frequently an indicator of the homeostatic state of the body at any given period of time and urine analysis is a rapid and inexpensive diagnostic tool.

The constituents that are found in urine can be divided into two major classes: *threshold* and *nonthreshold*. Threshold substances are generally valuable to the body; glucose is an example. In the plasma, the glucose level is 60 to 100 mg/100 ml, but in the normal urine the glucose concentration is zero. Frequently concentration of solutes in urine is given as a urine-to-plasma (U/P) ratio, and for glucose it would be 0/100 = 0. An example of a nonthreshold compound is *urea*, the chief nitrogenous end product of protein metabolism that is formed by the liver. In the plasma, the urea concentration is about 15 mg/100 ml, and in the urine, it is concentrated at 900 mg/100 ml; therefore the urea urine-to-plasma ratio = 900 ÷ 15 = 60. Two other important nitrogenous waste products are *uric acid* and *creatinine*, derived from the breakdown of nucleoproteins and muscle phosphocreatine, respectively.

A variety of other water-soluble compounds can be forced out of glomerulus to become part of the filtrate and even part of urine: vitamins, hormones, pigments, enzymes, and whole cells. The latter, for example, pus cells, appear in pathological situations.

Mention was made earlier that tubular cells are capable of secretion; that is, they can either extract substances directly from the peritubular capillaries, as distinguished from the glomerular capillaries, or the tubular cells will manufacture materials. Penicillin is one example of a substance that is actively removed from the plasma by the cells of the proximal convoluted tubule and "secreted" into the urine.

bladder physiology and micturition
The bladder receives urine as intermittent spurts from the ureters and stores and concentrates it. As the bladder fills and becomes distended, special receptor cells within the wall will be stimulated, which in turn will initiate a reflex contraction of the smooth muscles within the wall. As the muscles contract, the pressure within the bladder is increased to a point to overcome the sphincter closure at the bladder-urethra junction, and the voluntary elimination of urine occurs (*micturition*). Two sphincters control the flow from the bladder, but only the external one is

under voluntary control. The external sphincter can withstand rather forcible pressures; for example, the bladder will normally fill to about 350 ml before emptying, but the external sphincter can remain closed even when 800 ml of urine have accumulated.

regulation
of plasma
composition

The homeostatic regulation of the body fluids, particularly for the fluid portion of the blood, the plasma, is remarkably precise even under stress conditions. The regulation of body fluids involves a combination of both water balance and electrolyte balance. Body water, which constitutes about 60 percent of the total body weight (about 50 liters in an average adult), is divided into two compartments, intracellular fluid and extracellular fluid. Water homeostasis involves the acquisition of water and the controlled loss of water as shown diagrammatically in Figure 16-8. Under normal circumstances the kidney is the major organ involved in both water and electrolyte balance.

The protein components of the plasma, 7 g/100 ml, play a part in determining osmotic pressure (about 28 mm Hg). These large molecules do not readily pass through capillary membranes, nor are they normally

figure 16-8

WATER
DIURESIS,
HORMONAL
MECHANISM

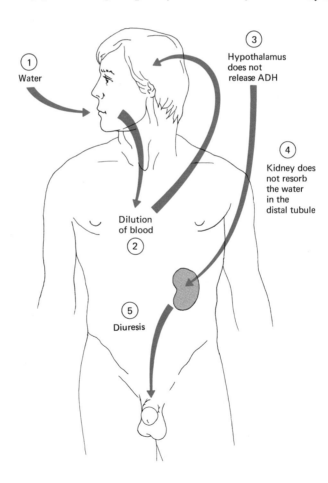

① Water

③ Hypothalamus does not release ADH

④ Kidney does not resorb the water in the distal tubule

② Dilution of blood

⑤ Diuresis

filtered in the healthy glomerulus. However, the other plasma contents, the electrolytes (mainly sodium, chloride, potassium, sulfate, phosphate, magnesium, and calcium), are both filtered and reabsorbed. Both passive and active mechanisms exist, regulating electrolyte concentration in the kidney. Active regulation is under hormonal control by the *antidiuretic hormone* (ADH) of the posterior pituitary and the *mineralocorticoids* of the adrenal cortex (particularly aldosterone). Both of these mechanisms are discussed in detail in Chapter 18. Under normal circumstances, the kidney is the major organ regulating electrolyte concentration, but in heat stress (severe sweating) and in gastrointestinal malfunctions, for example, diarrhea and vomiting, electrolyte concentration can be seriously altered.

Plasma glucose, the principal energy source, although not as carefully regulated as either plasma proteins or electrolytes, is kept within a comparatively narrow range even when ingestion or utilization varies. The normal plasma glucose level, 60 to 100 mg percent, is hormonally controlled by the pancreas (see Chapter 18) and controlled further in the tubular portion of the nephron. Under normal circumstances all glucose filtered in the glomerulus is reabsorbed, and no glucose is found in the urine; however, the work capacity per unit time of the renal tubules is limited, and for each substance there is a *tubular maximum* (TM) or maximum work load. If the tubular maximum of glucose is exceeded, as in diabetes mellitus, sugar will end up in the urine (*glucosuria*).

The level of nonprotein nitrogen (NPN) compounds in the plasma, such as uric acid, amino acids, creatinine, and urea, represents a good indicator of protein balance (for example, ingestion, breakdown, and excretion). In renal malfunction, excretion is impaired and nonprotein nitrogen rises.

The hydrogen ion concentration (pH) of the plasma varies, the arterial plasma being slightly more alkaline than the carbon-dioxide-rich venous plasma, but overall, the pH is fixed within narrow limits (about 7.4). A number of control systems help maintain this constancy, such as the liver, lungs, kidneys, and blood buffer system.

The blood buffer system responds quickly to changes in hydrogen ion concentration, utilizing the buffering capacities of bicarbonate, phosphate, and protein to keep the pH of the blood within normal limits of pH 7.4. The lungs contribute to the regulation of hydrogen ion concentration by eliminating carbon dioxide; when carbon dioxide levels increase, ventilation rates are elevated, and carbon dioxide is exhaled.

The kidney regulates hydrogen ion concentration in several ways. Hydrogen ions are secreted from the tubular cells into the tubular fluid, a process that depends on the conversion of carbon dioxide to carbonic acid in the tubular epithelial cells.

$$CO_2 + H_2O \xrightarrow{\text{carbonic anhydrase}} H_2CO_3 \rightarrow H^+ + HCO_3^-$$

CO_2	H_2O		H_2CO_3	H^+	HCO_3^-
carbon dioxide	water		carbonic acid	hydrogen ion	bicarbonate ion

The carbonic acid is ionized to bicarbonate and hydrogen ions, and the latter is secreted by the cells into the tubular fluid in exchange for sodium ions. The sodium ions in conjunction with bicarbonate ions move from the cell into the plasma.

$$Na^+ + HCO_3^- \longrightarrow Na^+ + HCO_3^-$$
$$\text{from tubular cells} \qquad \text{to plasma}$$

An increase in carbon dioxide level in the plasma leads to an increase in carbon dioxide levels in the tubular cells, thereby stimulating an increase in hydrogen ion secretion from the cells.

The glomerular filtrate contains bicarbonate ions and sodium ions, and the sodium ions are absorbed by the tubular cells in exchange for the hydrogen ions that are secreted. Hydrogen ions combine with the bicarbonate ion in the filtrate to form carbonic acid, which is broken down to water and carbon dioxide.

$$H^+ + HCO_3^- \longrightarrow H_2CO_3 \longrightarrow H_2O + CO_2$$

Carbon dioxide enters the tubular cells, and the water becomes part of the urine. The bicarbonate lost from the cell to the plasma is replaced by the formation of a bicarbonate from the carbon dioxide that enters the cell. Thus a balance in bicarbonate level is maintained in the tubular epithelial cell.

An upward shift in the pH of the blood (alkalosis) is accompanied by an increase in the bicarbonate ions, which are then secreted in the urine. This shift occurs because there are insufficient hydrogen ions in the tubular fluid for the bicarbonate ions to combine with to form carbon dioxide and water. The loss of bicarbonate ions shifts the pH of the blood toward its normal level.

In the case of low blood pH (acidosis), the problem is to eliminate excess hydrogen ions. When hydrogen ion secretion into the tubules is greater than bicarbonate ion filtration, the excess hydrogen ions are handled by the phosphate buffer system in the tubular fluid.

$$NA_2\,HPO_4 \longrightarrow 2Na^+ + HPO_4^-$$
$$\text{sodium} \qquad \text{sodium} \quad \text{phosphate}$$
$$\text{phosphate} \qquad \text{ions} \qquad \text{ion}$$

$$H^+ + HPO_4^{2-} \longrightarrow H_2PO_4^-$$

One of the sodium ions is exchanged for the secreted hydrogen ion, and the sodium ion moves with a bicarbonate from the tubular cell to the plasma. The gain of bicarbonate in the plasma raises the blood pH toward normal.

Another mechanism for handling excess hydrogen ions is by combination with ammonia to form ammonium. The ammonia is a product of amino acid breakdown and is secreted by the tubular cells. The ammonium ion that results is eliminated in the urine along with a chloride ion.

$$NH_3 + H^+ + Na^+ + Cl^- \longrightarrow NH_4^+ + Cl^- + Na^+$$

ammonia   ammonium

As in the previous example, sodium moves into the tubular cell and migrates to the plasma with a bicarbonate ion, thereby raising the plasma bicarbonate level.

Under normal circumstances the urinary pH is about 6.0, but following heavy exercise or metabolic disorders, it may fall to as low as pH 4.5 or rise to pH 8.0.

control

neural

A completely denervated (all nerves cut) kidney continues to form urine, which indicates that the basic physiological phenomena are under hormonal and other chemical control. The kidney does receive both sympathetic and parasympathetic stimuli, but these nerves probably function to regulate the smooth muscle in the walls of the larger blood vessels that nourish the kidney and are not in operation at the nephron level.

hormonal

The principal control of the urinary system is via a hormone called *vasopressin* or *antidiuretic hormone* (ADH), secreted by the posterior lobe of the pituitary. The hormone ADH is a small peptide that acts principally on the epithelial cells forming the distal convoluting tubule. By increasing the permeability of these cell membranes to water, ADH regulates the final fraction of water that is not automatically reabsorbed by the proximal convoluted tubule and the loop of Henle. How ADH alters permeability is unknown.

Drugs that either dilate or constrict the glomerular arterioles act to alter the glomerular rate and affect filtration. One commonly used substance, caffeine, not only dilates the afferent arteriole (increasing the filtration rate), but also inhibits tubular resorption of sodium. This may account for the frequent micturitions of coffee drinkers.

Other factors that affect hemoconcentration by causing water loss, profuse sweating, or diarrhea will decrease the glomerular filtration rate and urine volume.

factors influencing function

tubular resorption

As was seen earlier, the ultimate control of water loss is via the posterior pituitary hormone ADH. This means that any factors that alter ADH release will ultimately affect urine volume. Emotional stress is one common cause of increased urine production, since the hypothalamic centers that produce ADH are either directly or indirectly under the influence of higher neural centers in the brain. Under stress the synthesis and release of ADH are inhibited and diuresis results (increased urine formation).

The most usual cause of alterations in urine volume is the amount of water ingested orally. If a person drinks 1 liter of pure water, the blood is diluted; osmoreceptors in the hypothalamus are activated; and ADH release is inhibited. Within an hour, water diuresis reaches its peak (Figure 16-8). Conversely, water deprivation or dehydration stimulates ADH secretion, enhances tubular resorption, and decreases urine volume.

Various drugs—morphine, nicotine, barbiturates, and anesthetic agents—also inhibit the hypothalamic posterior pituitary system and increase the output of ADH, thereby decreasing urine volume.

Urine volume may also be affected by changing the concentration of solutes delivered to the tubules. Any osmotically active substance, for example, glucose, sucrose, and acid-forming salts such as ammonium chloride, acts as an osmotic diuretic. Any time the filtered load of solute exceeds the tubular maximum, the excess solute will carry water with it osmotically. This is often seen in diabetics who exhibit both glycosuria and polyuria (sugar in urine and excess of urine).

Apparently, ADH has no effect on sodium transport, and the reabsorption of this ion appears to be under the control of another hormone called *aldosterone*, which is secreted by the adrenal cortex. If the adrenal is diseased or removed and aldosterone is absent, sodium excretion in the urine is increased, which in turn means a decrease in plasma sodium. Low sodium levels in the blood will affect not only the shift of fluids toward the tissue, thus producing edema, but will indirectly affect the heart muscle.

Autoregulation

The amount of water and sodium lost by way of the urine is proportional to the glomerular filtration rate (GFR). The kidney appears to have an autoregulatory mechanism to insure that the blood pressure and blood volume remain high enough to affect a normal glomerular filtration rate. The precise location of the synthesizing cells and the exact nature of the stimulus are still unknown, but there is some indication that if blood volume decreases in the region near the afferent arteriole of the glomerulus, certain cells produce a substance called *renin*. A schematic representation of the relationship of renin to another chemical angiotensin is given in Figure 12-17. Apparently, angiotensin acts directly on the vascular smooth muscle, and even very small doses in the circulation will produce a rise in blood pressure (angiotensin is probably the most powerful vasoconstrictor agent known). By affecting the glomeration filtration rate, renin also affects the degree of water and sodium excretion or retention. Angiotensin also causes release of aldosterone.

glomerular filtration rate

Any change in the glomerular filtration rate will produce a parallel change in urine volume. Thus a multitude of factors that produce changes in arterial pressure will affect the glomerular filtration rate and urine volume. For example, in hemorrhage, the lowering of blood pressure affects the glomerulus, causing *oliguria* (little urine) or *anuria* (no urine production). Conversely, any elevation of blood pressure due to emotions, exercise, or such, will often increase urine formation. Changes in plasma protein concentration also affect the glomerular filtration rate and urine volume; hence a patient receiving a rapid infusion of saline solution will experience a dilution of his plasma protein concentration, and the effective filtration pressure will be increased (since osmotic pressure opposes glomerular hydrostatic pressure).

clinical considerations

renal hypertension

Any event causing *renal anoxia* (decreased renal blood flow) causes the systemic arterial blood pressure to become elevated. The renal hypertension is apparently initiated by the so-called *renal pressor system* (Figure 12-17). Pressor agents increase blood pressure by producing vasoconstriction of the arteriolar wall. Prolonged elevation of arterial blood pressure eventually involves not only the cardiovascular system but also the liver and kidneys.

glomerulo-
nephritis

A variety of infectious agents and poisons may cause swelling of the membranes of the glomerular capillaries. These structural changes in the glomerulus produce a disease state known as *glomerulonephritis*. In the initial or *acute* phase, the inflammatory reaction develops in the glomeruli, filtration is altered, and protein molecules and red blood cells escape. Red blood cells appear in the urine *(hematuria)*, as does protein *(proteinuria)*. However, the major pathological effects of glomerulonephritis are hypertension, edema, and the accumulation of electrolytes and nitrogenous compounds in the blood. If the inflammation persists and the disease becomes *chronic* (long term), the glomeruli become scarred, and complete renal failure may result.

tubular nephritis

Blockage or inflammation of the renal tubules may result from crush injuries, infection, or hemorrhage. The subsequent renal failure causes a spectrum of symptoms: low back pain, edema, hematuria, albuminuria, and, finally, a marked diminution of excretory function or *uremia*. As in glomerulonephritis, blood pressure is elevated.

renal calculi

Kidney stones or *renal calculi* may form in the collecting tubules, hilus, or ureters, causing obstruction of the urinary tract. There are many diverse types and causes for kidney stones, for example, *pyelonephritis* or infection of the hilus, which alters pH and may cause precipitation of massive magnesium ammonium phosphate stones. Calcium stones are common in patients with hyperparathyroidism. Another common cause of kidney stones is *hyperuricemia* or *gout*, a metabolic disease that causes elevated uric acid excretion. In the gouty patient, dehydration or acidification of the blood may precipitate many sharp urate crystals in the renal tubule causing excruciating low back pain, urinary frequency, and spasm of visceral structures.

diuretics

A number of medicinal agents increase urine production *(polyuria)* by either enhancing the glomerular filtration rate or by decreasing tubular resorption of water. The oldest diuretics in clinical use are mercurial compounds, which act osmotically in the tubule and also impede the resorption of sodium. *Alcohol* and *xanthines* both augment glomerular filtration at the renal level and depress ADH secretion centrally. Other diuretic agents such as sucrose are not readily resorbed in the renal tubule and act osmotically to decrease tubular resorption of water.

artificial kidney

If the kidneys fail (due to mechanical injury, poisoning, or infection), the blood nonprotein nitrogen soars, and toxic materials that would normally be excreted accumulate. In order to eliminate these toxic elements, an artificial kidney has been developed. This device consists of two plastic sheets surrounded by a considerable volume of dialyzing fluid (Figure 16-9). Arterial blood from the patient flows between the plastic sheets, which have pore sizes such that small molecules, as urea for example, move through by diffusion (from area of high concentration in the blood

figure 16-9
SIMPLIFIED
SCHEMATIC OF
AN ARTIFICIAL
KIDNEY

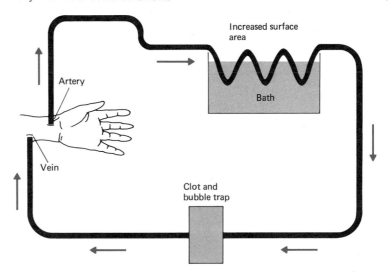

to area of low concentration, the dialyzing fluid). Protein molecules that are too large to pass through the plastic membrane pores are retained, and the dialyzed blood, now free of toxic products, is brought back into the patient by means of a venous catheter. The composition of the dialyzing fluid can be adjusted, but usually the electrolyte concentration in the fluid is the same as that of the plasma. To maintain the concentration gradient favoring removal of toxic products, it is necessary to replenish the dialyzing fluid frequently. The artificial kidney is of considerable benefit. Prolonged use has its limitations, such as the fact that anticoagulants are necessary to stop the blood from forming clots as it passes over the plastic membrane and prolonged use of anticoagulants is extremely dangerous.

summary

gross anatomy

1. Kidney: retroperitoneal, highly vascularized; blood vessels, nerves, and ureter join kidney at hilum
2. Ureters: tubes for carrying urine from kidney to bladder
3. Bladder: extensible muscular storage chamber
4. Urethra: duct from bladder to exterior; divided into prostatic urethra, membranous urethra, and cavernous urethra
5. Blood and nerve supply
    (a) renal and iliac arteries
    (b) extensive vasomotor supply from splanchnic nerve

cellular and tissue specialization

1. Functional unit is the nephron
2. Renal corpuscle: filtering portion of nephron includes the glomerulus and Bowman's capsule; high blood pressure due to differences in diameter of afferent and efferent vessels to glomerulus; glomerular-endothelium unit is sievelike
2. Tubular nephron
    (a) proximal convoluted tubule, loop of Henle, and distal convoluted tubule

   (b) epithelial cells with brush border, many mitochondria, specific transport mechanisms
   (c) renal cortex contains 1 to 3 million nephrons
3. Excretory ducts: renal medulla composed of ducts lined with transitional epithelium that are capable of sliding past one another for expansion
4. Bladder: cellular specialization like excretory ducts

physiology
1. Glomerular filtration rate: 1800 liters of blood filtered through kidney per day, forming 180 liters of filtrate; filtrate changed in tubules by tubular reabsorption and tubular secretion
2. Tubular activity
   (a) active transport responsible for reabsorption of almost all glucose, sodium ions, and water
   (b) transport of sodium ions results in passive movement of chloride ions and water
   (c) bulk of materials removed in proximal convuluted tubule
   (d) hormones act on distal convuluted tubules to regulate water absorption
   (e) tubular secretion moves potassium, calcium, and hydrogen ions out of the blood into urine
3. Urine
   (a) threshold compounds such as glucose
   (b) nonthreshold compounds such as urea
4. Receptors in distended bladder signal full bladder
5. Regulation of plasma composition
   (a) kidney important in water and electrolyte balance
   (b) electrolytes filtered, but reabsorption regulated by ADH and mineralocorticoids
   (c) nonprotein nitrogen good indicator of protein balance
   (d) bicarbonate and phosphate buffer systems aid in regulating blood pH; ammonia also aids in ridding of excess hydrogen ion; pH of urine generally near 6.0

control
1. Principally hormonal. ADH increases water uptake in distal convoluted tubule. ADH release activated by osmoreceptors in hypothalamus; low water concentration, ADH release activated
2. Aldosterone from adrenal cortex regulates sodium reabsorption
3. Low blood volume may cause release of renin, which produces angiotensin; angiotensin causes vasoconstriction and release of aldosterone

clinical considerations
1. Renal hypertension: renal pressor system responds to renal apoxia by elevating systemic pressure
2. Glomerulonephritis: structural changes in glomerulus leading to pathological changes in filtration
3. Tubular nephritis: blockage or inflammation of renal tubules
4. Renal calculi: kidney stones
5. Diuretics: compounds that increase urine production
6. Artificial kidney: mechanical dialysis of blood

integumentary system and thermal regulation

gross anatomy

microanatomy and cellular specialization
epidermis
dermis
nerve supply
hair
nails
cutaneous glands
blood and lymphatic supply

physiology

thermoregulation
heat exchange between
    man and his environment
heat production
the skin as an organ of
    temperature control
central control of
    temperature

clinical considerations
microbial infections
fever
hypothermia
heat cramps and heat
    exhaustion

17

The single largest and most diffuse body organ is the integumentary system composed of the skin and its derivatives (hair, nails, and a variety of glands). Because skin covers the outer surface of the body, it serves a multitude of passive and active functions. Its major passive function is to protect the internal structures from a variety of environmental stresses, for example, as a barrier to harmful bacteria. The active functions of the skin include sensing environmental change, regulating temperature, secretion, and excretion. The skin possesses a remarkable regenerative capacity and in response to damage is capable of proliferating rapidly. The total adult skin weighs about 9 to 10 pounds, and in a lifetime the body will form about 40 pounds of skin.

gross anatomy

Although the skin has basically the same anatomical structure over the entire body surface, there are highly specialized regional differences in texture, thickness, secretion, pigmentation, hair distribution, and sensitivity to touch, temperature, and pain. The skin, composed of an outer *epidermis* and an inner *dermis*, can be gossamer thin (over the eyelids, 0.5 mm) or very thick (on the callouses of the palmar surface or soles of the feet, +5 mm). In most parts of the body, it is loosely attached to a tough connective layer, the *hypodermis*, and is movable and elastic. However, in those regions most exposed to friction, such as the soles of the feet and the palms, it is very firmly attached to the underlying connective tissue. The multilayered epidermis has several layers of dead cells (forming the surface) that are periodically rubbed away or sloughed (Figure 17-1). The surface of the epidermis is ridged and grooved according to the genetic makeup of an individual. On the palms, fingers, soles, and toes, the patterns of ridges (whorls and loops) are so highly individual that they can be used for identification (Figure 17-2). Recent studies report that certain chromosomal abnormalities (Down's syndrome) produce a very typical fingerprint pattern, and it may be that certain abnormal states will be identified by the epidermal patterning. The ridges, which are so pronounced only on the hands and feet, may provide man with a rough large surface for friction, like the treads of a tire that grip the road better.

microanatomy and cellular specialization

epidermis

The stratified epithelial cells can be organized from two to five layers (see Figure 17-1). The surface is composed of several layers of flat, scalelike dead cells with cytoplasm that has been replaced by a tough insoluble protein, *keratin*. This layer is constantly being replaced from below by the rapidly dividing cells of *stratum germinativum* (basement layer) that show all the ultrastructure of actively proliferating cells, that is, ribosomes, glycogen granules, chromatin, and so on.

Since the epidermis is relatively translucent and in some regions very thin, the underlying colored objects show through; for example, veins of light-skinned people appear as blue where the skin is thin. In light-skinned Caucasians, skin color is generally pinkish, because red blood cells containing the pigment *heme* circulate through the capillaries lying close to the surface. When these vessels dilate, bringing more blood close to the surface (as in blushing), the skin color becomes quite reddish.

All peoples have varying numbers of pigment cells in the basement

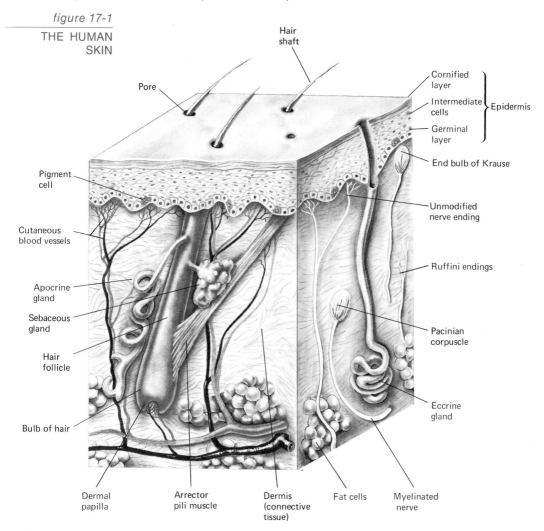

figure 17-1

THE HUMAN
SKIN

Hair
shaft

Pore

Cornified
layer

Intermediate
cells

Germinal
layer

} Epidermis

End bulb of Krause

Pigment
cell

Unmodified
nerve ending

Cutaneous
blood vessels

Ruffini endings

Apocrine
gland

Sebaceous
gland

Pacinian
corpuscle

Hair
follicle

Bulb of hair

Eccrine
gland

Dermal
papilla

Arrector
pili muscle

Dermis
(connective
tissue)

Fat cells

Myelinated
nerve

**The major structures described in the text are shown in this three-dimensional
section of human skin. (Note the variety of glands and sensory nerve endings
present.) The distribution of hair, the thickness of the outermost layer of dead
stratified cells, the numbers of oil and sweat glands, and the concentration of
sensory nerve endings vary with the part of the body being studied, the age and sex
of the individual, with the racial background, and may even be affected by environmental exposure.**

layer. These cells are called *melanocytes* and contain a brownish pigment, *melanin*. The dark skin color associated with certain races is due
to a wider distribution and greater concentration of melanocytes in the
epidermal layers. Tanning, which follows exposure to ultraviolet radiation, is due to the migration of melanocytes closer to the skin's surface,

figure 17-2

HUMAN
FINGERPRINT
ON A GUN

The characteristic patterning of the surface of the skin of the feet and hands is so highly individual that it may be used for identification. Even identical twins exhibit different fingerprint patterns. (Courtesy of Polaroid Corporation.)

as well as expansion of the melanocytes and darkening of the melanin. All people, dark or light, tan when exposed to ultraviolet light. This tanning process, as well as thickening of the epidermis following exposure to the sun's rays, is important in that the pigment absorbs the potentially harmful ultraviolet rays before they reach the sensitive underlying tissues. Another type of pigment cell contains carotene, a yellowish pigment that imparts a yellowish tinge to the skin. Localized colored regions (such as nipples and genital areas) are the result of concentration of pigment cells, *chromatophores,* in the underlying dermis of these areas.

dermis The deeper-lying dermis is penetrated by the epidermal germinative layer, but its constituents are primarily connective tissue fibers. Blood vessels, lymphatic vessels, nerve endings, sensory receptors, glands, hair follicles, and smooth muscles (the *arrector pili* muscles) are also found within the dermis. Figure 17-1 shows a composite of epidermal and dermal structures.

nerve supply A variety of specialized and unspecialized nerve endings are present in the dermis, some close to the surface and others lying deeper in the dermis. The endings are not uniformly distributed. Some regions are

figure 17-3

HAIR FOLLICLE
IN DETAIL

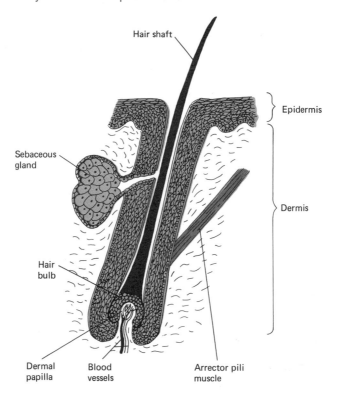

Hair shaft

Epidermis

Sebaceous
gland

Dermis

Hair
bulb

Dermal   Blood   Arrector pili
papilla   vessels   muscle

richly endowed with numerous sensory receptors and are sensitive to a
variety of stimuli, whereas other regions are almost devoid of sensory
endings and are nearly insensitive. Among the sensory modalities are
(a) touch (*Meissner's* plexus), (b) temperature (end bulbs of *Ruffini* and
Krause), (c) pressure (*Pacinian* corpuscles), and (d) pain (naked nerve
endings) (Figure 17-1). There are also motor fibers carrying impulses to
the erector pili muscles and muscles of the blood vessels. The latter are
primarily innervated by sympathetic nerve endings which regulate the
degree of constriction or dilation of the vessels by changing frequency
of impulses.

hair   Although an apparently "naked ape," man still retains hair distributed
over much of his body. In many areas, it is very fine and almost colorless; in some regions of the body, hair grows profusely at a rate of up to
6 inches or more per year.
    The hair follicle develops as a tubular invagination of the epidermis
and grows into the dermis forming a *germinal bulb.* From within the
bulb or *papilla*, the follicle (Figure 17-3) grows outward forming the
shaft that projects out of the skin. Attached to the hair follicles are the
arrector pili muscles, rudiments of the muscles used to raise the fur.
When these muscles contract in man, as during exposure to the cold or
when frightened, they produce *goose bumps*, and when contracted, they
produce the characteristic wrinkled appearance of the scrotum and

erection of the nipples. Although the hairy coat is much diminished in man, the contraction of these muscles still plays a small role in temperature regulation by contributing to the overall heat produced by muscle contraction. Small sebaceous glands are present adjacent to each follicle, and the secretion lubricates the hair unit. Modified sebaceous glands also may open directly to the exterior, producing the wax gland of the external ear and lubricating genital regions in females and males.

nails

Nails, which stiffen the fingers' ends, are modifications of the middle region of the epidermis. The cells of this area form a nail bed, and as mitosis occurs, a nail grows upward and forward. The exposed nail portion is composed of horny keratin similar to claw and hoof material. Nail growth is slower than hair growth, being only about twice the length of the exposed nail per year. For inexplicable reasons, nail growth is unequal; the nails on the little fingers are slowest to grow.

cutaneous glands

Sweat Glands

The sweat glands are shaped like corkscrews extending from the underlying dermis up to the surface through the epidermis (see Figure 17-1). Their secretion is almost colorless and contains small quantities of salts, primarily sodium chloride. However, urea and some enzymes may be excreted in sweat. Most sweat is odorless and sterile until it has been acted on by skin bacteria. In those regions richly endowed with sweat glands (the axilla, genital and anal regions, and toes), there are also great numbers of skin bacteria. Under extreme heat conditions, sweat glands are capable of excreting up to 4000 ml per hour for evaporative cooling. If thermal sweating occurs for a long period, the resulting water and salt loss can cause heat cramps, heat stroke, and even death.

Sebaceous Glands

The sebaceous glands are similar in structure to sweat glands (see Figure 17-1), but secrete an oily, salty secretion that keeps the skin lubricated. Each hair follicle has one or more sebaceous glands with a waxy or oily secretion, the *sebum*, that continually coats the hair and skin. The sebum provides waterproofing and additional protection and also makes the manipulative surfaces (fingertips) stickier. In some areas, such as under the foreskin of the penis, or around the clitoris, the combination of skin secretions and decaying skin cells produces a "cheesy" material, the *smegma.*

Specialized Glands

Other types of cutaneous glands are found in different regions of the body. The eyes have ciliary glands, and the mammary and wax glands are modifications of the previously mentioned sweat and sebaceous glands, respectively.

blood and lymphatic supply

Blood supply to the skin stems from rather large arteries located in the dermis that send out branches to the base of the epidermis. (The epidermis, composed solely of epithelial cells, does not contain blood vessels.) The vessels branch and form a network or *plexus* supplying the layers of skin, hair, nails, and glands. In some areas, direct connections between arterioles and venules are found in the skin. These anatomical modifications provide a mechanism for bypassing a capillary bed, a system involved in temperature regulation. Because of the vast number of cutaneous blood and lymph vessels, the skin is a desirable area for injections of materials.

physiology   The major functions of the skin are protection, secretion, excretion, and temperature regulation. The skin is a unique organ in that, for the most part, it is subservient to the needs of other tissues and organs. For example, the major heat loss of the body is at the interface of the skin and air, and the amount of blood circulation in the skin will determine the amount of heat dissipated to the environment. The degree of cutaneous circulation therefore depends not on the skin, but on what other organs are doing, especially the skeletal muscles which produce most of the heat.

thermo-   Man as a mammal is equipped with a remarkably precise mechanism
regulation   for regulating temperature. In a normal healthy individual, the temperature does not vary by more than $\frac{1}{2}$°F over a 24-hour span, although considerable individual variation exists. However, temperature may change several degrees in illness or after heavy physical exercise. The normal body temperature is set high, 98°F (plus or minus 1.5°F). Such a high temperature is metabolically expensive to maintain, and a great deal of man's total energy expenditure is applied to thermoregulation. This temperature setting is probably due to man's need to keep cool in environments in which the temperatures exceed 100°F for any period of time. If man's body temperature were set at only 80°F, there would be a great conservation of energy, but when the surrounding air temperature reached 100°F, it would be impossible for him to evaporate enough water to cool the body. In other words, man's temperature is high becase "it is easier to remain hot than to keep cool."

heat exchange   The maintenance of body temperature depends not only on metabolic
between man   heat production but also on a number of energy-exchange transactions
and his   between man and his environment. Heat is gained or lost passively
environment   through *radiation* (hot to cool), *conduction*, and *convection* (exchange of heat between skin and air). If the environment is hotter than the body temperature, heating results; if the environment is lower than the body temperature, the energy flow is from man to environment, or cooling.

Finally, there is *evaporational cooling.* In order to convert liquid water to gaseous water vapor, thermal energy is needed. When water evaporates from any surface, that surface is cooled. The two principal surfaces involved in evaporative cooling are the respiratory tract and the skin (via sweating). Evaporation of 1 gallon of water uses up 580 Calories and if man can refurbish his water supply, he is capable of using evaporative cooling to tolerate a rather large heat load. In Figure 17-4, the various sources of heat loss are shown for a nude man at 70°F.

heat production   Maintaining body heat is metabolically expensive, and basal heat production depends on a complex variety of energy-yielding reactions. For example, a 135-pound man will normally produce about 0.5 kcal per

figure 17-4

SOURCES OF
HEAT LOSS

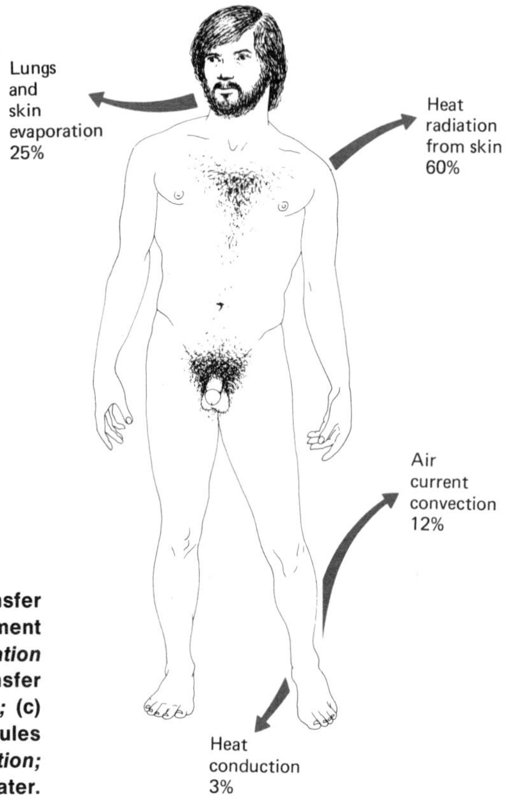

Sources of heat loss of
a nude man at 70° F

Lungs
and
skin
evaporation
25%

Heat
radiation
from skin
60%

Air
current
convection
12%

**Mechanisms for heat transfer
between man and his environment
involve (a) transfer by *radiation*
(infrared waves); (b) direct transfer
to another medium, *conduction;* (c)
movement of heated air molecules
by air currents called *convection;*
and finally (d) *evaporation* of water.**

Heat
conduction
3%

pound body per hour while maintaining all bodily functions. Under conditions of cold stress or maximum physical activity, however, he can increase his caloric utilization for a short time by about 18 to 20 times, which is a phenomenal heat production. Most of this heat production comes from muscular contraction. The dilemma faced by man is that to maintain a constant *core body temperature* (the temperature of deeper visceral structures, the brain, liver, and so on), he must be able to control both heat production and heat loss.

the skin as
an organ of
temperature
control

The skin surface of a 6-foot man may measure up to 15,000 square inches. Eighty-five percent of the body heat loss occurs from this great expanse of surface. The skin contains several structures contributing to overall thermal regulation. These are (a) thermal receptors sensitive to temperature changes, (b) subcutaneous fat deposits acting as an insulating layer, (c) the arrector pili, the muscles contributing to the body's heat production, (d) sweat glands that produce water for evaporative heat loss, and (e) the skin's vascular bed (see Figure 17-5).

figure 17-5

SOME FACTORS
INVOLVED IN
NORMAL AND
PATHOLOGICAL
CONTROL OF
TEMPERATURE

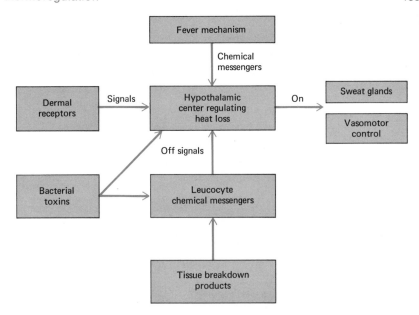

While dermal receptors reflexly control a local area, the master control center for temperature regulation is in the hypothalamus. Signals from the hypothalamus regulate endocrine control of metabolism (heat production), vasomotor changes (dilation or constriction), and sweating. Tissue damage or bacterial toxins affect the hypothalamic thermostat, causing its temperature setting to go up, thereby causing a fever.

central control of
temperature

The "human thermostat" is located in the hypothalamic control centers that coordinate a variety of sensory inputs from peripheral hot-cold receptors and central hot-cold receptors. The central receptors in the hypothalamus are sensitive to changes in core temperature of as little as 1.0°F. When the temperature of the blood bathing the hypothalamus changes, the appropriate mechanisms of heat loss or heat production are activated. The anterior hypothalamus center responds to rising temperature, and the posterior hypothalamic center responds to decreasing core temperature. Two transmitter substances, serotonin and norepinephrine, are involved in thermoregulation, and their effects may act to brake and accelerate around a given temperature set point. As is always the case, the higher center dominates the lower centers, and signals from peripheral thermoreceptors are overridden by the hypothalamic temperature sensors. In this way, core temperature always takes precedence over peripheral temperature (see Figure 17-5 and Module 17).

clinical
considerations

The skin is under almost constant abuse by its surroundings. It is subjected to a variety of mechanical shocks, blows, scrapes, punctures, and other noxious stimuli. Considering the variety of pathogenic organisms found on the skin surface and in the outside world, it is amazing how

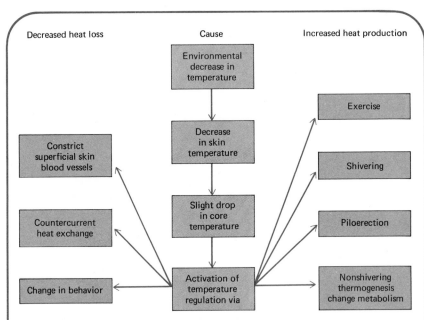

Decreased heat loss   Cause   Increased heat production

Most living things in both the plant and animal kingdoms are incapable of regulating their internal temperature, but birds and mammals have evolved this capability and maintain their body temperatures within relatively narrow limits. This reflexlike regulation of *core temperature* (temperature of brain and essential internal organs) involves a complex series of neural and endocrinological controls over both heat production and heat loss (or heat retention). Maintenance of a constant high core temperature which is independent of changes in environmental temperature is advantageous since the rate of all chemical reactions (enzyme action, etc) is temperature dependent. However, constancy of temperature requires precise regulation and if the core temperature exceeds 107° to 110°F for only a few hours, irreparable damage or death may result. In the normal human, temperature is not absolutely constant and thus normal core temperature varies slightly with activity and external temperature. All parts of the body do not have the same temperature; thus rectal temperature is about 1° higher than oral temperature and in the periphery (for example, toes, fingers) temperature may be considerably lower than the core temperature.

well the first line of defense works. The skin's ability to cope with these stresses is possible because of its remarkable repair capacity and excellent ability for inflammatory response, which seals off the traumatized or infected locus.

microbial
infections

The common pimple (acne) frequently seen in adolescents can be considered a typical skin infection. Pimples result from plugged or inflamed sebaceous ducts. Skin bacteria invade these inflamed areas, are killed by white cells, resulting in pus-filled *papules* or *pustules*, which are termed "blackheads" and "whiteheads." The area around the pustule is raised and red. The color is due to localized vasodilation, and the raised painful regions are due to swelling caused by leakage from the vascular bed. The underlying causes of acne are not clear. Skin bacteria, nutrition, endocrine factors, and excessive oiliness are all implicated. There is also evidence that emotional factors may play a role.

Boils are another manifestation of bacterial infection of the skin glands due to the invasion of *Staphylococcus aureus*. The latter bacteria are sometimes found in large numbers in the nose, nasopharynx, and perianal region. The staphylococci multiply rapidly, and the subsequent inflammation produces a painful pus and fluid-filled boil.

Foreign organisms cause a variety of skin conditions. *Warts*, localized excessive growths (hypertrophy) of the epidermis, are thought to be viral in origin. Strangely, they exhibit a psychosomatic component in that hypnosis and suggestion may have a curative effect. This probably accounts for the great variety of bizarre folk cures for warts. Various fungi invade the skin causing lesions, itching, and scaling. *Ringworm, athlete's foot*, and *jock itch* are examples of some of the more common fungal infections. *Pediculosis*, an attack on the hairy parts of the body by the common crab louse, is an example of infection caused by a blood-sucking parasite.

psoriasis
A skin inflammation that results in red areas covered with sloughing whitish scales, *psoriasis*, may be an inherited or genetic defect. Its cause is unknown, but there is the possibility that it may be viral in origin since it often occurs following an infection of the upper respiratory tract.

fever
A rapid rise in core temperature can be produced by a diverse number of inputs such as bacterial infection, viral infection, tissue breakdown, or trauma (burns, myocardial infarct, and so on). This rise in temperature is not mediated by enhanced heat production, since in most infections the increase is only about 20 percent (compared to 300 percent in heavy work). The temperature is caused instead by a disruption of the central nervous system temperature control mechanism regulating heat loss. In fever the set point for core temperature behaves as if it were a thermostat set for a higher temperature.

hypothermia
In some types of surgery, a patient may be cooled down to 25°C in order to reduce his metabolic rate to one-fourth the normal level. This permits both brain and heart to tolerate longer periods of circulatory arrest during the surgical procedure, thus decreasing the chance of anoxic tissue damage. Various drugs, which alter the effects of the neural and humoral transmitters, also modify temperature, and all anesthetics tend to depress body temperature.

heat cramps and
heat exhaustion
In an extremely hot environment, excessive sweating will result in excessive loss of Na^+ and Cl^-. When this happens, skeletal muscles may go into spasm, a process known as *heat cramp*. If replacement of salt and water is not initiated, the subject becomes weak as K^+ ions move into the interstitial space to replace sodium loss. The kidneys continue to excrete water, and this coupled with the water loss from sweat glands

figure 17-6

HEAT
EXHAUSTION

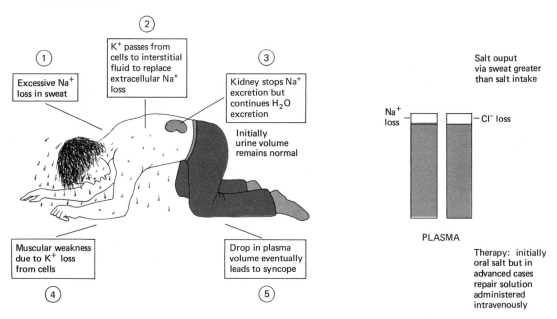

Prolonged exposure to intense heat may exceed the body's capacity for cooling, thereby causing heat exhaustion. The major changes associated with heat exhaustion are shown above.

causes the plasma volume to drop, leading to syncope (fainting) and even death (Figure 17-6).

summary

Skin is diffuse organ composed of varying thickness of an outer epidermis and an inner dermis attached to an underlying connective tissue layer, the hypodermis. Dermal derivatives include oil and sweat glands, nails, hair follicles, and a variety of nerve endings and sensory receptors.

gross anatomy

microanatomy and cellular specialization

1. Epidermis
   (a) stratified epithelial cell layers, the outermost being flattened scalelike dead cells
   (b) underlying stratum germinativum constantly replaces epidermis; contains melanin pigment cells which are responsible for the greatest percentage of skin color
2. Dermis: deeper layer made up of connective tissue, blood vessels, lymph vessels, hair follicle, and nerve endings
3. Nerve supply: a variety of receptors for touch, temperature, and pressure; also, naked nerve endings and motor fibers to blood vessels
4. Hair: hair follicle forms from a germinal bulb and grows outward;

arrector pili muscles attach to each follicle; sebaceous gland adjacent to each follicle lubricates hair shaft

   5. Nails: modified epidermal structures which stiffen ends of fingers and toes; nail made of horny protein keratin which grows out of nail bed

   6. Cutaneous glands

      (a) sweat glands: corkscrew-shaped tubular gland extends from dermis through the epidermis and secretes sterile, salty, clear fluid

      (b) sebaceous glands: somewhat similar in structure to sweat glands; they secrete a waxy or oily waterproof substance (the sebum)

      (c) specialized glands: modified sweat and sebaceous glands in genital region, mammary glands, wax glands of the external ear

   7. Blood and lymphatic supply: only in dermis; a rich network or plexus of vascular tissues supplies the skin, hair, glands, and nail bed

physiology   Three main functions: protection, secretion, and temperature regulation

thermo-regulation   1. Heat exchange between man and his environment: precise regulation of body temperature (about 98°F) balanced between heat production and retention, and heat loss; heat gained or lost by radiation, conduction, convection, and evaporational cooling

   2. Heat production: energy-yielding metabolic reactions mainly from muscle contraction produce heat; thyroid hormone increases heat production

   3. The skin as an organ of temperature control: the 15,000 square inch surface contains both hot and cold receptors; regulation of blood flow through the skin and control of sweat production are the major modes of temperature regulation

   4. Central control of temperature: the master temperature control center is in the hypothalamus and controls temperature of the body core by regulating both heat loss and heat production

clinical considerations   1. Microbial infections: the outer surface of our body is subjected to many traumas. If skin barrier is broken, a variety of microbes may enter and multiply, causing localized inflammatory reaction which seal off and repair damaged area, often leaving a pus-filled pustule; many fungi and viruses also cause skin abnormalities such as warts

   2. Fever: a rapid rise in temperature caused by bacterial or viral infections; disruption of central thermostat by chemical substance

   3. Hypothermia: lowering body temperature below normal levels; sometimes used in surgery to lower metabolic activities

   4. Heat cramps and heat exhaustion: excessive loss of sodium, chloride, and water may cause muscle spasms (cramps) due to imbalance between Na^+ and K^+ ion concentration in fluid spaces

18

the endocrine system

pituitary
gross anatomy
microscopic anatomy
physiology
clinical considerations

thyroid
gross anatomy
microscopic anatomy
physiology
clinical considerations

parathyroids
gross anatomy
microscopic anatomy
physiology
clinical considerations

pancreas
gross anatomy
microscopic anatomy
physiology
clinical considerations

adrenals
gross anatomy
microscopic anatomy
physiology of adrenal
    medulla
clinical considerations
physiology of the cortex
clinical considerations

The endocrine system is a dispersed collection of glands of internal secretion (endocrine); that is, their secretions are not carried by ducts, but are released directly into the bloodstream. The products of these ductless glands are different chemical messengers called *hormones*. Some hormones are small molecules such as amino acids, and others are larger units such as proteins and fatty substances. Hormones are effective in extremely small concentrations, as little as 10^{-10} to 10^{-13} M.

All endocrine glands are in intimate contact with the microcirculation, and in proportion to other tissues have the most extensive vascular supply. Thus their secretions are rapidly picked up by the capillaries and transported by the circulatory system to *target tissues* (tissues that respond to the hormone). The effect of the circulating hormone is determined by both the hormone and the specific target tissue. The message inherent in the hormone's chemical structure is interpreted differently by different cells; for example, some cells are stimulated, others are inhibited, and some cells do not respond at all.

Hormones generally affect the target tissues directly, but some hormones act in a *permissive* and *supportive* role by priming specific cells to make them responsive to a second hormone (Figure 18-1). Other hormones act *indirectly* by stimulating the *release* of a second hormone, which, in turn, affects target tissues.

The synthesis and release of all hormones are under regulatory control. Hormones are released in a rhythmical or cyclic fashion at a relatively constant rate or on physiological demand. In addition, all endocrine glands have a large functional reserve capacity that is called on in emergency or stress situations, and in such situations, the amount of messenger released is many times greater than normal.

After having performed their task, hormones are either broken down, inactivated by a carrier molecule (usually a protein), or excreted.

In this chapter only the major endocrine organs will be reviewed; other organs that have an endocrine function relevant to a specific organ or organ system are covered in those specific chapters; the endo-

figure 18-1

THE PERMISSIVE
ACTION OF
HORMONES

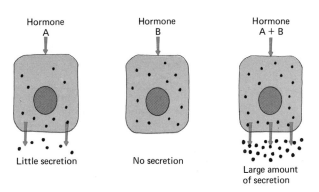

Hormone A   Hormone B   Hormone A + B

Little secretion   No secretion   Large amount of secretion

Some hormones do not exert a direct effect on a particular target tissue but instead may only prime or prepare that target to respond to a second hormone. In other cases one hormone may have just the opposite effect, that is, instead of priming the target tissue it renders the target unresponsive to a given hormone.

MAJOR
HORMONAL
CONTROL
SYSTEMS

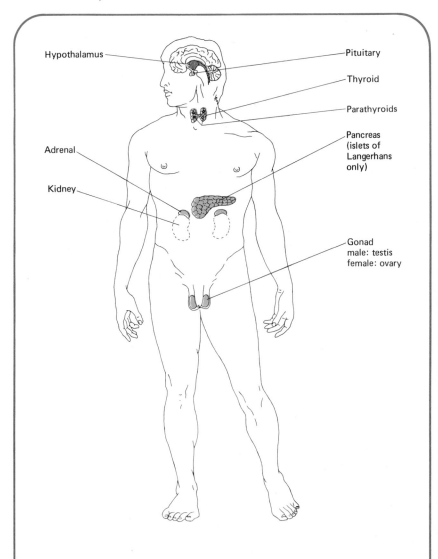

A group of specialized cells, tissues, and organs have evolved to produce chemical messengers (hormones) which carry information necessary for the coordinated activity of all tissues of the body. These specialized secretory tissues and organs form the endocrine system, a system which is remarkably diverse in form and embryonic development. The only justification for calling it a system is that (a) all endocrines are ductless glands secreting their product directly into the bloodstream and (b) endocrines all produce hormones. The major endocrine organs are shown in the above illustration, but there are a number of other hormones produced by diverse organs such as the thymus, stomach, intestine, kidneys, and other organs which will be discussed in other chapters in this book.

crine role of the kidney is discussed in the chapter on the urinary system; female hormones are discussed in the chapter on female reproductive system, and so on. The anatomical locations of the endocrine structures are seen in Module 18A.

pituitary   In the past the *pituitary* was considered the master gland of the endocrine system, but in actuality, pituitary function cannot be separated from that of the hypothalamic nuclei that order and control its activity. For the purposes of this discussion, the hypothalamus is considered a component of the endocrine system, even though it has other neural (nonendocrine) functions.

gross anatomy   The pituitary is a small (500 mg) ovoid structure on the floor of the brain directly below the hypothalamus (Figure 18-2). The well-protected pituitary sits in a cavity of the sphenoid bone and is surrounded by dense dura mater. It is directly connected to the hypothalamus by the *hypophyseal stalk* that penetrates the dura. Actually, there are three discreet anatomical entities making up this organ, the *anterior lobe* or *adenohypophysis*, the *posterior lobe* or *neurohypophysis*, and the *hypophyseal stalk.* Each lobe may be divided into three. The *adenohypophysis* is composed of the *pars tuberalis, pars intermedia*, and *pars distalis;* the neurohypophysis consists of the *median eminence,* the *infundibular stem,* and the *neural lobe.* The stalk of the hypophysis is actually composed of the infundibular stem and the pars tuberalis of the adenohypophysis, and is found directly behind the *optic chiasma* (Figure 18-2).

figure 18-2

THE ANATOMICAL RELATIONSHIP OF THE PITUITARY GLAND AND HYPOTHALAMUS

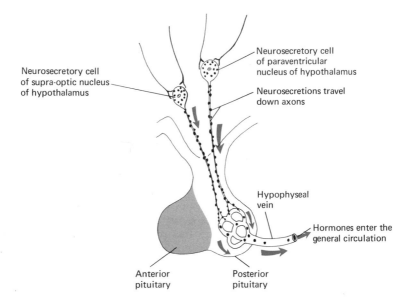

The hypothalamus by its anatomical location links much of the endocrine system indirectly to the nervous system. Thus both neural and endocrine influences on the hypothalamus determine pituitary function.

figure 18-3

THE
HYPOTHALAMIC-
HYPOPHYSEAL
PORTAL SYSTEM

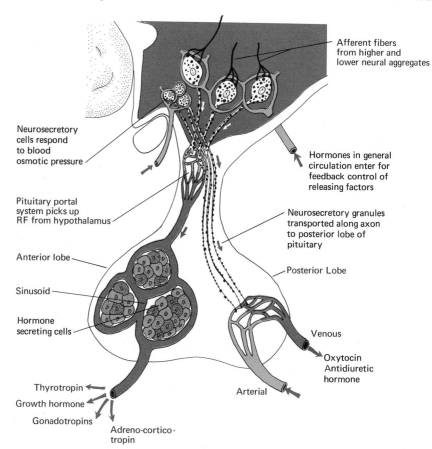

Afferent fibers
from higher and
lower neural aggregates

Neurosecretory
cells respond
to blood
osmotic pressure

Hormones in general
circulation enter for
feedback control of
releasing factors

Pituitary portal
system picks up
RF from hypothalamus

Neurosecretory granules
transported along axon
to posterior lobe of
pituitary

Anterior lobe

Posterior Lobe

Sinusoid

Hormone
secreting cells

Venous

Oxytocin
Antidiuretic
hormone

Thyrotropin

Growth hormone

Gonadotropins

Arterial

Adreno-cortico-
tropin

**Regulation of the anterior pituitary is brought about by specific releasing factors
(and inhibitors) produced by the neurosecretory cells of the hypothalamus. These
releasing factors are carried directly to the anterior pituitary by a portal system and
in this way the messenger molecules reach their target undiluted (RF= releasing
factor).**

The arrangement of blood vessels in this region is unique in that the
anterior pituitary has no direct arterial supply. Instead the entire blood
supply of the anterior lobe is provided by a *venous portal system*, which
arises from a dense bed of capillaries in the hypothalamus. As can be
seen in Figure 18-3, such an arrangement of blood vessels transports
secretions from the hypothalamus directly to the anterior pituitary. The
posterior lobe of the pituitary has the usual vascular arrangement, that
is, a direct arterial supply, capillary network, and venous drainage.

microscopic   The posterior lobe is nonglandular and composed mainly of *pituicytes.*
anatomy   It functions as a storage depot for *oxytocin* and *antidiuretic hormone*
that are produced by specialized neurosecretory cells in the *supraoptic*
and *paraventricular* nuclei of hypothalamus. These *neurosecretory*

cells are modified neurons (Figure 18-3) with axons that transport membrane-bound granules containing oxytocin and vasopressin to the posterior lobe of the pituitary, where they are stored until they are discharged.

The anterior lobe contains granular secretory cells that can be identified by their various staining characteristics. Each cell type is thought to be responsible for the synthesis and release of one of the six hormones of the anterior pituitary.

physiology

Posterior Pituitary

Vasopressin or *antidiuretic* hormone (ADH) is a peptide that acts on the distal convoluted tubules and collecting ducts of the kidneys to regulate water homeostasis. Two factors regulate the release of antidiuretic hormone: (a) osmoreceptors in the hypothalamus are activated by changes in blood dilution and (b) stretch receptors in the left atrium of the heart are activated by changes in blood volume. Both sensory mechanisms send nerve fibers to the neurosecretory cells that produce antidiuretic hormone. (See Chapter 16, Urinary System, for more complete discussion.)

The second hormone of the posterior lobe, *oxytocin* or *pitocin*, is also a peptide and has two major functions: (a) to enhance the milk-ejecting reflex in the mammary glands of lactating females and (b) to increase the contractility of the uterine muscles during labor and birth.

Anterior Pituitary

The anterior pituitary hormones are proteins and include *follicle-stimulating hormone* (FSH), *luteinizing hormone* (LH), *luteotropic hormone* (LTH), *thyrotropic hormone* (TTH), *adrenocorticotropic hormone* (ACTH), and *growth hormone* (GH) which is also called *somatotropic hormone* (STH). With the exception of growth hormone, the anterior lobe hormones stimulate the production of another hormone in a different gland, and it is the second hormone that affects the target tissue. For example, thyrotropic hormone stimulates the thyroid to produce thyroxine, which in turn increases the rate of cellular metabolism (target). Each of these indirect-acting hormones will be discussed in chapters dealing with the tissue they affect. The one direct-acting hormone, somatotropin, enhances protein synthesis and bone growth. Growth hormone is secreted throughout life, and recent studies suggest that the hormone is released during sleep in response to a decrease in blood sugar.

The regulation of the anterior pituitary is under a feedback control system and also responds to a variety of environmental inputs. The release of trophic hormones is generally controlled by specific releasing factors originating in the hypothalamus, and the production of these releasing factors is, in turn, primarily regulated by the concentration of circulating hormone of the target endocrine gland. For example, if the concentration of thyroxine in the blood is increased, the production and release of thyrotropin are inhibited; conversely, a decrease in the concentration of circulating thyroxine stimulates thyrotropin synthesis and release. Neural influences (stress, anxiety, and so forth) also play a role in regulating the release of thyrotropin by modifying the activity of the thyrotropin-releasing factor of the hypothalamus.

clinical
considerations

Posterior Pituitary

The major malfunction of the posterior pituitary is insufficient production or release of antidiuretic hormone due to trauma to the posterior lobe or hypothalamus. Without sufficient circulation of the hormone, there is a critical water loss via the kidneys and insatiable thirst. Such a syndrome is called *diabetes insipidus*, but with hormone-replacement therapy, the symptoms are alleviated.

Anterior Pituitary

Disease states of the anterior lobe are difficult to describe, since in some cases there is abnormal release of more than just one of the hormones although often tumors of one secretory cell type occur. For our purposes, only the growth hormone, somatotropin, is cited as an example here.

Hormone abnormalities produce markedly different effects, depending on the age of the individual at the onset of the disease. Usually the earlier the occurrence, the more severe and less reversible the defect. Insufficient growth hormones, that is, *hyposecretion,* during the early years cause *pituitary dwarfism,* a generalized diminution in growth and development that is sometimes reversible if treated with growth hormones in conjunction with other hormones. *Hypersecretion,* that is, excessive secretion of growth hormones during the developmental years, causes *pituitary giantism,* of which there are rare examples of persons reaching heights of 9 feet. After the long bones have stopped growing, hypersecretion of somatotropin increases the bone growth circumferentially, but not in the long axis. In this condition, called *acromegaly,* bony tissue continues to grow, hands enlarge, and features become coarse.

thyroid

gross anatomy

On either side of the larynx and attached to the thyroid cartilage *(Adam's apple)* is the reddish, H-shaped thyroid gland. Under normal circumstances the adult thyroid weighs only 30 to 40 g, but in disease it can hypertrophy (enlarge) to more than 10 times its normal size. The thyroid has an exceptionally rich blood supply, and numerous autonomic nerve fibers accompany the blood vessels, although the role of these nerves remains unclear.

microscopic
anatomy

The gland is composed of an aggregation of tubelike *follicles,* the size of which may vary considerably (Figure 18-4). The follicles are primarily composed of cuboidal epithelium that secrete an amber-colored gelatinous *colloid.* The colloid represents a storage form of the hormone, and thus the thyroid is unique in that its storage capacity is much greater than that of other endocrine organs.

physiology

Thyroid hormone is normally present in an inactive form bound to a globular protein, *thyroglobulin.* The exact mechanism involved in the release of the active principle, *thyroxine,* is uncertain. About 60 percent of the molecular weight of the hormone is iodine, and most of the dietary iodine is concentrated in the thyroid gland. (This fact is of clinical significance, since uptake of radioactive iodine can be used to measure thyroid activity.)

Thyroxine is important in maintaining the functional activity of all normal cellular metabolism, particularly oxidative metabolism and heat

figure 18-4

THE GROSS
ANATOMY OF
THE THYROID
GLAND AND
MICROSCOPIC
ANATOMY OF A
THYROID
FOLLICLE

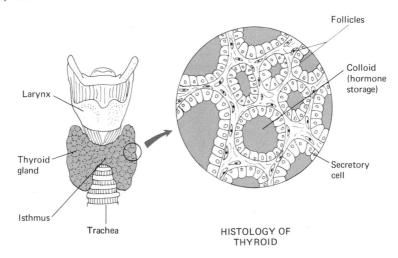

figure 18-4

THE GROSS ANATOMY OF THE THYROID GLAND AND MICROSCOPIC ANATOMY OF A THYROID FOLLICLE

production. Some investigators think that the effect of thyroxine is probably directly on the mitochondria, where the oxidation of both carbohydrate and fat is enhanced by thyroxine. However, some recent studies suggest that thyroxine has its primary effect on protein-synthesizing action (ribosome and nucleus), which may account for its role in early growth and development. For example, early thyroid researchers found that thyroxine was essential for tadpoles to develop into frogs. Neural influences such as stress and cold environments cause the hypothalamus to stimulate thyrotropin release, thus enhancing appetite, food utilization, and heat production.

The thyroid also contains cells that produce another humoral agent, calcitonin, a peptide hormone that lowers blood calcium (see Chapter 4).

clinical considerations

Hyposecretion

Cretinism is a *congenital* (acquired during development in the uterus) disease with a myriad of clinical manifestations: severe dwarfing, generalized growth failure, thickness of the tongue, low metabolic rate, severe mental retardation, and edema (Figure 18-5).

Myxedema is a term for thyroid hypofunction of children and adults, with clinical characteristics such as a lowered body temperature, low oxygen consumption, poor appetite, generalized mental and physical sluggishness, hair loss, tongue swelling, and subcutaneous fluid accumulation.

Goiter is a general term for thyroid abnormalities that produce a marked increase in thyroid mass (Figure 18-6). A variety of factors can cause goiter, such as an iodine-deficient diet, thyroid hypofunction, or even thyroid hyperfunction.

Hypersecretion

The effects of an excessive production of thyroxine (such as caused by a tumor) were first described by R. J. Graves (*Graves' disease*) and consist of a spectrum of symptoms associated with enhanced metabolic activity. The patient is nervous, highly active, and suffers extreme weight loss despite a ravenous appetite. Hyperthyroidism often causes hypertrophy

figure 18-5

THYROID
ABNORMALITIES-
CRETINISM

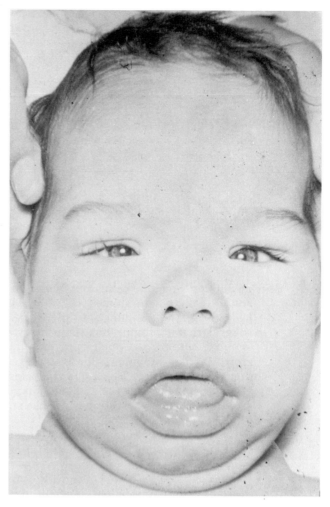

The lack of sufficient thyroid function during early development causes a spec-
trum of symptoms, the most dramatic of which is underdevelopment of the brain.
Such children are called cretins. (Courtesy of Dr. Boris Senior, Tufts University
Medical School.)

of the connective tissue behind the eyeballs, causing the eyes to bulge
out, a condition known as *exophthalamus.*

parathyroids

gross anatomy

Attached to or imbedded in the connective tissue covering of the thyroid
gland are four parathyroid glands (Module 18A). Two are located at the
superior end of the thyroid and two at the posterior poles. The total mass
of these vital endocrine glands is only about 0.2 g.

microscopic
anatomy

Each parathyroid consists of a highly vascularized mass of densely
packed cords of epithelial cells. There are two cell types, the *oxyphile*
and the more numerous *principal* or *chief* cell, which is probably the

figure 18-6

THYROID
ABNORMALITIES—
GOITER

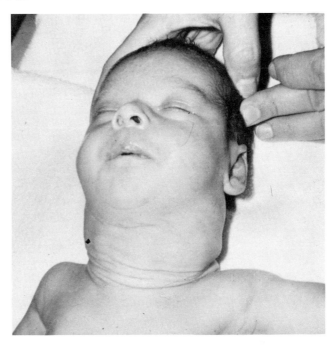

This child shows the classic symptoms of goiter, an abnormal enlargement of the thyroid gland which is clearly recognizable on external examination.

source of the parathyroid hormone (PTH), a peptide chain of 83 amino acids. These cells contain few secretory granules; hence we can conclude that relatively little parathyroid hormone is stored and that the hormone is synthesized and released on demand.

physiology   A principal function of the parathyroid glands is to regulate the calcium (Ca^{2+}) and phosphorous (PO_4) levels in the body. The Ca^{2+} ion is obtained from the diet and from reservoirs in bone that are mobilized on demand when blood Ca^{2+} level drops below the normal level of about 10 mg percent. Phosphorus (as phosphate) has a major role in carbohydrate and energy metabolism. Plasma phosphate is also regulated within narrow limits with bone as the major reservoir (see Chapter 4).

Calcitonin is produced by the thyroid and parathyroid tissues. This polypeptide hormone has a diametrically opposite effect to parathyroid hormone in that it moves blood calcium and phosphorus to bone. Calcitonin is also regulated by serum calcium levels. See Figure 18-7 for a diagrammatic presentation of calcium homeostasis.

clinical   Destruction or removal of the parathyroids results in a dramatic drop in
considerations   serum calcium levels followed by muscle spasms (*tetany*), convulsions, and death in a matter of days. Calcium, if you recall, is a cofactor to
Hyposecretion   acetylcholinesterase, which stops acetylcholine stimulation of muscle contraction.

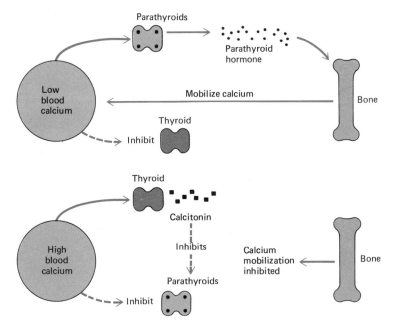

figure 18-7

CALCIUM
HOMEOSTASIS

The critical factor in calcium homeostasis is the serum calcium level. Changes in calcium ion concentration may activate either the release of parathyroid hormone (PTH) or calcitonin. The relationships are shown in the above diagram and described in the text.

Hypersecretion   In rare circumstances there is an excessive secretion of the parathyroid hormone. This hypersecretion causes a progressive demineralization of bone as bone calcium is continually removed and excreted by the kidneys and the gastrointestinal tract. The bones become fragile, brittle, painful, and easily fractured.

the pancreas   The endocrine pancreas is made up of about 1 million tiny islands (*islets of Langerhans*) of secretory cells surrounded by exocrine pan-

gross anatomy   creatic tissue that produces digestive enzymes. The whole pancreas weighs about 60 g, but the endocrine tissue collectively weighs about 1 g. The pancreas is set in the loop of the duodenum on the right side of the body; the anatomic relationship of the pancreas to adjoining structures is best seen in Figure 18-8.

microscopic   Each islet is 150 μ in diameter and contains different types of cells, but
anatomy   the two principal cells are dark-staining *beta cells* (β), which make up about 70 percent of the endocrine mass and are the seat of insulin secretion and storage, *alpha cells* (α), which secrete the hormone *glucagon*, also involved in carbohydrate metabolism.

physiology   Two active hormones produced by the pancreas are *insulin* and *glucagon*. The primary action of insulin is to promote the transfer of sugars

figure 18-8

THE GROSS
ANATOMY OF
THE PANCREAS

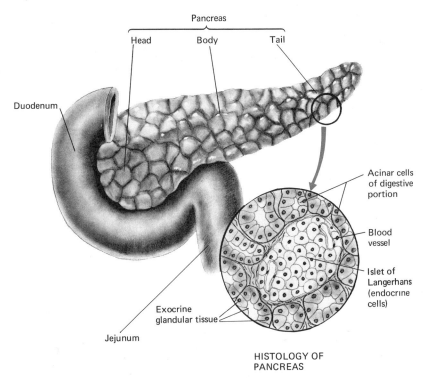

HISTOLOGY OF
PANCREAS

(for example, glucose and lactose) across cell membranes. Apparently sugar transport across the membranes requires an insulin-dependent (or activated) carrier mechanism. However, not all cells require insulin to move sugars across their membranes. Thus nerve, kidney, and red blood cells function quite well in the absence of insulin as long as normal blood sugar levels are maintained. Indirectly, insulin increases the storage of glycogen in the liver, possibly by activating an enzyme that converts glucose to its storage form, glycogen. Insulin also indirectly influences fat metabolism and protein synthesis in cells.

The regulation of insulin synthesis and release is not fully understood, since no tropic hormone or neural factors have been conclusively demonstrated. Other hormones such as epinephrine do affect the beta cells, possibly by producing *hyperglycemia* (excess blood sugar), which creates a demand for more insulin. It has also been shown that insulin is released by both high blood sugar levels and by amino acids in the blood. A proposed cellular mechanism of action for insulin release is shown in Figure 18-9. Recent research has shown that the mechanism involved in insulin release requires Ca^{2+} and cyclic adenosine monophosphate (AMP) (See Chapter 14 and Module 18B).

The other pancreatic hormone, *glucagon*, has an opposite effect on blood sugar levels to that of insulin. Glucagon elevates blood sugar by enhancing the breakdown of liver glycogen to glucose.

figure 18-9

POSTULATED
CELLULAR
MECHANISM FOR
THE RELEASE OF
INSULIN

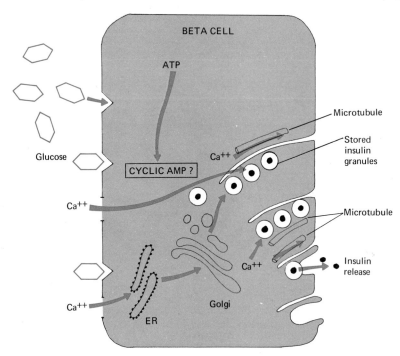

Insulin synthesis and release are triggered by an increase in blood sugar. The role of cyclic AMP is obscure but may play a role in the entrance of calcium ions into the cell. The calcium ions play a major role in the contraction of the microtubules, which in turn move insulin granules to the cell surface where they are secreted.

clinical
considerations

Hyperinsulinism

Hypoinsulinism

Hyperinsulinism, an excess release of insulin, produces a drop in blood sugar (*hypoglycemia*) because of the increased rate of glucose uptake by muscle and fat tissue and glucose conversion to glycogen in the liver. Hypoglycemia affects the brain, producing tremors, confusion, lethargy, and, finally, coma and even death.

Hypoinsulinism, exhaustion or malfunction of beta cells, results in a decrease in available insulin to cells dependent on this hormone (skeletal, muscle, and heart) and an increase in blood glucose. Since the excess glucose cannot be stored or utilized, it spills out into the urine. Normally glucose in the kidney filtrate is reabsorbed by the nephron, but in diabetics the excess of sugar is beyond tubular reabsorption and thus is excreted in the urine. The abnormal levels of glucose in the urine create an osmotic shift, with less water being absorbed by the nephrons (forming a dilute urine), and in the process abnormal amounts of water and salts are also lost as urine (*polyuria*). There is also a shift from carbohydrate to fat metabolism in diabetes. Lipids from storage depots are mobilized. Some of these lipids may be deposited in the blood vessels, causing a variety of vascular pathologies, particularly in the retinal vessels causing blindness. The shift to fat metabolism in diabetes (see Chapter 14, Metabolism) also markedly increases the production of meta-

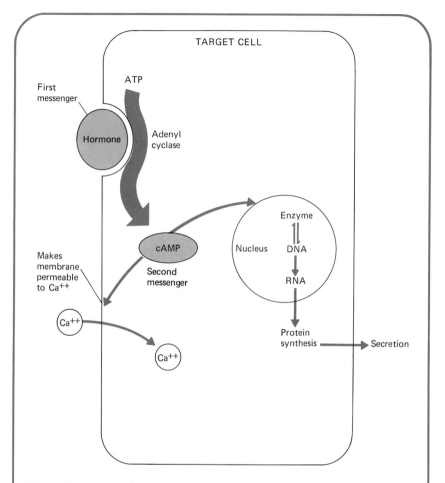

The cellular mechanism of hormone action on both target tissues and endocrine cells themselves has been in large part elucidated by the work of Nobel
Prize winner Earl W. Sutherland of Vanderbilt University. Fifteen years ago
Dr. Sutherland found that both norepinephrine and glucagon acted on liver
cells by triggering a second messenger system within the cell. This second
messenger then exerted its effect, breaking down glycogen to glucose thus
raising blood sugar levels. Since then a massive amount of work has shown
that many hormones act via this same second messenger, cyclic 3', 5' AMP
(cyclic adenosine monophosphate). It is postulated that many hormones fit
specific receptor sites on the surface of the target cell's membrane, causing
activation of the enzyme, adenyl cyclase. Adenyl cyclase in turn acts on ATP
to produce cyclic AMP, the second messenger. The altered level of cyclic
AMP activates intracellular enzymes, which produce the appropriate physiological response. In many if not all responses of the second messenger calcium ion appears to be necessary. The discovery of cyclic AMP not only
throws much light on the mechanisms of hormone action but is already beginning to be studied for its value as another tool in clinical diagnosis and treatment of disease.

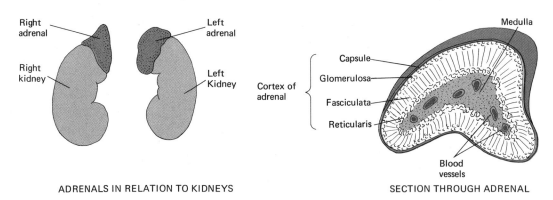

figure 18-10

THE GROSS
ANATOMY OF
THE ADRENAL
GLANDS

ADRENALS IN RELATION TO KIDNEYS   SECTION THROUGH ADRENAL

The adrenal gland is in actuality two glands, an outer cortex and an inner structure, the medulla.

bolic acids (ketone bodies) such as acetocetic acid, thereby producing *acidosis*. Metabolic acidosis may become severe and cause serious changes in electrolyte balance. The frequent urination that accompanies excretion of sugar can produce dehydration. In addition, the body is "robbing" itself of proteins that are needed for repair and regeneration of new cells. The sum consequences of these metabolic changes are that the individual is predisposed for a variety of diseases, the most serious of which appears to be a breakdown of blood vessel structure and function.

adrenals

gross anatomy

At the level of the first lumbar vertebra covering the superior pole of the kidneys are the flat, caplike adrenal glands (Figure 18-10). Each gland weighs 5 to 7 g (male adrenals being somewhat heavier). The adrenals anatomically are actually two glands, an inner medulla and an outer cortex (which accounts for 80 percent of the adrenal weight). The adrenals are copiously supplied with arterial blood vessels receiving branches from several sources (renal, pelvic, and gonadic arteries). Within the gland the vessels branch into sinusoids that exit by way of a large vein which joins the renal vein. The total blood flow can be as great as 8 ml blood per gram tissue per minute. Unlike most endocrines, secretion of the adrenal medulla is regulated by nerves from the sympathetic part of the autonomic nervous system.

microscopic
anatomy

The medulla of the adrenal derives its reddish-brown appearance from polyhedral-shaped chromaffin cells arranged into networks of connecting cords and from the copious blood supply. The cells have their origin from the embryonic nervous system that gives rise to the sympathetic neurons; the medulla cells function in a similar fashion to neurons. The adrenal cortex is more complex than the medulla, being composed of three discrete layers: the thin outer layer, the *zona glomerulosa;* the middle layer, the *zona fasiculata;* and an inner layer, the *zona reticularis.* The cell types of all three layers of the cortex are similar, composed of secretory cells loaded with lipid-filled globules of stored adrenocortical hormones. Each layer elaborates a number of different hormones; to date over 30 different hormones have been identified from the cortex.

physiology of adrenal medulla

The adrenal medulla elaborates two very similar hormones that are essential in preparing man for adverse environmental conditions, that is, *fight* or *flight* situations. The two active hormones are the catecholamines *epinephrine* and *norepinephrine.* The latter substance also is secreted at postganglionic sympathetic synaptic endings and in the brain (particularly in those parts of the brain having to do with alertness, arousal, and emotions). The predominant hormone of the medulla (80 percent) is epinephrine, which affects a number of target tissues in the following fashion: (a) the heart rate and strength of contraction increase; (b) the blood vessels to the heart and skeletal muscles dilate, while visceral vessels (kidney, gut, and reproductive tissues) are constricted, thus shunting blood to the active tissues; (c) smooth muscle to all visceral structures such as the gut, bladder, and bronchioles relaxes; (d) skeletal muscles contract more forcibly and fatigue less readily; (e) glycogen is broken down, and blood glucose levels are elevated; (f) the metabolic rate is increased; and (g) the brain is made more alert, a generalized arousal response to cope with the imposed environmental stress.

clinical considerations

Hypersecretion

Excess epinephrine secretion is uncommon, and when present, it is usually due to tumor of the chromaffin tissue. Hypersecretion causes hypertension, hyperglycemia with renal excretion of sugar, and a markedly elevated basal metabolism.

Hypofunction

There is no pathology associated with hypofunction of the adrenal medulla.

physiology of the cortex

The hormones of the adrenal cortex are all steroids and may be broken down into four major classes according to their function: (a) *glucocorticoids,* (b) *mineralocorticoids,* (c) *masculinizing steroids,* and (d) *feminizing steroids.* All have the same basic chemical structure, but subtle rearrangement of a few atoms within the molecule makes significant changes in function as can be seen in Figure 18-11.

The Glucocorticoids

One of the major ways the glucocorticoids (cortisone, cortisol, and corticosterone) work is to deplete the amount of protein in bone and muscle. The amino acids that are the products of this protein catabolism are then converted to glucose, and this increased blood sugar helps meet the emergency energy needs of the body. Another major beneficial effect of these steroids is their rather remarkable *anti-inflammatory* and *antiallergic* action. Any inflammatory response, for example, rheumatoid

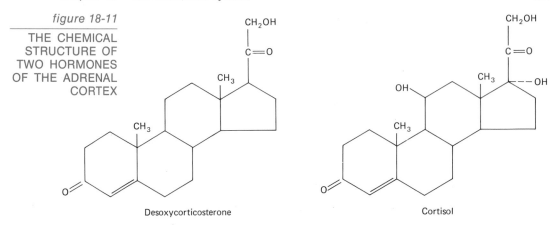

figure 18-11

THE CHEMICAL
STRUCTURE OF
TWO HORMONES
OF THE ADRENAL
CORTEX

Desoxycorticosterone   Cortisol

Subtle changes in the structure of the steroid nucleus, the change of only one or two atoms can significantly alter the coding of the message to target cells. Cortisol (right) inhibits the inflammatory process, while desoxycorticosterone (left) enhances some aspects of the inflammatory response.

arthritis, is alleviated by the glucocorticoids, and synthetic corticoids are used extensively in clinical practice. In Figure 18-12, the variety of effects of the glucocorticoids is summarized. Prolonged therapy with glucocorticoids may have serious adverse side effects, such as protein breakdown and susceptibility to infection due to lowering of the inflammatory response.

Glucocorticoids are secreted in any *physically* or *emotionally stressful* situation. The mechanism for increased glucocorticoid synthesis and release is well understood. Neural signals to the hypothalamus stimulate specialized neurosecretory cells to secrete *corticotropin-releasing factor*, which is then carried to the anterior pituitary via the hypophyseal portal system; the release of ACTH is thereby stimulated. The ACTH, in turn, stimulates both synthesis and release of glucocorticoids such as corticosterone and cortisone.

The *mineralocorticoids* are the second class of adrenocortical hormones and, as their name implies, are of extreme importance in electrolyte balance. The most important of these is *aldosterone*, elaborated by the cells of the zona glomerulosa in amounts up to 250 μg a day (as compared to 25 to 30 μg of glucocorticoids per day). In cases of decreased sodium intake (severe salt loss) or hemorrhage, the amount of aldosterone secreted may reach almost 1 mg per day. This increase gives some clue as to the major physiological effect of aldosterone, that is, the increased sodium retention and chloride resorption in the kidney tubules and sweat glands. At the same time that aldosterone is acting to retain sodium and chloride, it enhances the excretion of potassium and hydrogen ions.

The release of aldosterone does not depend completely or even primarily on ACTH, but depends, in large part, on other factors such as sodium-potassium levels in the blood and the release of renin from the

figure 18-12

THE ACTION OF
THE GLUCO-
CORTICOIDS

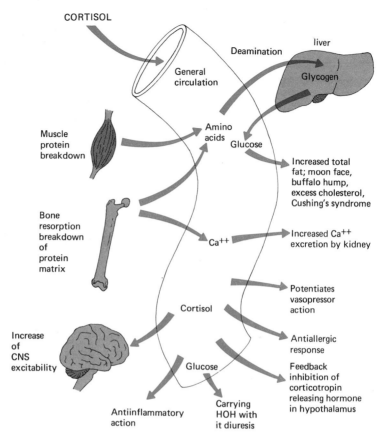

Some of the major functions of the glucocorticoids are shown diagramatically.

kidney. Aldosterone, in addition to its major role in the maintenance of
electrolyte metabolism, also plays a role in the maintenance of blood
volume and blood pressure.

clinical   Hypofunction of the adrenal cortex, *Addison's disease*, is characterized
considerations by (a) severe disruption in electrolyte balance and carbohydrate metabo-
                lism, (b) lowered blood pressure, (c) hyperpigmentation of the skin, and
Hyposecretion   (d) renal failure with both acidosis and dehydration. The disease can be
                controlled by hormone replacement therapy and increased dietary in-
                take of sodium.

Hypersecretion Excessive production of adrenocortical hormones, *Cushing's syndrome*,
                also seriously disrupts carbohydrate metabolism, electrolyte balance,
                and elevates blood pressure. The altered carbohydrate metabolism en-
                hances fat deposition particularly in the back of the neck, causing a
                telltale diagnostic sign, the so-called buffalo hump (Figure 18-13).
                Another characteristic symptom of adrenocortical hypersecretion in the
                female is masculinization due to elevated levels of circulating male
                hormone from the cortex.

figure 18-13

CUSHING'S
SYNDROME

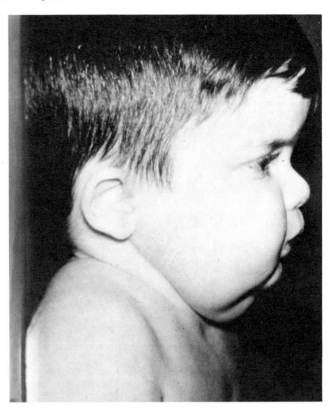

Cushing's syndrome is a constellation of metabolic abnormalities due to excessive cortisol production. The cause of the pathology in 75 percent of the cases (discovered by Dr. Harvey Cushing) is excessive pituitary production of ACTH. The remaining 25 percent of the cases are due to tumors of the adrenal cortex. (Courtesy Dr. Boris Senior, Tufts University Medical School.)

summary

endocrine system

pituitary

A diffuse collection of glands which secrete chemical messengers (hormones) into the bloodstream; hormones carry messages to specific target cells such as secretory cells, involved in homeostasis.

1. Under direction from the hypothalamus, the gland produces a variety of hormones
2 Gross anatomy
   (a) connected to the base of the brain below the hypothalamus by a thin stalk
   (b) bilobed, it can be divided into anterior and posterior lobes
   (c) a portal vascular system links hypothalamus and anterior pituitary
3. Microscopic anatomy
   (a) posterior lobe contains pituicytes, reservoirs for neurosecretory material from hypothalamus

   (b) anterior pituitary contains a number of granular cell types which produce the hormones in response to releasing hormones from the hypothalamus

4. Physiology
   (a) posterior pituitary: produces oxytocin, which affects uterine contractility and milk ejection, and vasopressin or antidiuretic hormone, which regulates water homeostasis by the kidney
   (b) anterior pituitary: produces growth hormone, gonadotropic hormones, adrenocorticotropic hormone, and thyroid-stimulating hormone; all except growth hormone stimulate other endocrine organs to secrete their hormones, which act in a regulatory feedback loop to inhibit pituitary hormone production usually by turning off production of hypothalamic releasing hormones

5. Clinical considerations
   (a) posterior pituitary: major malfunction of posterior pituitary causes severe diuresis (water loss)
   (b) anterior pituitary: difficult to describe since most diseases affect several different groups of hormone-producing cells; hence growth and metabolic abnormalities, and abnormal sexual differentiation are common manifestations of anterior pituitary disease

thyroid
1. Gross anatomy: a reddish, 40 g bilobed organ on either side of the Adam's apple
2. Microscopic anatomy: an aggregation of tubelike follicles filled with colloid material thyroglobulin
3. Physiology: active hormone thyroxine affects protein synthesis and plays a major role in oxidative metabolism and heat production
4. Clinical considerations
   (a) hyposecretion: during early development can cause cretinism (a severely retarded dwarfed individual with lowered metabolism); in older children and adults, the disease is called myxedema, and is characterized by lowered metabolism, fluid accumulation, and general sluggishness
   (b) hypersecretion: Graves' diseases; enhanced metabolic activity, weight loss, and hypertrophy of connective tissue behind eyeball causing eye to bulge out (exophthalamus)

parathyroids
1. Gross anatomy: four small masses of tissue imbedded in the mass of the thyroid gland
2. Microscopic anatomy: principal cells and oxyphile cells are densely packed and highly vascularized
3. Physiology
   (a) parathyroids regulate calcium and phosphorous levels in blood and bone
   (b) parathyroid hormone: mobilizes calcium from bone reservoirs when blood calcium drops
   (c) calcitonin: second hormone has opposite action

4. Clinical considerations

    (a) hyposecretion: a dramatic drop in blood calcium levels, muscle spasms, convulsions, and death if untreated

    (b) hypersecretion: demineralization of bone and enhanced renal excretion of calcium

pancreas

1. Gross anatomy: within the 60 g pancreas, located in the loop of the duodenum, are 1 million small islands of hormone-producing cells, the islets of Langerhans

2. Microscopic anatomy: islets are made up of insulin-secreting beta cells (70 percent of the islet cells) and alpha cells that secrete the hormone glucagon

3. Physiology

    (a) rise in blood sugar activates the beta cells to secrete insulin, which enhances transport of glucose across cell membranes and converts glucose to glycogen in the liver

    (b) glucagon working with epinephrine from the adrenal enhances glycogen breakdown and elevation of blood sugar levels

4. Clinical considerations

    (a) hyperinsulinism: causes a sharp drop in blood sugar (hypoglycemia); if severe may cause convulsions, coma, and death

    (b) hypoinsulinism: malfunction of beta cells, diabetes mellitus, decrease of available glucose to tissues while elevating blood glucose, the excess of which is excreted in the urine

adrenals

1. Gross anatomy: two small caplike organs covering the superior pole of the kidneys; are actually two glands in one, an outer adrenal cortex and the inner core, the medulla

2. Microscopic anatomy: the medulla is composed of chromaffin cells related to sympathetic nervous system; larger cortex is made up of three layers of lipid-filled secretory cells

3. Physiology of the medulla: emergency signals from CNS reach the medulla via the sympathetic fibers, which stimulate production of emergency "fight or flight" hormones adrenalin and noradrenalin; enhances heart rate, shifts blood to active organs, elevates blood sugar, blood pressure, and alertness

4. Clinical considerations

    (a) hypersecretion: usually due to chromaffin cell tumor; causes elevated blood sugar, high blood pressure, and elevated metabolism

    (b) hypofunction: no clinical entity associated with decreased hormone production

5. Physiology of the cortex: the cortex produces over 40 steroid hormones in three major classes.

    (a) glucocorticoids: inhibit allergy and inflammation and affect neuromuscular excitability

    (b) mineralocorticoids: retain sodium and water while enhancing K^+ excretion in the kidney

    (c) male and female sex hormones

      (d) pituitary control via ACTH is regulated by circulating levels of cortical hormones acting on hypothalamic neurosecretory cells, which produce releasing hormones

6. Clinical considerations
      (a) hyposecretion: Addison's disease causes salt: water imbalance, impaired carbohydrate metabolism, hyperpigmentation, low blood pressure, and renal failure
      (b) hypersecretion: Cushing's syndrome elevates blood pressure, elevates blood sugar, enhances fat deposition, causes breakdown of bone and muscle protein

19 male reproductive system

gross anatomy
testes
scrotum
penis
seminal ducts and vesicles
prostate
urethra and urethral glands
spermatic cord

microanatomy and cellular specializations
corpora cavernosa (penis)
seminiferous tubules
spermatogenesis

physiology
hormones
orgasm

control

factors influencing function
age
genetic defects

clinical considerations
castration
circumcision
hormonal hyperfunction
hormonal hypofunction
impotence
sterility
diseases of the prostate

The anatomical and behavioral differences between male and female have been recognized from the earliest times of human history, as is attested to by primitive cave drawings. However, it was not until modern times that we attained any real insight into the physiological basis for sexuality with the discovery of sex hormones. In the late 1800s scientists were aware that the male "sex principle" was produced in the testes. However, early attempts to extract male hormone failed, because the hormone at any given time is present in quantities too small to be detected by the chemical tools available at the time. In 1927 male hormones were obtained from extracts of testes, and by the mid-1930s the male hormone (testosterone) was isolated and synthetically produced.

The male sex is established at the moment of fertilization by the union of the egg containing the X chromosome and a sperm with the Y (male) chromosome. This genetic information on the Y chromosome programs maleness on the entire subsequent course of sexual development.

gross anatomy   The male reproductive system consists of the primary sex organs, the testes, and the accessory reproductive organs, which include the ducts (*epididymis, seminal* or *vas deferens, ejaculatory duct, urethra*), glands (*seminal vesicles, prostate, bulbourethral*), and the external genitalia (*scrotum, penis*). All structures are paired with the exception of the urethra, prostate, scrotum, and penis (Figure 19-1).

testes   Each ovoid testis is about 5 cm long and 2.5 cm wide and lies in its own compartment within the scrotum. Adjacent to the testis is the epididymis, the first segment of the genital duct system through which the sperm pass (Figure 19-1). The epididymis is a tortuous tube (uncoiled, it would be several yards long) that connects the germinal tissues to the seminal ducts.

scrotum   The scrotum is a thin-walled pouch that lies at the base of the penis. One landmark of the scrotum is the *raphe* (Figure 19-1), a ridge that marks the fusion point of the embryonic genital swelling; in the female, these swellings do not fuse, and become the outer fleshy genital folds (Chapter 20). The loose lining of the scrotum is continuous with the peritoneal layer of the abdominal cavity.

penis   The penis is composed primarily of three cylindrical masses of connective tissue joined by a tough connective tissue fascia (Figure 19-2). Traversing the interior side of the penis is the urethra. The distal end of the penis is enlarged and is called the *glans penis*. The skin in this region is folded to form a retractable casing called the *foreskin* or *prepuce*. The skin of the prepuce is quite thin and elastic, and it is easily retractable. In the nonexcited state, the penis is pendulous and flaccid and measures about 5 to 10 cm in length.

seminal ducts   The *seminal ducts*, also called the *vas deferens*, are continuations of
and vesicles   the epididymis and run from the testes into the pelvic cavity (Figure 19-1), where they join with the small canals leading from the seminal

vesicles. The *seminal vesicles* are a pair of secretory glands that lie close to the bladder. The union of the canal from a seminal vesicle and the seminal duct form the *ejaculatory duct,* a narrow tube about 2.5 cm in length that lies on one side of the superior end of the prostate gland; the ejaculatory ducts have a contractile mechanism that aids in the emission of the seminal fluid during an orgasm.

prostate

This gland is a large, doughnutlike structure that lies behind the symphysis, just below the bladder, where it surrounds the distal end of the urethra. The prostate enlarges at puberty and reaches full size in the adult. With old age the prostate usually regresses and decreases in mass, although frequently this gland does hypertrophy in elderly males.

urethra and
urethral glands

The urethra is a combined urinary and genital passageway extending from the prostate *(prostatic urethra)* and runs the length of the penis *(spongy urethra)* to the exterior. The entire structure is about 20 cm long and is found in the anterior surface of the penis (Figure 19-1).

The two *bulbourethral glands* are pea-sized structures lying adjacent to the urethra, just below the prostatic portion. These mucous glands secrete a thin fluid that enters the spongy urethra; other small urethral glands may be present in this area (Figure 19-1).

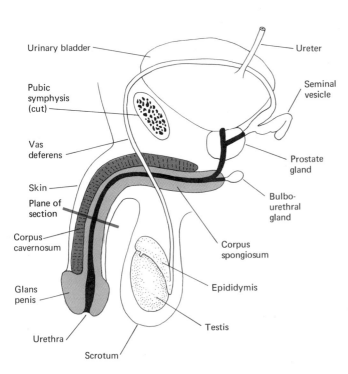

Figure 19-1 The anatomical organization of the human male reproductive system.

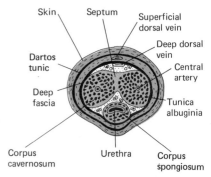

Figure 19-2 Cross section of the penis.

spermatic cord   In the embryo, the testes develop in the abdominal cavity near the point of origin of the kidneys and ovaries. During development, each testis is attached to the bottom of the scrotal sac by a ligament called the *gubernaculum*. The gubernaculum stops growing very early in the development of the embryo, but the embryo and fetus continue to grow so that the testes are "tied" to the scrotum. The blood vessels, nerves, lymphatic vessels, and ducts that descend with the testes as they migrate to the scrotum and the connective tissue wrapping constitute the *spermatic cord* (Figure 19-3). After the testes are within the scrotal sac, the pelvic musculature closes around the cord, obliterating the channel or *inguinal canal.*

microanatomy and cellular specializations   Two organs of the male reproductive system, the penis and testes, are highly specialized at the cellular and tissue level and are discussed in this section. The accessory male reproductive organs for the most part

figure 19-3

THE SEQUENCE
OF CHANGES IN
THE DESCENT OF
THE TESTIS

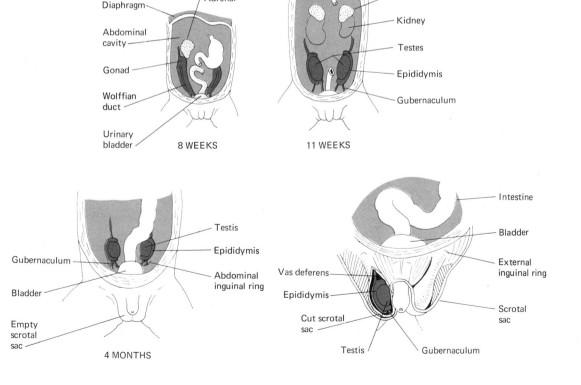

figure 19-4

THE
MICROSCOPIC
ANATOMY OF
THE
SEMINIFEROUS
TUBULES

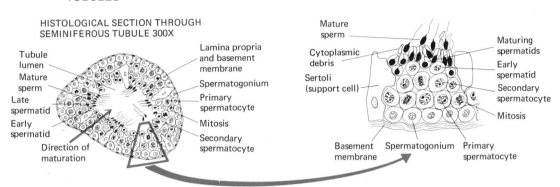

Various stages of spermatogenesis can be seen with the mature sperm in the lumen of the tubule.

are structurally comparable to similar secretory structures and ducts described for other systems.

corpora cavernosa (penis)
The copulatory organ of the male is primarily composed of three longitudinal columns of specialized connective tissue called the *corpora cavernosa*, a type of *erectile tissue*. Surrounding the corpora is a tough, inelastic fibrous sheath. The erectile tissue is quite spongy and can be engorged with large quantities of blood (Figure 19-2). The blood vessels supplying the erectile tissues do not terminate in capillary beds, but open directly into the cavernous, spongy spaces. During sexual excitement, the elastic cavernous spaces become filled with blood, causing the penis to become enlarged and erect. With the cessation of sexual excitement, the blood drains from the cavernous spaces, and the penis returns to its resting, flaccid condition.

seminiferous tubules
The testes perform two functions: (a) they produce the sex cells or gametes and (b) they produce the male hormones. The testis is composed primarily of *seminiferous tubules*, about 15 to 20 in number, located in lobules, each of which contains two or three tubules (Figure 19-4). Each seminiferous tubule is connected to the epididymis by a small duct, so that a closed channel system exists from the germinal tubules to the end of the urethra. The seminiferous tubules are composed principally of germinal cells, which are involved in sperm production (*spermatogenesis*), and *Sertoli cells*, which are believed to have a supportive role. Scattered between the tubules are clumps of *interstitial* or *Leydig cells*, which secrete the male hormone (Figure 19-4).

spermatogenesis

Spermatogenesis is the process by which mature male sex cells are formed, and it is distinguished by three major changes. First, the total number of chromosomes is halved from 46 to 23, and the *reduction division* is called *meiosis*. Obviously, mitosis alone is not suitable in male or female sex cells, because the number of chromosomes of the daughter cells is identical with the dividing cell. At fertilization, this would mean a double number of chromosomes (46 in the egg and 46 in the spermatozoon). In this case, mitosis of the fertilized egg would not proceed normally, and the egg would not develop. Second, at first stage of division, the homologous pairs of chromosomes come together, and invariably there is an exchange of genetic material. When the chromosome pairs come apart, each homologue has a different genetic content. This process provides much of the diversity we see in brothers and sisters. Third, the spermatazoa change size and shape (in ova the morphological changes are not as great). In essence, spermatogenesis produces a quantitative and qualitative change in the chromosome complement of the sex cells.

Meiosis involves two successive divisions, and the events in each are quite similar to the stages described for mitosis (see Module 2B). Only the first stage of meiosis I is unusual, when each chromosome pairs with its homologue and the genes are reshuffled. For every single sex cell that enters spermatogenesis, four mature cells are formed (Figure 19-5).

Spermatogenesis begins at puberty, when, under the influence of the male hormone, *spermatogonia* (46 chromosomes) undergo mitosis and form *primary spermatocytes* (also 46 chromosomes). The primary spermatocytes then undergo meiosis I and produce *secondary spermatocytes* (23 chromosomes). The secondary spermatocytes then go through meiosis II and are transformed first into *spermatids* and finally mature *sperm*. The latter step involves the morphological transformation of the immature cuboidal-shaped cell into the mature sperm with restricted cytoplasm, tail, and so on (Figure 19-6). The entire process takes about 72 days, and in man the cycle is almost continuous throughout his life. Spermatogenesis is not synchronous, except within given small regions of the seminiferous tubules; for example, all cells within a region are primary spermatocytes, whereas in an adjacent region only secondary spermatocytes are found. This lack of synchrony results in a continuous production of sperm, over 1 billion a day in the young adult.

physiology

hormones

The male sex hormones (*androgens*) are steroid molecules produced primarily by the Leydig cells of the testes and, to a lesser extent, in the adrenal cortex of both males and females. The most potent male sex hormone is *testosterone*. In the postpubertal male, testosterone production is relatively constant. Testosterone (Module 19) is not only essential for spermatogenesis but is required for the growth and development of the male sex organs and the other tissues that provide males with their secondary sex characteristics.

While the general effect of testosterone is to promote growth, the effect seems to be specific for certain tissues. Thus at puberty the larynx enlarges; the voice deepens; the sebaceous glands enlarge; the skin tex-

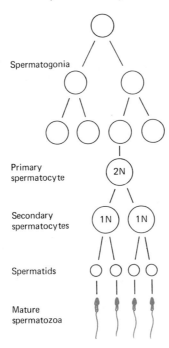

Spermatogonia

Primary
spermatocyte

Secondary
spermatocytes

Spermatids

Mature
spermatozoa

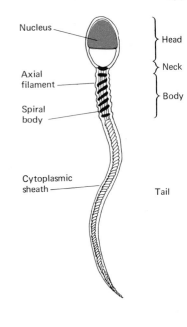

**Figure 19-5   Spermatogenesis, a di-
agrammatic summary. In meiosis each
diploid (2N) spermatogonium or stem
cell goes through a series of divisions,
which result in the production of eight
mature haploid (N) sperm.**

**Figure 19-6   The microscopic anat-
omy of a human sperm.**

ture changes; bone and muscle mass increase dramatically; and body
hair distribution becomes typically male, including certain types of bald-
ness which, while genetically determined, are homone dependent.
Testosterone probably also exerts an effect on the central nervous system, resulting in certain characteristic male behavior patterns. The
most clear-cut example is male sex drive, which declines fairly rapidly
after castration (removal of the gonads). Man's territorial and aggressive behavior has also been attributed to the effect of testosterone on the
brain, although these conclusions are primarily based on animal studies
and a few scanty clinical observations in man. It is exceptionally difficult
to separate environmental (cultural) influences from hormonal influences, but there appears to be sufficient evidence to suggest that some
masculine behavior is, in part, hormone dependent; how great a part
remains to be determined.

Synthesis of testosterone is continuous; about 8 μg is secreted daily.
The hormone is transported in the plasma bound to a carrier protein, and
only a small portion of the daily production affects target tissue. Most of
the testosterone in the circulation is broken down in the liver, and the
breakdown products are eventually excreted in the urine.

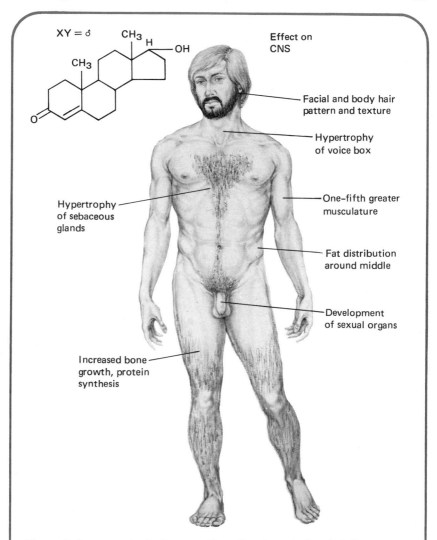

The male hormone, testosterone, either directly or indirectly influences all aspects of male reproductive function. Testosterone has a broad spectrum of effects on the testes and accessory reproductive organs as well as influencing sexual behavior, metabolism, and secondary sexual characteristics. Some of the major actions of testosterone are shown above.

Concerning our knowledge about human sexual behavior we have had to rely in large part on animal experimentation, where it has been shown that testosterone affects sex drive, aggressiveness, courtship behavior, and territorial drive. Recent work on primates suggests that hormonal influences in the last trimester of pregnancy and in early childhood produce early behavior manifestations of male type behavior. The production of sperm requires testosterone as well as the pituitary gonadotropins (LH and FSH). These pituitary gonadotropins have the same molecular shape in both males and females, but in males their only action is on the testes. LH in the male is sometimes referred to as ICSH (Interstitial-cell-stimulating hormone).

orgasm   Recent studies have helped to dispel some of our ignorance about the physiology of the human sexual response. Although a detailed review of male sexual activity is beyond the scope of this text, some of the salient features are worthy of mention. Males respond to a variety of sexual stimuli. The *primary erectile center*, part of the limbic system, sends volleys of nerve impulses to the *secondary erectile center* in the lower portion of the spinal cord. Impulses from the erectile center reach the penis via nerves and cause a rapid arteriolar dilation (5 to 10 seconds) of the blood vessels supplying the sinuses of the penis. Such erectile responses are seen in males from infancy onward. Stimulation of the sensory receptors, mainly around the glans penis, activates a complex *ejaculatory response*, during which *semen*, a mixture of sperm and secretions of male accessory glands, is forcibly ejected by a series of spasmodic contractions. The *ejaculatory response* is most often triggered by *masturbation* or by *coitus*, the sexual act of coupling. Accompanying the ejaculatory response are a number of other orgasmic responses: vasodilation of the skin, increase in blood pressure, increased muscle tone, involuntary contractions of the hand and foot musculature, hyperventilation, rapid heartbeat, and sweating. In most males, following the ejaculatory phase, there is a rapid decrease in muscle tone accompanied by relaxation.

The accessory male glands, the seminal vesicles, prostate, and bulbourethral glands secrete mucus and nutrient materials that make up 90 to 95 percent of the volume of the semen. During the orgasmic phase, the prostate contracts, adding to the semen a milky white alkaline secretion rich in sugars. Since sperm cannot survive in the acid medium of the vagina (pH 4) and because spermatozoa show maximum motility (1 to 4 mm/sec) at pH 6.5, it is thought that the alkaline secretions of the glands combine to protect the sperm from the vaginal acid environment as well as to adjust the pH to assure maximum sperm motility.

control   Testicular function, for example, sperm production and androgen secretion, is regulated by two anterior pituitary gonadotropic hormones. Both male and female pituitaries produce the same gonadotropins *follicle-stimulating hormone* (FSH) and *lutenizing hormone* (LH). To avoid confusion, it should be pointed out that LH in males is also called *interstitial cell-stimulating hormone* (ICSH), although the chemical structure of LH and ICSH is the same for both males and females. LH stimulates the Leydig cells to secrete androgens and, although LH alone can maintain sperm production for a short period of time, both LH and FSH are necessary for normal sperm production. The pituitary-gonadotropic feedback control system is similar to that described for the thyroid in the previous chapter; thus, the level of circulating androgen regulates gonadotropin release.

factors influencing function   Most of the factors that influence function of the reproductive system are complicated by hard-to-define psychosomatic responses (behavioral, anatomical and physiological). In such cases, cause and effect are difficult to define. The two examples cited in this section illustrate the complexity of the system.

age   Recent clinical evidence in man and some experimental studies on monkeys and rats have suggested that early in development the male sex hormone plays a role in the development of the central nervous system. Shortly after birth, at about three months of age, the testosterone-producing cells regress and do not function again until puberty, the time of transition from boyhood to manhood. This transition occurs in stages under the control of an unexplained clock mechanism of the central nervous system, which activates the gonadotropin release mechanism. Puberty usually starts somewhere between the ages of 8 and 11, but these early changes do not become apparent until the age of 10 to 15.

     The postpubertal male is believed to reach his sexual peak at about 18, and there is generally a gradual decline in sexual activity with the passage of time, although males usually maintain a fairly constant endocrine function into their fifties. In the aging male, psychological factors and a general decline in vigor are at least as important factors in the lessening of sexual activity as is regression of endocrine function.

genetic defects   Maleness, as was explained, is determined by the presence of the Y chromosome, but a delicate balance exists between masculinization and feminization in each individual. Except for the chromosome, the differences between males and females are essentially of degree. Both men and women have breasts, but usually these glands will develop in women, and rarely does this phenomenon occur in men.

     Males who have an extra X chromosome, the Kleinfelter syndrome (44 + XXY), have gangly arms and legs, infantile genitalia, enlarged breasts are not uncommon, and sterility is the rule. One can almost predict with certainty that a Kleinfelter child will show some degree of mental retardation and in some cases extreme loss of impulse control (aggression, rage, and so on). One might expect sterility or the excessive feminization, but why should an extra chromosome produce bizarre behavior?

     A similar situation in which behavioral aberration is the focal point of the genetic defect has recently been uncovered. Recent studies on prisoners institutionalized for violent, assaultive behavior have shown a very high frequency of another sex chromosome anomaly. Within this population, the frequency of an extra "Y" chromosome is about 5 to 12 percent, while in the general population, the frequency is estimated to be only 0.25 percent. Thus, it has been suggested that a male with an XYY may possibly be predisposed to violent aggressive behavior and that this behavior could be due to excessive amounts of testosterone. Today the evidence is far from clear, and there is considerable disagreement about both the data and the conclusion.

clinical considerations

castration   One of the earliest surgical procedures known to be performed was *castration*, the removal of the testes. Castration was and is practiced in raising livestock to produce plump, tender meat, and in the middle ages boy sopranos were castrated so that their voices would not change at puberty. If castration occurs before puberty, the male structures retain their juvenile condition, and sex drive never develops. Castration in adult males causes profound changes in structure and alteration of

figure 19-7
CIRCUMCISION

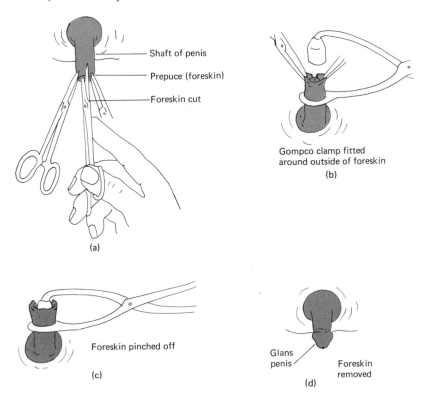

organ structure and function. However, sexually experienced castrated males may continue to show apparently normal sexual behavior for many months after the operation, which is indicative of the importance of the psychic aspects of sexuality.

circumcision
The earliest written account of human surgery is the operation of *circumcision*, the removal of the foreskin or prepuce of the penis (Figure 19-7). Examination of Egyptian mummies show that this operation was prevalent five millenia before Christ. Circumcision is thus an ancient rite that today is practiced by modern man both for hygienic and religious purposes. Most male babies in the United States are circumcised shortly after birth as a form of preventive medicine. Cancer of the penis is almost unknown in circumcised males.

hormonal hyperfunction
Premature or *precocious* puberty, due to abnormal function of the testes or anterior pituitary, is a relatively rare disease. When it does occur, adult masculine features will develop, even in young children. Hypersecretion in the adult also occurs, but the manifestation is difficult to assess.

hormonal hypofunction
Failure of the testes to descend *(cryptorchidism)* into the scrotum and tumors of the testes or pituitary cause hyposecretion and a spectrum of functional and structural changes similar to those described previously

figure 19-8

VASECTOMY

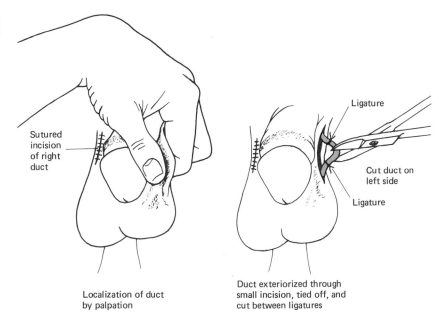

Sutured
incision
of right
duct

Ligature

Cut duct on
left side

Ligature

Localization of duct
by palpation

Duct exteriorized through
small incision, tied off, and
cut between ligatures

under castration; males display eunuchoid characteristics. Hormone therapy will often correct the defect.

impotence   Impotence is the inability to achieve or maintain an erection in an otherwise normal fertile male. In some instances, impotence may be due to nerve damage, sickle cell anemia, leukemia, or diabetes, but the usual cause is psychological. Anxiety, depression, fear, or anger may cause the erectile centers in the brain to be turned off. It should be emphasized that impotency is not a synonym for sterility.

Another primarily psychological problem that has effects similar to those of impotence is *premature ejaculation*, which involves sexual hyperexcitability and unusually rapid attainment of orgasm. While such males can produce offspring, the brevity of the sex act frequently prevents intromission and thus the sperm from being deposited in the vagina. Recent studies have shown that with counseling, the problem of premature ejaculation is largely correctable.

sterility   The normal fertile male produces 3 to 5 ml of semen per ejaculation. Each millimeter contains 70,000,000 to 100,000,000 viable spermatozoa. If sperm counts fall below 35,000,000 per milliliter, chances of conception are less than normal, and the individual may be *sterile*, incapable of producing offspring. A number of medications may produce transient depressions in sperm count. Permanent sterility can result from prolonged high fever or infection of the testes, which causes severe inflammation. For example, the common childhood disease mumps in postpubertal males may cause *orchitis* (inflammation of the testes), which produces sterility. Raising the body temperature for considerable lengths of time may also impair spermatogenesis.

diseases of the
prostate

The prostate is one of the most vulnerable glands to disease and is one of the few organs that may show enlargement (hypertrophy) as one reaches old age. Cancer of the prostate, a disorganized enlargement of prostatic tissue, is also frequently seen in older males. Hypertrophy does not only increase size and weight, but also increases secretory activity. Because of the anatomic relationship between the prostate and the urethra, hypertrophy of the gland can lead to obstruction of the ureters, thus blocking the flow of urine from the kidney to the bladder. Because of this condition, the individual must excessively contract the lower abdominal muscles to force the urine by the obstruction, and this extra pressure, if it is needed over a considerable span of time, may open the inguinal canal, and an inguinal hernia results.

summary

**gross
anatomy**

1. Testes: paired ovoid structures which lie within the scrotal sac; composed of germinal tissue connected to a highly coiled duct system (the epididymis and ductus deferens)

2. Scrotum: a thin-walled pouch below the base of the penis

3. Penis: a cylindrical, erectile shaft through which runs the urethra; distal end enlarged (the glans) and enfolded in a retractable, elastic layer of skin (the prepuce)

4. Seminal ducts and vesicles: paired tubular ductus deferens; run into pelvic cavity and join with glandular ducts from seminal vesicles and prostate; two ducts fuse to form a narrow tube, the ejaculatory duct; the latter enters the urethra (on each side)

5. Prostate: a large doughnut-shaped gland below the bladder surrounding the urethra

6. Urethra and urethral glands: common canal for urinary and genital systems; mucous-secreting bulbourethral glands also add secretions to urethral canal

7. Spermatic cord: contains blood vessels, nerves, seminal ducts; runs from the testes to points of origin in the abdominal cavity; a muscular ring forms around the cord, where it penetrates the abdominal wall

**microanatomy
and cellular
specializa-
tions**

1. Corpora cavernosa (penis): three specialized longitudinal columns of spongy, highly vascularized connective tissue; in sexual excitement can become engorged with blood (erection)

2. Seminiferous tubules: source of sperm cells; Leydig cells, between tubules, secrete male hormone

3. Spermatogenesis: meiotic division of primary spermatocytes through a series of divisions produces haploid sperm; up to half billion produced daily

physiology

1. Hormones: male sex hormones, androgens, produced by Leydig cells in testes and to a lesser degree by adrenal cortex, are responsible for all male primary and secondary sexual characteristics. The most potent androgen is testosterone which is secreted continuously

2. Orgasm: a complex ejaculatory response at peak of sexual excitement forcibly ejects about 3 ml of semen, a mixture of sperm and secretions of accessory male glands

control   The same anterior pituitary gonadotropins (FSH and LH) that stimulate ovarian function trigger continuous androgen production and sperm maturation in the testis; releasing hormone, which activates secretion of pituitary gonadotropins; respond to feedback inhibition by increasing blood levels of testosterone

factors influencing function   1. Age: in early development, testosterone may effect CNS development. At puberty transition into an adult male occurs, and testosterone secretion increases to a steady level; slow regression of testes occurs with advancing age, but the decline is extremely gradual

2. Genetic defects: any abnormality of extra X or Y chromosome impairs brain function and affects hormone production

clinical considerations   1. Castration: surgical removal of testis; in young males causes retention of prepubertal state; in adult males loss of source of male hormone affects primary and secondary sexual characteristics and behavior, as in hypofunction

2. Hormonal hyperfunction: early onset of puberty and slight enhancement of male characteristics above norm

3. Hormonal hypofunction: eunuchlike characteristics due to lack of male hormone; failure to develop full spectrum of adult male characteristics

4. Impotence: the inability to achieve or maintain an erection; often psychosomatic, but sometimes due to disease states or nerve damage

5. Sterility: low sperm count which reduces capability of impregnating healthy female; often due to inflammation of testes

6. Diseases of the prostate: often the site of gonorrheal infection; one of the few organs that sometimes increases in size with advancing age; primary site for cancer in older males

20

female reproductive system

gross anatomy
ovaries
Fallopian tubes
uterus
vagina
external genitalia
breasts

microanatomy and cellular specializations
ovaries
Fallopian tubes
uterus
vagina
external genitalia

physiology
estrogen

progesterone
control of secretion
menstrual cycle
orgasm

factors influencing function
age

clinical considerations
hyposecretion
hypersecretion
amenorrhea
dysmenorrhea
sterility
abnormal vaginal discharge
venereal diseases

Critical to the understanding of the reproductive system is knowledge of the sex hormones that are responsible for development and function of this system. In the male reproductive system, only one sex hormone is involved, but the female reproductive system involves two different sex hormones, both produced by the ovaries. Until 1500 the anatomist referred to the ovary as the "female testes," and it was not until the 1800s that the endocrine role of the ovary was elaborated. By 1923 it was shown that the ovary produced a feminizing hormone, but it took another 13 years of research before the primary female sex hormone, the steroid *estradiol*, was isolated, purified, and finally synthesized. During this same period a second female sex hormone was isolated and purified. This hormone, *progesterone* (also a steroid), is mainly involved in preparation of the uterus to receive a fertilized egg and to maintain the uterine lining during pregnancy, while the primary female sex hormone, estradiol, is responsible for the development of most primary and secondary female sexual characteristics (see Module 20). As will be seen later in this chapter, the plasma levels of these female sex hormones show a cyclical (monthly) rhythmicity.

gross anatomy

ovaries

Lying within the body cavity close to the lateral walls of the pelvis are two pinkish almond-shaped ovaries (Figure 20-1). Each adult ovary is about 3 to 5 cm in length, 1 cm thick, and 2 to 3 cm wide, and weighs about 6 g. The surface of the ovary is irregular, and in the mature female has many small patches of scar tissue that represents previous ovulations. The ovary is anchored in place by membranous ligaments: (a) the *mesovarium*, a broad ligament attached to the uterus, (b) the *ovarian ligaments*, also attached to the uterus, and (c) the *suspensory ligaments*, which attach to the pelvic wall.

Fallopian tubes

The uterine or Fallopian tubes that carry the eggs from the ovary to the uterus are each about 10 cm long, and they open into the uterus. The tubes are held in place by mesenteries, the mesovarium, which are described in greater detail in the next section (Figure 20-1). A funnel-like portion—the *infundibulum*, composed of many branched processes, the *fimbriae*—arches upward and surrounds most of the medial surface of the ovary. The infundibulum leads into a thickened portion, the *ampulla*, which then constricts, forming the narrow *isthmus* that leads into the uterus.

uterus

The nonpregnant uterus is a fist-sized, thick-walled, hollow muscular organ ($7.5 \times 5 \times 2.5$ cm) situated in the pelvis between the urinary bladder and the rectum. From above it receives the Fallopian tubes, and below it opens into the vagina. The *cervix* is the lowermost portion of the uterus that actually projects slightly into the vagina. The uterus can be divided into two major anatomical components, the *body* and *isthmus* (Figure 20-2). The body, which composes the bulk of the uterine mass, is pear-shaped, and the isthmus is the narrow portion that leads through an

---

* All steroids having feminizing effects are called estrogens; of the estrogens, estradiol is the most potent feminizing hormone.

THE PHYSIO-
LOGICAL ACTION
OF ESTROGEN

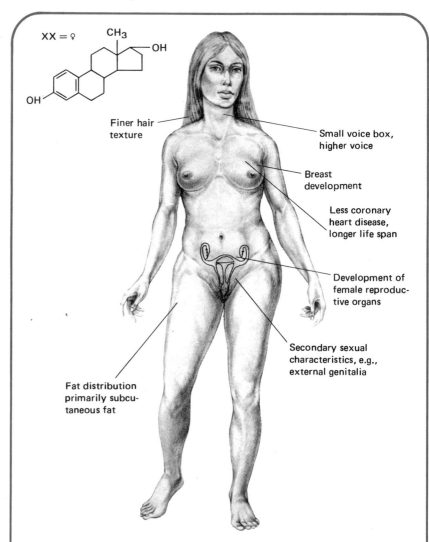

The hormonal control in females is much more complex than in males since two primary sex hormones are involved (estrogen and progesterone) and because, unlike the male the plasma levels of these hormones exhibit a cyclic rhythmicity. Many female characteristics are associated with the hormone estrogen, which is mainly secreted by the follicle cells in the ovary. Estrogen secretion is regulated by both anterior pituitary gonadotropins (LH and FSH), but what clock mechanism triggers the cyclic release of LH is still under investigation.

Estrogen in addition to markedly affecting the ovary, uterus, and associated reproductive organs exerts major control of secondary female sexual characteristics. In this respect estrogen is analogous to testosterone.

Estrogen also acts on nonreproductive tissues, causing typical female skin and hair texture, hair distribution, fat deposition, and in general has much less anabolic effect on other tissues, such as muscle and bone, than testosterone does.

Recent primate studies have suggested that estrogen may exert its effects in late fetal and in early postnatal development, causing behavior patterns which are more female. Some fragmentary information in humans tends to support this finding. The human female sexual response, unlike the male response, does not seem to be hormone dependent in that female sex behavior is not altered by castration (in this case removal of the ovaries). Other behaviors associated with cyclical changes in hormone level in females (premenstrual tension, etc.) may not be directly due to the plasma hormone level but may be the result of a number of the complex physiological changes associated with menstruation.

opening, the *internal os*, into the narrow *cervical canal*, which, in turn, opens into the vagina via the *external os*.

The uterus is loosely held in place by membranous ligaments (Figures 20-1 and 20-2), but is primarily kept in position by the floor of the pelvis, rectum, and bladder. Thus, the position of the uterus will depend, in part, on the fullness of the rectum and bladder. It should be noted that the uterus and vagina are not oriented in a straight line, but at right angles to each other when viewed in sagittal section (Figure 20-2). Because of this anatomic relationship, the uterus is frequently "out of position" (Figure 20-3).

vagina   A short but extensible muscular tube, the *vagina*, extends from the cervix to the external genitalia. At the cervical end, it attaches higher on the posterior side, so that it is about 9 or 10 cm long on the posterior side, but only 7 or 8 cm long on the anterior side.

external genitalia   The myriad structures that compose the female external sex organs are collectively called the *vulva* or *pudendum*, as shown in Figure 20-4. It is composed of (a) the *mons pubis*, a mound of fatty tissue, which overlies the *pubic symphysis* and is covered with coarse hair after puberty, and (b) the *labia majora*, two large fatty folds of skin that begin at the mons pubis and extend backward toward the rectum and form a cleft or valley into which both the urethra and vagina open. The outer portion of the labia majora is covered with hair, and the skin is pigmented like that of the scrotum. Within the labia majora are two hair-free smaller folds, the *labia minora*. Lying anteriorly within the labia minora is a small erectile organ, the *clitoris*. The clitoris is the homologue of the penis. The cleft behind the clitoris and between the labia is the *vestibule*, in which both the vaginal and urethral orifices lie, the urethral opening being anterior to that of the vagina. The vaginal orifice may be covered by a connective tissue membrane, the *hymen* or *maidenhead*. The hymen may totally occlude the vaginal opening, a relatively rare situation known as *imperforate hymen*. Since the hymen is so highly vari-

figure 20-1

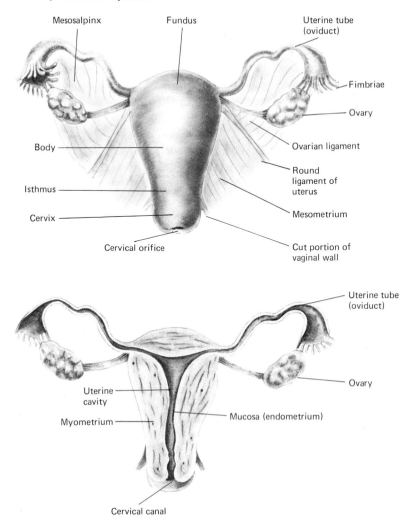

Mesosalpinx   Fundus   Uterine tube (oviduct)

Fimbriae

Ovary

Body

Ovarian ligament

Isthmus

Round ligament of uterus

Cervix

Mesometrium

Cervical orifice

Cut portion of vaginal wall

Uterine tube (oviduct)

Ovary

Uterine cavity

Mucosa (endometrium)

Myometrium

Cervical canal

able in shape and size and may persist even after repeated coitus, its absence or presence is not really a significant indicator of virginity.

breasts   The breasts are modifications of integumentary glands, and their role in the postpubertal female is that of accessory organs of reproduction. Although present in both males and females, development only takes place in the presence of female hormone (males given large doses of estrogenic hormones show mammary development). The immature breasts sit high on the chest wall, but with maturation they fill out and assume mature proportions (Figure 20-5). Each breast or *mammary gland* (there are usually only two, but extra or *supernumerary breasts* are not uncommon) is a skin-covered protuberance of glandular tissue, fatty tissue, and connective tissue attached to the pectoral region by

figure 20-2

THE FEMALE
REPRODUCTIVE
SYSTEM IN SITU,
A SAGITTAL
SECTION

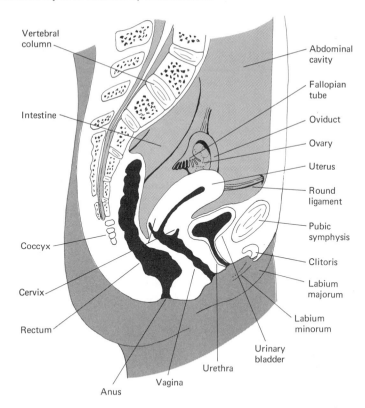

figure 20-2

THE FEMALE
REPRODUCTIVE
SYSTEM IN SITU,
A SAGITTAL
SECTION

fibrous connective tissue (Figure 20-6). Size is highly variable, as it is dependent on both endocrine and genetic factors. Each breast has a raised *nipple*, an area where the glandular ducts open to the exterior. Around the nipple is the pigmented hairless *areola*, a structure rich in sebaceous glands. Both the nipple and areola are capable of erectile responses.

microanatomy and cellular specializations

ovaries

Each ovary has an outer *cortex*, the *germinal layer*, which at birth contains up to a quarter of a million minute, immature *primary ovarian follicles*. Each primary ovarian follicle is composed of an *ovum* or egg cell surrounded by a ball of flat *follicular cells*, which, in the maturing follicle, are the source of estrogen (Figure 20-7). With the onset of menstruation, each month several primary follicles undergo maturation. The ovum in the developing follicle undergoes meiotic division and the surrounding follicular cells proliferate. A clear membrane, the *zona pellucida*, forms around the ovum, and connective tissue proliferates to form a *theca*, a fibrous coat rich in blood vessels, around the developing follicle. Many follicles start the maturation process, but only a few (usually one each month) complete the process. Thus, histological examination of the ovary reveals a variety of stages of follicular development, including primary follicles that underwent an abortive attempt at maturation and failed. Those follicles and ova that never complete de-

figure 20-3

THE UTERUS
AND VAGINA

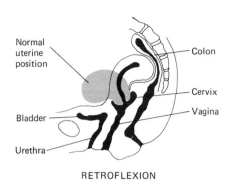

RETROFLEXION

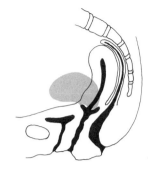

RETROCESSION

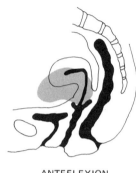

ANTEFLEXION

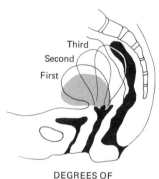

DEGREES OF
RETROVERSION

The normal uterus and vagina as seen in sagittal and several abnormal positions of the uterus.

velopment are called *atretic follicles*, and they are seen in various stages of regression within the ovarian tissue.

As development of the follicles progresses, they move outward to the ovarian cortex or *tunica albuginea*, where the ovum increases in diameter and undergoes other maturational changes (Figure 20-7).

Proliferative follicular cells form layers about the ovum, and a fluid, the *liquor folliculi*, fills in the follicular space. The fluid-filled cavity expands, forming a *Graafian follicle*. The ovum rests on a pillar of follicular cells, the *cumulus oophorous* (Figure 20-7). The maturing Graafian follicle migrates until it bulges out of the surface of the ovary from whence it ruptures out of the surrounding epithelium and tunica albuginea, freeing the ovum and its surrounding "crown" of follicular cells, the *corona radiata*, into the body cavity. The process of follicular rupture is ovulation (Figure 20-7).

Following ovulation the follicular cells repair the rupture and proliferate rapidly to form a ball of *granulosa cells* that surround a clot within the follicle, the *corpus hemorrhagicum*. The granulosa cells enlarge and elaborate a yellowish secretion, and together the cells and

figure 20-4

THE FEMALE
EXTERNAL
GENITALIA

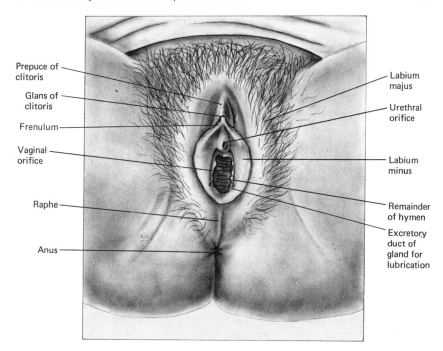

Prepuce of clitoris

Glans of clitoris

Frenulum

Vaginal orifice

Raphe

Anus

Labium majus

Urethral orifice

Labium minus

Remainder of hymen

Excretory duct of gland for lubrication

secretion fill the former follicular cavity. This yellow body or *corpus luteum* is the major source of progesterone and usually persists for only two weeks before undergoing regression, leaving behind a connective tissue scar, the *corpus albicans.* If pregnancy occurs, the corpus luteum persists and continues to enlarge, reaching its peak size at about the second month of pregnancy, and then gradually atrophies until birth when it quickly regresses totally (Figure 20-7).

Fallopian tubes   The uterine tubes consist of three layers: an outer *serous* coat of connective tissue, a middle double *muscular* layer containing both longitudinal and circular smooth muscle, and an inner *mucus* layer. The mucosa consists of a layer of simple columnar epithelium resting on a vascularized connective tissue bed. Some of the epithelial cells are ciliated, and the beat of these cilia plays a role in transporting the ovulated ovum to the uterus.

uterus   The uterus, like the ovary, exhibits cyclical changes. The outermost layer of the uterus, the *serous coat,* is composed of fibrous connective tissues from the peritoneum. The bulk of the uterus is the middle part made up of three layers of smooth muscle, called the myometrium, that collectively provide peristaltic contractions. The innermost mucosal lining of the uterus, the *endometrium,* is composed of secretory and ciliated columnar epithelium resting on a layer of loose connective tissue, within which are many blood and lymph vessels and coiled tubular uterine glands. The endometrium exhibits monthly cyclical changes in structure after puberty, and the tissue changes are hormone dependent.

figure 20-5

BREAST
DEVELOPMENT
AT VARIOUS
STAGES OF LIFE

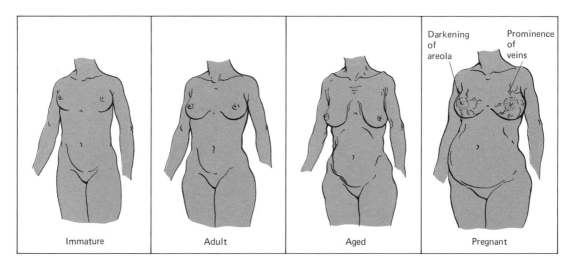

Immature   Adult   Aged   Pregnant

As progresterone from the corpus luteum declines, the thickened walls of the endometrium exhibit atrophic changes. (a) Capillary walls break down as do some smaller arterioles; as a result, bleeding occurs into the stroma of the endometrium. (b) The superficial portions of the endometrium are deprived of blood supply and are sloughed off or expelled along with blood and glandular secretions forming the *menstruum*, or "tears of the uterus."

vagina   The vagina is a muscular sheath and, like most tubular structures opening to the exterior, it has a *mucosa* composed of stratified squamous epithelium in which thickness varies with hormone levels. There are no distinct glands in the vagina, but mucosal cells appear capable of forming an exudate. The vaginal secretion, which is glycogen rich, permits bacterial breakdown of sugars and causes an acid vaginal environment, pH 4.5. The middle layer, the *muscularis*, is composed of both circular and longitudinal smooth muscles. The outer layer of the vagina is composed of highly vascularized connective tissue. Surrounding the vaginal orifice is a band of voluntary muscle, the *bulbocavernosus.*

external genitalia   Within the labia majora are numerous layers of sebaceous glands embedded in fatty, loose connective tissue. The clitoris contains two cavernous sinuses enclosed in connective tissue, whereas the free extremity or glans of the clitoris is highly vascularized erectile tissue richly endowed with sensory nerve endings. On either side of the vaginal orifice are the *Bartholin glands*, whose ducts discharge their secretions (quantity is minimal) via openings between the labia minora and hymen.

figure 20-6

THE
ANATOMICAL
ORGANIZATION
OF THE HUMAN
BREAST

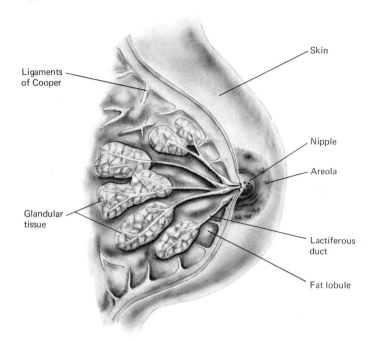

physiology

estrogen

Estradiol is responsible for development and maintenance of the reproductive organs as well as all female secondary sexual characteristics
(Module 20). Unlike male hormones, there is no apparent effect shown
on the libido, and removal of the ovaries in adult human females need
not affect sexual behavior.

Estrogen levels in the blood, and body temperature show cyclical fluctuations during the course of each monthly cycle (Figures 20-8 and 20.9).
Estrogen levels and temperature are lowest at menstruation. At ovulation, there is a sudden drop of temperature followed by a rise in basal
body temperature, which is maintained until just before menses begins.
Estrogen levels show two peaks during the cycle: one peak at ovulation
(9 to 11 days) and a second peak during the luteal phase (10 to 24 days).
Just prior to the onset of menstruation, the estrogen level shows a pre-
cipitous drop, but if pregnancy occurs, estrogen levels remain high until
the second trimester apparently due to estrogen production by the
placenta.

The primary female target tissues for estrogen are the linings of the
vagina and uterus, and the breasts. The vagina shows tremendous
growth changes, particularly in the epithelial cells, and involutes or
atrophies in the absence of estrogens. In the uterus, estrogens promote
proliferation of the endometrium as well as increase the contractility of
the uterine muscle. Estrogen also increases uterine blood supply and
may increase capillary permeability and overall metabolic activity. The
development of the mammary glands is affected by several hormones.
The principal activity of estrogen is to *prepare* the breasts for milk production, which is under control of other hormones. The duct system is
particularly estrogen sensitive.

figure 20-7

DIAGRAMMATIC
SUMMARY OF
CYCLICAL
EVENTS IN THE
OVARY

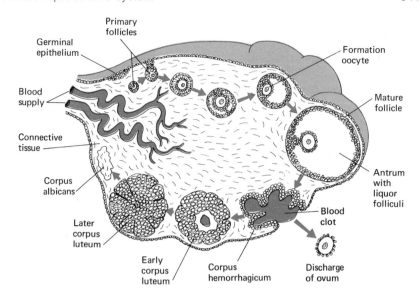

figure 20-7

DIAGRAMMATIC SUMMARY OF CYCLICAL EVENTS IN THE OVARY

progesterone

Early in this century it was discovered that removal of the corpus luteum early in pregnancy of rodents resulted in abortion. Thus it became apparent that the corpus luteum was producing a hormone needed for the maintenance of the uterine lining. This hormone is progesterone, and its functions extend beyond simple maintenance of the uterine lining. Progesterone interacts with estrogen to prepare the uterus for implantation of the fertilized egg (see Chapter 21) and stimulates growth of the secretory ducts of the mammary glands. The hormone also inhibits smooth muscle activity. Progresterone is synthesized and released in the second half of the menstrual cycle, and a sharp drop in plasma progesterone precedes the onset of menses (Figure 20-8).

control
secretion

The regular cyclical fluctuations in plasma levels of the female sex hormones in the adult female are due to a built-in clock mechanism in the central nervous system (probably in the hypothalamus).

Rhythmicity is apparently established prior to birth (last trimester of pregnancy) by estrogenic hormones present at this time acting on the developing brain. At puberty, this clock mechanism is activated, and the neurosecretory cells of the hypothalamus begin to produce *gonadotropic hormone-releasing factors*. These releasing factors eventually regulate the production and release of three pituitary gonadotropins: *FSH* (follicle-stimulating hormone), *LH* (lutenizing hormone) and *LTH* (luteotropic hormone). Thus, if the anterior pituitary or hypothalamus is destroyed, ovarian function ceases. Since the gonadotropins regulate ovarian hormone secretion, it is to be expected that there is a direct relationship between plasma gonadotropin level and the levels of estrogen and progesterone (Figure 20-8). Indeed, as the plasma concentration of estrogen and progesterone increases, there is a negative feedback to the hypothalamus suppressing the output of specific gonadotropic releasing factors (Figure 20-10).

figure 20-8

HORMONAL
CHANGES

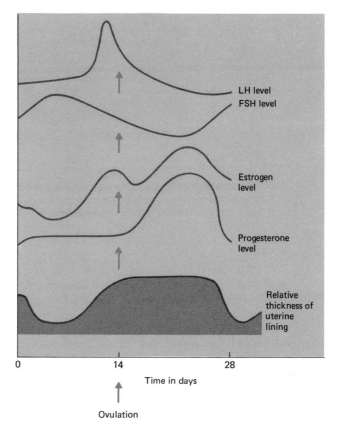

LH level
FSH level

Estrogen
level

Progesterone
level

Relative
thickness of
uterine
lining

0   14   28

Time in days

Ovulation

**Summary of hormonal changes during the menstrual cycle. Relative concentrations
of hormones are shown on the perpendicular axis.**

FSH is necessary for growth and maturation of the primary ovarian
follicles and also stimulates these follicular cells to secrete estrogen.
LH also appears to be necessary in the later stages of maturation of the
ovarian follicles and is also essential for ovulation and for the transformation of the emptied follicle into a corpus luteum. The third pituitary gonadotropin, LTH, aids in the maintenance of the corpus luteum
and, during pregnancy, plays a major role in the development of secretory activity of the mammary glands. In pregnancy the placenta becomes an endocrine organ producing HCG (human chorionic gonadotropin), which extends the functional life span of the corpus luteum.

menstrual cycle   Menstruation, a cyclical phenomenon of the postpubertal female,
represents the periodic preparation of the uterus to receive and nourish the fertilized egg. After the first menstrual period or *menarche,*
the cycle is repeated year after year for the next three or so decades when
menopause or cessation of the cycle occurs. There is considerable variation in the duration of the cycle ranging from 20 to 35 days with the
average duration being about 28 days. Although the cycle is a con-

figure 20-9

TEMPERATURE
CHANGES

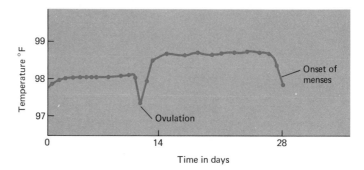

Temperature changes often seen during the menstrual cycle. Many women show characteristic changes in basal temperature (taken upon first arising in the morning) during the course of their menstrual cycle.

tinuum, for convenience it may be divided into three discrete phases, each dependent on hormonal changes, which are reflected by changes in uterine and vaginal function. The *proliferative* or *follicular phase* occurs prior to ovulation and is dominated by estrogen-induced changes described earlier. Starting with the first day of the cycle, this phase lasts about two weeks and is concluded at *ovulation,* or the release of the egg. The rupture of the mature follicle may be accompanied by the release of a small amount of blood and abdominal pain or *mittelschmerz* (German for middle pain). The ovum is transported into the Fallopian tubes, where fertilization may occur.

In phase two, the *secretory* or *luteal* phase is dominated by changes induced by progesterone and may last 10 days. During this phase the corpus luteum develops as a progesterone-producing endocrine organ, and the endometrium is able to maintain the implanted fertilized egg. If conception does not occur, however, the third phase of the cycle follows. The *bleeding phase* of menstruation is not induced per se, but occurs because the hormones that stimulate endometrial growth decrease in concentration; thus menstruation is a result of the withdrawal of estrogen and progesterone (Figure 20-8), with the latter hormone being more important. Prior to the onset of menses (2 to 6 days), the flow in the tortuously coiled endometrial arteries is diminished due to intermittent arteriolar clamping of the longitudinal band of smooth muscle that makes these arterioles unique. The resulting decrease in blood and lessened perfusion of nutrients to the outer third of the endometrium cause these tissues to become ischemic, and they begin to regress (that is, some epithelial cells start to die off). Immediately prior to menstruation these arterioles undergo prolonged clamping, up to 5 hours, and the anoxia is sufficiently severe to cause necrosis of the inner third of the endometrium. The arterioles then dilate, and this surge of blood helps initiate the sloughing off of the dead cells of the endometrium. Some hemorrhage occurs, but the arterioles constrict again, stopping the bleeding. Each of the endometrial arterioles only bleeds once during each period, but the time course of each arteriolar regression is not

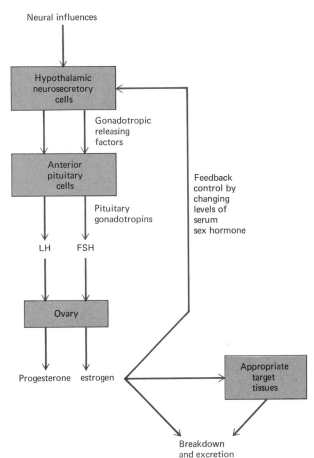

figure 20-10

SUMMARY OF
HORMONAL
CONTROL OF
THE OVARY

Neural influences

Hypothalamic
neurosecretory
cells

Gonadotropic
releasing
factors

Anterior
pituitary
cells

Feedback
control by
changing
levels of
serum
sex hormone

Pituitary
gonadotropins

LH   FSH

Ovary

Appropriate
target
tissues

Progesterone   estrogen

Breakdown
and excretion

synchronous; thus the menstrual flow lasts several days (3 to 6 days).

During the course of each monthly cycle, the vaginal lining also undergoes a series of cyclical changes. During the follicular phase of the cycle, the vaginal epithelium shows rapid growth, and the epithelial layer becomes partially cornified (converted into keratin). The vaginal smear taken at this time is mainly made up of "cornified" epithelial cells. During the secretory phase of the cycle, vaginal secretions increase. At the same time mucin is secreted, and the vaginal lining is invaded by many leucocytes. Thus the vaginal smear during this phase has both partially cornified epithelial cells and large numbers of white cells.

orgasm The sequence of events leading to and during the female orgasm in many ways parallels the stages observed for males. The initial phase is characterized by a surge of blood flowing to the genital region and to the breasts. The vasocongestion produces a swelling of the clitoris, expansion of the vagina, increased secretions, and erection of the nipples. Just prior to the orgasm, the clitoris withdraws, and the earlier changes in the vagina and breasts are heightened; even the uterus moves (upward and backward) for unexplainable reasons. Concomitant increases in heart rate and respiration also occur. The onset of the orgasm is distinguished by a series of muscular contractions, each lasting from several seconds to a fraction of a second. These contractions occur principally in the vagina, uterus, and rectum. The breasts and clitoris apparently are not reactive in this phase. The return to the preorgasm state usually takes less than 10 minutes.

factors influencing function

Recent clinical and experimental studies have suggested that early in development the female sex hormone may play a role in the development of the central nervous system. Shortly after birth, estrogen production declines until puberty, when some still unexplained clock mechanism triggers the release of gonadotropins and starts the hormonal tide

age

that brings about the transition to sexual maturity. In general, females tend to reach puberty sooner than males. After reaching sexual maturity, the female endocrine system continues to function regularly for the next three to four decades (there is wide variability), and then begins to show a marked decline in function.

The *menopause*, or so-called change of life, usually occurs between the years 45 to 50 and is a manifestation of aging of the female endocrine and reproductive system. It is characterized by a cessation of menstruation and sometimes a variety of other physical and psychological symptoms collectively known as the *menopause syndrome*. The symptoms during the *climacteric* (the total time leading to the cessation of the sexual cycle) may include dizziness, headache, palpitation of the heart, numbness of the extremities, hot flashes, insomnia, irritability, fatigue, and depression. In rare cases the emotional aspects become severe enough to alter the individual's sense of reality. This severe form of depression is known as *involutional melancholia*. Female hormone replacement therapy has proved to be of significant benefit in treating the menopausal syndrome so that many, if not most, symptoms can be alleviated.

clinical considerations

hyposecretion

Failure of the ovaries to develop completely (hypogonadism) may result in *sexual infantilism* (all primary and secondary female sex characteristics are maintained in a childlike condition) or *sexual juvenilism* (a state causing amenorrhea, dysmenorrhea, sterility, and underdevelopment of the sex organs). Treatment with both estrogenic and progestational hormones has proved to be effective in alleviating many of these symptoms.

hypersecretion

Although hypersecretion is relatively rare, it may occur, often in a relatively young girl, causing a precocious onset of puberty and menses. Sometimes ovarian hyperfunction may cause mammary glands to exhibit precocious or juvenile hypertrophy (Figure 20-11).

amenorrhea

The absence of menstruation is called *primary amenorrhea. Secondary amenorrhea* is cessation of menstruation in an individual who had previously experienced menstruation. This too is due to transient ovarian

figure 20-11

CLINICAL EFFECT
OF ESTROGEN
HYPERSECRETION

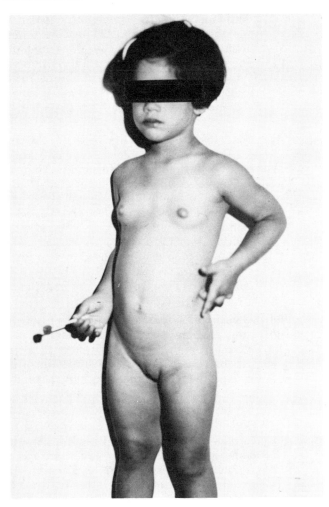

Precocious breast development in the five-year-old patient was due to hyperactivity of the anterior pituitary, which in turn stimulated ovarian function, prematurely raising estrogen levels in the plasma. This elevated hormone level causes hypertrophy of the mammary tissues. (Courtesy Dr. Boris Senior, Tufts University Medical School.)

hypofunction, which may be caused by a variety of chronic diseases, malnutrition, and emotional stress (anxiety, fear, depression, and so on). These psychosomatic cycle disruptions are particularly frequent in late teen-age and young adult females.

dysmenorrhea   Although generally not serious, the crampy pains, nausea, headache, and increased irritability sometimes associated with menstruation, that is, *dysmenorrhea*, can be transiently incapacitating. Psychic factors and the personality of the individual also contribute to the severity of the symptoms. Usually symptomatic relief may be provided by common analgesic medications. Another syndrome, *premenstrual tension*, can produce psychic factors, but the symptoms occur prior to menstruation. The symptoms of premenstrual tension include water retention and expansion of extracellular fluid volume, lower backache, feeling of tenderness or even pain in the breasts and nipples, a feeling of fullness of the abdomen, and occasionally changes in mood.

sterility   Contrary to older beliefs *sterility*, the inability to conceive, is not primarily a female problem, since at least 40 to 50 percent of the cases result from deficient sperm counts. There are a number of diverse causes of female sterility. One recent study found that in about 10 percent of the women studied, the vaginal secretions killed sperm, sometimes immobilizing the sperm in less than 10 seconds. However, the most common cause of female sterility is tubular occlusion. Infertility associated with ovarian failure often is correctable by hormone therapy. Despite numerous reports of psychosomatic infertility associated with emotional disturbances, there is relatively little or no clear evidence that emotional factors play a major role in the inability of females to conceive.

abnormal vaginal   Abnormal vaginal discharge may result from a great variety of causes,
discharge   ranging from hormonal disorders to infection or malignancy of the uterus, vagina, ovaries, or cervix. Since many conceptions abort spontaneously, a heavy prolonged episode of uterine discharge after a delay in expected time of menstruation may indicate such a spontaneous abortion. In any case, abnormal uterine bleeding or discharge indicates the need for gynecological examination.

venereal diseases   In many parts of the world today, venereal diseases have reached epidemic proportions (50 to 100 cases per thousand) in the young adult population. These infectious diseases are usually transmitted during sexual intercourse and are readily treatable with antibiotics. The two major diseases are *syphilis* and *gonorrhea.* The syphilis organism causes a localized lesion or *chancre* usually on the genitalia, but subsequently may be dispersed to many organs of the body such as the brain. The progress of the disease is remarkably slow, but if untreated, syphilis will eventually kill or cripple 25 percent of those persons afflicted. Gonorrhea is caused by a bacterium that enters the system through the genitourinary tracts of both males and females. The primary infection, if untreated within months, may spread to other parts of the body such as the joints and Fallopian tubes. The subsequent inflammation of the tubes may cause *salpingitis* (inflammation) and *scarring* of the tubes, which in turn causes sterility. In the joints the infection can cause a crippling arthritis.

summary

1. Ovaries: paired organs in body cavity anchored in place by membranes; source of ova (egg cells) and most female hormones

gross
anatomy

2. Fallopian tubes: paired funnels next to ovaries; channel egg (ovum) to the uterus; oviducts are not connected to the ovary

3. Uterus: muscular hollow organ between bladder and rectum; lower portion, the cervix, extends into the vagina

4. Vagina: a short extensible muscular tube leading from uterus to external genitalia

5. External genitalia: a number of external sex organs collectively called the vulva; composed of hair-covered mons, the labia majora and minora (lips of the vagina), and within the anterior labia a small erectile organ—the clitoris

6. Breasts (mammary glands): skin-covered protuberances of glandular fatty and connective tissue; glands open by way of a raised nipple; pigmented area around nipple called the areola

microanatomy and cellular specializations

1. Ovaries: Outer germinal layer contains 250,000 immature follicle cells made up of a single egg cell and surrounding flat cells; each month usually only one primary follicle undergoes meiosis and mitosis and forms a mature egg, which is released leaving a hollow follicle; the follicle is transformed to a solid ball of cells, the corpus luteum

2. Fallopian tubes: three-layered structure; outer serous layer (connective tissue), a middle muscular layer, and an inner mucous layer

3. Uterus
   (a) exhibits cyclical changes of innermost layer (endometrium), highly vascularized glandular mucosa
   (b) middle muscular layer and outer serosa are less involved in the sexual cycle

4. Vagina: changes in mucosa with monthly hormonal changes; cells become cornified

5. External genitalia
   (a) labia filled with sebaceous glands, fat deposits, and loose connective tissue
   (b) clitoris richly supplied with sensory nerve endings and contains vascular sinuses, which may become engorged with blood (erected)

physiology

1. Estrogen: female hormones mainly produced in ovary; shows cyclical fluctuations during menstrual period, peaking at ovulation and in the luteal phase (18 to 24 days); target organs are uterus and vagina, as well as nongenital tissues, such as breasts

2. Progesterone: female sex hormone produced by corpus luteum; maintains uterine lining during second half of cycle and in pregnancy; stimulates secretory ducts of mammary gland

3. Control of secretion: built-in biological clock in hypothalamus causes cyclical release of gonadotrophic releasing hormone, which stimulates the pituitary to release gonadotrophic hormones; these in turn stimulate ovarian production of estrogen and progesterone that act in a feedback mode to inhibit production of releasing hormones

4. Menstrual cycle: in postpubertal females, cyclical changes in female sex hormone follow a monthly rhythm with ovulation occurring between 9 and 14 days. Proliferative phase followed by secretory phase (second half of period) terminates in a bleeding phase when uterine lining is sloughed. In pregnancy the lining is retained

5. Orgasm: a psychological peak of sexual excitement which is released with considerable pleasure accompanied by a number of physiological changes in muscle tone, blood flow, heart rate, and so on

factors influencing function

Age: onset of female function at puberty when female hormones affect sexual development and function. Between 45 and 55, relatively rapid changes decrease function (menopause) often accompanied by psychological and physiological changes. Emotional state: anxiety and other states of stress can produce amenorrhea or dysmenorrhea.

clinical considerations

1. Hyposecretion: lack of gonadal function impairs development of secondary sexual characteristics

2. Hypersecretion: rare event in which precocious onset of puberty and menses occur due to release of gonadotropins

3. Amenorrhea: the absence of menstruation due to ovarian hypofunction; variety of causes both physiological and psychological

4. Dysmenorrhea: cramps, pains, nausea, and headache associated with menstruation

5. Sterility: inability to become pregnant due to ovulatory failure, blockage of Fallopian tubes, or toxic spermacidal factors in vaginal secretions

6. Abnormal vaginal discharge: a variety of fluidy discharges associated with hormonal disorders, infections, tumors, or early spontaneous abortions

7. Veneral diseases: epidemic microbial diseases primarily transmitted by sexual intercourse (mainly syphilis and gonorrhea), treatable by antibiotics if detected. Untreated disease can produce effects much later in brain, heart, joints, and other tissues

prenatal
development
and
birth

21

prenatal formation
growth and development
period of the trophoblast
embryonic period
fetal period

ecology of the uterus

labor and birth

contraception
male contraceptive
female contraceptive

abortions

prenatal
formation

Prenatal development refers to the 280-day time period (plus or minus 11 days) from conception (fertilization) to birth; following birth all development is *postnatal.* The prenatal stages of development can be condensed into three major time periods. The first is called the *period of the trophoblast,* which starts with fertilization and lasts for two weeks. During this period some remarkable changes occur, primarily in the arrangement of cells in preparation for subsequent growth of organs and systems. The next stage, the *embryonic period* (the second to the eighth week), encompasses the establishment of practically every organ and the differentiation of many cells. The last stage is called the *fetal period* and is characterized by a general growth and refinement of what has developed. At five months the fetus has all of its vital parts and theoretically should be capable of sustaining postnatal life except that it lacks the reserves and precise regulatory mechanisms that insure a healthy existence.

growth and
development

The physiologic processes utilized in the course of prenatal development are extraordinarily complex and involve programming by the individual's genetic mechanism (nature) and the environment and nutrition (nurture). At this point perhaps it would be of some value as background for this chapter to define the terms *growth* and *development.* Growth involves both the increase in the number of cells by the process of mitosis and the increase of cell size and components. Growth may go on in many directions simultaneously with different body parts growing at different rates; rates also vary from individual to individual. Usually growth is expressed as a percentage of the total for a given period of time. *Absolute growth* refers to the actual increase and *relative growth* to the percentage. Thus a 5-pound growth increase will be a 10 percent increase for a youngster weighing 50 pounds, but only a 2.5 percent increase for a 200-pound adult.

Development is a self-descriptive term that includes many activities. One major aspect of the developmental process is the change that leads to the specializations of cells, a mechanism called *differentiation.* As the fertilized egg undergoes cell division, the relatively uniform cell divides and specializes into many types of cells, for example, kidney, liver, and muscle. Differentiation therefore represents the limitation of the total range of developmental possibilities that an egg or any of its future cells will realize. Traditionally the term referred to the observable structural aspects of cell specialization, but now differentiation also includes related changes in the chemistry of the cells.

Although some tissues cease to divide and are wholly specialized early in life, most tissues retain the capacity for growth throughout the life of the individual. The tissue is constantly being broken down and being replaced, and the turnover of some tissues is rather remarkable. For example, the cells lining the intestine are replaced every day, and up to 25 percent of the solid matter in each bowel movement may be made up of epithelial cells from the gut lining. Other examples of cell life spans are (a) red blood cells, 120 days; (b) liver cells, 18 months; (c) muscle cells, life span; (d) nerve cells, life span (although up to 1000 or more are believed to be lost each day).

figure 21-1

TYPICAL CELL
TURNOVER

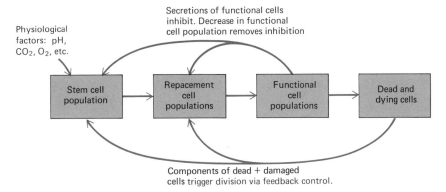

A typical cell turnover system and some proposed or known regulatory signals.

This continuous growth of cells is carefully regulated and is essential to the maintenance of the individual. A typical cell turnover system is diagrammed in Figure 21-1, and it can be seen that a number of factors can turn on and off the stem and replacement cell population. It has been estimated that if we could maintain the cell turnover rate of an individual at age 10, the average life span would be closer to seven centuries than to one century.

Growth may involve either an increase in cell numbers (*hyperplasia*) or increase in the size of existing cells (*hypertrophy*). We are all familiar with the hypertrophy in muscle of people doing heavy physical work. As it turns out, the maintenance of bone and muscle also requires continuous work stress. Patients subjected to enforced bed rest for only 24 hours show breakdown of muscle and bone protein and of bone calcium. Even in the weightless state of outer space where normal muscle work is diminished, breakdown of bone begins. The effect has been measured by means of X-ray examination in the astronauts before and after prolonged space flights. The shrinkage of muscle mass with disuse is particularly startling when a broken limb has been immobilized in a cast for several weeks, for upon removal of the cast, the limb musculature is severely *atrophied* (shrunken).

period of the
trophoblast

Fertilization

It is noteworthy that the beginning of human development is probably the least-known step in the total development of the organism. We know the spermatozoa will go to the oviducts from the uterus, but how the cells "home into" the ducts and swim to the egg is unclear. Probably the combination of sperm tail movement, the ciliary action in the oviduct, and the muscular contraction of the oviduct wall provides the mechanism for sperm propulsion. The spermatocytes reach the egg, usually in the upper third of the oviduct, and although thousands of spermatozoa surround the egg, one spermatozoon, and only one, will gain entry into the ovum to initiate fertilization. Once the spermatozoon head penetrates the egg, the tail breaks off, and the male nucleus moves toward the nucleus in the ovum. It appears that the fertilization phenomenon is

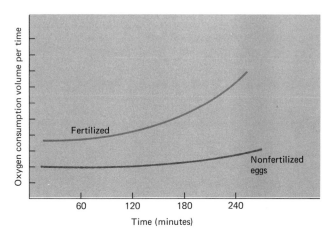

figure 21-2

OXYGEN
CONSUMPTION
OF EGG AT
FERTILIZATION

Increase in oxygen consumption of an egg at fertilization.

species specific, and this observation leads to the speculation that the relationship of the egg to the sperm may involve specific receptor sites on the surface or the secretion of chemicals that result in the specific "attraction."

Upon entering the egg, the spermatazoon triggers an immediate change in cell membrane structure. This change of the egg surface prevents *polyspermy* (many sperm entering the egg). The fertilized egg is a single cell about 0.14 mm in diameter, and it is believed to contain 100,000 pairs of genes that form a master blueprint.

Following fertilization, a variety of physiological changes occurs in the egg: (a) an increase in oxygen consumption is indicative of the overall increase of metabolism in the egg (Figure 21-2); (b) an alteration in the distribution of ions differs from the nonfertilized state; and (c) an increase in protein synthesis occurs, which produces more and new proteins.

The fertilization phenomenon can be summarized by imagining that during maturation the egg remains in a quiescent state because of chemical inhibitors, and the male nucleus lifts the inhibition and sparks the latent metabolic processes of the ovum. Once these inhibitors are removed or deactivated, the beginning of the expression of genes via protein synthesis occurs.

Cleavage Within 24 hours after conception, the first division of the fertilized egg occurs. The process called *cleavage* is synchronous (2, 4, 8, 16, and so on), but after five to six divisions, the mitotic timing becomes irregular. Cleavage can be looked on as a "parceling-out" process, since the mass of cytoplasm is not appreciably altered—only the number of cells increases. By dividing the original material into smaller units, called *blastomeres*, the fertilized ovum establishes the critical number of cells (increased DNA content, increased surface area, and so on) required for the specialized tasks that will start to develop in a matter of days (Figure 21-3).

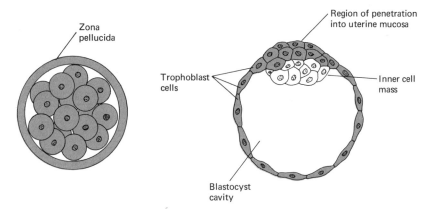

Figure 21-3   Early cleavage stages in a fertilized human egg cell.

Figure 21-4   The blastocyst stage of development prior to implantation (third day).

The dividing ovum meanwhile is moving down the oviduct toward the uterus. The explanation for this migration toward the uterus is still unknown; if the ovum for any reason should be stopped within the tube, however, development does not stop, and an *ectopic* or *tubal* pregnancy may occur. Because the oviducts are not specialized for fetal development, arrested development will occur shortly in this type of pregnancy. Growth of the embryo could lead to rupture of the tube and the need for surgical intervention.

As the blastomeres form they undergo a unique transformation of position to form a hollow ball, the *blastocyst*, rather than a solid mass. Only a small segment of the blastocyst, called the *inner cell mass*, is destined to become an embryo (Figure 21-4). The other cells are destined to form structures that assist in the development of the embryo. It is noteworthy that in the earliest stages of development, *morphogenetic movement* (the rearrangement and strategic positioning of cells) is a prerequisite for normal growth. These migrations follow a rigid pattern, and obviously any deviations from this pattern usually lead to arrested development with death or malformed structures. The blastocyst enters the uterine cavity around the fourth day and continues dividing in preparation for the next stage, called *implantation.*

Implantation and Placentation

The formation of the placenta is a unique event that starts at about the end of the first week of development. Although the placenta becomes functional within a matter of weeks, it takes about two months to reach full development. The placenta, as we shall see, is the morphological and functional link between the embryo and the mother.

An early step is the implantation of the blastocyst. The surface cells of the blastocyst, also called *chorion* cells, are specialized to secrete a proteolytic enzyme that erodes the endometrial lining of the uterus, wherever they make contact. By breaking down the epithelium, a gap is created, and the entire blastocyst sinks within the endometrial mucosa.

figure 21-5

PLACENTATION

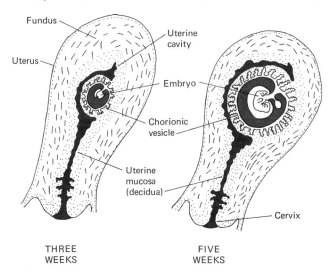

Early stages of placentation following implantation in the uterus lining.

The entry is sealed with a mucus plug, much like the healing of a wound, and a slight *hillock* is all that remains of the original site. This event marks the beginning of the attachment of the future embryo to the maternal tissue. The embryo literally grows in the wall of the uterus, and after the eighth week, as the fetus develops, it will expand into the uterine cavity. The implantation event is generally concluded by the end of the second week (Figure 21-5).

Placentation starts with the formation of the trophoblastic or *chorionic villi* that penetrate into the connective tissue of the endometrium (Figure 21-6). Each villus contains a capillary, which ultimately will be linked to the umbilical arteries entering the placenta. The blood collected from the capillaries of the villi drains into the single umbilical vein. The area of the uterine wall underlying the chorionic villi is called the *decidua basalis* and represents the maternal portion of the placenta; the villi of the chorion represent the embryonic portion. The details of the formation of the human placenta have not been documented as well as they have been for other mammals, but we do know that the following general morphological changes occur.

On the maternal side, irregular spaces called *lacunae* form around the villi, which are filled with maternal blood from ruptured endometrial arteries (Figure 21-6). Thus the chorionic villi are bathed in blood, and the materials that are to be exchanged between the respective blood streams of the mother and embryo need pass only through the epithelium of the chorionic villi and the endothelium of the villous capillaries. The formation of lacunae (microscopic lakes of blood) is a beautiful adaptation that enhances diffusion, since no limiting semipermeable membranes exist on the maternal side of the placenta.

The primary villi that form all over the chorion are soon lost, and secondary villi form that are restricted to a disc-shaped area called the

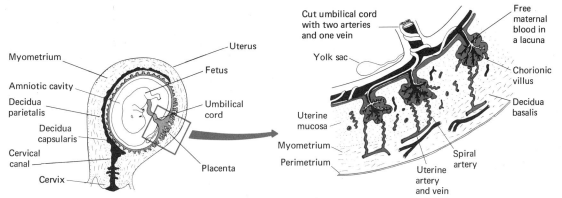

figure 21-6

PLACENTAL
STRUCTURE

Details of placental structure showing maternal and embryonic portions of placenta.

placental disc. This restricted area becomes the functional placenta, and as it develops, a fibrous connective tissue appears, which separates the placenta from the nonplacental connective tissue of the uterus. The fibrinoid material of this layer is broken down by some unknown enzyme just before birth, and brings about the separation of the placenta at its junction with the nonplacental uterine endometrium. Following the birth of the child, the placenta is expelled by the uterus and exits through the birth canal.

Where fully developed, the placenta is reddish brown (because of its great vascularity) similar to the general appearance of the spleen or liver. It weighs a little over 1 pound and measures approximately 8 inches in diameter.

During pregnancy the selectively permeable placenta performs many important physiological activities. It is involved in respiration, nutrition, and secretion. The placenta also acts as a substitute endocrine gland and secretes several hormones including chorionic gonadotropins that have the same effect as luteinizing and luteotropic hormones of the pituitary. These hormones stimulate continued estrogen and progesterone secretion from the corpus luteum. Estrogen and progesterone are also secreted by the placenta. "Morning sickness" is considered by some physiologists to be the result of excess hormone production during the first two months of pregnancy. Nausea and placental hormone production reach their peak about the eighth week, and then both begin to wane. Whether these events are parallel or related remains to be documented. Chorionic gonadotropin is the basis for pregnancy tests.

Organization of Primary Tissues (Second Week)

During the second week of development, remarkable rapid growth occurs in the trophoblast cells. First, there is a rearrangement of the cells of the inner cell mass (ICM) into distinct layers called the *primary germ*

figure 21-7

EMBRYONIC
GERM LAYERS

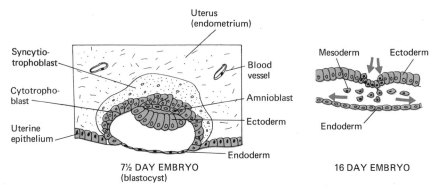

7½ DAY EMBRYO
(blastocyst)

16 DAY EMBRYO

The formation of the three primary embryonic germ layers: ectoderm, endoderm, and mesoderm. Cross-sectional view.

layers; all organs of the body are formed from cells that originate from these germ layers (Figure 21-7). They are called *ectoderm* (outer), *mesoderm* (middle), and *endoderm* (inner).

It is possible to map out the progressive changes in the inner cell mass and to trace the migration and development of the original cells. Not all of the cells of the inner cell mass become part of the embryo proper; some are destined to become *fetal membranes* that "service" the developing embryo and fetus. The subsequent development of the inner cell mass is the field of embryology, and only a brief summary of some of the highlights is provided here.

FETAL MEMBRANES   The chorion is one of the fetal membranes, and its function in placental formation has been discussed. Another important fetal membrane is the *amnion,* a sac that originates like a blister on top of the inner cell mass; it grows simultaneously with and outside of the embryo. Eventually the amnion surrounds the embryo, and as it grows, a fluid that possibly may be secreted by the amnion fills the sac. The amniotic fluid acts as a shock absorber against trauma for the fetus and prevents drying out. Before birth, the amnion breaks, and the fluid seeps out. The nutritive value of the amniotic fluid is questionable, as it is lymphlike with a little protein and sugar. It is known, however, that a fetus does drink amniotic fluid during its stay *in utero.* The amnion is dispelled along with the placenta following birth.

The *yolk sac* is another fetal membrane, but it is short-lived and has little function in human development. The sac is a carry-over from our inerasable past, from those animals without placental formation whose eggs contained a large amount of nutritive yolk and need a structure to envelope it. The human ovum contains no appreciable stored yolk material.

The *allantois* is a fetal membrane with a limited significance in human development. In nonmammalian animals it acts as a receptacle to store waste materials (example urea), and for respiration. Since the placenta takes over these functions, the allantois has become largely a vestigal structure. Its importance in the earliest stages of development

figure 21-8

THE FETAL
MEMBRANES

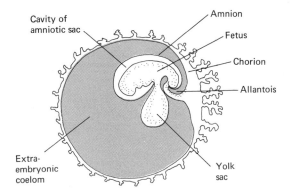

Cavity of
amniotic sac

Amnion

Fetus

Chorion

Allantois

Extra-
embryonic
coelom

Yolk
sac

is that the umbilical vessels start in the allantoic region and grow toward the area destined to become the placenta. Since the allantois and the yolk sac do not grow to any appreciable size, they are absorbed by the growing organism (Figure 21-8).

embryonic period During the embryonic period (second to eighth week), the embryo goes from the size of a dot to a structure weighing about 1 ounce and measuring 1 inch in length that looks like a miniaturized human being. In addition to the development of the viscera, the external anatomy undergoes dramatic change. The face develops around the formation of the nose; limbs form with demarcation (separation) of fingers and toes; the neck is recognizable; and genitals are present, but in a sexless condition (Figures 21-9, 21-10, and 21-11).

fetal period The fetus takes on more and more of the appearance of a newborn baby during the fetal period (ninth week to full term). Most organs "finish their specializations"; an increase in subcutaneous fat is apparent; and nonvital but important structures appear. For example, fingernails show up in the fifth month, eyelids and eyelashes appear during the sixth month (the eyes can open), and hairs are seen, although the skin is still so thin and translucent that the blood vessels show through. The skin secretes an oily substance known as *sebum;* this material mixes with sloughing epidermal cells to form a protective coat called the *vernix caseosa* that gives the newborn infant a cream-covered look. Although the fetus is capable of movement beginning in the embryonic period, the woman carrying the child does not "feel life" usually until about the twentieth week. During the last two months of pregnancy, there is a continuing increase of subcutaneous fat tissue for insulation and as a source of food, as well as final prenatal maturation of the lungs, CNS, and skeleton. This period is also the most difficult for the expectant mother, for the weight and size of the fetus are great enough to put a stress on her body. The pregnant woman must "function for two," which means increased heart rate, respiration, excretion, and so forth.

At the end of term the newborn will weigh in the vicinity of 6 to 8 pounds and can be approximately 20 inches in length. A formula for

figure 21-9

DEVELOPMENT
OF THE FACE

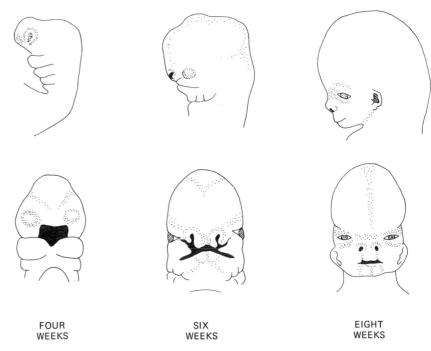

FOUR
WEEKS

SIX
WEEKS

EIGHT
WEEKS

measuring the size of the fetus during the first 5 months of development is to simply add the months preceding; for example, a *4-month old* baby equals $3 + 2 + 1$ or 6 inches. After 5 months, the number of the month is multiplied by 2; for example, an 8-month old baby equals 8 $\times 2$ or 16 inches.

Babies born before the thirtieth week would be only about 14 inches long and weigh around $2\frac{1}{2}$ pounds. They do not have the nutritional reserves to withstand the traumas of life outside of the uterus, although other factors are also involved, such as respiratory problems. In addition, at this stage the immunological mechanisms probably cannot perform all of their defense activities properly. Premature babies born after the thirty-second week have an excellent chance of surviving with the assistance of modern medical care. In Figure 21-12, stages in the growth of the fetus are shown to illustrate some of the changes that have been described above.

Fetal Circulation   Fetal circulation is explained because it provides additional insight into the relationship between mother and child *in utero*, and it also explains a common type of congenital heart defect. Because the placenta is functioning as the respiratory organ, there is no need to send blood to the fluid-filled fetal lungs, except for a small amount to keep the lung tissues alive and growing. Therefore, fetal circulation is essentially a modification to bypass the lungs. The following description will be more easily understood by referring to the diagram in Figure 21-13.

Blood low in oxygen goes to the placenta from the fetus by way of the two umbilical arteries. After oxygenation, blood is directed immediately

figure 21-10

DEVELOPMENT
OF THE HANDS
AND FEET

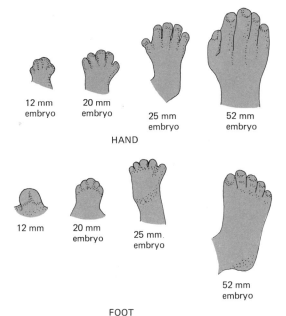

12 mm
embryo

20 mm
embryo

25 mm
embryo

52 mm
embryo

HAND

12 mm

20 mm
embryo

25 mm.
embryo

52 mm
embryo

FOOT

The development of the hands and feet during the second to eighth week of development.

to the liver by a single umbilical vein. Nutrients (glucose and amino acids) are extracted and stored by the liver (other substances, such as urea, are removed for excretion). Within the liver tissue there is a vessel called the *ductus venosus*, which can shunt a large bulk of the blood directly to the inferior vena cava. Depending on the needs of the fetus, blood may therefore circulate through the liver exchanging materials or bypass the liver cells by way of the ductus venosus. The ductus venosus is a structural adaptation to handle the large volumes of blood that the liver receives from the hepatic artery, hepatic portal vein, and umbilical vein.

The placental oxygenated blood leaves the liver and enters the right atrium through the inferior vena cava. Instead of passing directly into the right ventricle, a good percentage of this newly oxygenated blood "escapes" to the left side of the heart through an opening in the inter-atrial wall, the *foramen ovale* (actually the foramen ovale is two open-ings, since the interatrial wall is made up of two septa, as sketched in Figure 21-14). The highly oxygenated placental blood passes into the left ventricle and out to the body by way of the aorta, thus bypassing the lung. Of course, not all the blood in the right atrium is shunted into the left atrium via the foramen ovale; some goes into the right ventricle and then through the pulmonary artery to the lungs. Another structural adaptation is the *ductus arteriosus*, a small vessel that joins the pul-monary artery to the aorta. The lungs are collapsed and offer a high de-gree of resistance to flow, so that the little blood flowing in the pulmonary artery is almost completely shunted into the aorta through the ductus arteriosus, bypassing the lungs.

figure 21-11

DEVELOPMENT
OF THE
EXTERNAL
GENITALIA

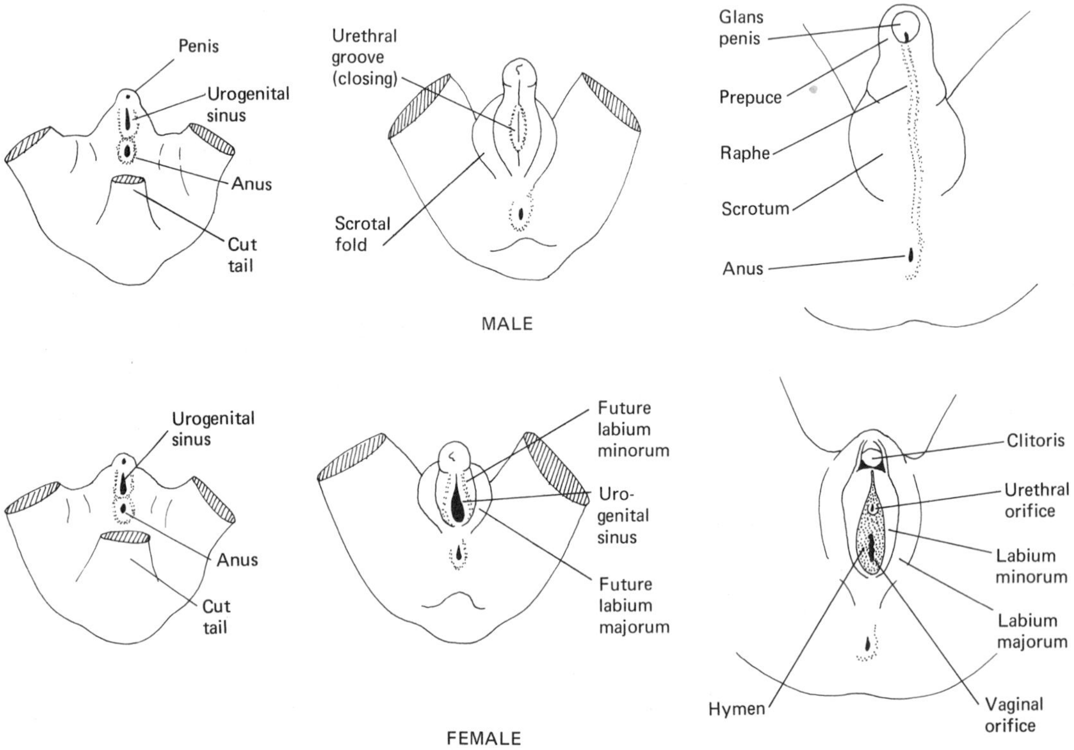

The development of the male and female external genitalia during the second to eighth week of development.

With the tying off of the umbilical cord at birth, the fetus is cut off from the placenta, and the ductus venosus becomes nonfunctional; it degenerates and becomes a liver ligament. The lungs inflate at birth and open up a vast new capillary circulation for gas exchange. The pulmonary bypasses are now unnecessary, and if they remain open (*patent*), there is a dilution of the highly oxygenated blood by the lower oxygenated blood coming from the right atrium. As more blood circulates to the lungs, more blood returns to the left atrium, and the pressure on both sides of the interatrial wall is equalized. Thus each septum blocks the opening in the other septum (Figure 21-14), and permanent closure takes about one year. About 10 percent of the population have a *patent* (open) foramen ovale, usually insignificantly small so that the slight exchange of blood between the atria is not serious enough to warrant surgery. If the patent foramen ovale is large, however, surgery is necessary to patch the hole.

figure 21-12

GROWTH OF
THE HUMAN
FETUS

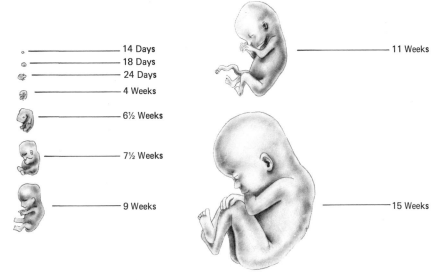

- 14 Days
- 18 Days
- 24 Days
- 4 Weeks
- 6½ Weeks
- 7½ Weeks
- 9 Weeks
- 11 Weeks
- 15 Weeks

Stages of growth of the human fetus through the first 15 weeks of development.

The ductus arteriosus is a highly elastic vessel that remains open as long as the flow of blood from the pulmonary artery into the aorta continues. With increased flow to the lungs, a correspondingly diminished flow in the ductus arteriosus occurs; the vessel recoils because of its elasticity and slowly narrows until it is obliterated (complete closure can occur as rapidly as two weeks). All that remains of the ductus arteriosus is a ligament that secures the proximal part of the aorta to the proximal part of the pulmonary artery. If the ductus arteriosus should fail to close, surgery is also required.

ecology of the uterus

In the early 1960s there was an outbreak of a neurological disease in Japan that had no known origin and was called *Minimata disease* because it appeared to be restricted to individuals that lived in the Minimata Bay area of Japan. Health officials finally uncovered the cause of the mysterious disease and correlated it with an intake of shellfish and fish from the bay that was being polluted by a methyl-mercury compound coming from the waste effluent (outpouring) from a nearby industrial factory. What is interesting is that during this same period of time, the statistics of cerebral palsy cases registered in a pediatric journal indicated an unusually high incidence in the Minimata area. It was subsequently shown that the mercury poisoning was also affecting pregnant women and the fetuses. This information was proof that metals can reach the fetus.

Although we are not totally ignorant about prenatal development, a detailed account of the relationship between *mother to fetus to environment* cannot be made. We have no idea, for example, how many spontaneous abortions occur in the earliest stages of development because

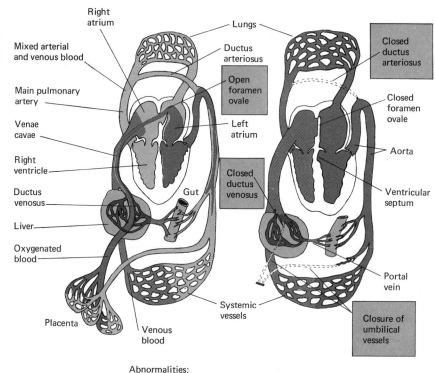

figure 21-13

THE FETAL
CIRCULATION
AND CHANGES
AT BIRTH

Right atrium

Lungs

Mixed arterial
and venous blood

Ductus
arteriosus

Open
foramen
ovale

Main pulmonary
artery

Venae
cavae

Left
atrium

Right
ventricle

Ductus
venosus

Gut

Closed
ductus
venosus

Liver

Oxygenated
blood

Placenta

Venous
blood

Systemic
vessels

Closed
ductus
arteriosus

Closed
foramen
ovale

Aorta

Ventricular
septum

Portal
vein

Closure of
umbilical
vessels

Abnormalities:

Foramen ovale: can stay open
Ductus arteriosus: can stay open
Ventricular septum: can be incompletely
  formed leaving hole

the mother might not even be aware of the pregnancy. We have only fragmentary information on what the state of an expectant mother's well-being has on the development of the child. A recent study concluded that heartbeat rhythm may have a distinct impact in human development, which can be interpreted to mean that mothers who have anxieties may influence fetal development by their increased heart rates.

Radiation exposure of the embryo or fetus during the first three months of pregnancy (first trimester) is known to cause a variety of birth defects (Table 21-1). The magnitude of the defects is both time and dose dependent. Maximum sensitivity is correlated with the developmental stage of a specific organ. Thus exposure to X-irradiation during early stages of heart development could produce heart defects; during limb development, it would cause limb defects; and so on. Sensitivity to radiation continues into the second and third trimesters, but primarily for the brain and hemopoietic centers. Expectant mothers in the later part of pregnancy in Hiroshima and Nagasaki, who were exposed to the radiation from the atom bomb, had offspring with smaller heads and lower IQs than children who were not exposed to irradiation in utero.

A 30 to 40 percent increase in the frequency of childhood leukemia was reported in children who received X-irradiation in utero following routine, diagnostic radiologic examination. Although these studies

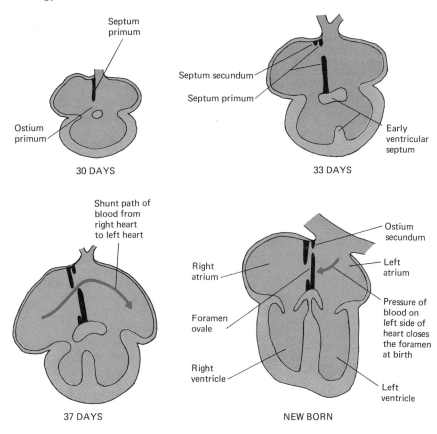

figure 21-14

THE FETAL
HEART
DEVELOPMENT

have not been confirmed, the statistics have alerted clinicians to radiation hazard, and caution is now being exercised so that *in utero* exposure is minimal.

The thalidomide incident of a few years ago can illustrate the type of problem that the developmental scientist must cope with. Thalidomide used as a tranquilizer primarily in Europe during the 1960s produced abnormalities in one out of five births if the expectant mother took the drug in the first trimester. The damage and suffering by this unnecessary error can never be estimated or reversed; however, a few "benefits" resulted from the tragedy. (a) It alerted the pharmaceutical companies and governments of the need for extreme caution and exhaustive testing before releasing products for public consumption. (b) It made the general community aware of the sensitivity of the growing embryo or fetus in the early stages of pregnancy. (c) It introduced an important consideration for scientists: Why were only 20 percent of the children maimed and why were the other 80 percent unaffected by a toxic substance?

Because over 90 percent of American women who are pregnant take at least one drug during their pregnancy, it might be of some value to illustrate the importance of the permeability of the placenta to certain substances. The selective permeability of the blood vessels to certain

table 21-1

THE EFFECT OF
IRRADIATION
ON THE HUMAN
EMBRYO

AGE OF GESTATION (DAYS)	LOWEST DOSE PRODUCING RETARDED GROWTH	DOSE FOR BIRTH DEFECT
0 to 9	5 r[a]	10 r
10	5 r	10 r
14	12 r	25 r
20	25 r	75 r
26	50 r	100 r
31	100 r	150 r

[a] r = unit of dose of X-rays, a physical measurement.

molecules and their rates of diffusion depend both on their physical-chemical characteristics and the needs of the fetus to utilize or eliminate them. Water, gases, urea, calcium, potassium, chloride, and other ions pass rapidly (milligrams in seconds) from the maternal to the fetal side of the placenta and vice versa. Steroids, sugars, amino acids, vitamins, and hormones are larger molecules than the group described previously, and they diffuse slowly, but usually they will pass through (milligrams perhaps in hours). Sometimes these substances move across the placenta by active transport mechanisms. Finally, even the very large molecules that would not be expected to leave a capillary can be exchanged between mother and fetus. The mechanism of transit is not known and may even involve pathology, such as an actual break in the vessel walls that allows for leakage (milligrams in days). In this category we would list antigens, antibodies, whole cells, and hard drugs. Substances or cells that can produce deformities of the embryo-fetus are frequently called *teratogenic* agents.

In conclusion, we could summarize by saying that when the mother is in doubt about ingesting or inhaling an unknown substance, she should assume that it will eventually reach the fetus. Even those materials that cross the membrane very slowly (milligrams per day) over the long period of pregnancy would accumulate in appreciable amounts within the fetus. Also, the fetal liver is immature during the gestation period; thus it is not completely capable of functioning as a detoxifying organ.

Last, caution is prescribed, not fear. The body is magnificently suited to take care of most of the problems it faces on a minute-to-minute or day-to-day basis. It is not necessary for an expectant mother to be overly concerned about her nutrition and to live only on rainwater and wheat germ. Since knowledge of the prenatal environment is still in its own embryonic period, all we can do at this time is to underline some of the measures that should be thought about to protect the fetus and to insure a quiet and healthy developmental period. Most pregnancies proceed in an uncomplicated way, and a minimum of supervision is needed. However, when in doubt, a woman should never hesitate or be embarrassed to seek the counsel of competent medical personnel.

labor and birth

The general sequence of events leading to birth is well known by the clinician, but the precise mechanisms involved in this extraordinary event are not fully understood.

In the latter months of pregnancy, placental functions slow down, and parts begin to break down. It is believed that this cessation of activity and tissue destruction is a major factor in initiating the birth phenomenon.

The initiation of labor is believed to be hormonally regulated, being correlated particularly to a *diminished* secretion of progesterone and an increased secretion of oxytocin from the pituitary. Progesterone exerts a stabilizing influence on the uterus by maintaining the endometrium in a highly active secretory state and by inhibiting myometrial activity. Oxytocin is a powerful stimulator of contraction of uterine smooth muscle. In all probability, other substances are involved in activating the uterus, because the muscles of the cervix begin to relax and the ligaments that tie the pelvic bones to the pubic arch soften before labor commences.

Labor is divided into three stages. The *first stage* (dilation) is from the onset of labor contractions to the complete dilation of the cervix (which opens to about 4 inches). The rhythmic contractions last for 20 to 30 seconds and occur at intervals of about 15 minutes; the abdominal musculature plays no role in this stage. The first stage is usually preceded by a vaginal discharge of mucus and blood, which represents the ejection of the mucus plug that blocks the cervix during pregnancy. These signs and the breaking of the amniotic membrane are excellent indicators that the birth process is about to take place. As the cervix dilates, it also stretches the upper part of the vagina. The course of the dilation can be determined by rectal examination, because the cervix can be felt through the rectal wall, which lies adjacent to it. The first stage lasts about 10 to 14 hours, and at the end of the stage, the baby's head appears (Module 21). The *second stage* extends to the actual delivery, and the duration varies from a few minutes to 6 hours. Labor contractions now occur at 1- to 2-minute intervals and last for about 1 minute. During this period, the abdominal musculature comes into play, and the mother may also be called upon to "help." The contraction of the abdominal muscles raises the intraabdominal pressure, which assists in the expulsion of the fetus. The *third stage* is the delivery of the placenta from the uterus.

The pain associated with labor is due to the violent contraction of the muscles and most of all to the stretching of adjacent tissues. The location of pain is highly variable from woman to woman, but is usually felt in the abdomen, thighs, and lower back. In *true labor* the pain occurs at regular intervals, and with time the intervals shorten and the pain increases. In *false labor,* the pain centers in the abdominal region, occurs irregularly, and with the same intensity; there is no discharge of the vaginal plug nor dilation of the cervix. Walking increases the pain in true labor, but neither affects nor diminishes the pain of false labor.

contraction The history of contraception is about as old as the recorded history of man. Prescriptions for both male and female contraceptives have been translated from ancient documents as early as 2800 B.C. In the United States the earliest known patent for a contraceptive device was taken out by a Dr. Beers in the early 1800s.

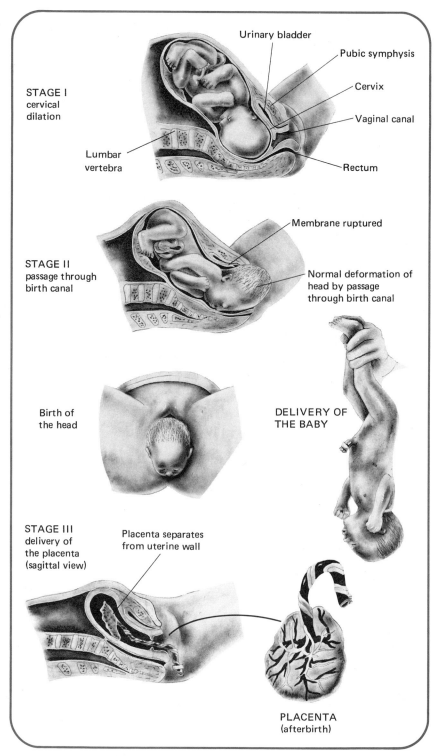

STAGE I
cervical
dilation

Urinary bladder

Pubic symphysis

Cervix

Vaginal canal

Lumbar
vertebra

Rectum

STAGE II
passage through
birth canal

Membrane ruptured

Normal deformation of
head by passage
through birth canal

Birth of
the head

DELIVERY OF
THE BABY

STAGE III
delivery of
the placenta
(sagittal view)

Placenta separates
from uterine wall

PLACENTA
(afterbirth)

male
contraceptive

The male contraceptives are generally devices that prevent the sperm from entering the female reproductive tract by covering the penis opening and isolating the sperm in a sac. The contraceptive materials are nonporous and elastic. The positive features of the male contraceptive are that they diminish the incidence of venereal disease; they are nontoxic; and they can be used with a minimum of discomfort. On the negative side, male contraceptives are less than 90 percent effective (a 10 percent error does not appear great, but in this country alone, it could account for millions of unwanted pregnancies), and they are expensive. A successful male chemical antifertility pill analogous to the female oral contraceptive is still in the research stage.

The use of surgery to affect sterilization appears to be increasing as a means of contraception; the procedure is called a *vasectomy*. The accessibility of the male genital ducts makes this procedure a minor operation. A small incision is made in the scrotum, and small segments of the sperm excretory ducts are removed; during an ejaculation, therefore, the fluid portion of the semen minus spermatocytes is discharged. A similar effect can be produced in the female, but the operation is slightly more complex because of the anatomic location of the oviducts.

female
contraceptive

Diaphragm

The most frequently used method of contraception in the past was the diaphragm or any reasonable facsimile that would block the opening of the cervix. Historical documents record the use of stones, buttons, leaves, plugs of wool and oil, and almost every possible combination that could be imagined by women who for countless centuries have wanted to limit the number of children they must bear. The modern diaphragm is a cone-shaped structure with a spring along its base to provide tension that fits over the cervix. The success of the diaphragm probably depends on a spermicidal cream, used in conjunction with the diaphragm, that is destructive to spermatozoa. The diaphragm itself merely inhibits the passage of the spermatozoa into the cervix and allows the spermicidal cream (or jelly) to act on the male sex cells.

The most important feature of the diaphragm is that it is made of an inert material that does not interfere with the normal physiology of the woman. On the negative side, the diaphragm is one of the less effective means of contraception presently used by the majority of women. It must be specially fitted to the individual by a well-trained person; it requires good vaginal tone to remain in place; it must be refitted after the birth of each baby; and, of course, its use requires a high degree of self-discipline in that it must be inserted prior to intercourse. The diaphragm also wears out and requires another fitting, and the additional expense. Since the greatest segment of the world population that wants and needs limited population growth never sees a physician or even a nurse between birth and death, it is foolhardy to believe that this means of regulating birth would be effective.

Intrauterine
Devices (IUD)

This technique is also quite old and was used by the ancient Greeks, Romans, and Jews. Basically all IUDs are objects inserted into the cavity of the uterus that act in an unknown manner to prevent pregnancy. Fertilized eggs have been recovered from the uterus of women with IUDs in place, so that it does not appear to affect the stages leading to conception. One positive feature of the IUD, assuming that an inert or nontoxic substance is used in its manufacture, is that once it is inserted, it is always present. The negative features are that the IUD must act in some manner as a foreign body to irritate the endometrium. For example, it might make the lining of the uterus hyperacid, which in turn would prevent cleavage after fertilization and thus act as a contraceptive. There is evidence that an IUD produces a mild inflammatory reaction with increased numbers of leukocytes and phagocytes appearing in the uterine tissues. It may be that these cells destroy the sperm. In addition, many of the present IUDs cannot be inserted into or retained by the virgin uterus. Last, the user is often not aware if the device was expelled. Until more is known about the long-time action of the intrauterine device on the structure and function of the uterus, it should be used with great caution and checked quite frequently by a physician.

Oral Contraceptives

In the United States the "pill" is rapidly becoming the primary means of contraception. It has been estimated that there are over 6 million users of oral contraceptives. The creation of an oral contraceptive had its beginning with the discovery in 1937 that progesterone (as well as other sex hormones) inhibits ovulation in rabbits. With this knowledge it was just a matter of time before proper dosage of female hormones could be used to inhibit the ovulation in other mammals. Although there are several types of pills marketed, the most popular one at the moment is the *combination pill* that contains a high amount of progesterone and a small amount of estrogen. Collectively these two hormones work on the hypothalmic-pituitary axis to prevent follicle-stimulating hormone and luteinizing hormones from being secreted in adequate amounts to cause egg cell maturation and ovulation.

The advantages of the pill are its convenience, its potential as a low-cost contraceptive, and the fact that it is the most effective known contraceptive (reported at 99 percent). On the negative side no one knows the problems that may result from taking hormones over a long period of time. General complaints of headaches, nausea, cramps, bloatedness, and minor ailments of this sort are reported that may not be serious. However, recent statistics indicate that the pill may, for certain women, increase the incidence of blood clotting disorders (thrombophlebitis and pulmonary embolism), although the risk of these diseases by the pill is less than from being pregnant.

abortions

It is the contention for the proponents for limiting population that abortion is the only satisfactory answer for overpopulation problems. The Women's Liberationists argue that to have or not to have a baby is solely the responsibility of the individual. Those who oppose legalizing abortions maintain that regardless of intent, the act is legalized murder.

The purpose of this section is to point out to the reader that abortion is a human problem involving the human body, and that much wisdom is needed as decisions are made. If overpopulation must be drastically curbed to assure the survival of mankind and if drastic measures are necessary, then it is essential that we monitor the cultural changes that will occur with legalized abortions. If abortions are not legalized, then the opponents of the law must come forth with alternative systems that work to eliminate the poverty and disease, the trauma and suffering, the destruction of the mind and body that are a by-product of overpopulation.

It is interesting to note that the first major laws against abortion, making it a crime, were established to protect women and not for any religious reasons. For over 165 years this country's law, based upon the *Common Law of England*, permitted abortions of pregnancies if they occurred in the early stages or before the "child quickened" (life was felt). Even if the operation was performed in late pregnancy or after quickening, the crime was only a misdemeanor (not a grave crime or felony). Historians believe that the abortion laws were put on the books to prevent immature, pregnant unmarried women, who were distraught, from undergoing the surgery of an abortion. In the early 1800s the rate of death following a major operation, such as an abortion, was 33 percent. In contrast the death rate from childbirth was merely 2 percent. The humanists of society who established these laws simply were saying, "Young lady, as bad as an unwanted pregnancy may be, it is still better than taking a one-third risk on your life." (Today, of course, the death rate from surgical procedures utilized in abortions is negligible, making the operation safer than natural childbirth.) The obstetrical and legal definition of abortion is the termination of pregnancy before the twenty-eighth week of gestation (varies slightly from state to state). In the eyes of the law, the fetus is not viable before 28 weeks, and it is not "taking a life."

Spontaneous abortions or *miscarriages* are quite common, probably more so than imagined, because there is an obvious tendency to under-report abortions. The best statistics show that 15 percent of all pregnancies terminate in spontaneous abortion with the highest frequency in women over 35. Of all the embryos recovered after spontaneous abortion, chromosomal abnormalities are present in about one-third of the cases.

One statistic worthy of consideration is the outcome of pregnancies in unmarried women. Only 5 percent of these pregnancies go to the full term with a live birth. Since 15 percent is the highest figure we can assign for spontaneous abortion and only 5 percent of pregnancies go full term, one is left with the incredible fact that approximately 80 percent of all pregnancies in unmarried women will be aborted by some induced means, and most of these operations will be performed illegally. Regardless of personal feelings and philosophical convictions, no one can deny that abortion is a major problem in our society, and it needs careful thought and judgment.

summary

prenatal formation

1. Pregnancy is a period of time, 280 ± 11 days
2. Stages of development
   (a) trophoblast: two weeks
   (b) embryonic periods: up to the eighth week
   (c) fetal period: from the eighth week to the termination of pregnancy

3. Growth
   (a) absolute growth: refers to actual increase in size
   (b) relative growth: refers to percentage increase
   (c) hyperplasia: increase in cell number
   (d) hypertrophy: increase in cell size
   (e) atrophy: shrinkage of cell size
   (f) differentiation: limitation of the total range of developmental possibilities that the egg or its future cells will realize
4. Example of cell life span
   (a) epithelial cells lining the gut – one day
   (b) erythrocytes – 120 days
   (c) liver cells – 18 months
   (d) nerve cell – can survive the entire life span of the individual
5. Fertilization
   (a) penetration of the spermatozoon into the ovum and the fusion of the chromosomes from both gametes
   (b) immediately following fertilization, a variety of changes occur such as the ovum becomes impermeable to other sperm cells; oxygen consumption is increased; and cell division will occur
6. Cleavage: within 24 hours of postfertilization, the first mitotic division or cleavage occurs; resulting cells called blastomeres in this early stage of development
7. Inner cell mass: a portion of the developing trophoblast that contains the cells destined to become the embryo
8. Implantation
   (a) process by which the trophoblast creates a gap and sinks into the uterine wall, beginning the attachment of the fetus to the maternal tissue
   (b) placentation: actual formation of the structural union between the organism and the maternal tissue; end point is that the respective bloodstreams will come in close approximation to one another, which facilitates exchange of nutrients and waste materials
   (c) placenta: reddish brown with a general appearance of liver; weighs a little over 1 pound; about 8 inches in diameter; involved in respiration, nutrition, and secretion of several female hormones
9. Primary tissues: the cells of the developing embryo rearrange themselves into three fairly distinct layers, and from these cells all organs develop
   (a) ectoderm: outer layer
   (b) mesoderm: middle layer
   (c) endoderm: inner layer
10. Fetal membranes: structures that "service" the fetus during development
   (a) amnion: protective sac that surrounds the embryo-fetus
   (b) yolk sac: vestigal structure in humans
   (c) allantois: site where the umbilical vessel develops
   (d) chorion: cells that contribute to the fetal portion of the placenta
11. Embryonic period: characterized by extraordinary growth and

differentiation; embryo develops from the size of a dot to a miniaturized human being about 1 inch in length

12. Fetal period: the "finishing" of organs already formed, such as lungs and central nervous system; new structures appear such as fingernails and eyelashes; storage of fat tissue as insulation and as a source of energy; at the end of pregnancy, the fetus will be about 28 inches in length and weigh between 6 and 8 pounds

13. Fetal circulation: specialized features include the circulation to the mother, shunting of fetal blood through the liver, and bypassing the collapsed lungs

  (a) ductus venosus: shunt through the liver
  (b) ductus arteriosus: shunt from the pulmonary artery to the aorta
  (c) foramen ovale: opening between the septa, which separate the right and left atria
  (d) umbilical vessels: two arteries and one vein going to and from the placenta

ecology of the uterus

1. Diffusion
  (a) molecules pass through the placental circulation dependent upon their physicochemical characteristics and the needs of the fetus
  (b) certain substances such as water and ions generally pass freely in a matter of seconds from one circulation to the other; larger molecules such as steroids and sugars diffuse more slowly
  (c) some molecules are transferred by active transport mechanisms
  (d) the process of transit for very large molecules, such as antigens and antibodies, is not known

2. Teratogenic agents: substances or cells that are capable of inducing abnormalities and deformities of the embryo-fetus

labor and birth

1. The exact mechanism that triggers labor is not known, but it is believed to be, in part, under the control of certain pituitary and ovarian hormones

2. Three stages of labor
  (a) onset of labor to the complete dilation of the cervix
  (b) rhythmic contractions occur at 1- to 2-minute intervals, which last for about 1 minute and continue until the fetus is delivered
  (c) the delivery of the placenta from the uterus

contraception

1. Male contraceptive: generally devices that prevent sperm from entering the female reproductive tract by covering the opening of the penis and collecting the sperm in a nonporous sac

2. Vasectomy: sterilization as a means of contraception; removal of a small segment of the sperm excretory duct

3. Female contraceptive
  (a) diaphragm: device that blocks the opening of the cervix and is used in conjunction with a spermatacidal cream
  (b) intrauterine devices (IUD): introduction of an inert foreign body which, in some unknown manner, makes the uterus non-receptive for the fertilized egg; a theoretical explanation is that

it creates a mild inflammatory reaction which is hostile to the fertilized egg

(c) oral contraceptive: the "pill" prevents fertilization by creating a "false pregnancy"; this state prevents hormones from being secreted in adequate amounts to cause egg cell maturation and ovulation

(d) sterilization: a similar operation to vasectomy can be performed on both oviducts

abortions The cessation of pregnancy by surgery, suction, irrigation, or other means; in the past few years, the courts have altered the abortion laws in the United States to a status of legality. One consequence of this dramatic change of law is that both committed groups, those who are for legalized abortions as well as those who are opposed, must enter into a period of dialogue. A culture with abortion laws as well as without laws has to face serious cultural changes. In the last analysis, abortion is a human problem involving the human body and that much wisdom will be needed so that the individual and his society will not be harmed.

cellular aspects of disease and defense

22

---

cellular self-protection

interferon

inflammation

specialized cells in the defense of the individual
phagocytes and reticulo-
  endothelial cells
antibody-producing cells

thymus and immunocompetence

**transplantation and im-
munological tolerance**
graft versus host reaction
autoimmune disease
hypersensitivity (allergy)
immunocompetence and
  cancer

chemotherapy

In the first two chapters, the importance of cell biology to the understanding of human structure and function was introduced. Throughout the book, we have tried to illustrate the interrelationships between the *micro* and *macro* levels of organization by describing the structure and function of specialized cells that are found in each system as well as the gross anatomy and organ physiology. In this chapter, we wish to elaborate on the concept that the cell is also the unit of pathology.

With infectious disease almost under control (infectious diseases are still rampant in certain countries because of economic reasons rather than scientific limitations), the clinical emphasis in the future will be directed toward maintenance of good health. This objective requires the clinician to recognize the metabolic or genetic defects that appear during prenatal growth and infancy, and to treat them as soon as possible after they occur. To obtain this type of information, diagnostic procedures will require precise quantitation that can only be obtained by analyzing cellular and subcellular components and relating whatever changes are observed at the cellular and molecular levels to the physiology of the organism. The field of molecular pathology requires that the specialists and the student, and eventually even the layman, have the same familiarity with terms such as ribosomes, lysosomes, and nucleus as they now have with the terms stomach, foot, and eye.

cellular self-protection

The cell has many ways of "defending" itself against harmful agents. In all probability, each cell secretes and is enveloped by a highly specific coating of proteins and sugars quite similar to that described for "the blood-brain barrier." This personalized secretory envelope could account for many of the specific characteristics that give cells their individuality: surface electric charge, permeability, and adhesiveness to similar cells. The secretion of part of a cell's own external environment implies that the cell has some degree of autoregulation in response to the many small but numerous changes in the environment. Cells have evolved many systems to handle potentially adverse conditions. For example, if the cytoplasmic concentration of cations increases, the cell membrane has pumps that literally remove the cations from the cell (Figure 22-1). One theoretical explanation of a type of cell death is based on the limited ability of cells to isolate and store free calcium when it is in excess. If a cell cannot recycle, remove, or sequester (isolate) the excess calcium, then its homeostasis is severely and irreversibly altered, and the cell will die. Cells can also deactivate or remove unwanted material by complexing (combining) the material with some intracellular component. The limitations of this type of response are related to the quantities of the agent that is to be removed and the coupling material. Cells, of course, have their individual "organs of digestion," the lysosome that contains enzymes for the removal of foreign substances or the lysis of damaged parts of cells. Sometimes the trauma is so great that the defense unit becomes self-destructive, as is the case with *autolysis* in which the entire cell is digested by its own enzymes.

interferon

An example of a natural cellular defense mechanism is the synthesis of *interferon,* a substance that is capable of inactivating viruses. (A virus requires the protein-synthesizing machinery of a living cell in order to

figure 22-1

CALCIUM
SEQUESTERING

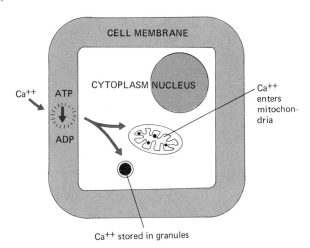

Metabolic pumps in the cell membrane move calcium against a concentration
gradient. Excess calcium may be isolated (sequestered) in storage granules to prevent homeostatic disruptions.

reproduce.) All cells appear to have the ability to respond to the invasion
of a virus by producing interferons, small proteins, or polypeptides that
are active in very small concentrations. In some manner interferon
"interferes" with the ability of the viral DNA to utilize the host's RNA,
thereby preventing further reproduction of the virus. The gene for the
production of interferon is repressed in cells until the infectious virus in
some manner initiates a lifting of the repression of the gene *(derepression)*, and synthesis of interferon begins. Since interferon does not work
directly on the virus but on the reproduction of new viruses, the infected
cells may die before the virus is inactivated. The interferon that is synthesized is released and can enter the adjacent cells to establish their
resistance to the infectious virus. In this respect interferon is not truly
a cellular "self-defense" mechanism but, rather, a defense at the tissue
level (Figure 22-2).

Because virus infections are so commonplace, the discovery of interferon is of great significance. The specificity of interferon is not very
great, so that an interferon developed against one type of virus usually
will provide at least partial protection against other types of viruses.
Because of this characteristic, interferons could be widely used for the
prevention of diseases such as measles, encephalitis, certain types of
cancer, and even the common cold. One problem is that interferons,
although not very specific against viruses, are very *species specific*; that
is, the interferons synthesized in nonhuman animals are not suitable for
human activity, and vice versa. The human interferon has not been
"harvested" in appreciable amounts because of the obvious difficulties
of research on humans, although such programs are now under study at
the National Institutes of Health. A more promising approach would be
to discover or synthesize a chemical that could mimic the action of the
viral nucleic acid sufficiently to turn on interferon synthesis. If such a
chemical compound was available, individuals with a virus infection

figure 22-2

THE SYNTHESIS
OF INTERFERON
IN RESPONSE TO
A VIRAL
INFECTION

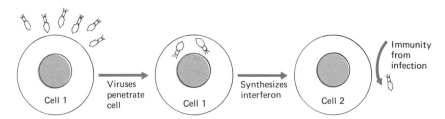

Interferons, small proteins or polypeptides, are produced by cells in response to a viral invasion. Interferon prevents viral replication by interfering with the ability of the viral DNA's utilization of host cell RNA.

could simply receive a shot of the artificial "virus," which would automatically turn on interferon synthesis. A number of research laboratories are currently seeking such synthetic interferon-stimulating compounds. If they succeed, many current untreatable viral diseases will be brought under control. This type of research is an excellent example of the importance of research in molecular and cellular biology to the promotion and maintenance of the general health and welfare of the public.

inflammation   A tissue's most effective means of defense in response to trauma is *inflammation*, a conglomeration of activities principally involving connective tissue cells and the cells of the microvascular system (endothelium, blood cells, and mast cells). Without the inflammatory response, the body would quickly succumb to bacteria, viruses, and fungi. It is significant, however, that although events listed in this section and in the general schema presented in Figure 22-3 usually occur, they are not necessarily related either in time or in sequence. Any one phenomenon can occur, with or without the others. For example, the change of permeability of a capillary region does not necessarily mean that there is an accompanying leukocyte migration into the adjacent tissue, and likewise there can be leukocyte migration from the blood through the capillary wall without altering the capillary permeability. An additional limitation of the inflammatory response as a defense mechanism is that in certain tissues, prolonged inflammation is detrimental to the individual. Types of arthritis and gout are examples in which a person would be better off if the inflammatory response could be curtailed. Accepting these limitations to the reaction, inflammation can be qualitatively described as follows.

1. Once injury occurs to a tissue, the cells will release, because of changes in permeability or because of death, a variety of intracellular substances (amines, proteins, RNA, enzymes) that collectively or individually can increase the permeability of the capillaries. Some of these substances also act on other cells to induce a release reaction of stored material, particularly *histamine.* Histamine is stored by mast cells, platelets, and basophils, and the release of histamines causes marked vasodilation and increasing capillary permeability.

2. The increased permeability will produce a localized edema with the retention of sodium and water in the extravascular tissue spaces. The

figure 22-3

STAGES OF THE
INFLAMMATORY
RESPONSE

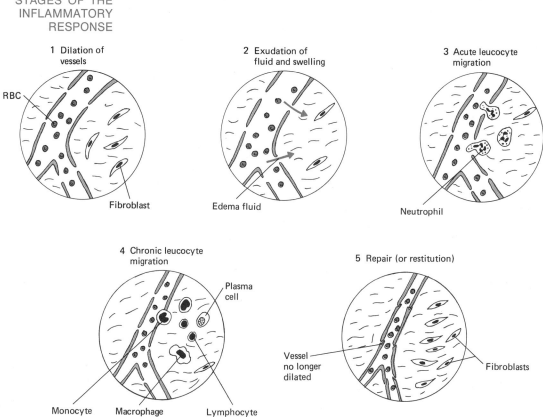

1 Dilation of
vessels

RBC

Fibroblast

2 Exudation of
fluid and swelling

Edema fluid

3 Acute leucocyte
migration

Neutrophil

4 Chronic leucocyte
migration

Plasma
cell

Monocyte   Macrophage   Lymphocyte

5 Repair (or restitution)

Vessel
no longer
dilated

Fibroblasts

loss of water from the blood will also help to produce a blood stasis with red blood cell clumps, platelet aggregates, and the conversion of fibrinogen to fibrin.

3. Within minutes, leukocytes adhere to the capillary walls in the area of inflammation and then emigrate (1 to 6 hours later) into the connective tissue to form macrophages, which phagocytize the bacteria and debris that result from the trauma.

4. If the injury and blood stases are extensive, the tissue will become necrotic because of the ischemia (localized anemia), and as more cells die, more inflammation-producing substances are released, enhancing the local inflammatory response. The lack of circulation also has some positive features in that it tends to isolate the bacteria that increase rapidly in the necrotic tissue. In this way the infection is walled off from the healthy tissue.

5. Some of the released enzymes have the ability to break down proteins (such as collagen and fibrinogen) into smaller products that have been shown to have *chemotaxic effect*, namely, that they attract leukocytes to the area of the inflammation.

6. It is believed that a *leukocyte-promoting factor* is a part of the substance released from traumatized cells. The leukocyte-promoting factor is believed to be a protein hormonelike material that has the ability to stimulate the marrow to increase the production of leukocytes (*leukocytosis*) and to release neutrophils into the bloodstream.

7. Eventually, the damaged area is sloughed or phagocytized and replaced by *granulation tissue*, which forms a bond between the trauma site and the adjacent normal tissues. Fibrin exudates help to "glue" these areas. Granulation tissue is composed of fibroblasts, new collagen, blood cells, and new capillaries.

Sometimes an inflammatory response is referred to as being *acute* or *chronic* even though the overall pattern of response is the same. The major difference that distinguishes both types of inflammation is that in the chronic type (of long duration) as opposed to the acute type, the macrophages remain in the damaged site and multiply, filling the spaces formed by the removed dead tissues. In acute inflammation, macrophages enter the wound from the bloodstream and are transient.

specialized cells in the defense of the individual

phagocytes and reticuloendothelial cells

In the early chapters on the cell the phenomenon of pinocytosis was detailed and illustrated as a general characteristic of cell membranes. Phagocytosis is merely an enhancement of the pinocytotic mechanism in that substances that contact the cell membrane and are engulfed by the cell are much larger. Harmful bacteria and cellular debris are removed and isolated by phagocytosis, followed quite frequently by digestion and expulsion of the degradation products.

The specialized phagocytic cells of the body are two types of leukocytes: *neutrophils* and the *monocytes.* Outside the circulation these cells become enlarged and are called *macrophages.* Macrophages are found in the tissues and as cells lining the blood and lymphatic sinusoids; they are found particularly in organs such as the spleen, bone marrow, and lymph nodes. The lining cells, regardless of the organ in which they are located, are conveniently lumped together as the *reticuloendothelial* system, although they do not truly constitute a system. At any time, reticuloendothelial cells can leave their primary location, become mobile, and enter adjacent tissue. They are then called *histiocytes,* a term that is merely a synonym for macrophage.

antibody-producing cells

Another defense mechanism of the body is the ability of specialized cells to produce antibodies, substances that neutralize or deactivate the harmful materials that invade the tissues. The many types of antibodies form a major protein constituent of the blood, the *immunoglobulins.* The harmful materials called *antigens* are often a high-molecular-weight protein. The body immediately recognizes antigens as being genetically different; even toxins or poisons can be classified as genetically dissimilar, since the source of the poison is usually derived from genetically dissimilar cells. Antibody production is part of the *immunological* system, and the cells primarily responsible for this function belong to the lymphocyte group (immunocytes). Without a doubt, this system is the major mechanism for protecting an individual against disease (Module 22).

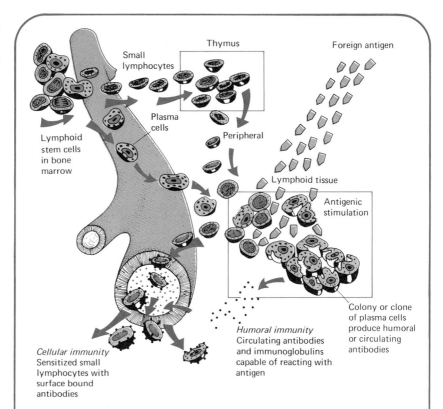

Thymus

Foreign antigen

Small
lymphocytes

Lymphoid
stem cells
in bone
marrow

Plasma
cells

Peripheral

Lymphoid tissue

Antigenic
stimulation

Colony or clone
of plasma cells
produce humoral
or circulating
antibodies

Humoral immunity
Circulating antibodies
and immunoglobulins
capable of reacting with
antigen

Cellular immunity
Sensitized small
lymphocytes with
surface bound
antibodies

**Although many steps in the stimulation of antibody (immunoglobulins) syn-
thesis and deactivation of antigens are known, the precise molecular-cellular
mechanism is still unexplained. The immunological competent cells, those
capable of producing antibodies, are lymphocytes and plasma cells, the latter
being a specialized, differentiated form of lymphocyte. The lymphocytes produce two general types of antibodies: (a) an immunoglobulin which adheres
to the surface of the lymphocytes (surface bound antibody) and (b) immunoglobulins that leave the lymphocyte and circulate freely in the blood (humoral
antibodies). The surface bound antibodies are involved in rejection of grafts
and in allergic responses, whereas the circulating antibodies (plasma cells)
protect the body by inactivating foreign proteins such as bacteria. The first
type of antibody response is very limited and the whole cell, as well as the
surface bound antibody, appears to be involved in the defense mechanism
(cell-mediated response). The production of circulating immunoglobulins is
the body's major defense system.**

**It is believed that the lymphocytes involved in tissue immune response
(graft rejection) stem from or are programmed in some manner by the thymus
gland. Lymphocytes with antibodies that intereact with foreign proteins are
not *thymus-dependent.***

**Within the lymphoid tissue the thymus-dependent and independent lympho-
cytes (plasma cells) clone (form colonies) of like cells, forming surface attached antibodies and circulating or humoral antibodies.**

figure 22-4

TYPES OF
IMMUNITY

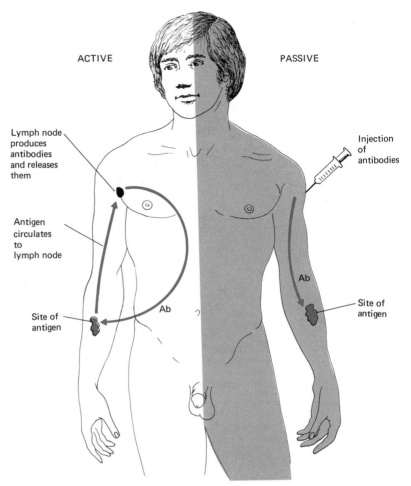

ACTIVE   PASSIVE

Lymph node
produces
antibodies
and releases
them

Injection
of
antibodies

Antigen
circulates
to
lymph node

Ab

Ab

Site of
antigen

Site of
antigen

The concept that the body has an immune mechanism had its origin in antiquity, for it seems that man has always thought, albeit empirically, that if he could survive a disease, he would be protected against the disease for life. The fundamentals of the mode of action of the immune response are detailed in Module 22. The current accepted explanation is the *clonal selection theory*. This theory proposes that an immunocyte has receptor sites for antigens, and the contact of the antigen stimulates the cell to form specific antibodies against that antigen. The antigen also stimulates the antibody-producing cell to divide, producing a progeny of cells or a *clone* (an aggregation of like cells capable of responding to the antigen that stimulated cloning). The sequence of events involved in the clonal selection mechanism is called *active immunity*, and it may be acquired by exposure to a disease or by the injection of small amounts of antigen (Figure 22-4). In addition each individual has a *natural immunity* that he is born with. Natural immunity is regulated by the genetics of the individual, and an example would be the antibodies found in the plasma against different types of red blood cells. *Passive immunity* is a condition that results when protective antibodies are derived from a source other than self. For example, the fetus may obtain antibodies *in utero* from the mother (also called *innate passive immunity*). Another way of obtaining passive immunity is by receiving an injection of gamma globulin or antitoxin *(artificial passive immunity)*.

Two types of antibodies are produced. The lymphocytes produce surface-bound antibodies (immunoglobins), which adhere to the lymphocyte's cell membrane. Such immunoglobins are involved in graft rejection and allergic responses. Some lymphocytes transform into plasma cells, which produce antibodies that are free in blood plasma. These antibodies interact with antigens, causing aggregation and inactivation of foreign material. These aggregates are eventually phagocytized by granular leukocytes (Module 22).

We are still a long way from understanding the molecular-cellular mechanism of antibody production and the means of deactivating an antigen by complexing with an antibody. There is increasing evidence, however, that certain classes of antigens must be modified before they can become antibody inducers. For example, labeled antigens injected into an individual have been found circulating in his system many months later. Evidently the body can tolerate certain levels of antigens without producing antibodies. Obviously these circulating antigens must be mediated by some process before they are capable of stimulating antibody production. (The term *immunogenic* is sometimes used to connote the actual antibody-stimulating quality as opposed to the potential.)

thymus and immuno-competence

In the second century, the Greek physician, Galen, described the thymus as the "seed of courage," and this poetic description of function was almost the limit of understanding the thymus until very recent times. In 1961 a theory was postulated that the thymus was the "master gland" of the lymphoid system and that it had the capability of programming non-thymic lymphocytes (for example, lymph nodes, marrow, and spleen) to become *antigensensitive* (to become *immunocompetent*). It was also established by others that *thymectomy* (removal of the thymus) in newborn animals produced a disease that had many manifestations of an *immunological deficient state;* that is, the animals were not able to handle the stresses of an infection and were "slowly wasting away." It was also known that if thymectomy was performed at any period beyond the first few postnatal weeks, the animal functioned normally. The conclusion was that whatever the thymus did to develop immunologically competent individuals, it did so prenatally and continued to do so for only a few days after birth.

The exact relationship between the thymus and the pool of immunologically competent cells found in other lymphoid organs is unknown. The thymus is the first lymphoid organ to form, and when the peripheral lymphoid organs develop, the thymus somehow confers a state of competence on their newly developed lymphocytes. One theory has lymphocyte stem cells migrating from bone marrow to the thymus and then to the

figure 22-5

HYPOTHETICAL
MECHANISMS IN
THE THYMUS-
DEPENDENT
IMMUNE
RESPONSE

**Two modes of immunolo-
gical programming shown
at the right have been
postulated. (a) The thy-
mus confers a state of immunological competence
by seeding (giving rise to)
clones of lymphocytes
capable of producing antibodies (Ab), or (b) the
thymus produces a hor-
monelike agent which ac-
tivates lymphocyte pro-
duction of antibody.**

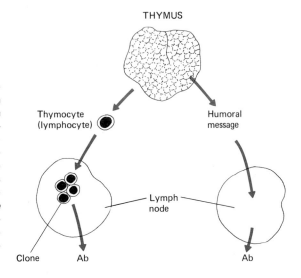

lymph nodes. These *thymus-dependent* cells seed the lymph node and
are responsible for certain types of immune responses. The other lymphocytes of the nodes come directly from the marrow and are *thymus
independent.* A second but less acceptable explanation of thymic responsibility is that it acts as an endocrine gland and produces a hormone
that has, as its specific target, the developing lymphocytes of such
organs as the spleen and lymph nodes. The hormone activates the lymphocyte RNA or genes that produce the protein for antibody synthesis,
and thus the sensitized lymphocytes become part of the immunological
mechanism. Both systems may be part of the immunological programming system, operating either at different stages of development or
possibly the duplication functions as a fail-safe mechanism. In Figure
22-5, two modes of thymic action are depicted.

The thymus becomes less important with the passing of years, going
into semiretirement after puberty. It maintains just enough activity to
insure that the pool of immunocompetent lymphocytes stays at a steady
state. The thymus is very well suited for its role as a master gland of the
immunological system. To operate effectively, the thymus should not be
"bothered" by the host of antigens that circulate, for this sensitivity
would only interfere with its role of programming lymphocytes. The
thymus is protected against circulating antigens by several anatomical
adaptations. (a) It is not near the skin's surface or lumen of the gastrointestinal tract, as are many lymph nodes, but buried within the mediastinum; (b) it has no afferent lymphatic vessels, so lymph does not enter
and percolate through its tissues; and (c) the thymic capillaries have an
identifiable coating, which is presumed to act as a blood-thymic barrier.

Immunological competence appears to be divided into two distinct
systems. In one, thymus-dependent immunocytes play the key role in
graft rejection (see next section) and hypersensitivity, but have little or
no effect on antibody production against bacteria. In fact, in this system

figure 22-6

GRAFT
REJECTION

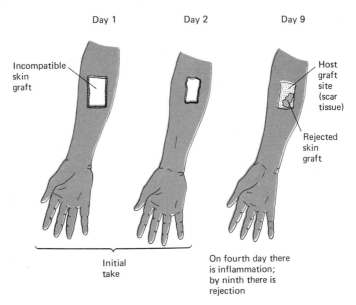

Day 1   Day 2   Day 9

Incompatible
skin
graft

Host
graft
site
(scar
tissue)

Rejected
skin
graft

Initial
take

On fourth day there
is inflammation;
by ninth there is
rejection

Foreign tissues grafted onto the host trigger immune responses which ultimately reject the graft.

the antibody response is very limited, and the whole cell appears to be involved in the protective mechanism *(cell-mediated response)*. In the other group, the immunocytes are thymus independent. These cells respond to bacterial invasion, maintain normal levels of circulating immunoglobulins, and are not involved in graft rejection. The latter group may be thought of as the major *antibody-producing system*.

transplantation and immunological tolerance

Death is discussed in the final chapter but long before a person dies, parts of his body wear out, become diseased, or are affected by a traumatic event. Sometimes the loss is compensated for by another organ taking on the load (one kidney doing all the work) and sometimes by drug therapy, but in most cases, there is no solution but to replace the defective part or organ with an artifiical unit *(prosthesis)* or a transplant of the living tissue. *Dentures* or false teeth are a common example of a prosthesis, and a blood transfusion is an example of a transplant, albeit temporary.

If a graft of skin is transplanted from one individual to a genetically nonrelated recipient, the graft will be rejected in a relatively short period of time. The tissue first shows signs of inflammation on about the fourth day, and by the ninth or tenth day most of the cells will be dead (Figure 22-6). Except for exchanging tissue between identical twins and occasionally between closely related individuals (mother and child), this rejection reaction is the rule. For years, the rejection of foreign tissue by a host was believed to be due to a failure in the vascularization of the graft. It has now been demonstrated conclusively that the complex process of tissue rejection is part of an immune mechanism that is similar to

table 22-1

NOUN	ADJECTIVE	DEFINITION
Autograft	Autologous	Graft in which donor is also the recipient
Isograft (Homograft[a])	Isogeneic	Graft between individuals that are identical in histocompatibility antigens
Allograft	Allogeneic	Graft between genetically dissimilar members of the same species
Xenograft (Heterograph[a])	Xenogeneic	Graft between species

[a] Old terminology.

Modified and taken from *The Biology of Tissue Transplantation.* P.S. Russell and A. P. Monaco. Boston: Little, Brown, 1965.

the body's response to any antigen. Since there is a grace period of several days before inflammation starts during the rejection phenomenon, it appeared probable to investigators that tissue rejection was not part of a rigid, immutable system, that in all probability, the immunological response could be manipulated, either to enhance or paralyze it.

Not too many years ago it was believed that only *autografts*, the exchange of tissue from one area to another area of the body, would be successful, and in this category the exchange of tissues between identical twins is included (see Table 22-1 for the nomenclature used to identify types of transplants). We now know that the same cells that produce immunity also produce tolerance, a condition that permits or "tolerates" foreign substances.

To date, the various aspects of tolerance are still theoretical, but clinicians have developed several techniques empirically that will "trick" the body to accept foreign tissue or at least minimize the rejection. The common denominator for almost all of the artificial means of inducing tolerance is to remove or reduce drastically the number of immunocytes in the body.

The first step of a kidney transplant is to find a donor who is immunologically close to the recipient. An identical twin is the ideal donor, but frequently other close relatives may be *isogenic* (have the same histocompatibility); that is, there may be a successful exchange of tissues because the individuals have similar genes for tissue-antibody synthesis.

The method of testing the donor involves an exchange of tissues between the two participants in the transplant operation and an observation of the degree of the inflammatory response. Obviously, if a small graft of the skin is transplanted and the recipient has a classical rejection response, the skin donor would not be classified as a suitable kidney donor. Once an acceptable donor is found (donor's cells do not elicit the classical graft rejection in host because of histocompatability), the immunological mechanism of the recipient must be suppressed. An example of this technique would be to give antilymphocyte serum (ALS) to the host to produce tolerance (other procedures used are irradiation or cortisone injections). Antilymphocyte serum is made by injecting the recipient's lymphocytes into an animal, for example, a horse or a rabbit, and after a suitable period of time, the animal is bled and the antibodies made against the human lymphocytes extracted.

By destroying the host lymphocytes with the serum, the antibody-producing system is temporarily paralyzed, and the foreign kidney given a chance to take hold. Of course, during the antilymphocyte serum therapy, the host is extremely vulnerable to other antigens, bacterial or fungus, and he must be isolated to minimize exposure to these antigens; otherwise, we would have the unfortunate situation of "The operation was successful, but the patient died."

One critical aspect of this procedure that cannot be explained is that following the cessation of antilymphocyte serum treatment, most kidney transplants will survive, even though the lymphocyte population returns to normal. Evidently, the kidney per se is not very antigenic, and it is other cells such as donor leukocytes trapped within the kidney that are the immunogenic substances.

Another technique that is used less frequently is to produce a *chimera* (a chimera is a mythical animal with a lion's head, goat's body, and serpent's tail). For example, the host's hemopoietic tissue can be depleted (x-rayed, cortisone injections, antilymphocyte serum), and the patient is then given marrow from the prospective donor (prior to the kidney transplant). For a period of time, the majority of the circulating host lymphocytes will then be genetically similar to the kidney that is to be transplanted, producing a temporary state of tolerance. After the operation, the host's own lymphocyte population is restored, but the donor lymphocytes remain at a relatively steady number. Thus the recipient is now a chimera in that he has two different types of lymphocytes circulating in his bloodstream.

Chimeras are also made experimentally by exchanging other tissues, such as skin. Why it is that certain tissues will provide a state of tolerance for another tissue, such as using skin prior to a kidney transplant, is not yet known. This response indicates that although at times a high degree of discrimination against one type of cell can be produced, homograft reactions are not always highly specific.

graft versus host reaction

One manifestation that may occur in transplant operations is the graft versus host reaction (GVH). In this situation, the graft tissue or organ, even though quantitatively inconsequential compared to the vast amount of host tissue, becomes the center of the reaction so that it is capable of building up antibodies and rejecting the host. The graft versus host reaction in experimental animals is called the "wasting disease," but it is also occasionally present in man. It is a syndrome that occurs in infants born with a deficient immunological mechanism, for example, an atrophic or functionally inactive thymus. Such an individual could not survive very long with this immunologic deficiency; consequently, these infants are given marrow transplants or lymphocyte transfusions. In a number of cases, the donor tissue initiates the graft versus host reaction, and the child will die in a few months.

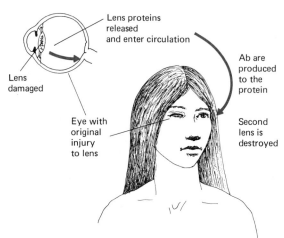

figure 22-7

AN EXAMPLE OF
AN AUTOIMMUNE
REACTION

SECTION OF EYE

Lens proteins
released
and enter circulation

Lens
damaged

Eye with
original
injury
to lens

Ab are
produced
to the
protein

Second
lens is
destroyed

autoimmune
disease

Until quite recently, it was intellectually "forbidden" for life scientists to assume that an organism would make antibodies against itself. The mechanism seemed to contradict homeostasis and the very essence of life itself. As our clinical knowledge increased, it became evident that there are a number of maladies that can only be explained by this rare immunological activity, *the body producing antibodies against itself* (Figure 22-7). One can think of the autoimmune disease as the result of (a) relaxation of the immunological system, (b) the release of intracellular substances such as protein from muscles or from neurons after these cells die (these molecules are not normally seen by reticuloendothelial cells and the proteins sensitize the immunological mechanism), (c) nonantigenic substances becoming antigenic, and (d) a metabolic failure in the body. Some forms of rheumatism, arthritis, and anemia are believed to involve an autoimmune reaction.

Further discussion of the significance of the autoimmune disease is included in the next chapter as one of the explanations of aging.

hypersensitivity
(allergy)

The immune response is not always beneficial, and for a fairly large segment of the population, harmful antigen-antibody reactions can produce a *hypersensitivity* or *allergy* that can be quite serious. Delayed hypersensitivity was discussed in the previous section on transplantation rejection. The reader will recall that this response was associated with cellular reactions rather than with circulating antibodies, such as gamma globulins. Some of the features discussed were (a) the response is the basis for transplantation rejection; (b) following an intradermal injection of an antigen, a skin reaction can be detected; and (c) the sensitivity can be transferred by injecting lymphocytes from a sensitized donor. Delayed hypersensitivity is responsible for certain drug allergies and for specific reactions, for example, poison ivy, and is the basis of the tuberculin diagnostic skin test.

figure 22-8

IMMEDIATE
HYPERSENSI-
TIVITY TO AN
ALLERGEN

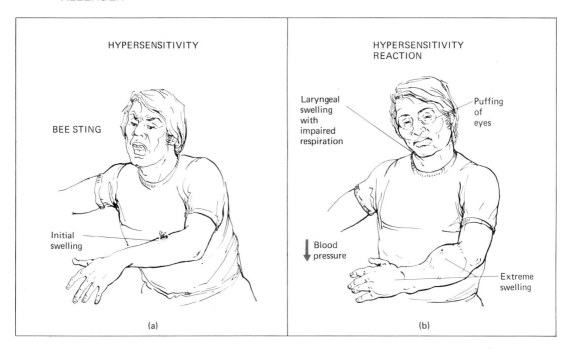

HYPERSENSITIVITY

HYPERSENSITIVITY
REACTION

BEE STING

Initial
swelling

Laryngeal
swelling
with
impaired
respiration

Blood
pressure

Puffing
of
eyes

Extreme
swelling

(a)

(b)

In an allergic individual previously sensitized to a foreign substance (an allergen) subsequent exposure to the allergen (in this case bee venom) triggers the release of histamine and a typical hypersensitive reaction.

The most common type of allergic response, however, is *immediate hypersensitivity* (Figure 22-8). The classic example of this type of hypersensitivity is *serum sickness*. If an individual receives an injection of horse serum (horses are commonly employed for the production of antibodies, for example, for tetanus), the immunological system will build up antibodies against the foreign protein in the horse serum. Usually, no reaction occurs with the first inoculation, because by the time the antibody level is high enough to produce a reaction, most of the foreign protein has been metabolized. Some cells can "remember" the reaction (also called the *recall phenomenon* or *anamnestic response*), so that if a second shot is received, even years later, the synthesis of antibodies is rapid, and the resulting antibody-antigen complexes are toxic. High fevers and aching joints are manifestations of this disease.

The recall phenomenon can be produced by a variety of foreign substances, and into this category would fall most of the allergies against antibiotics and against those allergens that produce asthma, hay fever, or food sensitivity. Allergy can be detected by injecting small amounts of an antigen (pollen) into the skin, and if the sensitivity is present, a

figure 22-9

LOCALIZED
REACTION TO
TRAUMA OR AN
ALLERGEN

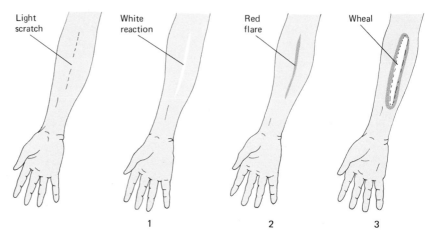

The so-called classic triple response is shown in sequence above. Following the white reaction a red flare appears due to the release of histamine or histaminelike vasodilators. The dilated vessels leak fluid into the tissue spaces, causing the formation of a raised fluid-filled wheal.

localized reaction will appear in minutes producing a *wheal* or *flare* (Figure 22-9). Because the skin is especially sensitive to antigen-antibody reactions, it is possible to test an individual against a large number of allergens. In minutes, a fairly complete hypersensitivity profile can be determined.

Most individuals have some hypersensitivities, but they are not serious enough to warrant the taking of medication or injections to minimize the antigen-antibody reaction. In a small segment of the population, a hypersensitivity can be so great that if sufficient localized adsorbed antigens and antibodies are present, an extreme reaction called *anaphylaxis* may occur and even cause death. Anaphylaxis induces the release of large quantities of *amines* (histamine, serotonin), which, in turn, will produce contractions of smooth muscle and changes in vascular permeability. The respiratory system is particularly sensitive to amines, and spasms of the laryngeal muscles and other respiratory changes will produce suffocation and shock. If an individual receives large injections of antihistamines or epinephrine before or right after the onset of an anaphylactic reaction, most of these symptoms are relieved; for example, epinephrine produces bronchodilation. An example of an anaphylactic reaction is seen in individuals who are extraordinarily sensitive to the venom of bees. These individuals frequently carry with them an epinephrinelike drug that they can ingest or, in some cases, even an injection kit for antihistamines and epinephrine.

immuno-
competence
and cancer

Immunity against infection is a significant evolutionary adaptation with a high survival value. We might then ask why a recognition system against malignant tumors has not evolved? Once a critical mass of tumor tissue develops, an immune response to the foreign tissue should occur; however, when we look at the blood and lymph for tissue antibodies or an increase of globulins, there is no evidence of immune reaction. Even when the body is saturated with tumor tissue, demonstrable antibodies are difficult to detect. There is some experimental evidence that if a thymectomy is performed on newborn mice, which receive injections of virus-induced tumor cells, the animals have no resistance to the tumors and succumb. If the thymectomy is performed later, several weeks after birth, the animals are resistant to the virus tumor. Under these conditions, we would conclude that tumors are exempt from the immunological mechanism; however, adjacent lymphoid tissue draining the tumor region is enlarged and microscopically exhibits an immune response (increased number of plasma cells). Therefore we must assume that at some stage of tumor genesis there is a immunological response by the body similar to that seen following transplants or infections.

It is possible that the programmed lymphocytes and their antibodies against tumors are short-lived or cannot cope with the tumor antigen system. We never really know how successful the immunulogical mechanism is all through life in repressing tumors, since there is no way of obtaining this information. Another possible explanation is that cancer cells are more invasive than normal cells (it is known that tumor cells will cross a placental barrier that is normally impenetrable to other types of cells), and because of this unique characteristic, the cancer cells may reach areas not readily drained by the lymphatic system. If so, the abnormal cells would be isolated for a long enough period of time before the body's defense mechanisms could be mobilized, and this delay would be sufficient to give the tumor a foothold. This response would be similar to the kidney transplant following the antilymphocyte serum therapy; once the kidney obtains a foothold, it is tolerated by the body. Eventually a tumor would probably be rejected. Unfortunately, before that point of time is reached, which might take years, the tumor has caused so much secondary damage – blocking blood vessels, replacing healthy vital tissues, or producing anemia – that the individual dies.

We might predict for the future that as our knowledge of the cellular aspects of the immunological mechanism increases, clinicians will be able to manipulate the rejection and tolerance status to fit the specific needs of the patient. Using the techniques of immunology, we could develop specific antibodies against the foreign material, for example, a tumor, in the same manner that antivenoms are now made. Patients with tumors may be cured by grafting tissues to enhance the immune reaction that would not only destroy the new graft, but also the tumor. We also hope that because organ procurement is a logistic problem, grafts between species may be possible. One method would be to create chimeras (this could start at infancy) with donor tissue from nonhuman primates or other mammals. Immunosuppressive procedures, such as the antilymphocyte serum therapy, might also be used for interspecies transplantation.

chemotherapy Although man has used natural products in the treatment of his diseases (quinine bark was used for centuries as a "cure" for malaria), the substances were used without any knowledge of their effect on cells and cell parts. Paul Ehrlich's use of an arsenic compound for the treatment

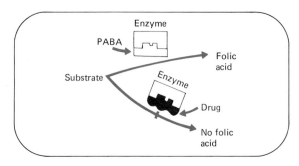

figure 22-10

THE BACTERICIDAL
ACTION OF A
DRUG

The drug sulfanilamide acts by competing with PABA for the active site on the enzyme which forms folic acid. Folic acid is essential for bacterial growth; thus by inhibiting folic acid synthesis bacterial growth is suppressed.

of syphilis in the early 1900s was the modern beginning of *chemotherapy;* his procedure represented a systematic treatment of a disease by a natural or synthetic compound that affects cell structure and function. The chemotherapeutic agent must not only work specifically against the disease without injuring or destroying healthy cells, it also should not interfere with the body's natural immunological mechanisms. Agents that are nonselective, such as *germicides,* are not considered to be chemotherapeutic substances.

In 1935, a sulfur-containing compound called *sulfonamide* was shown to have *bactericidal* properties (capable of destroying bacteria). The action of these so-called sulfa drugs is based on the mechanism of *competitive inhibition,* whereby a molecule that is structurally similar to a substrate of an enzyme interferes with the reaction between the substrate and the enzyme. This is illustrated by the action of *sulfanilamide,* one of the sulfa drugs, which has a structure similar to para-aminobenzoic acid (PABA) (Figure 22-10). This acid is a component of folic acid (vitamin B), which bacteria must synthesize in order to grow and reproduce. Sulfanilamide competes with para-aminobenzoic acid for the enzyme that is involved with folic acid synthesis, thus inhibiting production of folic acid and curtailing growth of the bacteria. Unfortunately not all foreign cells are sensitive to sulfanilamides, and many bacteria become resistant to the drug after prolonged use.

Using this principle of competitive inhibition, a variety of compounds have been tested for their ability to arrest cancer metastases, unfortunately with little success. For example, the compound methotrexate resembles the vitamin, folic acid, except at two positions:

$$\text{methotrexate} \quad \text{—CO—NH—C}_5\text{H}_7\text{O}_4$$

(OH)   (H)
methotrexate
(folic acid)

However, the differences are sufficient to make methotrexate a *nonsense substance* as far as the cell is concerned. It is analogous to constructing a supporting wall of bricks, some of which are made of lead and others of foam rubber—the bricks look alike, but their value is certainly different. If large quantities of methotrexate are injected into a patient, tumor cells will take up methotrexate instead of folic acid, and the net effect will be that cell division stops (folic acid is needed for mitosis). This inhibition of mitosis will occur in all cells, but the rationale is that the methotrexate will be localized in the tumor cells, because the mitotic rate of cancer cells is far greater than that of normal tissues. The clinician is taking a calculated risk that although normal cells will also be killed by this technique, a greater number of cancer cells will be affected. In essence, this complication of the methotrexate therapy is the major problem in cancer chemotherapy, mainly that the selectivity of the compound must be very great. Most agents that kill or inhibit division of cancer cells also affect normal tissues.

Chemotherapeutic agents affect aspects of the cell other than cell division. Perhaps the most famous natural antibiotic is *penicillin*, which is extracted from the common mold found as a contaminant of old bread. Bacteria walls are made of proteins and sugars, and the wall rigidity depends on the deposition of a specific protein called *murein*. Murein forms a bridge between the various components of the cell wall, with the amino acid glycine as the final linkage. Penicillin prevents the attachment of glycine to the other components and creates a weak wall; eventually, the wall gives, and the cellular contents burst forth. Although bacteria have, in general, a similar cell wall structure, penicillin is not always effective against all types of bacteria. The antibiotic may form nonspecific complexes with other components in bacteria. For all intents and purposes under these circumstances, the penicillin is isolated and of no therapeutic value. A variety of other antibiotics also act as inhibitors of normal cell wall formation.

Chemotherapeutic agents have been developed that affect respiration, nucleic acid synthesis, protein synthesis, mitosis, and intracellular movement, such as the release of stored materials. The mechanisms are equally varied, but because of the systematic approach of chemotherapy, the target of each agent is related to some known subcellular structure or function. For example, a vital protein synthesis can be inhibited by turning off DNA, by blocking the transfer of the message to the RNA, by preventing the mRNA from attaching to the ribosome, by breaking up the ribosome so that the mRNA message cannot be utilized by preventing the amino acids from leaving the ribosome, and so on. By knowing all the steps of the synthesis of a protein, any one step is a potential target for chemotherapeutic action.

summary

cellular self-protection

1. Cells have evolved many ways of protecting themselves against harmful agents

2. Protective coat: certain cells, such as the endothelial cells of the brain blood vessels, can form an extracellular coat, which creates a blood-brain barrier

3. Phagocytosis: the ability to engulf harmful agents that come within a cell's environment

4. Detoxification: foreign substances that get into the cell can complex with some intracellular material and thus inactivate it

5. Pumps: excess cations, such as calcium, can be removed by pumping the material out of the cell

6. Lysosomes: "intracellular organs of digestion" that lyse foreign material

7. Interferon

    (a) substance capable of inactivating viruses

    (b) usually a protein or polypeptide

    (c) interferes, in an unknown manner, with viral DNA utilizing the host's RNA, thus preventing further reproduction of the virus

    (d) interferons synthesize from one cell can enter an adjacent cell and confer this defense mechanism

inflammation

1. A conglomeration of activities in response to a trauma to a given tissue

2. Principally, the mechanism involves blood cells, connective tissue, and the circulatory system

3. Stages

    (a) release of substances such as histamine, which increases capillary permeability

    (b) increased capillary permeability produces local retention of water and salts in the extravascular spaces (edema)

    (c) the water loss from the blood may produce stasis in the area of the trauma, which in turn stimulates localized thrombosis and clotting

    (d) leukocytes adhere to the capillary walls in the inflammatory areas and then pass through the vessels into the adjacent tissue, where they act as macrophages

    (e) if injury and blood stasis are extensive, tissue becomes necrotic because of insufficient blood perfusion

    (f) dead cells release enzymes that appear to have a chemotaxic effect on attracting leukocytes to the injured area; a leukocyte-promoting factor is believed to be released from dead cells that stimulates leukocyte production

    (g) granulation tissue eventually replaces the damaged tissue

specialized cells in defense

1. Phagocytes: neutrophils and monocytes become macrophages when they leave the circulatory system

2. Reticuloendothelial system: the lumping together of phagocytic cells that form part of the lining of blood vessels and sinusoids of any organ

3. Immunocytes

    (a) cells capable of producing antibodies in response to an antigen

    (b) antigen: generally a large protein, and is foreign to the body

    (c) natural immunity: regulated by the genetics of the individual; blood types due to specific antigens on the erythrocyte are examples of natural immunity

(d) active immunity: exposure to a disease or injection of a small amount of antigen will stimulate sufficient antibody production to confer some degree of immunity

(e) passive immunity: protective antibodies are derived from a source other than self; injection of gamma globulin or antibodies that cross the placenta from the mother to the fetus are examples

thymus and immuno-competence

1. The immunocompetence of the body is genetically derived, and the programming during prenatal development is a function of the thymus gland

2. The exact mechanism of programming is unknown, but one theory is that lymphocytes of lymphoid organs come from stem cells that were seeded by the thymus

3. Another explanation is that thymus is an endocrine gland and secretes a hormone that activates or affects differentiation of developing lymphocytes

4. The thymus is significantly important in the prenatal and neonatal stages and becomes less important with aging; by puberty it begins to involute (actually becomes smaller)

trans-plantation

1. The process of accepting or rejecting a graft of tissue is part of the immunological mechanism

2. Autograft: exchange of tissue from one area of the body to another

3. Isograft: exchange of tissue between donor and recipient that have similar genetic makeups; an ideal donor would be an identical twin

4. Allograft: exchange of tissue between genetically dissimilar members of the same species; requires producing tolerance in the host

5. Tolerance: a state in which the individual will tolerate the presence of a foreign substance; the body can be "tricked" into a tolerant state by a number of techniques, such as depleting the organism of his immunocompetent cells

6. Graft versus host reaction: on rare occasions, a graft will reject the host; this reverse rejection is also called "wasting disease"

7. Autoimmune disease: a state in which the body produces antibodies against self; certain forms of rheumatism and anemia are believed to involve an autoimmune reaction

8. Hypersensitivity

(a) allergy: an overreaction of responding to an antigen; symptoms of the response are debilitating (high fevers, aching joints, skin eruptions)

(b) anaphylaxis: an extreme state of hypersensitivity that may even lead to death; characteristic to this response is an extraordinary release of histamine and serotonin, which affect the blood vessels and muscles of respiration

chemotherapy

1. Systematic treatment of a disease by using a natural or synthetic compound that will alter cell structure and/or metabolism

2. Sulfa drug: one of the early chemotherapeutic drugs, which acts

by competitive inhibition; the sulfa molecule is structurally similar to a natural substrate of an enzyme required for cell growth; thus the cell does not survive because the sulfa molecules "compete" with the natural substrate of the vital enzyme

3. Penicillin: most famous natural antibiotic, which acts on the developing bacterial walls by preventing a specific amino acid from attaching to the protein; the net result is that a weak wall is created that soon bursts, and the bacterium dies

aging
and
death

theories on senescence
cross-linkage and diffusion
  theory
somatic mutation theory
immunological theory

future of aging research

aging and behavior
progeria

death

It is apropos that the closing chapter of this book on human structure should be a discussion on aging and death, because this process is a true human common denominator. This fact alone should give the study of the phenomena the highest priority in every educational system. Yet professionals of all types (including scientists) shy away from discussing the problems related to aging and death with an almost studied intent. In *Future of Man*, Medawar points out the curious observation that there is no word in the English language for the "mere increase of years." The term *aging* has overtones of deterioration, and that is why he restricts the term *aging* to mean merely the *passing of years*. Medawar, uses *senescence* to describe the decay and metabolic decreases in the body that accompany aging.

Even in the most progressive clinical institutions, it is possible for a scientist, physician, or paraclinician to complete his advanced training without any education related to the mechanism of aging and without any guidance on how to communicate with patients and their families when death is imminent. It is time for man to appreciate that living and dying are parts of the developmental process, and the dilemma of mortality is that death begins at birth. Greater information and insight into the process of senescence would help to establish a new attitude that could aid individuals in many ways.

1. There is the problem of minimizing the pathology and alleviating suffering that comes with old age.

2. There is the further effort to increase longevity. For decades, the longevity curve has been climbing, but recently it reached a peak of a mean age of 70 years and started to decline so that at present the average life span is closer to 68 years (individuals in the U.S.A.). This statistic indicates that environmental factors are now present (such as smoking, pollution, and tension) that counteract the medical progress that has occurred.

3. Greater insight could reverse the trend of our present *youth-oriented culture* that unconsciously sensitizes us to ignore and, even worse, to dislike the old. Old people in too many cases spend their last few years in a pathetic state of resignation and despair. There should be new roles assigned to individuals who have managed to withstand both the physical and psychological traumas of life for 70 years, so that they have the opportunity if they desire to pass on to subsequent generations whatever wisdom they have gathered. The least civilization can do is to improve the low quality of care that most terminal patients receive. It is paradoxical that the richest and one of the best-educated nations in the world has abdicated its responsibility to the aged. It is even more unbelievable that this is done with the full awareness of its citizens that they too will someday be a part of the "senescent generation."

4. There is still the unsettled question about "terminating life." Is the prolongation of a terminally ill patient a humanitarian act or should society establish regulations for "mercy killing" *(euthanasia)*?

What is aging? Throughout the book we have made a continual reference to the fact that a living organism, unlike any other form of matter, is an *open system;* that is, the body can continually make new matter and energy from a variety of sources to produce more of itself, and the machinery for this process is genetically controlled. Senescence could simply be viewed as a process that interferes with the mechanism of tissue homeostasis by preventing a proper balance between the creation of new cells and their destruction. Aging is a disorganizational process that increases an individual's vulnerability. In other words, aging makes the individual more likely to die from external as well as random causes with each passing year. If, for example, a man maintains throughout life the capacity to repair and make new tissues that he had between the ages of 10 to 13 years, it is reasonable to predict that he could live for seven to nine centuries (remember the bible has Methusala dying at 969 years). The study of aging is called *gerontology,* and gerontologists predict that if medical progress continues at its present rate and if we can curb the physical insults from the environment, the mean life span by the year 2000 should reach 100 years, and by 2050 the mean age can be extended to 150 years. Of course, one of the problems is not merely to keep individuals alive for a longer period of time, but to keep them healthy and alert; it is no real advancement to be 150 years old, but to feel 300 years old. In addition, improved medical care will also increase the number of individuals who will reach maximum life span.

In summary, the object of this chapter is to introduce the reader to the discipline of gerontology, both for practical reasons and to stimulate your awareness of a new social phenomenon. Knowledge of living, senescence, and death can help to blunt the impact of the knowledge of an incurable disease. Survival is good, but mortality is not necessarily negative; aging may have positive aspects. Biologically, it is good to die for no other reason than to make room for the next generation.

Without aging, there would not be certain specializations that realize more fully our human potential. Sexual maturity, a positive feature of aging, includes procreation and all of the events of a familial existence that gives us a conscious enjoyable interexperience that separates us from other living forms. The price of these positive features is death, and perhaps it is worth it. (Table 23-1) In the old testament, King Solomon states, "There is a time to live and a time to die."

theories on senescence

To the best scientific knowledge, senescence is not due to any one alteration in structure or function, or even to any single disease. Of course, there are certain predictable changes found in an old person—for example, cholesterol deposits in the blood vessels, arthritis, brittle bones—but these and any other condition that could be mentioned are also found in young individuals. In other words, the debilitations are part of the profile of old age, but in themselves they are not the cause of senescence.

In the chapter on prenatal development, it was pointed out that a premature baby younger than 30 weeks fails to survive because of lack of reserves. The aged could possibly die for the same reason; that is, the sum total of a variety of factors collectively decreases the reserve of the individual. Gerontologists have proposed at least a dozen special theories to describe aging, and a few of the more popular concepts are presented here as examples.

table 23-1

NUMBER AND
MAXIMUM AGES
OF CENTENAR-
IANS DYING
IN ENGLAND
AND WALES
(REGISTRAR-
GENERAL'S
STATISTICS)[a]

YEAR	NUMBER AND PROBABLE MAXIMUM AGE	
	MEN	WOMEN
1940	20 (105)	102 (108)
1941	18 (112)	91 (108)
1942	12 (107)	79 (108)
1943	21 (108)	92 (106)[b]
1944	21 (109)	85 (105)[b]
1945	19 (105)[b]	71 (106)[b]
1946	22 (105)[b]	94 (108)[b]
1947	19 (106)[b]	97 (108)[b]
1948	19 (103)[b]	107 (115)
1949	27 (104)[b]	133 (106)[b]
1950	22 (102)[b]	131 (107)[b]
1951	33 (104)[b]	142 (109)[b]
1952	24 (105)[b]	147 (107)[b]

[a] Reprinted from Alex Comfort, *Aging.* New York: Holt, Rinehart and Winston, 1964.
[b] Verifiable by birth certificate.

cross-linkage
and diffusion
theory

The basis for the *cross-linkage theory* is that molecules chemically combine with other molecules, and the linkage alters the structure and function of the original units (Figure 23-1). The rate of combination increases
with age because of the accumulation of organic free radicals, hydroxyl
groups (OH), hydrogen (H), electrons, and so forth, that the body is slow
to excrete. If, for example, the free radicals combine with DNA molecules, the latter might be changed in such a way that they form "nonsense" proteins, molecules that are similar to the normal body proteins,
but that do not fit in either a structure or as part of a function. Nonsense
proteins nevertheless can catalyze cross-linking of normal similar proteins and in this manner deactivate them (Figure 23-1).

The result of excessive cross-linkage over a period of years could be
far-reaching. For example, collagen fibers account for more than one-

figure 23-1

CROSS-LINKING
TO FORM
NONSENSE
PROTEIN

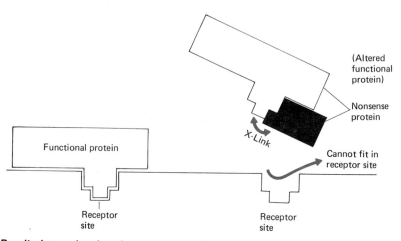

By altering molecular shape as shown diagrammatically above critical proteins
can no longer perform their function.

third of the total body protein mass, and it is known that this molecule is easily cross-linked. Since collagen is the principal constituent of most organs, the collagen linkage could transform porous fibrous tissue into a dense barrier. This condition would hinder the diffusion of molecules, and tissues would be cut off from their nourishment. The pressure of the highly cross-linked connective tissue might even press down on the capillaries sufficiently to close them off, and thus interfere with nourishment and respiration of the adjacent tissues. The effect of cross-linking need not always involve major structural alterations. Suppose an important oxidative enzyme underwent cross-linking because of the presence of an abnormal amount of a lipid pigment (a product of fatty degradation) and accumulated with age. This essential enzyme would no longer function in its special physiological niche and possibly would produce a disruption of a vital step in a chain of events.

somatic mutation theory The essence of this theory is that the body is constantly bombarded with physical factors that can produce mutations in somatic cells. The popularity of the mutation theory stems, in part, from the fact that radiation, a powerful mutagenic agent, can also produce symptoms associated with aged tissues (Figure 23-2). Accelerated aging in experimental animals can be produced by subjecting them to sublethal doses of X ray. Let us assume for the sake of argument that at least 2500 genes are essential for normal cell functioning, and that thousands of other genes play lesser roles. If any two homologous genes of the 2500 are hit by mutations, the cell would then become inoperative. Or if the homologous chromosomes carried a dominant gene for a normal activity and a recessive "abnormal" gene, respectively, theoretically only one hit on the dominant gene would be necessary to produce malformation or malfunction. Because most mutations are harmful, the genetically altered cells would continually divide to reproduce abnormal cells. For example, if a stem red blood cell mutated, after a period of time a good number of abnormal blood cells would accumulate. If the mutation altered hemoglobin production, then the individual's tissue would suffer from a lack of oxygen and operate at a less efficient level. This type of change could accelerate the aging process.

The somatic mutation theory is also attractive because it can incorporate many aspects of senescence. A variety of chemical agents and viruses may also have a similar effect on DNA as that produced by X ray. Altered DNA might synthesize slightly abnormal proteins (one amino

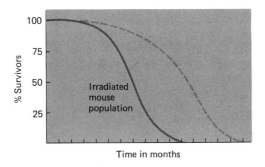

figure 23-2

THE EFFECTS OF X-IRRADIATION ON SURVIVAL

% Survivors

100

75

50

25

Irradiated mouse population

Time in months

Exposure to irradiation shifts the entire survival curve to the left when compared to a control unirradiated population.

acid deleted or out of sequence) that would not be incorporated into the cell structure or activity. These proteins would become antigens and stimulate the production of antibodies. The antibodies might not be able to discriminate between the normal proteins and the missynthesized counterpart and bring about degradation of both proteins (see next section).

immunological
theory

At approximately the fifth decade, there is a sudden increase in circulating gamma globulins; the ratio of splenic weight to body weight reaches its peak; and plasma cells (associated with antibody production) are more numerous than the mature lymphocyte. These age-related immunochemical and cellular changes suggest that the body is actively involved in antibody synthesis. However, it is well established that there is a *decrease* in the immunological state in old people, except for their ability to reject foreign grafts, a response that stays "youthful" all during life. The question then arises—if there is not a general acceleration of immunological activity in older individuals, what substances are stimulating the increase of antibodies that appears around 50 years of age? The prevalent concept is that as the body ages, it is in a chronic or prolonged state of *histoincompatability.* For unexplainable reasons, cells fail to recognize *self,* and the immunological system produces antibodies against *normal* or *self-cells.* The process is similar to the *autoimmune* disease described in the previous chapter. The key to this theory, of course, is to discover what happens to cells with age that transfers them from "self" to "foreign" cells. The mutation theory would assume that an altered DNA would produce foreignness, but according to the autoimmune theory, genetic alteration is not necessary.

future
of aging
research

Each theory described has strong and weak points, and the overlap is obvious even in this limited treatment of each theory. No one explanation on the syndrome of senescence "fits all the facts," yet each theory does provide a reasonable explanation of one or more important aspects of the phenomenon. We can predict that any explanation of senescence will certainly have to be an *integrated theory* and include at least two mechanisms: one that has a genetic basis for accommodating change due to congenital defects and somatic mutations, and the other that will be nongenetic and explain the ravages of age on the failure of the homeostatic mechanism to maintain a proper metabolic balance between the organism's internal and external environments.

Man has, and will probably continue, to look for an elixir to provide perpetual youth. Although it is obvious that such a goal is unobtainable, the quest will produce fringe benefits on how to delay the decay that accompanies old age. If cross-linking is a major contributor to aging breakdown, then the possibility of injecting an enzyme to erase the cross-linkages is not farfetched. We could simultaneously inject the necessary molecules for the repair of the proteins at the cross-linkage sites.

Recent evidence suggests that certain materials have *special* nutritional value that may lengthen the life span; to date, the only successes have been obtained in guinea pigs, rodents, and other experimental animals. Sulfhydryl compounds (sulfur amino acids) that are found in meat and eggs fall into this special category, and if they are of value, they probably implement tissue repair and trap free radicals. Another special group, *antioxidants*, are theorized to operate by removing free radical groups and by stabilizing cell membranes. Vitamin E is one of the better-known antioxidants. Other vitamins believed to be of special value in the process of senescence are vitamin C and the B complex. It appears that deficiencies of these vitamins hasten the "aging process"; however, excess amounts apparently do not lengthen the life span.

Finally, hormone therapy might also be an important tool to retard the "defects" of the aged. Synthetic sex hormones implanted in postmenopausal women and elderly men appear to have a beneficial effect by postponing certain degenerative senescent diseases (arthritis, high blood pressure, and so on). Hormone therapy in females undergoing menopause has produced good results in alleviating symptoms of fatigue, anxiety, and vascular problems. Even the incidence of cancer of the breast and uterus was decreased when a group of elderly women were treated with female hormones and compared with a similar group of nontreated women.

aging and behavior

The reader will recall that nerve and muscle tissue do not readily regenerate new cells once organogenesis is completed. Continuous mitosis of brain tissue would lead to chaos, because memory would not be possible. Nerve cells, of course, are not immortal, and a number die each day (in the very old, as much as one-third of the total nervous tissue has disappeared). The adverse effect of this neuronal loss begins to become apparent about the fiftieth year and manifests itself in a general slowdown of motor behavior. The *conduction velocity* of an impulse in a nerve fiber decreases; *sensory activation* is slow; and *reaction times* to stimuli as manifested even by simple movements of a finger or feet are delayed.

Information extrapolated from brain wave patterns of electroencephalograms from young and old subjects is interpreted by some investigators to indicate that a *master timing device* is present in the brain, and this center is a focal point of the deteriorative process. If such a center truly exists, it could add another dimension to the understanding of aging senescence and death. We could use the analogy of a car. Even if all the automotive parts are in A-1 condition, when the timing device is off, the motor will eventually stall, and the car will lose its specific function.

Probably one of the most significant alterations of behavior related to the passage of time is the tendency of the presenile and senile individual to forget recent experiences even though long-past experiences can be recalled with vivid detail. This loss of function is not clearly understood, although it is not believed to be directly related to a gradual deterioration because of neuron loss. Subjects tested by remembering either *nonsense syllables* or *meaningful words* appear to show this manifestation around the age of 40, and another appreciable loss does not manifest itself until about 60 (Figure 23-3). Evidently, other maturation factors are involved than numbers of neurons.

figure 23-3

AGING AND THE
CENTRAL
NERVOUS
SYSTEM

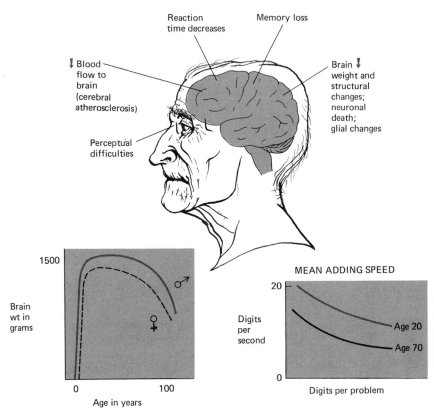

progeria   Progeria is a rare "aging disease," and it is included in this section because its very bizarreness can serve the reader as a model or microcosm
of the effects of aging. A general description of the disease is that *time
has accelerated;* dependent upon the onset of the disease, individuals
will progress through the various stages of life and die of old age before
30. Congenitally, it appears more frequently in men. They show many
signs of senility: arthritis, cataracts, heart and vascular problems,
wrinkled skin, excessive pigmentation, loss of bone, muscle, and nervous
tissue, loss of memory, impotence, and sterility. Progeria is believed to be
the result of a chromosomal defect that affects a key cellular enzyme
system that is involved in monitoring the timing mechanism of metabolism. When this enzyme system is inoperable, the rate of living accelerates, and the entire life span is telescoped into two or three decades.
There is some statistical evidence that the mode of action seen in progeria is by way of the pituitary gland and its trophic hormones.

death   Immediately following Christian Barnard's first successful heart transplant, the search for suitable organ donors became so intensified that it
was reported that at one large southwestern medical center, patients
were placing signs at the foot of their bed that read, "Please I am only
sleeping." The story is probably apocryphal, but it is worthy of retelling

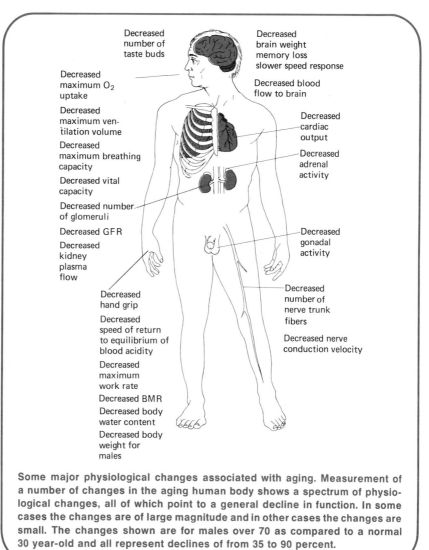

Decreased
number of
taste buds

Decreased
brain weight
memory loss
slower speed response

Decreased
maximum O₂
uptake

Decreased blood
flow to brain

Decreased
maximum ven-
tilation volume

Decreased
cardiac
output

Decreased
maximum breathing
capacity

Decreased
adrenal
activity

Decreased vital
capacity

Decreased number
of glomeruli

Decreased GFR

Decreased
gonadal
activity

Decreased
kidney
plasma
flow

Decreased
hand grip

Decreased
number of
nerve trunk
fibers

Decreased
speed of return
to equilibrium of
blood acidity

Decreased nerve
conduction velocity

Decreased
maximum
work rate

Decreased BMR

Decreased body
water content

Decreased body
weight for
males

Some major physiological changes associated with aging. Measurement of a number of changes in the aging human body shows a spectrum of physiological changes, all of which point to a general decline in function. In some cases the changes are of large magnitude and in other cases the changes are small. The changes shown are for males over 70 as compared to a normal 30 year-old and all represent declines of from 35 to 90 percent.

both as an editorial and as a reminder that death is not simple to ascertain. Death is a process as well as an event, and although there are many signs that serve as a harbinger of the end, each manifestation in itself is not proof that irreversible extinction has occurred. Even after *clinical death* has been pronounced, the body is not biologically dead. The hair continues to grow for several hours; the liver converts glycogen to glucose; and muscles will contract (*rigor mortis*). Rigor mortis apparently is due to the irreversible conversion of ATP to ADP that provides the energy for muscle contraction. Muscle tissue stores ATP, and evidently the quantity is sufficient to provide the energy for muscle contraction after death as the ATP breaks down. Therefore, rigor mortis generally begins 2 hours after death, and the muscles will stay contracted for about 30 hours because there is no resynthesis of ATP needed for muscle relaxation. Rigor mortis disappears because the ATP is utilized, and the muscle cells themselves break down and the flaccid condition prevails.

The criteria for death are not fixed, and only quite recently has the medical profession made an attempt to provide guidelines for making this decision. The heart, lungs, and brain form the vital trinity upon which the standards for irreversible death are established, and the criteria would include (a) an absence of respiration, (b) an absence of heartbeat, and (c) a flat electroencephalogram for several hours. Couple these signs of loss of function with such obvious alterations as the absence of pupillary reflexes, the clouding of the cornea, and an absence of body movement, and we can quite certainly declare that death has occurred.

The field of *resuscitation* (restoring function) after clinical death is now a very common occurrence, especially since surgery of the heart and lung is so widely practiced. Sometimes the mere manipulation of these organs brings about cessation of heartbeat and/or normal breathing for minutes, and such patients have been "brought back to life" and have survived to live a normal life. The difficult question to answer is when to institute resuscitation. For example, a brain inadequately perfused with blood for as little as 5 minutes will have irreversible damage. If survival is achieved after this period of time, the patient may not recover consciousness; or the individual may regain consciousness, but be totally unaware of self and environment, with total dependence. Notwithstanding the heroic efforts of the clinicians, is survival at any cost good? Can any individual be nonaccountable for his actions? Obviously, who should be resuscitated and when are philosophical as well as clinical problems. As our knowledge of events leading to death increases, there will be a parallel increase in the sophistication of the artificial units utilized to assist the body (especially to keep the brain tissue nourished) during these traumatic moments. Hopefully our wisdom will maintain an equal rate of growth.

summary

theories on senescence

1. The study of aging is the discipline of gerontology
2. To the best of scientific knowledge, senescence is not due to any one alteration in structure or metabolism or even to a single disease
3. Cross-linkage and diffusion theories
   (a) the rate of molecules combining with other molecules increases with age because of the accumulation of free radicals, such as hydroxyl groups, electrons; the body is slow to excrete these molecules
   (b) some of the free radicals may combine to produce "nonsense proteins" that are similar to normal proteins, but do not fit in either a structure or a function
   (c) excessive cross-linking of collagen fibers could transform porous connective tissue into a dense barrier; this condition would limit the diffusion of molecules, and tissue would be cut off from their nourishment

4. Somatic mutation theory
   (a) the body is constantly bombarded with physical factors that can produce mutations
   (b) most mutations are harmful, and the genetically altered cells might continually divide and produce abnormal cells
   (c) mutation might also alter the DNA so that faulty proteins are made
   (d) radiation, which can produce mutations, also accelerates the aging process in experimental animals

5. Immunological theory: the prevalent concept is that as the body ages, it is in a prolonged state of histoincompatibility; that is, for unexplainable reasons, cells fail to recognize "self," and the immunological system begins to produce antibodies against normal or "self-cells" (similar to the autoimmune disease)

future of aging research

1. No one explanation fits all the facts of senescence

2. Some scanty evidence suggests that certain materials have special nutritional value that may lengthen life span; in experimental animals, sulfhydryl compounds fall into this special category

3. Hormone therapy may be an important tool to retard aging defects; sex hormones implanted in postmenapausal women do postpone certain degenerative senescent diseases associated with the cessation of menstruation

aging and behavior

Probably one of the most significant alterations related to aging is seen in behavior. Since adult brain cells do not undergo mitosis, any degeneration or mortality to nerve cells is much more significant to the individual than if the damage was directed to epithelial or connective tissue cells. Some investigators believe that a master timing device, which is the center of aging, is present in the brain, and behavioral changes related to aging stem from this center

progeria

A very rare aging disease is mentioned because of its bizarreness. The general description of the disease is that in individuals with progeria, "time has accelerated"; an individual will progress through the various stages of life and die of old age frequently before 30

death

1. Death is a process as well as an event

2. Even after clinical death has been pronounced, the body is still not totally biologically dead; the hair continues to grow; liver cells will convert glycogen to glucose; and muscles will contract (rigor mortis)

3. Although criteria for death are not fixed, certain standards involving the heart, lungs, and brain have been established and include
   (a) absence of respiration
   (b) absence of heartbeat
   (c) a flat electroencephalogram for several hours

glossary

abdomen part of the body between the diaphragm and pelvis

abduction movement away from the midline

absorption the uptake of fluids by cells, tissue, blood vessels, and so on

accommodation eye adjustment for various distances, accomplished by changing the curvature of the lens

acetylcholine chemical released from certain nerve endings

acetylcholine esterase enzyme which breaks down acetylcholine

acid excess hydrogen ions producing a pH less than 7

acidosis decrease of alkali in body fluids in proportion to the acid content

actin protein found in the thin filaments of the sarcomere of skeletal muscle; combines with myosin

action potential electric current set up in nerve, muscle, or other excitable tissue; a transient reversal of the membrane potential

active transport movement of ions and molecules across a membrane and against a concentration gradient requiring energy usually in the form of ATP

actomyosin combination of the proteins actin and myosin that forms the basic contractile unit of muscle

acute of a short period

Adam's apple enlargement especially in the neck of males formed by the large cartilage of the larynx

adaptation modifications of an organism or its parts to fit the environment

adduction movement toward the midline or beyond

adenohypophysis anterior lobe of the pituitary

adenosine triphosphate (ATP) found in all cells and the major source of energy

adipose type of connective tissue; fat

adrenal hormone synthesizing glands located just above the kidneys

adrenergic nerve fibers that liberate norepinephrine at their endings

adventitia outer coat of an organ or blood vessel

aerobic chemical reactions requiring oxygen; existing in air

afferent moving or bringing to or into, for example, afferent nerves going to the brain

agglutinin antibodies that clump antigens

agonist a muscle whose contraction is controlled by an opposite muscle (antagonist)

aldosterone adrenal cortex hormone involved in metabolism of ions, for example, potassium

alkalosis condition with an excessive amount of alkali in the blood

allergy exaggerated reactions to substances that usually do not affect the majority of the population

allergic related to allergy

alimentary pertaining to nutrition or food, for example, stomach is part of the alimentary canal

allantois one of the fetal membranes

alveolar small cavities

amenorrhea absence of menstrual cycle

amino acid unit of structure for protein

amnion one of the fetal membranes that encloses the fetus

amorphous lacking definite shape

amplitude extent of change from some average value, as in a muscle contraction or nerve impulse

amylase enzyme that splits polysaccharides, for example, starch, glycogen

anabolism synthesis of complex chemical compounds from simpler ones

anaerobic chemical reactions that occur without the presence of oxygen; living without oxygen

analgesia diminished sensitivity to pain

anamnestic response also called *recall phenomenon;* response calling forth past immunological events; a second graft of foreign tissue would be rejected faster because the immunological mechanism "recalls" the first graft

anaphylaxis hypersensitivity

from previous exposure and sensitization with an antigen

anastomose to communicate or to join by connecting channels, for example, two blood vessels joining

androgens male hormones

anemia loss of red blood cells or hemoglobin from the blood

aneurysm a dilation or ballooning of a small area of an artery

angiotensin blood substance that produces vasoconstriction

angstrom (Å) $1/10$ millimicron or about $1/250$ millionth inch

anoxia decreased oxygen in tissues and organs

antagonist action opposing the action of something else (agonist)

anterior in front of or the ventral part

antibody substance produced in response to an antigen and characterized by reacting with the antigen

anticoagulant substance preventing coagulation

antidiuretic substance that inhibits urine formation

antigen foreign substance which on gaining access to the bloodstream of an animal stimulates the formation of certain antibodies

antioxidants substances that inhibit oxidation

anuria absence of urine formation

aorta main systemic blood vessel emerging from the left ventricle

aperture opening

aphasia loss of ability to understand or to use words; frequently seen as a loss or defect in speech

apnea lack of respiration

apocrine cells of a coiled, tubular gland that may contribute part of their protoplasmic substance to their secretion

apposed fitted together; contact of two substances

areola small area; frequently refers to the pigmented area of the nipple that is rich in glands

areolar type of connective tissue

aqueous humor watery fluid that fills the anterior and posterior chambers of the eye

arrhythmia loss of rhythm

arterioles smallest muscular arteries continuous with capillary networks

arteriovenous shunt the passage of blood directly from arteries to veins without going through a capillary network

arteriosclerosis hardening of the arteries caused by thickening of the intima, loss of elasticity of the walls, calcification, and so on

articulation motion between adjacent parts loosely connected

artifact modification or product produced by technique (by man) as opposed to a natural occurrence

-ase suffix used to denote enzymatic activity, for example, carbohydrase, lipase, protease

association tract nerve fiber tract connecting parts of the brain on the same side

astigmatism unequal curvatures of any refractive surfaces of the eye; focus of the image is diffuse on the retina

ataxia loss of muscle coordination

atherosclerosis arteriosclerosis characterized by lipid deposits in the intima

atom ultimate particle of an element composed of smaller particle; for example, protons, neutrons, electrons

atomic weight weight of an element in relation to the weight of carbon-12 used as the standard

atresia closure of an opening or sac

atrioventricular node specialized muscle fibers located near the opening of the coronary sinus in the right atrium

atrophy decrease in size or wasting away of tissue or organ

audition sense of hearing

autocatalytic chemical reaction in which the products as they form increase the rate of the reaction

autografts the transferring of tissue or an organ from one part of the body to another area on the same body

autoimmunity production of antibodies against individual's own tissue

autolysis self-digestion of cells by their enzymes

autonomic capable of independent control; in the nervous system refers to regulation without conscious awareness, for example, heart rate

autoregulation ability of a local area to regulate itself independently of central regulating centers as seen in blood flow of certain areas

autosomal chromosomes chromosomes other than the sex chromosomes

axilla armpit

axon cytoplasmic extension of the nerve cell that conducts impulse to a target site

axoplasm cytoplasm of the axon

bactericide bacteria-killing agent

basal relating to a minimum or base

basal ganglia basal nuclei of the telencephalon

basal metabolic rate (BMR) related to the base, hence the minimum amount of metabolism needed to maintain the vital processes in operation

base nonacid, characterized by excess of OH ion and a pH greater than 7

basophil leukocyte characterized by a pale nucleus and large, densely basophilic granuoles

bel a measure of sound intensity

beta-oxidation important in fatty acid metabolism; oxidation of the β carbon (#3) of a fatty acid

bilateral referring to both sides of the body

bile alkaline fluid secreted by the liver that aids in the digestion of fats

-blast usually used as a suffix denoting immature or embryonic stage, for example, osteoblast, an embryonic bone cell

blastocyst stage in early development of the embryo, characterized by hollow ball of cells

blastomere one of the cells which results from division of the fertilized egg

blind spot area in the retina in which there are no light receptor cells

blood-brain barrier special mechanism that blocks the passage of materials from the blood to the cerebrospinal fluid and brain; for example, toxins that would ordinarily pass into tissues from a blood vessel in the muscle are blocked by the "barrier"

Bowman's capsule capsule containing the glomerulus; depression in tubular system of nephron which surrounds a network of capillaries

bradycardia slowing down of the heart beat

bronchus subdivision of the trachea carrying air to and from the lungs

bronchiole finer division of the bronchial tubes

Brownian movement random movement of particles suspended in liquid or gases

Brunner's glands secretory tissue of the duodenum; secretions counter gastric acidity

buffer compound that combines with an acid or with a base and thereby reduces the change in hydrogen-ion concentration

bundle of His bundle of modified cardiac muscle fibers that is part of the system that initiates and controls contraction of the heart muscle

calculi stones formed in the body composed of salts

Calorie heat unit; amount of heat needed to raise the temperature of 1 kgm of water 1°C

calorimetry measurement of heat liberated in a chemical reaction

capillary smallest blood vessel which connects arterioles to venules; site where exchange among cells, tissue fluid, and blood occurs

carbohydrate organic compound containing carbon, hydrogen, and oxygen in certain specific proportions (such as sugar and starch)

carbonic anhydrase enzyme that catalyzes the conversion of carbon dioxide to carbonic acid and the reverse reaction

carcinoma malignant (endangering life) growth of epithelial cells

cardiac output blood flow from the heart

castration removing the testes or ovaries

catabolism breakdown of complex chemical compounds into simpler ones

catalyze to increase the rate of the reaction without contributing any energy

cataract loss of transparency of the crystalline lens of the eye, or its capsule

cecum first part of the large intestine (blind gut, cul-de-sac)

centimeter (cm) unit of measure; 2.5 cm equals 1 inch

centrifugation sedimentation of solids suspended in a fluid by means of the centrifuge

centriole small organelle lying in the centrosome that serves to organize the mitotic spindle

centromere structure that joins each pair of chromatids

cerebellum part of the brain that is associated with coordination of voluntary motion

cerebrum largest portion of the brain composed of the cerebral hemispheres, basal ganglia, and olfactory brain

cervix necklike; in the uterus the lower narrow portion that extends into the vagina

chemoreceptors sensory cells that are stimulated by chemical substance, as in the taste buds

chemotaxic attraction of cells or cytoplasm to chemical stimuli

chemotherapy treatment of disease by means of chemical substances or drugs

chiasma X-shaped crossing of nerves, of chromosomes

chief cells term applied to secretory cells of certain organs

chimera an individual resulting from the joining of embryonic parts of one individual with the embryonic parts of another individual

choanae posterior openings of the nasal fossa

cholecystokinin hormone stimulating the contraction of the gall bladder

cholesterol a steroid present in all cells and fluids, especially high in cell membranes

cholinergic related to nerve fibers of the autonomic and nonautonomic portions of the nervous system that liberate acetylcholine at the nerve endings

chondrocyte cartilage cell

chorion outermost of the fetal membranes

chromatid one of the two filaments making up a chromosome

chromatin deep-staining substance in the nucleus of cells; divides into chromosomes during mitosis

chromaffin tissue tissue that reacts with a certain stain, generally

chromatography separating chemical substances and particles by differential movement through a two-phase system

chromatolysis breakdown of colored compounds in nerve cell, generally associated with decrease or loss of function

chromatophore pigment-bearing cell found mainly in the skin, also chromophore

chromosome deep-staining, rod-shaped bodies in cell nucleus, containing the genes

chronic disease of long duration or slow progress

chylomicron microscopic particle of fat, about 1 μ

cilia hairlike motile projections of cytoplasm and plasma membranes

circumcision excision of the foreskin of the penis

circumduction movement of a part in a circular direction

cleavage mitotic divisions of the egg

clitoris small erectile body usually about 1 to 2 cm in length projecting between the labia minora; it is the analogue of the penis

coccygeal relating to the coccyx

coenzyme a substance that is needed in the activation of an enzyme

coitus act of introducing semen into the female reproductive tract

collagen main protein of skin, tendon, bone, cartilage, and connective tissue; extracellular

collateral side branch of a nerve axon or blood vessel

colloidal solution solute particles with diameters of 1 to 100 millimicrons

colon part of the large intestine that extends from the cecum to the rectum

commissural tract bundle of nerve fibers connecting brain structures from one side to the other side

compound substance formed by the joining of two or more elements, usually differing entirely in physical characteristics from its components

concave depressed or hollowed surface

conductivity transmission of certain forms of energy as heat, sound, and electricity, without measurable motion in the conducting body

cone nerve cell in retina responsible for color vision

congenital existing before or at birth

contraception voluntary prevention of conception or impregnation

convex curved or bulged outward

coping behavior (cope) competing, striving, behavior; to dispute, struggle, engage

cornea a transparent layer of cells forming the outer coat of the eyeball

coronary encircling; usually refers to the heart, for example, coronary arteries

corpora cavernosa two parallel columns of tissue making up the major portion of the penis and clitoris

corpus luteum yellow body, the stage following ovulation when the follicle fills with cells

cortex the outer portion of an organ

costal pertaining to ribs

cranium bones of the head, skull

cretinism severe congenital thyroid deficiency leading to physical and mental retardation

cribiform sievelike

cross linkage chemical bonds linking fibrous molecules

cutaneous relating to the skin

cyclic adenosine monophosphate chemical compound that is produced by cells in response to presence of many hormones; called the *second messenger*

cytochemistry study of specific chemical reactions in cells by means of staining reactions

cytochrome iron containing protein whose principal function is electron and/or hydrogen transport

cytology study of cells

cytopenia reduction or lack of cellular elements in the circulating blood (leukocytopenia is lack of white blood cells)

cytoplasm the substance of a cell exclusive of the nucleus

cytosis a condition characterized by more than the usual number of cells, for example, leukocytosis (increased white blood cells)

deamination removal of a NH_2 group from a compound

decidua basalis part of mucous membrane that is lost in menstruation, also part of the placenta

decompression release from pressure or compression

decussation crossing over the midline of a band of fibers, such as in the brain and spinal cord

defecation excretion of solid wastes

dehydration loss of water from body or from food

dehydrogenase enzymes that catalyze the removal of hydrogen from certain molecules

dendrite a branching cytoplasmic process of a nerve cell that conducts impulses to the nerve cell body

denervation cutting off the nerve supply

deoxyribonucleic acid (DNA) nucleic acid constituent of chromosomes; chemical basis of heredity; carrier of genetic information

depolarization neutralizing polarity

depth perception to measure visually distance in space

derepression turning on of an enzyme system that has been previously turned off

dermis lower connective tissue layer of the skin

desmosome specialized site of adhesion between two cells

diabetes mellitus: condition characterized by excessive urine formation, faulty sugar metabolism, lack of insulin; **insipidus:** excessive quantity of urine formation due to faulty secretion of pituitary hormone

dialysis separation of molecules in solution by means of their unequal rates of diffusion through a semipermeable membrane

diapedesis passage of blood and blood cells through the intact walls of blood vessels

diaphysis shaft of a long bone

diarthrosis articulation that is freely movable

diastole period when the heart chambers dilate and fill with blood

diencephalon section of forebrain that gives rise to the thalamus, epithalamus, hypothalamus, retina, and so on

differentiation visible change in the structure and function of general or nonspecialized cells; part of the process of cell maturation

diffusion random movement of free molecules in solution or suspension toward a uniform distribution in the given volume

digit finger or toe

dilation stretching or enlarging of a vessel or cavity

dioptric refractive

disaccharide the product formed of the binding of two monosaccharides

distal farther from any given point

diuresis increased excretion of urine

DNA *see* deoxyribonucleic acid acid

dorsal toward the back; posterior

ductus arteriosus fetal vessel that shunts blood from the pulmonary artery to the descending aorta

ductus deferens spermatic duct, genital tract (testes)

ductus venosus fetal blood vessel which shunts blood through the liver into the hepatic vein

dysmenorrhea abnormal or irregular menstrual cycle

ectoderm outermost germ layer

ectopic pregnancy pregnancy that occurs in regions other than the cavity of the uterus

edema accumulation of an excessive amount of fluid in cells, tissues, cavities

efferent carry outward, for example, nerves, vessels, ducts conducting outward

ejaculatory duct male excretory duct of the seminal vesicle opening into the prostatic urethra, and contracts during orgasm

electrocardiogram (ECG or EKG) record of the heart's activity obtained with an electrocardiograph

electrolyte any substance in solution that becomes an ion conductor

electron a negatively charged particle

embolus a moving blood clot that may stop and form a plug or wedge

embryo generally restricted to the developing organism between the second and eighth weeks

emmetropic normal vision; image is sharply focused on the retina

encephalon brain

endergonic a chemical reaction that absorbs energy from its surroundings

endocardium innermost layer of the heart

endocrine ductless gland; secreting hormone directly into the blood

endoderm middle layer of the three primary germ layers

endometrium lining of the uterus

endoneurium connective tissue covering of individual nerve fibers

endoplasmic reticulum network of parallel flattened sacs or vesicles in the cytoplasm

endothelium single layer of epithelium lining blood vessels

enterokinase digestive enzyme secreted by the intestine

enzyme catalytic substance formed by cells

eosinophil white blood cell staining readily with acid dyes

epididymis first portion of the excretory duct of the testis; sperm are stored here

epiglottis flap that covers the opening of the glottis

epinephrine adrenaline, hormone from the adrenal medulla

epineurium outermost layer of connective tissue surrounding a nerve trunk and binding together the bundles of nerve fibers

epiphysis end portion of a long bone in early life separated from the shaft by cartilage plate that disappears around the twentieth year

epithalamus a small area of the diencephalon, forming part of the root of the third ventricle

epithelium covering of the internal and external surfaces of the body

equilibrium balance

erector pili muscle muscle cell located at the base of hair follicle

ergosterol chemical compound that is converted to vitamin D

erythrocyte (RBC) red blood cell

erythropoietin substance secreted by the kidney into plasma and believed to be involved in erythrocyte formation

essential amino acids amino acids that cannot be synthesized by the body therefore must be part of the diet

estrogen female sex hormones that regulate sex cycle, and so on

ethmoid sievelike; referring to

ethmoid bone with many openings

eupnea normal respiration

Eustachian tube tube leading from the tympanic cavity to the nasopharynx

euthanasia so-called mercy killing of individuals with painful and incurable disease

evagination outpocketing

eversion turning outward

exergonic reaction that takes place with release of energy to the immediate environment

exocrine gland which empties its secretions to a free surface of the body via ducts

exophthalamus protrusion of the eyeball; pop-eyes

expiration exhalation; breathing out

exponent symbol indicating the number of times a factor is to be multiplied; for example, $10^3 = 10 \times 10 \times 10$

extension movement away from the body

extracellular outside the cell

fallopian tube uterine tubes; run from the region of the ovary to the uterus

fenestration pertaining to fenestra or windowlike openings

fertilization process of joining egg and sperm

fetal relating to the unborn young in the uterus

fibrillation exceedingly rapid contractions of groups of muscle fibers or single fibers, but not of the muscle as a whole; sometimes occurs in atria and ventricles of the heart

fibrinogen soluble blood protein which is converted to the insoluble fibrin by enzymatic action such as seen in blood clotting

fibroblast an elongated cell present in connective tissue, capable of forming collagen

fibrous composed of or containing fibers; long

filtrate liquid remaining after passage through a filter

fimbriae fingerlike projections that extend outward from the opening of the oviduct

fissure a slit, furrow, or cleft

fixing, fixative substance used for the preservation of gross and histologic specimens of tissue or individual cells

flexion bending of a joint so as to diminish the angle between the bones

focal length the distance light rays travel before converging after passing through a convex lens

follicle small sac such as the ovarian cells that surround an ovum

foramen perforation through a bone or membranous structure

foramen ovale the oval-shaped opening between the atria in the fetal heart

fossa pit or depression

free energy energy from a chemical reaction that is capable of doing useful work

free radical group atom or group of atoms having at least one unpaired electron

frequency number of recurring events in a given time

frontal concerning the anterior part of a body in front

gametogenesis production of gametes, for example, sperm and ova

gamma globulin division of proteins in plasma that have antibody function

ganglion aggregation of nerve cell bodies outside the central nervous system

gastrin hormone that stimulates gastric juice secretions

gastrointestinal related to the stomach and intestine

gel semisolid or solid phase of a colloidal solution

gelatinous jellylike

generator potential potential established on receptor or sensory cells in response to stimulus

genitalia referring to genitals, the reproductive organs

germinal embryonic or original

gerontology study of aging and old age

gingiva fibrous connective tissue covered with a mucous membrane that encloses the necks of teeth

glaucoma disease of the eye caused by increased intraocular pressure

glomerulus capillary tuft found at the beginning of the nephron

glottis opening into the larynx; glottis folds help to produce sound

glucagon peptide secreted by the pancreas whose hormonal action raises blood sugar by the mobilization of liver glycogen (glycogenalysis)

glucocorticoids adrenal cortex hormones that affect sugar metabolism and have anti-inflammatory action

gluconeogenesis formation of simple sugars from noncarbohydrate sources, for example, proteins

glucose monosaccharide or simple sugar; principal blood sugar

glucosuria urinary excretion of glucose

glycogen principal carbohydrate storage compound composed of many glucose units

glycogenesis formation of glycogen from glucose

glycogenolysis breakdown of glycogen to glucose

glycolysis utilization of sugar, specifically the conversion of glucose to lactic acid with release of energy

goblet cell mucosal epithelial cell that assumes a goblet shape when it discharges its secretion

goiter any disease of the thyroid gland can be termed a goiter; frequently visible as a swelling of the neck

Golgi complex lies adjacent to the nucleus; concerned with secretion

gonadotropins pituitary hormones that stimulate the secretory activity of the gonads (ovary and testis)

graft joining something with something such as skin or bone

gram molecular weight amount of a chemical compound with a weight in grams numerically equal to its molecular weight, also called a mole

granulation tissue vascular connective tissue involved in wound healing

ground substance amorphous material of connective tissue in which the structural elements occur

gubernaculum fibrous cord that connects the testis to the base of the scrotum

gyrus convoluted or rounded ridges between grooves on the surface of the brain hemispheres

half-life period that a radioactive substance reduces its radioactivity by one-half of the original value; for example, half-life of 1 year means that in 4 years only 12.5 percent of the original radioactivity would be present

hallucination an imaginary situation; perception not based upon reality

hematocrit percentage (value) of red blood cells in whole blood

hematopoiesis formation of blood cells and other formed elements

hematuria urine containing blood

hemoconcentration increase in the concentration of red blood cells

hemoglobin iron-containing protein in red blood cells which combines with oxygen

hemolysis release of hemoglobin from red blood cells

hemorrhage large flow (loss) of blood from a vessel

hemostasis arrest of bleeding

heparin chemical that has anticoagulant properties

hillock small hill

histamine substance found in tissues that constricts bronchial smooth muscle; produces vasodilation of arterioles (and capillaries); depresses blood pressure; produces shocklike effects

histocompatibility state of similar immunological competence permits successful transplanting

histology study of tissue

holocrine type of gland with secretions consisting of disintegrated cells of the gland

homeostasis tendency toward a state of equilibrium between various parts of the body with respect to function and to chemical compositions of the fluids and tissues, and to the environment

homogenous similarity of structure

homograft transplant of tissue

from a donor to a host of the same species

homologous similarity of structure based upon heredity

hormone organic compound that is produced by endocrine gland and produces an effect on other cells

host the recipient of a graft

hydrochloric acid acid secreted by the stomach as part of gastric juice

hydrogen ion hydrogen atom minus its electron; carrying a unit positive charge

hydrolysis "split by water"; hence chemical transformation following reaction with water

hydrophilic association with water molecules; attraction of water molecules

hydrophobic opposite of hydrophilic; repels water molecules

hymen (maiden head) thin membrane that partially closes off the external opening of the vagina in a virgin

hyper- prefix denoting above normal; for example, hypersecretion

hyperbaric high atmospheric pressures

hyperglycemia abnormally high concentration of glucose in the blood

hypermetropia farsightedness

hyperplasia the increase of numbers of cells in a tissue

hyperpnea rapid or accelerated respiration

hypersensitivity excessively sensitive

hypertension high arterial blood pressure

hypertonic having a greater degree of osmotic pressure

hypertrophy overgrowth; abnormal enlargement

hyperventilation increased pulmonary ventilation

hypo- prefix denoting a location beneath something else; or below normal

hypophyseal stalk stalk of the pituitary gland

hypothalamus group of nuclei at the base of diencephalon; forms part of the inferior wall of the third ventricle

hypotonic having a lesser degree of pressure (osmotic)

hypoxia amount of oxygen in tissue

immolation to kill or destroy

immunity ability to resist a disease

immunocompetence capable of confering immunity

immunocyte leukocyte that produces antibodies

immunoglobulins proteins with antibody activity

impermeable does not permit passage of particles or fluid

implantation insert in living tissue of the body

impotence inability of the male to copulate

impulse nerve action potential

inclusions particles within the cytoplasm, for example, pigment granule

infarction death in a local area (for example, heart muscle) due to obstruction of the terminal artery nourishing the area

inferior lower; below another structure

inflammation local response to injury marked by capillary dilation, redness, heat, and so on

inguinal pertaining to the groin

insertion (muscle) attachment of a muscle to the more movable part of the skeleton

inspiration breathing in, inhalation

insulin pancreatic hormone essential for carbohydrate metabolism

integration coordination of parts and function into a harmonious unit

intercostal located between the ribs

interstitial cells cells of the testes that secrete male hormones

intima innermost coat of a blood or lymphatic vessel

intracellular within the cell

in utero inside the uterus

inversion turning inward

in vitro observed in an artificial system, for example, a reaction in a test tube

in vivo occurs within the living body

ion atom with either a positive or negative charge of electricity

ischemia local anemia due to obstruction of the blood supply

islets of Langerhans small aggregates of cells of varying sizes in the pancreas that produce hormones, insulin, and glucagon

isogenic having the same histocompatibility or state of immunological similarity to permit successful grafting

isometric contraction muscular contraction that occurs without change in length of the fibers

isotonic denoting solutions having the same osmotic pressure

isotonic contraction opposed to isometric; muscle contraction with shortening of the fibers

isotope term referring to either of two or more nuclides that are chemically identical but differing in mass number since their nuclei contain different numbers of neutrons

karyokinesis division of the nucleus

karyotype chromosome characteristics of an individual or of a group of cells

keratin albuminoid present largely in skin structures such as hair and nails

ketone substance with the group—C=O linking two carbon atoms; acetone is a common ketone

ketosis condition characterized by the overproduction of ketone bodies

kinetosome small granule at the base of a cilium

Krebs cycle citric acid cycle; a series of energy-yielding steps in the catabolism of carbohydrates; named after Hans Krebs, Nobel laureate and codiscoverer (with Fritz Lipmann)

labia plural of labium, which means liplike; the large fleshy outer folds and the inner narrow mucous membrane folds of the female genital region are called the labia majora and minora, respectively

lacrimal gland gland that secretes tears

lactation secretion of milk

lactic acid intermediate product in the metabolism of carbohydrate; the end point of anerobic glycolysis

lacunae small space or depression

larynx voice box, part between pharynx and trachea

latent period period elapsing between the application of a stimulus and the response

lateral on the outer side

leukocyte (also leucocyte) white blood cell (WBC)

leukocytosis abnormally large number of leukocytes

limbic system part of the nervous system concerned with the control of emotions and of autonomic activity

lipase fat-splitting enzyme

lipid fat and fatlike compounds

liter volume occupied by 1 kgm of water at standard atmospheric pressure; equivalent to 1.057 quarts

lobe curve or rounded projection

local circuit electrical circuit covering a limited area of the axon membrane

locus place; plural, loci

lumbar region of back and side between the ribs and pelvis; loins

luteinizing hormone from the pituitary that stimulates the development of the corpora lutea in the female and interstitial cells in the male

luteotropic hormone from the pituitary and it has a stimulating action on the corpus luteum secretory activity

lymphocytes white blood cells formed in lymphoid tissue; involved in phagocytosis and antibody formation

lysosome membrane bound granules that contain enzymes

macro large, extensively developed

macrophage large, wandering phagocyte

macula (eye) spot or region in the retina containing only cones

malnutrition poor diet that eventually will produce abnormal structure and function

mandibular relating to the lower jaw

manubrium part of the sternum

marrow highly vascular modified connective tissue that occupies the cavities of most bones and produces blood cells

mast cell connective tissue cell with coarse granules containing, for example, heparin and histamine

mastication chewing

media middle coat of a blood or lymphatic vessel

medial relating to the middle or center

mediastinum septum of the thoracic cavity that encloses the viscera except the lungs

medulla inner or deep part of an organ

megakaryocyte large cell with a multilobed nucleus; present in bone marrow but not in circulating blood; gives rise to platelets

meiosis process by which the chromosome number is halted in dividing sex cells

melanin dark brown or black pigment

melanocytes melanin pigment cell of the skin

membrane potential potential across the membrane of cells, especially of nerve and muscle fibers

memory trace a pattern for remembering; theory that each impulse creates molecular changes in the nervous system

meninges three membranes that envelope the brain and spinal cord

menopause permanent cessation of the menstrual cycle

menses menstrual cycle

merocrine gland that is repeatedly functional; secretions are not part of the cell (opposite of holocrine)

mesencephalon midbrain

mesenchyme embryonic connective tissue consisting of mesenchymal cells

mesentery membranes that support, connect, and enclose viscera

mesothelium single layer of epithelium-lining serous membranes

mesovarium broad ligament attached to the uterus

messenger RNA type of RNA that carries the DNA "message" to the exact cytoplasmic area where protein is assembled

metabolic pathway series of chemical reactions by which a compound is synthesized or degraded

metabolism complex process by which food is utilized by a living organism

metencephalon anterior of the two divisions of the rhombencephalon; area that forms cerebellum and pons

microgram 10^{-6} grams, or one one-millionth of a gram

micron (μ) unit of measurement in the metric system equal to 10^{-3} millimeter or 10^{-6} meter

microtome instrument for making thin sections for microscopic examination

microtubules cylindrical cytoplasmic elements of at least 250 Å in diameter; spindle fibers are microtubules

microvilli projections of cell membranes that increase surface area

micturition urination

midsagittal median line

milligrams percent milligrams of a substance in 100 ml of blood

mineralocorticoids term for a group of adrenal cortex hormones that influence salt metabolism

mitochondria cytoplasmic organelles that are the principal energy source of the cell

mitosis division of cells

mitotic spindle tubular structures in dividing cells attached to the two poles and also to the chromosomes

mittelschmerz abdominal pain that supposedly indicates the release of an egg from the ovary

molecule smallest possible quantity of a substance that retains the chemical properties of the substance

monosaccharide carbohydrate that cannot form any simpler sugar by simple hydrolysis

monosynaptic nerve pathway involving only one synapse

mons pubis elevation or prominence of fatty tissue over the pubis in the female

morphogenetic movement part of the process of differentiation in the early embryo to establish the form and structure of organs

mucosa mucous membrane

mutation alteration of the gene that is perpetuated in subsequent mitosis of the specific cell in which it occurred

myelencephalon part of the hind brain, or medulla

myelin substance arranged in layers around the axons of nerve fibers; gives white matter its characteristic shade

myeloid pertaining to the bone marrow

myenteric plexus mass of tubules in the muscular coat of the intestine

myocardial relating to the muscular middle and largest layer of the heart

myofibril microscopic fiber occurring in muscles fibers or cells

myoglobin oxygen-transporting protein of muscle

myometrium thick middle layer of muscle in the uterus

myopia nearsightedness

myosin protein found in the thick filaments in the sarcomeres of skeletal muscle; when combined with actin, forms the basic contractile unit of muscle

NAD, nicotinamide adenine dinucleotide attached to a protein; it serves as a coenzyme

nares nostrils

necrosin active principle isolated from exudates of acute inflammation that causes death of cells

nephritis inflammation of kidneys

nephron the kidney's functional unit

neurilemma sheath enclosing nerve fibers

neurofibrils fibrils in the cell body, dendrites, axon, and sometimes the synaptic ending

neurogenic starting from or caused by the nervous system

neuroglia (glia) non-nervous elements of nervous tissue; supportive, protective, and nutritive

neurohypophysis posterior lobe of the pituitary gland

neuromuscular junction area where a muscle and nerve membrane are apposed; specialized for transmission of the impulse from the nerve to the muscle

neuron nerve cell; functional and structural unit of the nervous system

neurosecretory release of a chemical substance by neural tissue into the circulatory system

neurotic nervous, relating to or suffering from a functional nervous disorder

neutrophil white blood cell that

stains readily with neutral dyes

Nissl bodies substance in nerve cell which stains readily; contains RNA

norepinephrine chemical released from certain nerves, as in the postganglionic fibers of the sympathetic division of the autonomic nervous system

nuclease enzyme that splits nucleic acids

nuclei (brain) mass of gray matter, composed of nerve cells, in any part of the brain

nucleic acid substances of large molecular weight, found in chromosomes, nucleoli, mitochondria, and cytoplasm of all cells and in viruses

nucleolus small structure composed in part of RNA within the nucleus

nucleoplasm colloidal portion of the nucleus of a cell (cytoplasm of the nucleus)

nucleus spherical or oval structure within a cell containing the chromosomes

nuclide species of atoms with defined characteristics and properties of its nucleus (number of protons and neutrons, amount of energy)

obesity excessively overweight

occipital relating to the back of the head; name of bone and division of brain

ocular relating to the eye

olfaction sense of smelling

oliguria little urine formation

organ any structure of the body which exercises a specific function

organelle one of the stable structures found in cytoplasm concerned in the functions of metabolism, locomotion, and so on

orgasm the summit or consummation of the sexual act

origin end of a muscle that remains fixed during contraction

oscilloscope instrument that is used to record the small electrical charges associated with membranes

osmoreceptors receptor in the CNS that responds to changes in the osmotic pressure of the blood

osmosis type of diffusion; movement of water through a semipermeable membrane from an area of greater concentration of water (or lesser concentration of dissolved materials) to an area of lesser concentration of water (or greater concentration of dissolved materials)

osseous bony

ossification formation of bone

osteoblast bone-forming cell

osteoclast large multinucleated cell functioning in the absorption and removal of bone

osteocyte mature bone cell

ovagenesis (oogenesis) process of formation and development of the ovum

ovary primary sex organ of the female; reproductive gland

overlapping junction a type of cell connection

ovum female gamete; egg

oxidation combination with oxygen or the loss of H or an electron from an atom

oxytocin hormone that stimulates labor and release of milk during lactation

pacemaker rhythmic center which controls the activity of the heart

palate roof of the mouth

palatine referring to palate

palpated touching or feeling by the sense of touch

papilla nipplelike projection

parasympathetic division of the nervous system concerned primarily with activities that occur during nonemergency or stressful periods; restorative regulation

paravertebral alongside vertebrae

parenteral introducing a substance by some other means than through the intestinal canal, for example, injection into the skin or vein

parietal wall of any cavity

parietal cells hydrochloric acid secreting cell of the gastric glands

parietal pleura membranous layer lining chest walls

partial pressure the pressure exerted by one gas in a mixture of gases, for example, oxygen in air

patent open, unobstructive

pathogenic causing disease

pathology study of disease

pelvic relating to the pelvis the basin-shaped structure of the posterior part of the trunk

penis male organ of copulation

pepsin a digestive enzyme that splits proteins

pericardium membrane surrounding the heart

perineurium connective tissue sheath surrounding a bundle of nerve fibers in a peripheral nerve

periosteum connective tissue covering the entire surface of a bone except its articular cartilage

peripheral outer part or surface, related to the periphery

peristalsis wavelike contraction and relaxation of tubular organs, for example, intestine

peritoneum the sac of mesothelium and connective tissue (serous membrane) that lines the abdominal cavity and covers the organs

  visceral p., the layer covering the organs

  parietal p., the layer lining the abdominal walls

Peyer's patches lymphoid tissue in intestinal wall

pH symbol commonly used in expressing hydrogen ion concentration

phagocytosis process of ingestion and digestion by cells

pharynx common chamber for respiratory and digestive systems between mouth and nasal cavities superiorily and esophogus and trachea inferiorily

phase microscope a special interference light microscope

phosphocreatine source of energy in the contraction of muscle, furnishing energy phosphate for the resynthesis of ATP from ADP

phospholipid lipid containing phosphorus

phosphorylation adding a phosphate group to a compound

pinna the external ear

pinocytosis cellular process of actively engulfing liquid

pituitary endocrine gland attached by a stalk to the brain

placenta vascular structure that joins the fetus to the maternal uterus

plasma liquid portion of blood

plasma cell a type of white blood cell that acts in the formation of antibodies

plasmalemma boundary of all cells; regulates permeability and other cell surface activities

platelets specifically a blood platelet; a fragment or subdivision of a megakaryocyte involved in blood clotting and hemostasis

pleura serous membrane that encloses lungs and lines the thoracic cavity

plexus network of nerves and blood vessels

polymerize process whereby high molecular weight substances are produced by additions or condensations of a simpler compound

polysaccharide carbohydrate containing a large number of simple sugars

polyspermy penetration of more than one sperm into the ovum

pons bridgelike formation connecting two or more parts of the same organ, for example, fibers that bridge the medulla to cerebellum; form part of the pons

posterior situated behind or toward the rear

postganglionic neuron beyond a ganglion; the second autonomic neuron that goes to the target structure

postnatal subsequent to birth

precapillary sphincters last muscular unit for regulation of arterial blood flow; may consist of single muscle fiber wrapped around a terminal arteriole

precursor anything preceding another from which something is derived, as in glycogen synthesis from glucose

preganglionic neuron neuron of the autonomic nervous system that precedes the ganglion existing

prenatal before birth

pressor raising blood pressure; involving vasoconstriction (narrowing of blood vessels)

pressoreceptors sense organ that responds to changes in pressure

pressure head force exerted in a given direction against resistance

primary germ layers three layers of cells (ectoderm, mesoderm, and endoderm) from which all organs are formed; some organs are derived primarily from one layer

progeria accelerated aging; a young person with the appearance and symptoms of senility (old age)

progesterone hormone produced by the corpus luteum and in pregnancy by the placenta; regulates menstrual cycle and helps maintain uterus in active state

pronation face down

proprioceptor sensory receptor stimulated by impulse arising in the deeper structures such as the muscles, tendons, and joints

prostate gland surrounding the urethra in the male, secreting a milky fluid discharged with semen

prosthesis fabricated substitute for a missing bodily part, for example, false teeth and artificial limb

protein macromolecule consisting of long sequences of amino acids

proteinuria protein in urine

proteolytic capable of breaking down proteins

proximal nearest; closer to point of reference

psychosomatic interaction of mental and body phenomena; generally in reference to individuals who have mental and body symptoms because of a mental problem or conflict

puberty condition of becoming capable of sexual reproduction

pulmonary relating to the lungs

pulse pressure difference between systolic and diastolic pressure

Purkinje fiber interlacing fibers formed of modified cardiac muscle cells, used as a pathway for conduction of an impulse

pyloric sphincter circular muscle band that controls the opening of the stomach to the small intestine

pyruvic acid intermediate compound in the metabolism of carbohydrates

radial diverging in all directions from a given point

radioactive isotopes an unstable isotope which decays to a stable state

radiography record produced by X rays or radioactive material

ramus branch; a primary division of a nerve or blood vessel

receptor sensory nerve ending in the skin and organs of sense (such as eye, nose, tongue, ear)

reciprocal countering the effects created by another part

reduction the reverse of oxidation, or the gain of one or more electrons by an ion or compound

refraction light ray deflection when it passes from one medium into another of differing optical densities

refractory period period during which a cell is unresponsive to stimulus

regurgitation vomiting

releasing factors substance capable of accelerating the rate of hormone secretion

renal relating to a kidney

renin enzyme found in the kidney

rennin protein splitting enzyme in stomach

replication process of reproduction

residual volume left over air in the lungs after exhalation

respiratory quotient ratio of the volume of carbon dioxide expired to the volume of oxygen consumed

resuscitation revive from unconsciousness or apparent death

reticular cell connective tissue cells forming a network

reticulocyte young red blood cell

reticuloendothelial connective tissue cells that are phagocytic

retina eyeball's nervous tunic

retinene vitamin A-like compound; part of visual purple pigment compound involved in the chemistry of vision

retroperitoneal behind the peritoneum

ribonucleic acid (RNA) protein synthesizing substance

rotation turning or movement of a body around its axis

rod nerve cell in retina responsible for black and white vision

saccharide sugar, carbohydrate

sacral relating to the sacrum (lower vertebrae)

sagittal a plane or section parallel to the long axis of the body

saltatory conduction conduction in which the nerve impulse "jumps" from one node of Ranvier to the next

sarcoma tumor, frequently malignant, arising from connective tissue (or any nonepithelial tissues)

sarcomere skeletal muscle unit

Schwann cell neurilemma cells, cells of the sheath enfolding nerve fibers; produces myelin

sclerotic pertaining to sclerosis, the hardening by inflammation or excessive cell growth

scrotum external pouch that contains the testes

sebum secretions of the sebaceous glands

secretagogue substance that stimulates secretions

secretin duodenal hormone that stimulates secretion in the pancreas

selective permeability the passage of only certain molecules through a semipermeable membrane

seminal vesicles small sacs containing semen

semipermeable membrane membrane that allows the passage of water and small ions or molecules but not of large molecules

senescence state of growing old

sensitized to make sensitive

septum thin dividing wall between two cavities or masses of tissues

sequester to separate and remove from the immediate environment

serotonin substance liberated by the blood platelets; inhibits gastric secretion, stimulates smooth muscle contraction (in blood vessels produces vasoconstriction)

serum portion of blood minus cells, other formed elements, and fibrin

sex chromosomes pair of chromosomes responsible for sex determination

sinoatrial node pacemaker of the heart

sinusoids an amorphous blood channel found in marrow, spleen, and so on, with a lining that is partly composed of phagocytic cell

sol colloidal dispersion of a solid in a liquid

solute dissolved substance

solvent substance that dissolves or can dissolve

soma body, including the head, neck, without the limbs; also used to denote the body of a cell as opposed to its processes

somatic referring to the nonvisceral parts of the body, for example, framework

somesthesis bodily sensation; the "consciousness of the body"

spastic increased muscle tone

spermatic cord cord that contains blood vessels, lymphatic, and nerves running from the testis to the pelvic cavity

spermatogenesis sperm formation

spermatozoon motile male gamete or sex cell

spermicidal sperm-killing agent

sphincter muscle able to contract and close an opening

spirometer instrument for measuring air entering and leaving lungs

splanchnic visceral; for example, splanchnic nerves going to the stomach and intestine

steady state state where input is equal to output

stenosis narrowing of a canal

sterility unproductive, barrenness

steroid large group of substances that include vitamin D, bile acids, hormones, and so on

sterol steroid containing —OH groups, for example, cholesterol

sucrose disaccharide made up of glucose and fructose

sulcus groove or furrow on the surface of the brain

sulfhydryl sulfur hydrogen (—SH) group on an organic compound

superficial relating to on, or near the surface

superior above another structure, higher; the head is at the superior end of the body

supination to bend backward; to turn forearm and hand palmar side up

surfactant substance secreted

by lung cells which reduces the surface tension of the tissue fluid

sympathetic division of the autonomic nervous system concerned generally with emergency situations

synapse region where an impulse is transmitted between two adjacent neurons or between a neuron and muscle fiber

synarthrotic immovable articulation

syncope loss of consciousness

syncytium multinucleated protoplasmic mass formed by the secondary union of originally separate cells

syndrome collection of symptoms or signs that indicate a "common denominator cause"

synthesis formation or putting together of simpler compounds or elements to more complex substances

systemic relating to a system, as in the urinary system

systole rhythmical contraction of the heart

tachycardia rapid heartbeat

tactile relating to touch

tarsal glands sebaceous glands of the eyelid

temporal relating to the temple; name of skull bone and part of brain

testes primary male reproductive organ

testosterone the major male hormone secreted by the testes

thalamus large ovoid mass of gray substance making up most of the walls of the third ventricle; relay station for sensory stimuli to the cerebral cortex

thermodynamics branch of science that deals with heat, energy, and their conversions into mechanical work

thoracic relating to the chest, thorax

threshold point where a stimulus begins to produce a sensation; the lower limit of perception of a stimulus; in the neuron the point at which an impulse is initiated

thrombus clot, formed on a blood vessel wall

thymectomy removal of the thymus gland

thyrocalcitonin hormone secreted by the thyroid gland that inhibits the resorption of bone; produces low calcium levels in the blood

thyroglobulin protein hormone secreted and stored in the thyroid

thyroxine active thyroid hormone

tidal volume air inspired or expired during normal quiet breathing

tight junction type of connection between cells in which the plasma membranes are believed to fuse

tissue collection of similar cells and the intercellular substances with similar functions

tissue fluid extracellular fluid in tissues, excluding the blood and lymph

tolerance ability of the body to retain a graft or transplant

tone firmness of the tissues

trace element elements present in minute amounts in the body

tracer element or compound containing atoms that can be distinguished from their normal counterparts by physical means and thus used to trace the course of normal substances in metabolism or similar chemical changes

tract path

transamination reaction in which an amino group ($-NH_2$) is transferred from an amino acid to a keto acid

transfer RNA short chain RNA molecules capable of combining with a specific amino acid

transient short-lived, having little duration

transplant remove from one area and place or introduce elsewhere

transverse crosswise

transverse tubules small tube passing from muscle membrane across myofibril of striated muscle

trauma injury to living tissue caused by an extrinsic agent; also used to describe phenomenon that produce mental disorders

triglyceride fat composed of glycerol and three fatty acids

trophoblast embryonic outer cell layer covering the blastocyst which erodes the uterine mucosa in the formation of a placenta

true solution solution containing dissolved substances

trypsin proteolytic enzyme formed in the small intestine and secreted into the lumen

tumor growth of tissue that grows independently of its surroundings and has no physiological value

tunic one of the layers of an organ

twitch denotes rapid contraction of a muscle

tympanic membrane ear drum; membrane marking the boundary between the external ear and the middle ear

ulcer break in skin or mucous membrane

urea chief end product of nitrogen metabolism formed by the liver and excreted in the urine; it accounts for most of the nitrogen excreted by the body

uremia excess of urea and other nitrogenous wastes in the blood

urethra canal that carries urine from the bladder and in the male serves also as a genital duct

uterus hollow thick-walled muscular organ in which the fertilized egg develops into an infant; about 3 inches in length in a nonpregnant adult woman

vacuoles clear space in the cytoplasm; sometimes serving as temporary storage structures

vagina short muscular tube that extends from the uterus to the exterior part of the birth canal

vas deferens see ductus deferens

vasoconstriction narrowing of the diameter of blood vessels

vasodilation enlarging the diameter; in blood vessels leads to increased blood flow

vasomotor nerves causing dilation or constriction of the blood vessels

vasopressin pituitary hormone that increases blood pressure and decreases urine flow

vegetative involuntary growth or functioning unconsciously, for example, heart contractions, endocrine secretions

ventilation circulation and exchange of air

ventral situated in front; anterior

ventricle small fluid-filled cavity in the brain, also heart chamber

vermiform wormlike extension of the colon, veriform appendix

vernix caseosa fatty substance

which covers the skin of the fetus

vesicle small membrane-bound structure in the cytoplasm, often containing some sort of secretory material, as in the nerve endings

villi projections from the surface especially of a mucous membrane

visceral relating to the internal organs; viscus (singular)

visceral pleura membranous layer enveloping lungs

viscosity resistance to flow of a substance as a result of molecular interaction; water has a low viscosity, whereas vegetable oil has a high viscosity

visual acuity ability of the eye to see two close point sources of light

visual purple chemical in retinal cell which changes with light and initiates the nerve impulse, also called rhodopsin

vitamin group of organic substances present in minute amount in food that are essential to normal metabolism

vitreous body colorless, transparent gel in the posterior chamber part of the eyeball

wheal suddenly formed elevation of the skin surface

yolk sac one of the fetal membranes; limited function in human development

Z line dense, repeating lines in skeletal muscle; forms the boundary of the sarcomere

index

index

Page numbers in italics refer to definitions of terms.

Abdominal cavity, 84
Abortions, 542, 543
  spontaneous, 543
Absorption, intestinal, 361
Accessory reproductive organs, 491
Accommodation, 249
Acetoacetic acid, 392
Acetyl CoA, 49, 391
Acetylcholine (*see* Synapse, neuro-
  muscular junction)
Achilles reflex, 238
Achilles tendon, 165
Acid (*see* specific acid)
Acid base balance, 280
Acidosis, 392, 449, 482
ACTH (*see* Adrenal cortex; Anterior
  pituitary)
Actin, 167, 168
Action potential, 135, 137, 138
Active immunity, 554
Active transport, 549
Actomyosin, 168
Adam's apple, 413
Addison's disease, 485
Adenoid tonsil (pharyngeal tonsil), 347
Adenosine triphosphate (ATP), 18, 44
  in muscle contraction, 168, 175
  production in lipid metabolism, 392
  to drive reactions, 44
ADH (*see* Antidiuretic hormone)
Adrenal cortex, 483
  feminizing steroids, 483
  glucocorticoids, 483
  masculinizing steroids, 483
  mineralocorticoids, 483
  physiology, 483

Adrenal medulla, 483
Adrenals, 482
Adrenergic nerves, 232
Adrenocorticotropic hormone, 473
Adventitia, 314
Afterbirth, 540
Aging, 85, 560, 570-576
Agranulocytes, 272
Albumin, in plasma, 273
Aldosterone, 330, 332, 451, 484, 485
Alimentary tract, 344
Alkali reserve, 281
Alkalosis, 449
Alkaptonuria, 400
Allantois, 530
Allergy, 560, 561
Allograft, 558
All or none law, 135, 172, 177
α receptor, 329
Alveolar ducts, 416, 419, 420
Alveolus, 419, 420
  gas exchange, 421
Ameboid movement, 59
Amenorrhea, 518
Amino acid metabolism, ammonia
  production, 396
  oxidative deamination, 396
  transamination, 395
Amino acids, 367
Amnion, 529, 530
Amygdaloid nuclei, 209
Anaerobic metabolism, 46-48
Anamnestic response, 561
Anaphylaxis, 562
Anatomic dead space, 423
Anatomic position, 81

Androgens, 495
Anemia, 560
Aneurysm, 331
Angina pectoris, 309
Angiotensin, 330, 332, 451
Anorexia nervosa, 375
Anoxia, 428
Anterior chamber, 243
Anterior pituitary, 473, 474
Antiallergic action, 483
Antianemic factor, 372
Antibody (ies), 270, 279, 555
Antibody defense mechanism, 553
Antibody producing cells, 552, 557
Anticoagulants, 279
Antidiuretic hormone, 448, 450, 472, 473
Antigens, 552, 555
Antihemophilic globulin (AGH), 286
Antihistamines, 562
Anti-inflammatory action, 483
Antilymphocyte serum, 559
Antioxidant, 575
Anuria, 451
Anus, 350
Aorta, 293
Aortic body, 306, 427
Aortic reflex, 306
Aphasia, 213
Apnea, 423
Apocrine glands, 78
Appendicitis, 373
Appendix, 337, 349, 350
Appetite, 375
  hypothalamus centers, 376
Aqueous humor, 243
Arachnoid layer, 189
Areola, 509
Areolar, 71
Arterioles, 315, 316
Arteriosclerosis, 332
Arteriovenous shunts, 317
Artery, 315
  aorta, 292, 313
  adrenal, 313
  axillary, 313
  brachial, 313
  brachiocephalic, 313
  celiac, 313, 353
  common carotid, 313
  common iliac, 313
  coronary, 293
  deep palmar arch, 313
  digital, 313
  dorsalis pedis, 313

Artery (Continued)
  elastic, 315
  femoral, 313
  gastric, 353
  hepatic, 353
  hypogastric, 313
  inferior mesenteric, 313, 353
  internal thoracic, 313
  lateral femoral circumflex, 313
  muscular, 315
  ovarian (testicular), 313
  profunda femoris, 313
  pulmonary, 292, 293
  radial, 313
  renal, 313
  spiral, 529
  splenic, 353
  subclavian, 292, 313
  superficial palmar arch, 313
  superior mesenteric, 313, 353
  tibial, 313
  ulnar, 313
  uterine, 529
  vertebral, 313
Arthritis, 119, 560
Arthrology (see Articulation)
Articulation, 115, 116
Artificial immunity, 555
Artificial kidney, 452, 453
Ascorbic acid, 370
Association areas, learning, 196
  tracts, 191
Asthma, 430
Astigmatism, 249
Ataxia, 213
Atherosclerosis, 332
ATP (see Adenosine triphosphate)
Atria, 291
Atrio-ventricular node (A-V node), 295
Atrophy, 525
Auricle, 257
Autograft, 558
Autoimmune disease, 560, 574
Autolysis, 548
Autonomic nervous system, 201, 229
  parasympathetic division, 230
  reciprocal action, 233
  role of adrenal medulla, 232
  sympathetic division, 229
Autonomic reflexes, 234

Baroreceptors, 331
Barr body, 272
Basal ganglia, 191, 196, 207
Basal metabolic rate, 403-405

Basal metabolic rate (Continued)
  effect of age and sex, 404
  effect of climate, 405
  effect of hormones, 405
Basement membrane, 317
Basilar membrane, 260
Basophil, 270, 272, 275
Bends, 428
β-hydroxybutyric acid, 392
Beta oxidation of fatty acid, 391
β receptor, 329
Bicarbonate ion, 280
Biceps reflex, 238
Bicuspid valve, 293
Bile, 350, 351, 361
Bile ducts, 351
Bilirubin, 361
Biliverdine, 361
Biopsy, 23
Birth, 524, 539, 540
Birth canal, 540
Birth control, 539-542
Bladder, 436, 437, 446, 447
Blastocyst, 527
Blastomeres, 526, 527
"Bleeder," 286
Bleeding times, 279
Blood, 269
  buffering action, 280
  cell development, 71
  cell types, 270
  clotting factors, 277
  defense, 279, 281
  gases, 281
  nutrition, 281
  pH, 280
  prothrombin activator, 277
  respiratory functions, 279
  stem cells, 275
  temperature control, 279
  transport, 281
  wastes, 281
Blood-brain barrier, 321
Blood clot, 114, 274
Blood electrolytes, 273
Blood flow, 321, 326
Blood plasma (see Plasma)
Blood pressure, 323
Blood smear, 71
Blood transfusion, 282
Blood types, 281, 282
Blood volume, 325
Body fluids, 447
Body organization, 81
Bone(s), carpal, 104

Bone(s) (Continued)
  clavicle, 103
  diaphysis, 113
  epiphysis, 113
  ethmoid, 95
  femur, 106
  fibula, 107
  flat, 91
  fontanels, 97
  formation, 110
  frontal, 97
  humerus, 103
  hyoid, 97
  ilium, 105
  incus, 97
  innominate, 105
  irregular, 90
  ischium, 105
  lacrimal, 97
  malleus, 97
  mandible, 97
  maxilla, 97
  metacarpals, 104
  metatarsals, 106
  nasal, 97
  occipital, 95
  palatine, 97
  parietal, 97
  patella, 106
  phalanges, 104
  physiology, 109
  protection, 115
  pubis, 105
  radius, 103
  ribs, 103
  scapula, 103
  sphenoid, 95
  stapes, 97
  sternum, 102
  symphysis pubis, 105
  tarsal, 106
  temporal, 96
  tibia, 107
  ulna, 103
  vertebrae, 99, 100, 115
  vomer, 97
  zygomatic, 97
Bone callus, 114
Bone classification, 90
Bone fracture, 112, 114
Bone landmarks, 91, 93
Bone marrow, 555
Bone repair, 114
Bone support, 115
Botulism, 150

Bowman's capsule, 439, 441
Brachial plexus, 227
Brain, 184
Brain transmitters, 213
Breast(s), 508, 513
  development of, 512
Breast bone (see Sternum)
Breathing, 412, 421
Broca's areas, 191
Bronchioles, 416, 420
Bronchitis, 430
Bronchus, 412, 416, 420
Brownian motion, 30
Brunner's glands, 353
Buffers, 32, 280
Buffy coat, 269
Bulbourethral gland, 438, 491, 492

Calciferol, 371
Calcification, 113
Calcitonin, 116, 477
Calcium, 111, 116, 117, 277, 549
Calcium homeostasis, 478
  calcitonin, 477
  parathyroid hormone, 477
Calories, 376, 378
Calorimetry, 402
Canal of Schlemm, 244
Cancer, 563
Capillary(ies), 86, 316
  endothelium, 320
  filtration, 325
  gas transport, 426
  membranes, 319, 320
  permeability, 319
  ultrastructural, 319
  vesicles, 320
Capillary blood pressure, 323
Carbaminohemoglobin (or carboxy-
  hemoglobin), 426
Carbohydrate, 34-35, 368
Carbohydrate metabolism, 385-390
Carbon dioxide, 212
Carbon dioxide transport, 426
Carbon monoxide (CO) poisoning, 427
Carbon acid, 280
Carcinoma, 118
Cardiac arrhythmia, 301, 308
Cardiac centers, 304
Cardiac cycle, 297, 298, 300, 326
Cardiac failure, 309
Cardiac inhibition, 304
Cardiac muscle, 296
Cardiac output, 307, 326
Cardiac reflex, 305
Cardiac reserve, 308

Cardiac valve deficiencies, 308
Cardioinhibitory center, 305
Caries, 122
Carotene, 458
Carotid body(ies) 306, 427
Carotid sinus, 415
Carotid sinus reflex, 306
Cartilage cells, 107
Cartilage replacement bone, 110, 113
Castration, 499
Catabolism, 46, 391
Cataracts, 249
Cathartics, 374
Cation(s), 367, 548
Cavernous urethra, 437-438
Cecum, 349, 350
Cell, 5, 548
  cytology and disease, 22
  selective permeability, 15
  semipermeable barrier, 15
  separation of components by ultra-
    centrifugation, 9
  subcellular separation, 7
  surface specialization, 13
Cell connections, 14
Cell life spans, 524
Cell membrane, 549
Cell theory, 2
Cell turnover, 525
Central dogma, 2
Centrifuge, 7
Centriole, 19, 57
Centromere, 57
Cerebellar functions, coordination, 205
  equilibrium, 205
  postural reflexes, 205
  stretch reflexes, 205
Cerebellum, 187, 192, 205, 207
  anatomy, 192
  cytoarchitecture, 192
Cerebral cortex, 190
  Broca's areas, 191
  motor projection, 195
  pyramidal cell, 190
Cerebral hemisphere(s), 184
Cerebral palsy, 212, 535
Cerebrospinal fluid (CSF), 189
Cerebrum, 185
  cross section of, 188
Cervical plexus, 227
Cervix, 505
Chemical energy, 401
Chemical transmitters, 232
  acetylcholine, 232
  noradrenaline, 232
  norepinephrine, 232

Chemistry of vision, 253
Chemoreceptors, 306, 331, 427
Chemotaxis, 551
Chemotherapy, 563, 564
Cheyne-Stokes breathing, 430
Chimera, 559
Choanae, 413
Cholecystokinin, 365
Cholesterol, 36, 368
Cholesterol plaque, 333
Cholesterol synthesis, 393
Cholineric nerves, 232
Chondrification, 109
Chondrocyte, 107
Chorion, 528
Chorion cells, 527
Chorionic gonadotropins, 529
Choroid plexus, 189
Chromatid, 57
Chromatin, 5, 22
Chromatography, 8, 9
Chromatophores, 458
Chromosome(s), 22, 57
    autosomal, 25
    drumstick, 270
    sex chromosomes, 25
Chromosome analysis, 25
Chromosome defects, 499
Chronic otitismedia, 262
Chylomicrons, 390
Cilia, 13, 14, 59, 67
Ciliary body, 243
Ciliospinal reflex, 238
Cingulate gyrus, 209
Circumcision, 500
Cisterna chyli, 336
Cisternae vesicles, 16
Citrate, 279
Clasped knife reflex, 236
Cleavage, 526
Clitoris, 534
Clonal selection theory of immunity,
    554
Clot, 274
Clot retraction, 279
Clotting times, 279
Coagulation, 111, 272
Cobalt, 367
Cochlea, 259
Coclear duct, 259
Coenzyme, 391
Coenzyme A, 48
Colloid, 474
Colon, 349, 350
Color blindness, 253
Coma, 212

Competitive inhibition, 564
Conditioned reflex, 237
Conductance, 139
Conduction, 461
Cones, 251-252
Conjunctivitis, 254
Connective tissue, 65
    blood supply, 72
    cell types, 70
    classification, 69, 71
    functions, 72
    matrix, 69
    nerve supply, 72
Constipation, 374
Contraception, 539
Convection, 461
Copper, 367
Cord reflex(es), 234
Cornea, 243
Corneal reflex, 238
Corona radiata, 510
Coronary artery disease, 309
Coronary circulation, 294
Coronary sinus, 293
Corpus albicans, 511
Corpus callosum, 185, 191
Corpus luteum, 511
Corpus striatum, 192
Cortex, 186
Coughing, 415
Cramps, 178
Cranial nerves, 221-225
    abducens, 222, 223, 224
    accessory, 225
    acoustic, 224
    facial, 224
    glossopharyngeal, 224
    hypoglossal, 222, 223, 225
    oculomotor, 224
    olfactory, 222
    optic, 222
    trigeminal, 224
    trochlear nerve, 224
    vagus, 186, 222-225
Creatine, 169
Creatinine, 446
Cremasteric reflex, 238
Cretinism, 476
Cristae, 17
Cross-extensor reflex, 236
Cryptorchidism, 500
Cumulus oophorous, 510
Cushing's syndrome, 485, 486
Cyclic adenosine monophosphate, 387,
    394, 479, 481
Cytochemistry, 6

Cytology, 2
Cytoplasm, *11*, 12
Cytoplasmic organelles, 5

Deafness, 261
Death, 570, 579
Death statistics, 572
Decibel, 260
Decidua basalis, 528
Decidua capsularis, 529
Deciduous teeth, 120
Decompression sickness, 428
Defense, 548
Dehydration, 374
Delayed hypersensitivity, 560
Demyelinating diseases, 213
Deoxyribonucleic acid (DNA), 38
    replication, 41
Depth perception, 250
Dermatones, 227
Dermis, 458
Descending reticular activating sys-
    tem, 204
Descending tracts, 194
Descent of testis, gubernaculum, 493
    inguinal canal, 493
    spermatic cord, 493
Desmosome, 14
Development, 524
Diabetes insipidus, 474
Diabetes mellitus, 448
Dialysis, *31*, 452
Diapedesis, 275
Diaphragm, 292, 348, 541
Diaphysis, 90
Diarrhea, 373
Diarthrotic joint, 116
Diastole, 297
Dicumarol, 279
Diencephalon, 186, 190, 192
Dieting, 379
Differentiation, 524
Diffusion, *52*
Digestive system, 344
    absorption, 361
    blood supply, 353
    enzymes, 359, 366
    gross anatomy, 345, 347
    hormone regulation, 362
    microanatomy, 352
    nerve supply, 351
    neural regulation, 363
    physiology, 361
    secretions, 359
Disaccharide, 34
Disease, 548

Disc, slipped, 119
Diuretics, 452
Down's syndrome, 25
Drugs and brain chemistry, 213
Ductus arteriosus, 533, 535, 536
Ductus venosus, 533, 536
Duodenum, 348
Dura mater, 185, 188
Dust cells, 275
Dyspnea, 423

Ear, anatomy, 257-258
    physiology, 258-263
Ectoderm, 530
Ectomorph, 82
Ectopic or tubal pregnancy, 527
Edema, 323, 339, 550
EDTA, 279
Egg, 525
Egg development, 509
Ejaculatory duct, 491, 494
Electrocardiogram (ECG), 300
Electrolyte balance, 447
Electromyography, 178
Electron microscopy, 4
Embolus, 333
Embryo, 528, 530
    external anatomy, 531, 532, 533
Embryonic germ layers (*see* Primary
    germ layers)
Embryonic period, 524
Emetics, 373
Emphysema, 430
Endergonic reactions, 45
Endocrine glands, 79
Endocrine system, 469
Endocytosis, 20
Endoderm, 530
Endolymph in ear, 259
Endometrium, 527, 530
Endomorph, 82
Endoplasmic reticulum, 5, 16, 17, 19
Endothelial cells (*see* Endothelium)
Endothelium, 65, 275, 314, 317, 319,
    419
Energy balance, 401
Energy liberated from food, 402
Enterocrinin, 365
Enzymes, *37*
    cofactors, 47
    kinase, 385
    mechanism of action, 37
    phosphatase, 389
    phosphorylase, 387
Eosinophil, 270, 272, 275
Epidermis, 456

Epididymis, 491
Epiglottis, 356, 413
Epilepsy, 212
Epinephrine, 483, 562
Epiphyseal plate or cartilage, 113, 117
Epiphysis, 90
Epithalamus, 192
Epithelium, 65
  blood supply, 68
  ciliated, 67
  classification, 68
  columnar, 65
  cuboidal, 65
  functions, 68
  nerve supply, 68
  repair and regeneration, 68
  squamous, 65
  stratified, 67
  transitional, 67
Equilibrium, 263
Erythroblastosis fetalis, 283
Erythrocyte antigens, 281
Erythrocytes, 269, 275, 284, 287
  degradation, 275
  life span, 275
Erythropoietic stimulating factor (ESF), 276
Erythropoietin, 276
Esophagus, 347
Estradiol, 505
Estrogen, 506, 513
Eupnea, 423
Eustachian tube, 257
Evaporational cooling, 461
Exercise, 406
Exergonic reactions, 45
Exocrine glands, 78
Expiration, 421
External acoustic meatus, 257
External genitalia, 507, 512, 534
  cervical canal, 507
  internal os, 507
  vulva, 507
External respiration, 412, 423
Extrapyramidal system (pathway), 207, 210
Eye, anatomy, 242-244
  physiology, 244-257
Eyelids, 244

Face, development of, 532
Facilitation in nerve, 144
Fallopian tubes, 505, 511
False labor, 539
False pelvis, 106

Farsightedness, 248
Fat cells, 21
Fats, 368, 390
Fatty acids, saturated, 35
  unsaturated, 35
Feces, 358
Feet, 106
  development of, 533
Female contraceptive, 541
Female external genitalia, 511
Female orgasm, 517
Female sexual characteristics, 505
Fenestrations, 319
Fertility, orchitis, 501
  sperm count, 500
Fertilization, 525, 526
  physiological changes, 526
  polyspermy, 526
Fetal circulation, 532, 536
Fetal heart development, 537
Fetal membranes, 530
Fetal period, 524
Fetus, 529, 531
  growth, 535
  size, 532
Fever, 465
Fiber, 75
Fibrillation, 178, 308
Fibrin, 277, 278
Fibrinogen, 273, 277, 278
Fibrinolysins, 279
Filtration, 442
Fingerprint, 456
Fixation, 4
Flexor reflex, 236
Flower spray receptors, 236
Fluid therapy, 287
Focal length, 247
Folic acid, 564
Follicle-stimulating hormone, 473, 514
Fontanels, 98, 117
Foreskin or prepuce, 491
Forman ovale, 533, 536, 537
Fornix, 209
Free energy, 45

Galactosemia, 399
Gall bladder, 348, 350, 351
Gall stones, 373
Gamma globulin, 279
Ganglion, 75
Gas exchange, 421, 424
Gas laws, 423
Gastrin, 364
Gastrointestinal tract, 344

Gene, 39
Generator potential, 147
Genetic code, 42
Genetic control, 399
Germinal cells, 494
Glands, apocrine, 78
  cellular, 78
  endocrine, 79
  exocrine, 78
  holocrine, 78
  merocrine, 78
  mucus, 78
  serous, 78
Glans penis, 491
Glaucoma, 253
Glia (see Neuroglia)
Glomerulus, 439, 440, 441
  function of, 442, 445, 451
  disease of, 452
Glottis, 413
Glucagon, 387, 478, 479
Glucocorticoids, 483, 484, 485
Gluconeogenesis, 389
  amino acids in, 396
Glucose, 34
  enzymes acting on, 385, 389
  plasma levels, 273
Glucosuria, 448
Glycogen, 21, 385
  storage and disease, 178
Glycogenolysis, 387
Goblet cells, 78, 353
Goiter, 477
Golgi complex, 5, 18, 19
Golgi tendon organ, 236
Gonadotropins, 514
  control of, 514
Gout, 452
Graafian follicle, 510
Grafts of tissue, 558, 559
  rejection reaction, 557
Granulation tissue, 85, 552
Granule, 5
Granulocytes, 272
Gray matter, 75
Greater omentum, 346
Ground substance, 70
Growth, 524
Growth hormone, 117, 473

Hair, 459
  erector pili, 459
Hair cell in ear, 260
Half-life, 10
Hands, development of, 533

Haustra, 350
Haversian canals, 109, 110
Headaches, 213
Heart, 291-293, 537
  blood supply of, 293
  conduction system of, 295
  factors modifying, 299, 307
  hormonal control of, 306
  neural control of, 296, 302-305
  valves, 294
Heart block, 308
Heartburn, 372
Heart sounds, 302
Heart transplant, 306
Heat cramps, 465
Heat energy, 401
Heat exchange, 461
Heat exhaustion, 466
Heat loss, 462
Heat production, 461
Height chart, 377
Hemocyte destruction, 275
Hemocytopoiesis (hematopoiesis), 274, 276
  centers for, 284
Hemodynamics, 324
Hemoglobin, 269, 280, 425
Hemolysis, 281
Hemophilia, 279, 287
Hemorrhagic diseases, 286
Hemorrhoids, 332
Hemostasis, 270, 277, 278
Heparin, 271, 279
Hepatic ducts, 348
Hepatitis, 374
Hexokinase, 285
High altitudes, 428
Hippocampus, 209
Histamine, 270, 307, 364, 550
Histiocytes, 552
Histoincompatability, 574
Histology, 11
Homeostasis, 61, 269, 447, 548
Hormones, 469
Hunger, 375
Hyaline membrane disease, 422
Hyaloid canal, 244
Hydrochloric acid, 362, 363
Hydrogen ions (H^+) (see pH)
Hydrolysis, 344
Hymen, 507
Hyoid bone, 413
Hypercalcemia, 116
Hyperglycemia, 479
Hypermetropia, 248

Hyperplasia, 26, 525
Hyperpnea, 423
Hypersensitivity, 560, 561, 562
Hypertension, 333
Hyperthyroidism, 404
Hypertrophy, 525
Hyperventilating, 415
Hypothalamic-hypophyseal portal system, 472
Hypothalamus, 192, 201, 202, 209, 463, 471
  releasing hormones of, 212
Hypothermia, 465
Hypoxia, 428
Hypovolemia, 333

ICSH (see Interstitial cell-stimulating hormone)
Ileocecal valve, 349
Ileum, 348
Immunity, 550, 552, 554, 562,
Immunocompetence, 555
Immunoglobulins, 552
Immunological deficient state, 555
Immunological programming, 556
Implantation, 527
Inclusions, 11, 21
Incus, 258
Indirect calorimetry, 402
Infarction, 308
Infectious disease, 548
Infectious mononucleosis, 285
Inflammation, 550, 551, 552, 557
Inguinal, 336
Inhibitory neurons, 142
Inner cell mass (ICM), 527, 529
Inspiration, 421
Insulin, 389, 478, 479, 480
Interconversion of sugars, 385
Internal brain spaces, 189
Internal capsule, 192
Internal respiration, 425
Interneuron, polysynaptic, 234
Interstitial cell-stimulating hormone, 498
Intervertebral discs, 102
Intima, 314
Intracellular membranes, 16
Intracranial pressure, 189
Intrauterine devices (IUD), 541
Intrauterine life, 535
Iodine, 367
  isotope of, 10
  see also Thyroid hormone
Ions (ionization), 31

Iris, 243
Ischemia, 308, 333
Isometric contraction, 156, 173
Isotonic contraction, 156, 173
Isotonic solution, 287
Isotope, 8
IUD (see Intrauterine device)

Jaundice, 373
Jejunum, 348
Joint capsule, 80
Joints (see Articulation)

Karyotyping, 25
Keratin, 456, 460
Ketogenesis (ketone bodies), 392
  ketogenic amino acids, 396
Kidney, 436, 437, 441
  blood supply of, 438
  buffering in, 448-449
  homeostasis by, 447, 448
  hormones of, 450
  neural control of, 450
  retroperitoneal location, 436
Kidney stones, 452
Kinetic energy, 401
Kinetosome, 19
Kleinfelter syndrome, 499
Knee jerk reflex, 234, 238
Krebs citric acid cycle, 176, 388

Labium majorum, 534
Labium minorum, 534
Labor, 539
  stages of, 539-540
Lacrimal glands, 244
Lactation, 513
Lacteals, 353, 354
Lactic acid, 47, 176
  in exercise, 408
Large intestine, 348
Larynx, 412-413
Law of conservation of energy, 401
Lens, 243
Leukemia, 284
Leukocytes, 269, 284, 287, 551
Leukocyte-promoting factor, 552
Leukocytosis, 284, 552
Leukopenia, 284
Leydig cells, 494
LH (see Luteinizing hormone)
Limbic system, 199, 209, 211
  see also Psychosomatic; Visceral brain
Lingual tonsil, 345

Lipid metabolism, 390-394
Lipids, 21, *35*, 368
    fatty acids, 35
    phospholipids, 36
    triglyceride, 35
Lipoprotein, 390
Lithium salts, 215
Liver, major functions of, 352
Local circuits in neuron membrane, 138
Lockjaw, 150
Lower motor neuron, 207
LTH (*see* Luteotropic hormone)
Lumbar plexus, 228
Lung(s), *416-417*
    buffer system, 448
    cancer, 430
    histology, 419
Lung capacity, 422
Lung volumes, 422
Luteal phase, 516
Luteinizing hormone, 473, 514
Luteotropic hormone, 473
Lymph, 335
Lymph flow, 339
Lymph fluid, 335
Lymph nodes, 335-336, 556
Lymphatic system, 335-338
    fat absorption by, 338
Lymph vessels, 335
Lymphocyte, 270, 272, 275, 555
Lymphoid elements, 274
Lymphoid organs, 555
Lysosomes, 20

Macronutrients, 367
Macula, 252
Male contraceptives, 541
Male sexual response, 498
Mammary gland, 508
    see also Breast
Manganese, 367
Marrow, 113, 274
Mast cell, 108, 279, 317
Media, 314
Mediastinum, 84, 291, 412
Medulla oblongata, 193, 205
    major tracts in, 205
    psychosomatic symptoms, 205
    vital control centers in, 205
Megakaryocyte, 272
Meiosis, 495
Melanin, 459
Membrane bone, 112
Membrane potential, 133-135

Membranes, *11*
    mucous, 80
    serous, 79
    synovial, 80
Membranous labyrinth, 259
Membranous urethra, 437, 438
Memory and learning, 197, 199
Menarche, 515
Meniere's disease, 262
Meninges, 188, 195
Menopause, 515, 518
Menses, 513
Menstrual cycle, 515
    hormonal changes during, 515
    phases of, 516
Menstruation, 515
Menstruum, 512
Merocrine glands, 78
Mesencephalon or midbrain, 187, 192, 202
    cross section, 191
Mesenchymal cell, 108
Mesoderm, 530
Mesomorph, 82
Mesothelium, 65
Mesovarium, 505
Messenger RNA, 42
Metabolic pumps, 549
Metabolic rate, 403
Metabolism, 46
    aerobic, 48-50
    anaerobic, 46-48
    efficiency, 48, 51
    glycolysis, 46
    Krebs cycle, 49
Metencephalon, 193
Methotrexate, 564
Methyl mercury, 215
Micron, 3
Micronutrients, 367
Micropores, 22
Microtome, 6
Microtubules, 13
Microvasculature, 321
Microvilli, 13, 67
Midbrain, 192
Middle ear, 257-258
Mineral metabolism, 367
Mineralocorticoids, 484
Minimata disease, 535
Minor pelvis, 106
Miscarriages, 543
Mitochondria, 5, 16, 17
    ATP production, 50
    electron transport, 50

Mitosis, 55-58
Mitral valve, 293
Molarity, 31
Mongolism (*see* Down's syndrome)
Monocyte(s), 270, 272, 275, 279, 285
Monosaccharide, 34, 387
Morning sickness, 529
Motor cortex, 195
Motor homunculus, 196, 201
Motor pathways, 207
Muscle(s), abductor hallucis, 181
    abductor pollicis, 180
    abductor pollicis longus, 164
    adductor pollicis, 164, 180
    adductors, 180
    agonist, 156
    anatomy, 157
    anconeus, 180
    antagonist, 156
    aponeurosis, 159, 161
    arm extensors, 163
    arrector pili, 459
    attachment to bone, 158
    auricular muscles, 159
    biceps, 154, 156, 163
    biceps brachii, 164, 180
    biceps femoris, 155, 180
    blood supply, 157
    brachialis, 156, 180
    brachioradialis, 164
    buccinator, 159, 179
    cardiac, 166, 177, 178, 181, 296
    components, 157
    contraction, 111
    coracobrachialis, 180
    deltoid, 154, 155, 160, 179
    depressor anguliaris, 159
    depressor labii inferioris, 159
    diaphragm, 161, 162, 180, 292
    digiti minimi, 164
    extensor carpi, 180
    extensor carpi radialis, 164
    extensor carpi radialis brevis, 164
    extensor carpi radialis longus, 164
    extensor digitorum, 164, 166
    extensor digitorum communis, 180
    extensor indicis, 180
    extensor pollicis, 180
    extensor pollicis brevis, 164
    extensor pollicis longus, 164
    extensors, 154, 155, 163, 181
    external intercostals, 180
    external oblique, 154, 155, 160, 162,
        163, 180
    fascia (of rectus abdominus), 160

Muscle(s) (Continued)
    flexor, 163, 181
    flexor carpi, 180
    flexor carpi radialis, 164
    flexor carpi ulnaris, 164
    flexor digitorum, 180
    flexor digitorum profundus, 164
    flexor digitorum superficialis, 164
    flexor pollicis, 180
    flexor pollicis brevis, 164
    fibrillation, 178
    frog gastrocnemius, 172
    gastrocnemius, 155, 165, 166, 181
    genioglossus, 179
    gluteal muscles, 180
    gluteus maximus, 155
    gluteus medius, 155
    glycogen, 176
    gracilis, 180
    hyoglossus, 179
    iliocostalis, 161, 179
    iliopsoas, 180
    inferior oblique, 179
    inferior rectus, 179
    infraspinatus, 155, 180
    insertion, 157
    intercostal, 160
    internal intercostals, 180
    internal oblique, 162, 180
    lateral rectus, 179
    latissimus dorsi, 154, 155, 161, 180
    levator labii, 159, 180
    levator labii alaegue nasi, 159
    levator scapulae, 180
    longissimus, 179
    masseter, 159, 179, 345
    medial rectus, 179
    mentalis, 159, 179
    nerve supply, 158
    obturator, 180
    occipitalis, 179
    omohyoid, 179
    opponers, 164
    orbicularis oculi, 159, 179
    orbicularis oris, 159, 179
    origins, 157
    palmar, 163
    palmaris, 180
    palmaris longus, 164
    pars frontalis, 159
    pars occipitalis, 159
    pectineus, 180
    pectoralis major, 154, 160, 180
    pectoralis minor, 160, 180
    peroneus, 154, 165, 166, 181

Muscle(s) (Continued)
plantaris, 166, 181
platysma, 159
popliteus, 180
posterior, 163
pronator teres, 164, 180
psoas, 179
pterygoid, 179
quadriceps, 154, 180
quadriceps femoris, 165
quadratus lumbarum, 179
rectus abdominis, 154, 160, 163, 179, 180
rectus femoris, 165
rhomboid, 180
risorius, 159
sacrospinal complex, 179
sacrospinalis, 161
sartorius, 165, 180
scalenus, 179
semimembranosus, 180
semitendinosus, 155
serratus, 179
serratus anterior, 160
skeletal, 166, 175, 178, 181
smooth, 166, 172, 175, 176, 177, 181, 182
soleus, 155, 165, 166, 181
splenius capitis, 179
sternoclavomastoid, 159
sternocleidomastoid, 154, 159, 179, 345
sternohyoid, 179
sternothyroid, 179
striated, 172
structural components, 167
styloglossus, 179
subscapularis, 180
sufraspinatus, 180
superior oblique, 179
superior rectus, 174
supinator, 180
temporalis, 179
tensor fasciae latae, 180
teres major, 155
teres major/minor, 180
tibialis, 165, 166, 181
transverse abdominis, 160, 162, 180
transversus, 163
trapezius, 154, 155, 179
triceps, 154, 155, 156, 163
triceps brachii, 164, 180
vastus lateralis, 165
vastus medialis, 165
zygomaticus, 159, 179

Muscle contraction 172-174
isometric, 173
Muscle metabolism, 175, 176
Muscle myoglobin, 177
Muscle relaxing system, 168, 170
Muscle spasms, 178
Muscle spindle, 235
annulospiral receptor, 235
intrafusal fibers, 235
Muscle tissue, 65
blood supply, 74
classifications of, 73
functions of, 74
nerve supply, 74
regeneration and repair, 74
Muscle tone, 174-175
Muscle twitch, 154, *172*
Muscular dystrophy, 178
Myasthenia gravis, 150
Myelencephalon, 187, 193
Myelin, 75
Myelin sheath, 131
Myeloid, 274
Myocardial infarction, 308
Myocardial ischemia, 308
Myoglobin, 177
Myometrium, 529
Myopia, 248
Myosin, 167, 168

Nails, 460
Nares, 413
Nasal cavity, 412
Natural immunity, 554
Nearsightedness, 248
Nephron, 439
blood supply, 440, 441
distal tubule, 440
function, 443
homeostatic role, 443
loop of Henle, 440
proximal tubule, 440
Nerve, 75
Nerve tissue, 74
blood supply, 76
classification, 75
functions, 76
nerve supply, 76
repair and regeneration, 76
Neurilemma, 75
Neurocranium, 92
Neuroglia, 74, 190
astrocytes, 190
microglia, 190
oligodendrocytes, 190
Neuromuscular junction, 131

Neuron, 74
  axon, 129
  axoplasm, 129
  chromophilic substance, 128
  collaterals, 129
  dendrites, 128
  endoneurium, 221
  epineurium, 221
  metabolism, 149
  neurilemma, 131, 221
  neurofibrils, 133
  Nissl bodies, 128
  perineurium, 221
  soma, 128
  synaptic terminals, 129
Neuronal circuits, convergent, 145
  divergent, 145
  parallel, 145
  reverberating, 145
Neuronal pools, 144
Neurosecretory cells, 201, 472
  releasing factors, 201
Neurotropic viruses, 213
Neutrophil, 270, 272, 275
Newborn, 531
Niacin, 370
Nicotinamide adenine dinucleotide (NAD), 48
Nicotinic acid, 370
Nipple, 509
Nitrogen poisoning, 428
Nodes of Ranvier, 131
Noise pollution, 260
Nonprotein nitrogen (NPN), 448
Norepinephrine, 231, 483
Nuclear membrane, 5
Nucleic acid, 38
Nucleolus, 5, 22
Nucleoplasm, 11
Nucleus, 11, 22
Nuclide, 8
Nutrition, 344, 365, 376
  minerals, 367
  water requirements, 366

Obesity, 376, 378
Ocular muscles, 244
Oddi, sphincter of, 350
Olfaction, 264
Oliguria, 451
Olmentum, 85
Oogenesis (see Egg development)
Optic disc, 251
Oral cavity, 412
Oral contraceptives, 542

Organ of Corti, 259
Organelles, 11, 16
Organs, 65
Organ systems, 66
Orgasm, 498
Oscilloscope, 136
Osmosis, 53
Ossification, 109, 113
Osteoblast, 107, 113, 117
Osteoclast, 111, 116
Osteocyte, 107
Osteomalacia, 118
Osteoporosis, 117
Otoconia, 263
Otoliths, 263
Otosclerosis, 263
Oval window, 259
Ovarian ligaments, 505
Ovary, 505, 509
  cyclical events, 514
  germinal layer, 509
Overlapping junction, 14
Overpopulation, 542
Overweight, 377
Ovum, 509
Oxalate salts, 279
Oxidation-reduction reactions, 47
Oxygen, 212
Oxygen debt, 176, 407
Oxygen transport, 425
Oxyhemoglobin, 280, 425
Oxyhemoglobin dissociation curve, 425
Oxytocin, 472, 473, 539

Pacemaker, 295
Pain, 199, 237, 459, 539
  perception, 200
  referred pain, 238-239
  visceral, 238
Palate, 97
Palatine tonsil, 345
Pancreas, 348, 350, 351, 478
  beta cells, 478
  gross anatomy, 479
  islets of Langerhans, 478
  microscopic anatomy of, 478
  neurogenic control, 364
Pancreatic duct, 351
Pancreozymin, 364
Pantothenic acid, 370
Papanicolaou smear, 24
Parapalegia, 357
Parathormone, 111
Parathyroid, 476, 477
Parathyroid hormones, 116

Parenteral feeding, 287
Parotid gland, 345
Parturition (*see* Birth)
Passive immunity, 555
Passive transport, 54
Patent foramen ovale, 534
Pathology, 22
Pavlov, 365
Pco₂, 424, 427
Pellagra, 370
Pelvis, 105
Penicillin, 446
Penis, 491, 534
   corpora cavernosa, 494
   erectile tissue, 494
Pentose monophosphate shunt, 388
Pentose sugars, 389
Pericardial cavity, 84, 291
Pericarditis, 309
Pericardium, 291
Perichondrium, 109
Pericyte, 317
Peridontal disease, 122
Perilymph in ear, 259
Periosteum, 114
Peristalsis, 354
Peritoneum, 85
Peritonitis, 373
Permeability, 550
Pernicious anemia, 370
Peroxidase, 271
Petechiae, 286
Peyer's patches, 348
pH, 31, 280, 427
Phagocytes, 552
Phagocytic cells, macrophages, 552
   monocytes, 552
   neutrophils, 552
Phagocytosis, *20*, 270, 271
Pharyngeal tonsil, 345
Pharynx, 412, 413,
Phase microscopy, 6
Phenylketonuria, 400
Phlebitis, 332
Phosphocreatine, 169
Phospholipid synthesis, 394
Phrenic nerve, 426
Physical training, effect of, 408
Pia mater, 189
Pigments, 21
Pill (*see* Oral contraceptives)
Pinna, 257
Pinocytosis, *55*
Pitocin (*see* Oxytocin)
Pituitary, 117, 471

Pituitary (Continued)
   anterior lobe, 471
   dwarfism, 474
   giantism, 474
   hypophyseal stalk, 471
   hypothalamic control, 203
   posterior lobe, 202, 471
Pituitary gonadotropins, 514
Placenta, 527, 528, 529, 533, 536, 539, 540
   anatomy, 529
   formation, 527, 528
   permeability, 538
   separation, 529
   substitute endocrine gland, 529
Plantar reflex, 238
Plasma, 269, 273, 447
   gases, 273
   ion composition, 273
Plasma, composition of, 273
Plasma cell, 271, 279
Plasma membrane 13, 14
   active transport, 54
   diffusion, 51
   facilitated diffusion, 53
   pores, 51
   structure, 51
Plasminogens (*see* Fibrinolysins)
Platelets, 269, 270, 272, 278, 287
Pleura, 412, *416*
   parietal, 416
   visceral, 416
Pleural cavities, 84
Pleural space, 417
Pneumonia, 284, 431
Pneumothorax, 431
Po₂, 423, 425, 427, 429
Poliomyelitis, 178
Pons, 185, 193
   respiratory reflex center, 202
Posterior chamber, 243
Posterior pituitary, 473, 474
Potassium, in blood, 273
   in nerve activity, 132, 137-138
Potential energy, 401
Precapillary sphincter, 316
Precocious puberty, 500
Pregnancy, 537, 539
   nausea, 529
   radiation, 536
Pregnancy tests, 529
Premature babies, 532
Premature ejaculation, 500
Prenatal development, 524, 540
Primary germ layers, 529, 530

Primary male sex organs, 491
Primary ovarian follicles, 509
Primary tissues, 65
Progeria, 574
Progesterone, 505, 514, 539
Projection tracts, 191
Proprioceptors, 234
Prostate, 438, 492
Prostatic urethra, 437
Protein-bound iodine, 405
Protein metabolism, 394-397
  regulation, 396
Proteins, 36-37
  amino acids, 36
  peptide, 36
  structure 36
  synthesis, 43
Prothrombin, 277, 278
Prothrombin activator, 278
Psychosomatic, 201
Pulmonary arteries, 417
Pulmonary veins, 417
Pulmonic valve, 293
Pulse, 301, 302
Pulse pressure, 327
Pupil, 243, 249
Pupillary light reflex, 238
Pyelonephritis, 452
Pyloric sphincter, 348
Pyramidal tract, 207, 209
Pyruvic acid, 47, 388

Radiation, 461
Radioautography, 10
Recall phenomenon, 561
Receptor cells, 147
Rectum, 348, 349, 350
Red blood cells (see Erythrocytes)
Red flare, 562
Red nucleus, 202
Referred pain, 238
Reflex activity, 234-237
Reflex arc, 148-234
  see also Reflex activity
Refraction, 246
Refractory period, muscle, 173
  nerve, 137
Refractory state, 173
Regulation of metabolism 397
Relaxing factor, 168, 170
Renal anoxia (see Angiotensin)
Renal calculi (see Kidney stones)
Renal corpuscle, 439, 442
Renal filtration (see Glomerulus, function of)

Renal pressor system (see Renin; Renal anoxia; Aldosterone)
Renin, 330, 332, 451
Respiration, barriers, 421
  chemoreceptors, 415
  control of breathing, 415
  CO_2, 415
  earth's atmosphere, 429
  exercise, 427
  factors which influence breathing, 415
  ventilation, 427
Reticular activating system, 202, 203, 204, 207
Reticular formation, 192
Reticulocyte, 271
Reticuloendothelial cells, 552
Reticuloendothelial system, 280
Retina, 251-252
Retinene, 253
Rh, 286
Rheumatism, 560
Rhinencephalon, 209
Rhodopsin, 253
Ribonucleic acid (RNA), 38, 42
Ribosomes, 16, 42
Right lymphatic duct, 335
Rigor, 175
Rigor mortis, 577
Rods, 251-252
Round window, 259
Rugae, 353, 359

Sacral plexus, 228
Salivary glands, 344
Saltatory conduction, 140
S-A node (see Sino-atrial node)
Sarcomere, 167, 168, 171
Sarcoplasmic reticulum, 168, 171
Scab, 86
Scala vestibuli, 260
Scar tissue, 74, 84
Schwann cell, 131
Sclera, 243
Scrotum, 491
Scurvy, 370
Sebaceous glands, 460
Sebum, 531
Second messenger theory, 388, 481
Secretagogues, 363
Secretin, 364
Secretary vacuole, 5
Semen, 498
Semicircular canals, 263
Seminal ducts, 491

Seminal vesicle, 438, 491, 492
Seminiferous tubules, 494
Senescence (*see* Aging)
Sensory input, 198
Sensory projection areas, 196
Serotonin, 272, 307
Sertoli cells, 494
Serum, 272, 274
Serum sickness, 561
Sexual infantilism, 518
Shock, 333, 334
Sickle-cell anemia, 285, 286
Sino-atrial node, 295
Sinuses, 98
Sinusoids, 317
Skeletal muscle, 73, 166
    contraction, 168, 169, 171
    ultrastructure, 170, 171
Skeleton, aging, 117
    appendicular, 90, 103
    axial, 90
    calcium requirements, 117
    gross anatomy, 90
    growth and maintenance, 111
Skin, 456, 457
    blood supply, 460
    color, 456
    functions, 461
    layers, 456
Skin pathology, 464, 465
    boils, 465
    psoriasis, 465
    sensory receptors, 458, 459
    warts, 465
Sleep, 206
Sliding filament model, 167, *168*, 171
Slipped disc, 119, 120
Small intestine, 348, 350
Smell, 264
Smooth muscle, 172, 176, *177*
    pacemaker activity, 177
Sneezing, 415
Sodium, in blood, 273
    in nerve activity, 132, 137-138
    in urine, 444
Sodium pump, 134
Soft palate, 356
Soft spot (*see* Fontanel)
Solar plexus, 230
Solutions, 30
    hypertonic, 53
    hypotonic, 53
    isotonic, 53
    molar, 31
Somatotropic hormone, 473, 474
Sound, 259, 260

Speech-making, 416
Sperm, 495, 496, 525
Spermatic cord, 493
Spermatogenesis, 494, 495, 496
Spermatogonia, 495
Sphygmomanometer, 327
Spinal cord, 188, 193, 197, 205
    tracts, 194
Spinal nerves, 102, 225, 226, 227
Spinothalamic tract, 199
Spirometer, 423
Splanchnic nerves, 229
Spleen, 337
Stapes, 258
Starling's law, 299
Starvation, 374
Stereoscopic vision, 250
Sterol synthesis, 393
STH (*see* Somatotropic hormone)
Stomach, 347, 348, 350
    acidity, 353
    gastric fluid, 353
Stool, 358
Stratum germinativum, 456
Stress, 484
Stretch reflex, 234
Striated muscle (*see* Skeletal muscle)
Stroke, 213
Subcortical nuclei, 191
Sublingual gland, 345
Submandibular gland, 345
Sucrose, 34
Summation, in muscle, 173
    in nerve, 142
Supernumerary breasts, 508
Surfactant, 422
Suspensory ligaments (eye), 243, 505
Sutures, 95
Swallowing, 356, 358
Sweat glands, 460
Synapse, 131
    chemical transmitters, 141
    neuromuscular junction, 178
    synaptic fatigue, 146
    synaptic vesicles, 140
Synaptic delay, 148
Synarthrotic joints, 116
Syncope, 212
Synovial joint, 115
Synovial membrane, 80
Systems, 65
Systole, 297

Taenia coli, 350
Target tissues, 469
Tarsal glands, 244

Taste, 263-264
Taste buds, 263
Tectorial membrane, 259
Teeth, *119*
  blood supply, 122
  cementum, 121, 122
  crowns, 120
  dentin, 121, 122
  extraction, 122
  pulp, 122
  roots, 120
  types, 121
Temperature, 461, 464
  core body, 462
  heat production, 462
  regulation, 462, 463
Tendon, 157
Teratogenic, 538
Testes, 491, 494
  descent, 493
  function, 498
Testicular regulation, interstitial cell
    stimulating hormone, 498
  luteinizing hormone, 498
Testosterone, 495, 497
Testosterone and behavior, 499
Tetanus, 173
Tetany, 477
Thalamus, 192, 199, 209
Thalidomide, 537
Thermoregulation, 461
Thoracic cavity, 84
Thoracic duct, 335, 336
Thrombin, 277
Thrombocytopenia, 285
Thromboplastin, 277, 278
Thymectomy, 555
Thymus, 337, 555, 556
Thyroid, 292, 475
Thyroid cartilage, 413
Thyroid diseases, cretinism, 475
  goiter, 475
  Graves' diseases, 475
  myxedema, 475
Thyrotropic hormone (thyrotropic
    stimulating hormone), 473
Thyroxine, 117, 474
Tight junction, 14, 319
Tissue fluid, 70, 269
Tissue pressure, 323
Tissues, 65
Tocopherols, 371
Tolerance, 558
Tongue, 344
  papillae, 263
Tonsils, 337, 347

Tonus, 74
Toxins, 552
Trachea, 292, 412, 416, 420
  cartilages, 413
Tranquilizer, 537
Transcapillary exchange, 320, 323
Transfer RNA, 43
Transitional epithelium, 441
Transmitters (*see* Chemical trans-
    mitters)
Transplantation rejection, 560
Transverse or commissural tracts, 191
Transverse tubules, 168
Triceps reflex, 238
Tricuspid valve, 293
Trophoblast, 524, 527
True labor, 539
Tubal tonsil, 345
Tuberculosis, 284, 431
Tubular nephritis, 452
Tubular secretion, 445
Tumor genesis, 563
Tympanic membrane 257

Ultracentrifugation, 9
Ultracentrifuge, 7
Ultrastructure, 2
Umbilical arteries, 532
Umbilical cord, 529, 534
Umbilical vein, 533
Upper motor neuron, Betz cell, 207
Urea, 446, 448
  formation, 396
Ureter, 433, 436, 437, 438
Urethra, 436, 437, 492
  prostrate, 492
  spongy, 492
Urethral glands, 492
Uric acid, 446
Urinary bladder, 438
Urinary system, 436
Urine, constituents, 444
  drug effect, 450
  formation, 445, 446
  threshold materials, 446
  volume, 451
Urine-to-plasma ration, 446
Urogenital sinus, 534
Uterus, 505, 510, 511, 513, 528, 529,
    530, 535
  endometrium, 511
Utricle, 263

Vacuoles, 21
Vagina, 507, 510, 512, 513
Varicose veins, 332

Vascular tone, 329
Vascularity, 184
Vasectomy, 541
Vasoconstriction, 329
Vasodilation, 329
Vasomotor center, 331
Vasomotor regulation, 329
Vasopressin, 450
Vater, ampulla of, 350
Vein(s), 315
  adrenal vein, 313
  anterior tibial vein, 313
  axillary vein, 313
  basilic vein, 313
  brachial vein, 313
  brachiocephalic, 292, 313
  cephalic vein, 313
  common iliac vein, 313
  digital veins, 313
  dorsal venous arch, 313
  external iliac 313
  external jugular vein, 313
  femoral, 313
  great saphenous, 313
  hepatic, 313
  hepatic portal, 319, 533
  inferior vena cave, 292, 293, 313
  internal iliac, 313
  internal jugular, 313
  median antebrachial, 313
  median cubital, 313
  ovarian (testicular), 313
  palmar venous network, 313
  popliteal, 313,
  pulmonary, 293
  renal, 313
  subclavian, 292
  superior vena cava, 293, 313
  umbilical 533
  valves, 293
Venereal disease, 54
Ventilation, 412, 422
Ventricle(s), brain, 186, 189
  central canal, 189
  cerebral aqueduct, 189
  foramen of Monro, 189
  heart, 292, 293
Ventricular fibrillation, 301
Ventricular septum, 536
Venule, 316
Vermiform appendix, 349
Vernic caseosa, 531
Vertebrae, cervical, 100, 101
  thoracic, 100
  lumbar, 100
  sacral, 100

Vertebral column, 117
Vertebral discs, 119
Vertebral foramen, 102
Vesicles, 21
Vestibular apparatus, 263
Vestibular organs, 205
Villi, 353, 354
Viral infection, 550
Virus interferon, 548
Visceral brain, 208, 233
Viscosity, 327
Vision, 242, 249
Visual acuity, 250
Visual purple, 253
Vital capacity, 422
Vitamin(s), 369
Vitamin A, 111, 117, 369
Vitamin B_{12}, 277, 368
Vitamin B complex, choline, 370
  cyanocobalamin (B_{12}), 370
  folic acid, 370
  niacin, 370
  pantothenic acid, 370
  pyridoxine (B_6), 370
  riboflavin (B_2), 369
  thiamine, (B_1), 369
Vitamin C, 111, 117, 370
Vitamin D, 111, 117, 371
Vitamin E, 371
Vitamin K, 277, 279, 371
Vitreous body, 244
Vocal cords, 416
Volkmann canals, 109
Vomiting (emesis), 373

Wasting disease, 559
Water balance, 447
Water, properties of, 12, 30, 461
Wheal, 562
White blood cells (see Leukocytes)
White matter, 75
White reaction, 562
Wisdom teeth, 120
Work, 407
  definition, 407
Wound healing, 86

X chromosome, 499
Xenograft, 558
X-ray, 525

Y chromosome, 449
Yolk sac, 529, 530

Zinc, 367
Zonula, 243